W9-BIM-815

QUANTITATIVE CHEMISTRY

QUANTITATIVE CHEMISTRY
Measurements and Equilibrium

WILLIAM B. GUENTHER
The University of the South

ADDISON-WESLEY PUBLISHING COMPANY
Reading, Massachusetts · Menlo Park, California · London · Don Mills, Ontario

This book is in the
ADDISON-WESLEY SERIES IN CHEMISTRY

Consulting Editor
FRANCIS T. BONNER

 Library of Congress Catalog Card No. 68-20927.

And so for weeks I was alone in the laboratory, taking photographs, gazing under the red lamp at films which still dripped water, carrying them to the light and studying them until I knew every grey speck on them, from the points which were testing my structures down to flaws and scratches on the surface. Then, when my eyes tired, I put down my lens and turned to the sheets of figures that contained the results, the details of the structure and the predictions I was able to make. . . For days my predictions were not only vaguely right, but right as close as I could measure. I still possess those lists of figures, and I have stopped writing to look them over again. It is ten years and more since I first saw them and yet as I read:

Predicted	*Observed*
1.435	*1.44*
2.603	*2.603*

and so on for long columns, I am warmed with something of that first glow. . . It was as though I had looked for a truth outside myself, and finding it had become for a moment part of the truth I sought; as though all the world, the atoms and the stars, were wonderfully clear and close to me, and I to them, so that we were part of a lucidity more tremendous than any mystery.

C. P. Snow, *The Search*

PREFACE

This text presents a quantitative study of chemical equilibrium which emphasizes ionic solutions and the study of homogeneous and heterogeneous separation processes. The purpose of the laboratory section is to provide practice in carrying out quantitative procedures through projects on equilibrium and quantitative methods, as well as some traditional determinations of unknowns. Thorough grounding in precision chemical work and its interpretation is still needed in the chemistry curriculum. This text is an attempt to meet that need, along with others, with a course somewhat different from the classical course in "Quantitative Analysis."

The role of quantitative analysis in experimental chemistry curricula varies from a negligible part to a very large one. In some plans it is included in courses in physical chemistry, chemical equilibrium, chemical separations, etc.* The purpose of this text is to provide an approach and materials suitable for both class and laboratory work in the newer courses, which continue the study of equilibrium and physical chemistry of solutions begun in the general chemistry course. Because of the wide variety present in evolving college chemistry programs, this text is an attempt to steer a middle path between repeating too much of the material covered in the general or elementary physical chemistry courses and assuming more fluency in chemical theory than sophomores or juniors are likely to have. The material is divided into 26 chapters and may be adapted to a variety of presentations.

A major aim of the classroom portion of this course is to extend the student's insight into the mathematical expression of ideas in physical science. Plotting data, getting slopes and intercepts, finding maxima or minima, as well as the physical significance of these procedures are repeatedly stressed along with the realization that reliability limits of data and results must be recognized in the proper interpretation of experiments.

The topics of gases, liquids, and chromatography contribute to a course well suited to premedical students, who need this study but who commonly do not take courses in physical chemistry. These topics, which fit naturally into the quantita-

* A symposium on this subject, sponsored by the American Chemical Society, is reprinted in the *Journal of Chemical Education* **44,** 312, (1967).

tive chemistry sequence, can be coordinated to release equivalent time in other courses where they are sometimes given.

The rigorous and logical mathematical treatment of equilibrium in more advanced books by Butler, Fleck, and others,* is used here. This approach is easier for the student in the long run because it unifies most of the equilibrium calculations to be studied. If the basic methods and ideas of this approach, explained in Chapters 5, 6, and 8, are thoroughly mastered, applications to titration, extraction, and complex equilibria should follow with less difficulty than is experienced with the approximate methods used to introduce undergraduates to equilibrium calculations. Progressively less detail is given in solving examples in the later chapters.

No claim is made that so great a variety of topics is presented in the detail that each of us might like. Most chapters are intended to serve as self-teachers, where the student learns to solve problems by following through the worked examples with pencil and paper. Other chapters may appropriately be assigned as supplemental reading. The emphasis throughout the book is on using equilibrium theory to solve problems encountered in chemical work. Reading the problem assignments and the list of laboratory projects should reliably convey the nature of the course.

Those wishing to present a complete-equation approach to equilibrium calculations from the beginning of the course, may prefer to combine Chapters 5 and 6. So far, the author has used Chapter 5 first to try to instill some feeling for acid-base equilibrium situations. Facility in manipulation of the complex complete equations is of little value if it is but an algebraic exercise unassociated with the chemical situation involved. To keep close to realistic situations, many problems are derived from the student laboratory work and recent literature in chemistry. Compound-*A* and -*B* type problems have been avoided.

Above all, one must encourage the use of the student's curiosity and imagination, that he may grow in the pleasure of intellectual discovery expressed by C. P. Snow in the Frontispiece. The laboratory project work with its requisite reference to the library should foster this development. A research approach in the laboratory can be approximated by varying the conditions, introducing new compounds, etc., in the projects. I rarely repeat them without changes. They are presented to suggest possibilities, rather than as finished exercises for unvaried repetition.

In the laboratory section, there should be enough work to allow wide variation in the proportions of projects and unknown determinations. Some of the projects may seem long until one sees that much of the learning value can be realized by each student through getting only one or two of the points on a curve compiled from class data. As usual in advanced courses, laboratory work has to be adapted to local students, curriculum, and equipment. Some further comments are available in a teacher's manual. More than enough experimental work for two semesters (60 laboratory periods) is given.

---

* See the General References, p. 376.

For college students today, laboratory work related to significant chemical research problems is of greater interest and value than determination of unknowns alone. However, using unknown exercises on new methods is still a valuable means to teach the required techniques before starting a project.

References are given to sources of information that have been found valuable. No doubt, many other apt examples can be supplied by each instructor. Three advanced texts have been especially important in shaping this course: those by J. N. Butler, H. A. Laitinen, and H. F. Walton.*

I record my grateful indebtedness to my teachers at Oberlin College and the University of Rochester and to my students, who have participated in the course over the last eight years. I thank the administration of the University of the South for providing research facilities and a sabbatical leave for writing. National Science Foundation grants for student research participation have been most welcome in making possible equilibrium investigations which suggested some of the projects in this text. Of greatest value has been the leadership of David B. Camp both in chemical ideas and in pacific departmental administration.

I had long hoped that a comprehensive text for a course of this type, which is being taught at many institutions, would be developed. My present selection of interesting and necessary topics is but one of many possible sets. In waiting for a text, I prepared notes for the students and eventually arrived at a full manuscript, which the staff at Addison-Wesley has tirelessly edited into readable form. My thanks to them are unbounded. For my mistakes, which undoubtedly remain, I repeat the explanation of Dr. Johnson, who, when asked why he had written a particularly strange and erroneous definition, replied, "Ignorance, Madame, pure ignorance."

Sewanee, Tennessee
January 1968

W. B. G.

CONTENTS

CHAPTER 1

MEASUREMENT IN SCIENCE

Recent improvements in long-known chemical methods as well as the rapid development of many new instrumental methods for obtaining measurements have made possible the flood of new information by making possible easier, more rapid, and deeper probing of nature. This text presents some of these methods with emphasis on their uses in investigating the equilibria involved in their operation.

Why did not the rapid scientific progress occurring in the last two centuries start much earlier? Surely men did not suddenly become more intelligent. The complexity of literary and mathematical development of several ancient peoples rules out such an explanation.

Formulation of the laws of chemical reaction and the atomic theory had to wait until reliable, sensitive balances were developed about the time of Lavoisier (1743–1794). The study of energy relations, thermodynamics, required information obtainable only with a good mercury thermometer, which was invented in 1714. Improvement in the quality of glass and in optical instruments in the seventeenth century opened the door to the examination of the small and the distant in nature. The development of the spectroscope and of gas-discharge tubes in the late nineteenth century made possible knowledge about atomic structure. The development of rapid and accurate techniques of chemical investigation has brought about extensive understanding of chemical reactions and knowledge of the means of controlling them.

One sees that scientific advance depends on the tools available for the discovery of new information as well as on the ability to interpret and use information. This text aims to teach the student how to make chemical measurements and how to use various graphical and mathematical devices to extract information from data.

The raw material of physical science consists largely of measurements. In chemistry one measures mass, volume, temperature, pressure, and the optical and electrical properties of matter. The data used are scale readings. The measurements of length, area, and volume depend on some standard scale. Temperature is measured by the length of mercury expansion on a scale. Weights are compared by the motion of a pointer on a scale. Time is measured by the scale reading of a periodic motion. Pressure, thermal, and electrical measurements are made by a combination of these and some other scale-reading devices. For intelligent use of this raw material, one must know the source and reliability of the readings. In *none* of these cases does a scale reading give the "true" value of the property sought.

To produce an accurate *estimate* of the mass, volume, temperature, or pressure, corrections from the raw readings of an instrument must be made. This chapter presents some of the important corrections required for accurate chemical measurements. Chapter 2 shows mathematical procedures for interpreting results and judging their reliability.

1.1 MASS

Mass is a measure of amount of matter. A mass is usually measured in the laboratory by comparing its weight with that of standard masses, called *weights*. Weight is a measure of the force of gravity on a mass. Force and mass are related by Newton's second law, $F = ma$, force equals mass times acceleration. Here, weight $= m \times g$, where g is the gravitational constant of the earth at that spot. Since this is the same on both balance pans, the masses are directly compared, if an equal-arm balance is used. Error due to inequality of balance arms is avoided by substitution weighing: weights on the same pan as the object being weighed are removed until balance is restored against a constant load on the other pan. Single-pan semiautomatic balances operate this way. Figure 1–1 shows the construction of a substitution-type single-pan balance.

The gram was originally intended to be the mass of 1 cc of water at its maximum density, at 3.98°C. But the experimental difficulty of accurately weighing water made it desirable to choose a standard weight made of a noble metal alloy. Each nation's standard kilogram weight can be compared with the prototype in Paris to within a few parts in 10^9. An independent mass scale is that based on $^{12}C = 12$ used to compare isotopic masses in the mass spectrometer. Its relation to the kilogram is known to 25 ppm, but this is of little use. No one has yet thought of a good, independently reproducible, mass standard like those we have for length and temperature.

To determine weight accurately, one must test the mechanical condition of the balance, the accuracy of the weights, and consider possible buoyancy corrections. Disturbances caused by a magnetic field or a source of heat must also be avoided. The presence of a warm object near a balance will cause it to behave erratically. For reliable weighing, objects to be weighed must be at room temperature.

Table 1–1 shows the tolerances set up by the National Bureau of Standards for several classes of weights. Single-pan balances usually have steel weights adjusted to within class S tolerances. We see from the table that an object weighing 31.6000 g could be in error by ± 0.3 mg at worst, assuming that all errors are in the same direction. However, most chemical work will involve subtracting two such weights to find a smaller sample weight. For example, to find the weight of a sample, subtract the weight of the empty crucible (31.0000 g) from the weight of the crucible plus sample (31.6000 g), giving 0.6000 g as the weight of the sample.

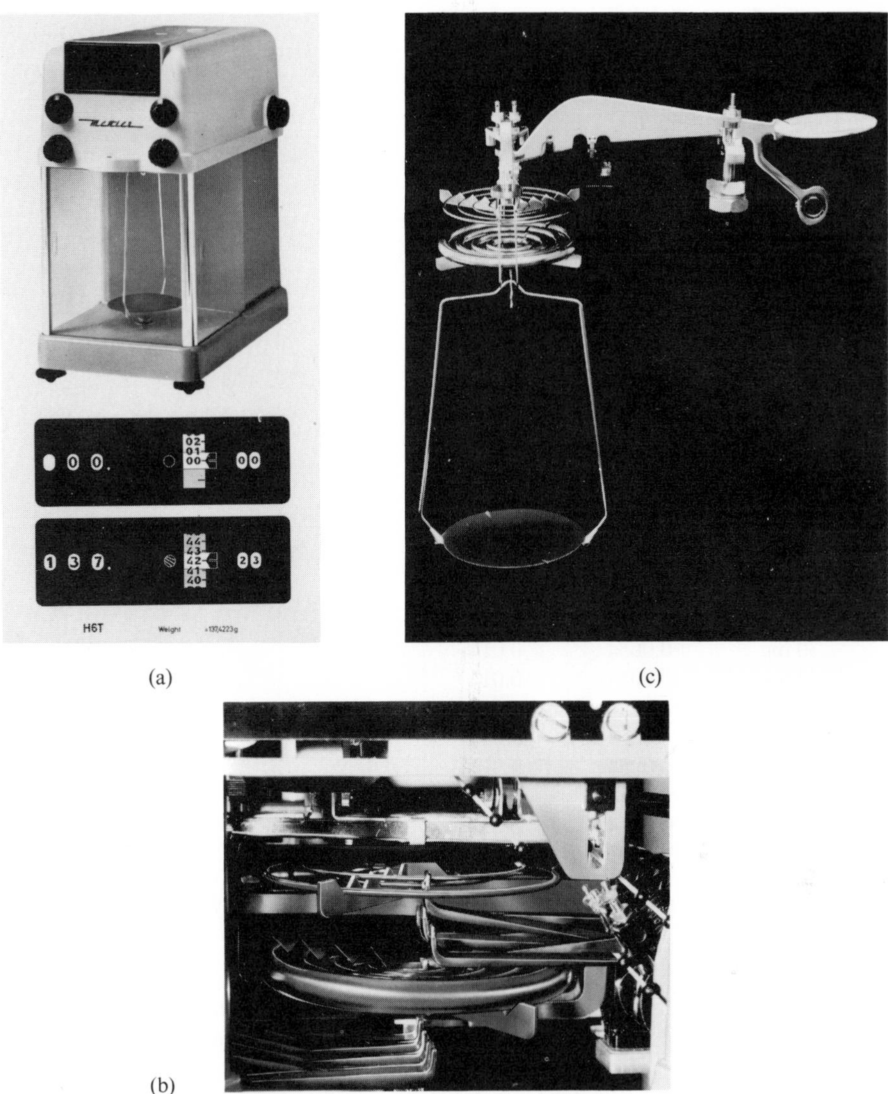

Fig. 1–1. (a) A single-pan balance. Side entrance through sliding glass windows. On model H6T, scale readings are shown for zero weight and for a weight of 137.4223 g. (b) Weight lifting mechanism within the balance case above the pan. Two Bakelite® fingers lift each circular weight off the rack. Weights are removed equal to the weight of the object placed on the pan. A typical analytical balance of this kind has eight ring weights: 1, 1, 2, 5 g above, and 10, 20, 40, and 80 g below. (® Bakelite is a registered trademark of Union Carbide Corp.) (c) Cut-away view of main working parts of the balance: beam, weights, pan, and small circular glass scale at opposite end. The scale moves up or down in a light path so that its divisions are projected onto a screen at the front of the balance case. It has divisions for 100 or 1000 mg in various models. The vane above the scale moves in a box so that air damping of the beam motion brings it to rest. The fulcrum near the front end is a sapphire knife edge. (Courtesy of Mettler Instrument Corporation.)

Table 1–1. Weight Tolerances, in mg

Denomination	Class M	Class S	Class S-1	Class P	Class Q
1000 g	5.0	2.5	10	20	50
500 g	2.5	1.2	5.0	10	30
300 g	1.5	0.75	3.0	6.0	20
200 g	1.0	0.50	2.0	4.0	15
100 g	0.50	0.25	1.0	2.0	9.0
50 g	0.25	0.12	0.60	1.2	5.6
30 g	0.15	0.074	0.45	0.90	4.0
20 g	0.10	0.074	0.35	0.70	3.0
10 g	0.050	0.074	0.25	0.50	2.0
5 g	0.034	0.054	0.18	0.36	1.3
3 g	0.034	0.054	0.15	0.30	0.95
2 g	0.034	0.054	0.13	0.26	0.75
1 g	0.034	0.054	0.10	0.20	0.50
500 mg	0.0054	0.025	0.080	0.16	0.38
300 mg	0.0054	0.025	0.070	0.14	0.30
200 mg	0.0054	0.025	0.060	0.12	0.26
100 mg	0.0054	0.025	0.050	0.10	0.20
50 mg	0.0054	0.014	0.042	0.085	0.16
30 mg	0.0054	0.014	0.038	0.075	0.14
20 mg	0.0054	0.014	0.035	0.070	0.12
10 mg	0.0054	0.014	0.030	0.060	0.10
5 mg	0.0054	0.014	0.028	0.055	0.080
3 mg	0.0054	0.014	0.026	0.052	0.070
2 mg	0.0054	0.014	0.025	0.050	0.060
1 mg	0.0054	0.014	0.025	0.050	0.050

From National Bureau of Standards Circular 547; M = (master) weights for reference standards, S = scientific working standards, S-1 = routine analytical weights, P (formerly S-2) = rough analytical weights, Q = technical weights for trip scales, etc.

We only need to consider the error in the 600 mg of weights (or optical scale). For the class S weights, this could be 0.05 mg or about one part in 10,000 in this example.

The condition of the balance and weights can be checked against a standard set of laboratory weights to reveal mechanical failure of the instrument and any large error in its weights. The optical scale can also be checked by following the instructions given by the maker of the instrument. This is simple to do, and the span of the scale can be quickly readjusted if it is not perfect.

Buoyancy

By Archimedes' principle, 1 liter of a certain stainless steel of mass 7.86 kg (17.3 lb), which is a cube about 3.9 in. on a side, weighs only 6.86 kg under water because it displaces 1.00 kg of water. In the much less dense air, d = 1.2 g/liter, its weight would not differ from its mass to the three significant figures given. However, if this cube were weighed more precisely and its mass were 7.8624 kg, the weight in air would be 7.8612 kg. If it were balanced against steel weights, the air displacement would be the same on object and weights, so that buoyancy effects just cancel each other, and a "weight" equal to the mass is obtained. The mass is often called the weight in a vacuum.

From the example just given, it is apparent that buoyancy correction will sometimes be required for precision when the density of object and weights are different. The reader can satisfy himself that this equation holds

$$M = W_{\text{vac}} = W_{\text{air}} + W_{\text{air}} \frac{d_{\text{air}}}{d_{\text{obj}}} - W_{\text{air}} \frac{d_{\text{air}}}{d_{\text{wts}}}, \tag{1-1}$$

where M is mass, W, weight, and d, density. This equation reads, mass equals the apparent weight in air, plus the buoyancy (mass of air displaced) on the object, minus that on the weights. (In the buoyancy terms, $W_{\text{air}} \cong M$ for liquids and solids.)

For weighings with steel weights, $d = 7.86$ g/ml and $d_{\text{air}} = 0.0012$ g/ml, Eq. (1–1) becomes

$$M = W_{\text{air}} \left[1 + \frac{0.0012}{d_{\text{obj}}} - 0.00015 \right] \text{g}. \tag{1-2}$$

For liquids of density near 1 g/ml, Eq. (1–2) becomes

$$M = W_{\text{air}} (1.0011). \tag{1-3}$$

This means that 1000.0 apparent grams of water would weigh 1001.1 g in a vacuum. For quantitative work to a precision of one part per thousand, buoyancy corrections will be needed on most liquids, but not on solids of density greater than 3 g/ml.

The value given for the density of air is for average conditions. Variations in atmospheric pressure, temperature, and humidity would usually affect the fifth significant figure in the mass. For instance, reduction of the pressure to 700 mm and addition of 50% humidity only affect the mass by about one part in 10,000 after the buoyancy correction.

Schoorl, in 1918, proposed a system of "rational" atomic and formula weights containing the buoyancy correction. This system is based on the rough generalization that atomic volumes are additive upon compound formation. Therefore densities and buoyancy corrections are also additive. The rational formula weight is then the apparent weight in air of one mole of the substance. Calculation of a number of moles or a percentage from an experimental weight can then be made with these rational weights to give values corrected for buoyancy. This approximation is reliable in the fifth figure, which is usually the first one affected. For solids the correction is slight, even for a low-density material like potassium acid phthalate(KHP), with formula weight, 204.23 and rational formula weight, 204.15. One standard for which the difference is important is constant boiling HCl. Tables usually give the air weight required to contain one mole of HCl after distillation at a stated pressure. At 760 torr, it is 180.19 g (see p. 308).

1.2 LENGTH AND VOLUME

Originally (in 1791), the meter was intended to be such that the circumference of the earth would be 40,000 km. This value is within 0.1% of modern values. Later, the meter was defined as the length on a platinum alloy bar kept in Paris. In 1960, the meter was more precisely defined as 1,650,763.73 times the wavelength of the orange-red krypton-86 line. Actual lengths on the order of centimeters can be compared with this standard using a Michelson interferometer.

From the geometry of a container we know that volume can be measured as a length cubed. However, it is much easier to weigh glass apparatus accurately than to determine its volume from length measurements. Therefore the liter was defined as the volume of 1000 g of water at its maximum density at 3.98°C. This was thought to be also one cubic decimeter or 1000 cc. More accurate measurement has shown that 1000.000 cc of water at 3.98°C has a mass of 999.973 g, so that 1 ml was 1.000027 cc, a difference of 0.027 ppth. This difference is negligible for ordinary work. The liter was redefined as exactly 1000 cc by international agreement in 1964.

Accurate measurement of solution volume has long been the most common technique in analytical chemistry. However, with the development of rapid balances and sintered glass and porcelain filter crucibles, gravimetric determinations and even weight titrations may return to extensive use. The time required for weighings and crucible preparation had made gravimetric methods far more time-consuming than volumetric ones.

No volumetric container can be used without being calibrated by the user or the manufacturer. A vessel is calibrated by weighing the water contained in or delivered by the vessel, depending on its use. Even 1 ml of water can be weighed to 1 part in 10,000, that is, 0.1 mg out of 1 g, although evaporation makes tenths of milligrams difficult to get. For a 1 liter flask, weight to 0.1 g would be 1 part per ten thousand. Thus this method is capable of achieving a high degree of accuracy for large apparatus. Corrections must be applied for buoyancy and density of water at the temperature used. For apparatus used to deliver a known volume, strict attention to cleaning and drainage time is required if reproducible volumes are to be obtained.

As we derived in the preceding section, the buoyancy correction for water weighed with steel weights is

$$M = W_{\text{air}}(1.0011).$$

Thus at 25°C the volume is:

$$V = M/d = W_{\text{air}}(1.0011)/0.99704 \text{ g/ml} = W_{\text{air}}(1.0041).$$

To speed calibration calculations, Table 1–2 lists values obtained in this way for various temperatures. For example, if a student finds that, at 25°C, his pipet delivers 24.898 g of water weighed in air against steel weights, he need

Table 1–2. The Volume of 1.0000 g of Water Weighed in Air with Steel Weights at 18 to 32°C

Temperature, °C	Density g/ml	Volume, ml/apparent g	Temperature, °C	Density, g/ml	Volume, ml/apparent g
18	0.99860	1.0025	26	0.99678	1.0043
19	0.99840	1.0027	27	0.99651	1.0046
20	0.99820	1.0029	28	0.99623	1.0049
21	0.99799	1.0031	29	0.99594	1.0052
22	0.99777	1.0033	30	0.99565	1.0055
23	0.99754	1.0036	31	0.99534	1.0058
24	0.99730	1.0038	32	0.99502	1.0061
25	0.99704	1.0041			

In this table, milliliters and cubic centimeters are assumed identical. In older tables, the densities used here would be described as g/cc. This only affects the rounding off in the fifth figure in five cases of the apparent volume.

only multiply this by 0.0041 on the slide rule and add to get 24.898 + 0.102 = 25.000 ml. He then knows that, for his four-figure work, his pipet delivers 25.00 ml and no correction is needed.

If the container is used at a temperature more than 10°C from the calibration temperature, the change in volume of the glass itself must be calculated with the cubical expansion coefficient of the glass (1×10^{-5} per degree for Pyrex® glass). This is not included in the table because vessels are usually calibrated and used at about the same temperature so that no correction is needed.

The reciprocal of the last column in Table 1–2 gives the apparent weight of 1.0000 ml of water. For example, to mark a flask at 1000.0 ml, one should weigh into it at 25°C 1000.0/1.0041 = 995.9 apparent grams of water.

The density and specific volume of water change about 2 parts in 10,000 per degree. That is why it is pointless to try for precision in the fifth significant figure in volumetric work if, as is usual practice, the temperature is not known to within several degrees. To obtain five significant figures, one would have to control the temperature to within 0.5°C for all measured volumes of aqueous solutions, or make a correction after taking the temperature at each measurement.

A careful but thoughtless student might get the following values for the weight of water from a 10 ml pipet:

first trial,	9.9706 g,
second trial,	9.9684 g.

He has read the temperature with an ordinary thermometer as 21°, but it was really 20.5° the first time and 21.5° the second. "What, 2.2 mg difference?" says

® Pyrex is a registered trademark of Corning Glass Co.

he. But these weights vary only the 2 parts in 10,000 which correspond to a one-degree change in the water temperature.

This is a major reason that usual analytical work has been scaled to a precision level of one part per thousand, the limitation imposed by the $\pm 5°$ range of laboratory-solution temperatures.

1.3 TEMPERATURE

The concept of temperature as a quantitatively measurable property is relatively recent. Good thermometers were not available until after 1700. Galileo (1597), Pascal (1643), and Newton (1701), experimented with liquid-containing devices. Fahrenheit, in 1714, made the first sealed mercury thermometer.

The temperature concept is easily accepted on the basis of experience, but it is difficult to define clearly. It is certainly not a direct measure of the "heat" in a body. One calorie raises the temperature of 1 g of aluminum about 5°, but it raises the temperature of 1 g of water only 1°.

Temperature has been lightly defined as that property measured with a thermometer. But, then one must specify which thermometer is meant. Each real fluid expands at a different nonlinear rate upon heating. Consider trying to use water as a thermometric fluid between 0° and 10°C. Its volume goes through a minimum at 3.98°C. Mercury is much more nearly linear, but against what standard can one check it? The absolute thermodynamic temperature will be discussed later. Here we can use the fact that it appears in the ideal gas law, $PV = nRT$ or

$$T = (V/nR)P,$$

so that the absolute temperature could be measured by the pressure in a constant-volume apparatus, if we had an ideal gas. In such a gas thermometer, helium has been calculated to deviate from ideality to make a temperature error of less than 0.002°C between $-50°$ and 200°C. Our common temperature degree, however, is defined as a mercury degree, which is $\frac{1}{100}$ of the distance of mercury expansion from the ice point to the normal boiling point of water. Because the mercury does not expand linearly with thermodynamic temperature, there is a difference of 0.1° at 50°C between the mercury and the ideal gas thermometer.

To get correct temperature measurements, a mercury thermometer must be used in the same way it was calibrated or a correction must be applied. Clearly, the reading will be different depending on whether only the bulb is immersed in a boiling liquid or whether the whole thermometer is raised to the same temperature. Tables for the emergent stem correction are available in handbooks. Some thermometers are intended to be immersed only to a line on the stem. When there is doubt, it should be calibrated at a temperature near that needed. Table 1–3 describes a few standard calibration points. Several other, usually small, corrections may be needed under some conditions. After a large change in temperature,

Table 1–3. Some Standard Temperature Calibration Points

Temperature, °C		System and remarks
0.00		Clean crushed ice mixed with about equal volume of distilled water. Must be well stirred with thermometer.
32.384		$Na_2SO_4 \cdot 10H_2O$ moistened in a large test tube; warm slightly to melt. Stir with thermometer while cooling in air. Seed with $Na_2SO_4 \cdot 10H_2O$.
	Pressure, torr	
100.00	760	Thermometer must have good contact with both liquid and vapor H_2O. Use a distillation flask.
99.26	740	
98.49	720	
97.72	700	

a thermal hysteresis correction may be required. High pressure can also change the volume of the bulb. Special tables can be consulted to determine these corrections.*

In many calculations the absolute temperature is used so that, at room temperature, 298°K, a precision of 1 ppth corresponds to 0.3°C uncertainty in the temperature.

Temperature scales in use are:

a) International Practical Celsius, °C, formerly centigrade: The ice point is 0.00° (or, the triple point of water is 0.01°, no air present). The boiling point of water at one atmosphere is 100.0°, and other fixed points are used.
b) International Practical Kelvin: $T°\mathrm{K} = t_{\mathrm{p}}^{\circ} + 273.15$, where t_{p}° is the practical °C in (a).
c) Thermodynamic Kelvin: The triple point of water is 273.16°K. This one and only defined point fixes the size of the degree.
d) Thermodynamic Celsius: $t_{\mathrm{th}}^{\circ} = T°\mathrm{K} - 273.15$.

The size of the degree is not exactly the same in the thermodynamic and practical scales. The practical degree varies slightly in different parts of the scale. Interpolation between fixed points of the practical scales is described in terms of platinum resistance thermometers and thermocouples to which mercury thermometers must be compared. Very low or high temperatures require special techniques; mercury melts at −38.9°C and boils at 356.6°C. Common glass thermometers are limited by the difficulty in making the tubing in uniform bore. Extensive calibration is required to use them to better than 0.1°.

* For further information and calibration systems, consult handbooks and J. R. Partington, *An Advanced Treatise on Physical Chemistry*, Vol. 1. New York: John Wiley, 1949, Section VI-A.

1.4 PRESSURE

The mercury barometer was invented by Torricelli in 1643. The measurement of atmospheric pressure from it is needed for some quantitative procedures: finding vapor densities, preparing constant boiling HCl, and correction of boiling points. The standard atmosphere is now defined as 1,013,250 dynes/cm^2, which is 14.696 pounds per square inch, and 760 mm of Hg (torr) under the conditions given below.

The barometer reading is *not* the atmospheric pressure. Atmospheric pressure was defined as the height of ice cold (0°C) mercury supported in a tube with a perfect vacuum above the mercury, in a place where $g = 980.665$ cm sec^{-2} (45° latitude). Therefore the reading is affected by the following factors:

1. temperature, which affects density and vapor pressure of Hg and expands the scale,
2. capillary depression of Hg in narrow tubes,
3. altitude and latitude, which affect g,
4. difficulties in construction (scale position and lack of good vacuum).

Tables listing correction factors for the first three are given in handbooks. Only the first two usually affect the reading to more than 0.1 torr. The second, capillarity, is usually compensated for in the construction of the scale in commercially made models. The temperature, however, is variable, and its effect is large, usually about 2 to 4 torr. The mercury and scale corrections are contained in one table. The vapor pressure of mercury is only about 10^{-3} torr at room temperature.

Example. To estimate the atmospheric pressure from the barometer reading, add in all the correction factors:

barometer reading at 26°C at 50° N latitude and 500 m (or 1640 ft) elevation	738.66 mm
temperature correction	−3.12
latitude effect on g	+0.34
altitude effect on g	−0.12
	735.76 torr atmospheric pressure.

Note that the meteorological tables for "reduction to sea level" are not the ones used here. Rather, use tables for reduction to sea-level gravity at 45° latitude. However, for pressures to the nearest torr, the temperature correction alone is adequate in most places.

SUMMARY

Intelligent use of data requires knowledge of how the measurements are made, their inherent errors, precision, and accuracy. The student should be especially alert to these factors in his basic operations: weighing and volume measurements.

SUGGESTIONS FOR FURTHER READING

HIRSCH, R. F., "Modern Laboratory Balances," *J. Chem. Educ.* **44,** A1023 (1967) (Part One), **45,** A7 (1968) (Part Two).

LANG, S. B., and R. L. PECK, *J. Chem Educ.* **44,** 48 (1967). This article discusses the mathematics of the distribution of integral weights in one- and two-pan balances.

WILSON, E. B., JR., *An Introduction to Scientific Research*, New York: McGraw-Hill, 1952.

PROBLEMS

1. Find the minimum number and denomination of gram weights that can be used on one side of the fulcrum in a single-pan balance to weigh up to at least 120 g.
2. Find the minimum number and denomination of gram weights that can be used on both sides of the fulcrum of a two-pan balance to weigh up to 121 g.
3. How many parts per thousand is the buoyancy correction on CCl_4 (density 1.6 g/ml) weighed with steel weights?
4. Show that buoyancy correction is required for four-figure work with water but not with sodium chloride.
5. A 100.0 ml glass bulb with stopcock weighs 47.2002 g when full of air of density 1.207 mg/ml. Find the weight when the air is replaced with hydrogen under conditions at which it has density 0.077 mg/ml?
6. How will the common (Torricellian) barometer react to weightless conditions at atmospheric pressure, in a space ship?
7. Calculate the buoyancy-correction factors for platinum and for aluminum weighed with steel weights.
8. A student makes a solution with distilled water at 20°C in a 1 liter volumetric flask. His calculated molarity was 0.2011. By the time he used the solution, it had warmed to 24°C. What was the new molarity? Assume the same expansion as with pure water.
9. A student prepared an As(III) solution as directed which requires neutralization of a large amount of base with acid. He forgot to cool it after this exothermic reaction and made it up to 1.000 liter when it was actually at 43°C. The next morning, it was at 24°C. What volume of it would seem to have evaporated?
10. Derive the buoyancy corrections in Eq. (1–1). Show with vector arrows the effects on object and weights. Demonstrate that the same effects operate in two-pan and single-pan (substitution) weighings. Discuss the validity of the approximation, $W_{\text{air}} = M$. (See Problem 5.)

CHAPTER 2

TREATMENT OF DATA

2.1 SIGNIFICANT FIGURES

Scientists do not knowingly make false claims about their results. However, lack of regard for the degree of reliability of measurements often has led to reports of results to more figures than can be justified. This can be very misleading as some of the following examples will show.

It is tempting to retain an arithmetical result such as 1385 even if it came from multiplying two figures one of which had only three significant figures. For this reason, scientific notation is preferred for careful and clear reporting. The use of this notation also simplifies calculation. Scientific notation is formed as follows. Put the decimal point after the first digit. Then write only as many figures as are significant. Then multiply by ten raised to the power that correctly sets the magnitude of the quantity. Write the units.

Examples

1. The above number 1385 is 1.38×10^3.
2. A measurement such as 0.03779 liter should be written 3.779×10^{-2} liter or 3.779×10^1 ml.

(The second example shows that the units chosen have no connection with the significant figures or the reliability of a measurement.) For simplicity in such low powers of ten, most people will write 37.79 ml for the last result. No ambiguity is introduced here, but consider a number such as 53,000. Does the person mean five significant figures? Or, does he mean 5.3×10^4?

The number of significant figures in a measurement is made up of all the certain digits ending with one that may be uncertain, an estimate. On the usual 50 ml buret, one can read tenths of a milliliter with certainty and can estimate hundredths to about ± 0.01 ml. Thus an initial reading of 0.07 ml and a reading of 23.09 ml after titration gives 23.02 ± 0.02 ml delivered (± 0.01 at each reading). Therefore the uncertainty is about 1 ppth. If the final reading had been 43.09, then the delivered volume would be 43.02 ± 0.02 ml, where the uncertainty is reduced to 0.5 ppth.

Here let us list some rules for consistent, logical use of numbers:

1) Round off a five, when needed, to the nearest even number:

$$1.975 \rightarrow 1.98, \qquad \text{but} \qquad 1.965 \rightarrow 1.96.$$

2) In multiplication and division, each number contributes its own fractional uncertainty to the result:

$$(388 \pm 2)(489 \pm 7) = 189{,}732 \pm 36\bar{9}4 = (1.90 \pm 0.04) \times 10^5.$$

(Here, the first figure has an uncertainty of $\pm 0.5\%$ and the second $\pm 1.4\%$. Thus the product has an uncertainty of $\pm 1.9\%$.) The rough rule is that the least precisely expressed number determines the number of significant figures in the product or quotient. However, consider the example,

$$(101 \pm 1)(989 \pm 1) = 99{,}889 \pm 10\bar{9}0 = (9.99 \pm 0.11)10^4.$$

The rough rule requires three figures, 9.99×10^4, which is plainly not justified by the two uncertainties, 1% and 0.1%, of the starting figures. Therefore the sum of the uncertainties of the starting figures is a more reliable guide to the right number of significant figures than is the rough rule. This sum approximation is usually valid when the uncertainties are less than 10%. This is deduced from the magnitude of the last term in the product: examine the example given above, with higher uncertainties inserted.

3) In addition and subtraction, columns with unknown digits are not used. Digits to the left of the ones given are known to be zeros, but, those to the right are not. Consider the following two examples:

i) To 1000.0 ml water, add two dilute solutions of 10.05 ml and 1.066 ml:

$$\begin{array}{r} 1000.0xx \text{ ml} \\ 10.05x \text{ ml} \\ 1.066 \text{ ml} \\ \hline 1011.1xx \text{ ml.} \end{array}$$

Here x is used to emphasize the columns where addition cannot take place because some of the digits are not available.

ii) If the initial and final buret readings are 20.66 and 22.99, the net volume is 2.33 ml. As explained above, this has uncertainty of ± 0.02 ml or about 10 ppth. One must be alert to this common loss of significant figures when the calculation requires a subtraction.

4) Logarithms are exponents, and only their mantissas convey significant figures. Such common expressions as pH = 11.88 and $pK_a = 12.32$ contain only two significant figures each. The antilog table permits the assignment of uncertainties. For example, pH = 11.88, assuming ± 0.01 unit, is: $(H^+) = 10^{-11.88} = 10^{0.12} \times 10^{-12} = 1.32 \times 10^{-12}$, and from the antilogs of 0.11, 0.12, and 0.13, one can see that the uncertainty is $(1.32 \pm 0.03) \times 10^{-12}$.

But, beware of the beginning of the log table. Antilog 0.992 ± 0.001 is 9.82 ± 0.02, but the antilog of 0.005 ± 0.001 is 1.012 ± 0.002.

The last figure which is significant is sometimes indicated by a bar over it. When an additional figure is carried for subsequent calculations, it is sometimes shown as a subscript:

$$10\bar{3}50, \qquad 1.03_5 \times 10^4.$$

Measurements are limited in precision, the amount of information they convey. The number of significant figures presented should give some idea of how precisely the result is known. More definite expression of precision is described in the following section. It should be understood that the information contained in data is strictly limited and, in general, is not subject to unlimited increase by refinement of techniques. (See the discussions of the limits of fundamental measurements in Chapter 1.)*

2.2 ERRORS

Errors which can be assessed and for which corrections can be applied are *determinate* errors. Volume expansion with temperature, buoyancy, flask calibrations, etc., are determinate errors. Limitations in the equipment and methods as well as variations in judgment of estimated readings (of the last significant figure) are *indeterminate* errors. They may introduce variation into a set of results. This type of error is not to be equated with mistakes or gross errors. The kind of error we are treating here is unavoidable error. It may sometimes be reducible, but by its nature, it cannot be eliminated.

Accuracy is defined in quantitative chemistry as the closeness of a result to an expected, published, or theoretical value. *Precision* is the closeness of replicate results to each other. A set of results which are not very precise might have an accurate average, while a set of very precise results might have a very inaccurate average because of a consistent source of error. For example, consider the following results for the atomic weight of silver (accepted value 107.870):

a)	b)
107.861	107.777
107.870	107.778
107.881	107.779
107.892	107.780
The mean is 107.876.	The mean is 107.778.

Set (a) is more accurate, but less precise, than set (b). The accuracies of the mean values are:

for set (a),	+0.006 amu	or	0.06 ppth;
for set (b),	−0.092 amu	or	−0.85 ppth.

Parts per thousand are convenient units for much chemical analysis.

In the measurement of an unknown quantity, the accuracy cannot be determined if there is no value to compare it with. Thus precision is used to express the

* The case for proper use of significant figures, especially where small numbers of measurements make statistical methods less valid, is clearly presented by R. C. Pinkerton and C. E. Gleit, *J. Chem. Educ.* **44**, 232 (1967). See especially p. 234.

reproducibility of the result. The simplest way to express the precision is as the deviation from the mean of the set. Signs are not used for this. The deviations and the average deviation of the above sets of values are:

a)	0.015 amu	0.14 ppth
	0.006	0.06
	0.005	0.05
	0.016	0.15
	The mean is 0.010.	The mean is 0.10.
b)	0.001 amu	0.01 ppth
	0.000	0.00
	0.001	0.01
	0.002	0.02
	The mean is 0.001.	The mean is 0.01.

This average deviation is clearly

$$\bar{d} = \sum d/n,$$

where d is the deviation and n is the number of results. Of more statistical significance is the term *standard deviation*, defined as

$$\sigma = (\sum d^2/n)^{1/2}$$

for a very large set of results with random positive and negative errors. It is the half-width at the inflection of the normal-error curve:

$$\frac{dN}{N} = \frac{e^{-d^2/2\sigma^2}}{\sigma\sqrt{2\pi}}\,dx, \tag{2-1}$$

where N is the number of results, and d is the difference between the mean and a certain result, x, or d is the deviation from the mean μ. See Fig. 2–1 for a diagram of the normal-error curve. This law may or may not be followed by any chosen sample of a set of a *finite* number of results from this infinite population of possible results.

Two-thirds, approximately, of the infinite set lies between $\pm\sigma$ of the mean. For a sample from the infinite set, the *estimated* standard deviation, s, can be calculated as follows,

$$s = [\sum d^2/(n - 1)]^{1/2}.$$

In the above sets of values for silver, we see that for set (a),

$$s^2 = (2.25 + 0.36 + 0.25 + 2.56) \times 10^{-4}/3,$$
$$s = 0.013 \text{ amu} \quad \text{or} \quad 0.12 \text{ ppth},$$

and for set (b),

$$s^2 = (1 + 0 + 1 + 4) \times 10^{-6}/3 = 2 \times 10^{-6},$$
$$s = 0.001_4 \text{ amu} \quad \text{or} \quad 0.01_4 \text{ ppth}.$$

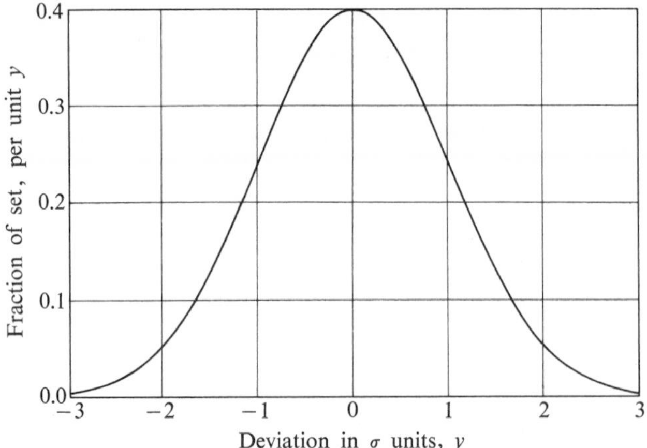

Fig. 2–1. Normal-error curve. Equation (2–1) for the normal-error curve can be simplified by substituting $y = d/\sigma$, where $d = x - \mu$, and thus, $dx = \sigma\, dy$. (The new variable, y, is just the deviation expressed in sigma units.) The instantaneous value of the fraction of the set within a one-sigma unit interval at deviation y is $dN/N\, dy = e^{-y^2/2}/\sqrt{2\pi}$.

It must be stressed that s, the estimated standard deviation, may be very different from σ. However, all the following methods based on s assume the equality of s and σ.

Confidence limits can be obtained from the abbreviated table of t values, Table 2–1, by use of the relation,

$$\mu = \bar{x} \pm t(s/\sqrt{n}).$$

That is, the true mean, μ, of a very large set of determinations has the given probability (95 or 99% in the table) of lying within $\pm\, t(s/\sqrt{n})$ of the observed mean, $\bar{x}$, of a small set of n results of standard deviation s.

For example, in the sets of values for silver above,

	95% confidence limit	99% confidence limit
Set (a):	$\dfrac{3.2(0.013)}{\sqrt{4}} = \pm 0.021$ amu	$\dfrac{5.8(0.013)}{\sqrt{4}} = \pm 0.038$ amu
Set (b):	$\dfrac{3.2(0.001_4)}{\sqrt{4}} = \pm 0.002_2$ amu	$\dfrac{5.8(0.001_4)}{\sqrt{4}} = \pm 0.004_1$ amu.

If one has an estimate of σ (say, the s from 50 or more previous results by the method) one then may use the ∞ value in the table for t in calculating the confidence limits for a new group of m values: $\pm 1.96\sigma/\sqrt{m}$, or $\pm 2.58\sigma/\sqrt{m}$, for 95 and 99%.

Various statistical tests of the significance of differences among sets of results obtained by different methods or persons have been devised. Extensive tables of

Table 2–1. Values of t and Rejection Quotient, Q, for n Results (Degrees of Freedom are $n - 1$)

n	2	3	4	5	6	7	8	9	10	∞
t (95%)	12.7	4.3	3.2	2.8	2.6	2.5	2.4	2.3	2.26	1.96
t (99%)	64	10.	5.8	4.6	4.0	3.7	3.5	3.4	3.25	2.58
Q		0.94	0.76	0.64	0.56	0.51	0.47	0.44	0.41	

critical values for the t test, F test, and chi-square test are readily available in reference books and in *Handbook of Chemistry and Physics* (ed. by R. C. Weast, Cleveland: The Chemical Rubber Co., 1967.)

The *t test* can be used to test the hypothesis that two means, from two sets of results, do not differ significantly. From the formula for confidence limits given above, solved for t, one gets,

$$t = (\bar{x} - \mu)\sqrt{n}/s.$$

For two sets of n results each, one can use this formula with the difference of the means and a pooled s calculated as follows:

$$s^2 = \frac{\sum d_1^2 + \sum d_2^2}{(n_1 - 1) + (n_2 - 1)}.$$

In the two sets of four silver results above, one gets

$$s^2 = \frac{5.42 \cdot 10^{-4} + 6 \cdot 10^{-6}}{3 + 3} = 9.1 \cdot 10^{-5},$$

$$s = 9.5 \cdot 10^{-3}.$$

With $n = n_1 n_2/(n_1 + n_2)$,

$$t = \frac{0.098}{9.5 \cdot 10^{-3}}\sqrt{2} = 14._5.$$

The number of degrees of freedom (the number of independent values in the mean, the denominator of the s^2 calculation) is six. Therefore one looks under $n = 7$ in the t table to find that the critical value of t is 3.7 at the 99% level. One concludes that, since the calculated t is in excess of 3.7, the two sets differ significantly for some reason.

The *F test* compares the variances of the sets, rather than the means,

$$F = s_1^2/s_2^2.$$

For the two sets of silver results,

$$F = 1.7 \cdot 10^{-4}/2 \cdot 10^{-6} = \overline{8}5.$$

The critical value of F when both sets have 3 degrees of freedom is 29 (F-value tables are given in the *Handbook of Chemistry and Physics* or in the references).

Thus, again there is a 99% probability that the difference between the two sets is real, whether because of analytical errors or a difference in the original material taken.

Such significance tests as these might reasonably be applied when large groups of students perform analyses by different methods or on different samples of materials.

The chi-square test of data deviation from an expected frequency of appearance is sometimes useful in chemical situations such as detection of number bias in readings of graduations on burets and balances. Its use and tables are given in handbooks and reference books.

Rejection of Results

One may use the rejection quotient to test the advisability of omitting a result which seems very far out of line. This quotient, Q, is found as follows:

a) Arrange the results in order of increasing magnitude and take the *difference* between the suspect value and its nearest neighbor.

b) Get the *range* of the set: the highest minus the lowest value, including the suspect value.

c) Get the rejection quotient, $Q = a/b =$ difference/range.

If Q is greater than the critical value in the table, the result may be rejected with 90% assurance that it contains some gross error. For example: in the cases for silver discussed above:

a) Range = 0.031 and the difference between the last two values is 0.011, so that

$$Q = 0.011/0.031 = 0.35,$$

which is less than 0.76 required for rejection in the table for four results.

b) The rejection quotient,

$$Q = 0.001/0.003 = 0.\overline{3}3$$

for either end result in the set. However, if a fifth result were 107.788,

$$Q = 0.008/0.011 = 0.73,$$

which is greater than the 0.64 required for rejection with five results. Note the irony here that one must reject the most accurate of his results. This danger always exists, and one must maintain a healthy skepticism toward even the most gratifying precision.

Rejection by this method should be used only when no reason is known for the deviation of the suspected result. If some accident has occurred in handling one sample, that result may be rejected without any statistical test.

Statistical treatment cannot improve data. However, it may reveal what may not be obvious upon inspection of the set of results. In the example using the determination of the atomic weight of silver carried through this section, one found that, although no specific value of either set could be rejected, the statistical tests clearly showed a significant difference between the sets. Without these tests one might have concluded only that one set was less precisely determined than the other.

2.3 RELIABILITY LIMITS

From the discussion of significant figures, one can see why a statement such as "the sample contains 5% iron" is unclear. Does it mean between 4% and 6%, between 4.9% and 5.1%, or what? The figures 5% ± 1%, 5.0% ± 0.1%, etc., would clarify the meaning. This section treats methods of estimating uncertainty and assigning reliability limits, the ± figure.

From Section 2.2 one can determine confidence limits based on the normal-error curve. However, these are so unreliable for the small sets of results usually obtained in laboratory work that more realistic estimates of the limits can be made from reliabilities of the original data and chemical considerations.

Examples

1) Three results obtained in a determination of the percentage of Na_2CO_3 in soda ash were 38.80%, 38.81%, and 38.82%. The average value is 38.81%. The average deviation is 0.007 units, or 0.2 ppth, and the standard deviation is 0.01 units, or 0.3 ppth.

The chemist doing the work knows that the burets and solution concentrations can only be reliable, here, to about 1 ppth as explained in Section 2.1. Therefore the good precision of the three results is fortuitous, and he reports 38.81 ±0.04%, an estimated 1 ppth reliability range at best. Such an estimate is justified because three results do not warrant use of statistical methods, *and* because the chemist has other knowledge about the precision of the method. Without this knowledge, more determinations would be required. (See the following example.)

2) For the percentage of Sb in an ore, these values were obtained:

46.00 The average of first 3 = 46.06, $\bar{d}$ = 1.7 ppth, s = 2.2 ppth.
46.01
46.18
45.88
45.69
45.55
The average of 6 values = 45.86, $\bar{d}$ = 4.0 ppth, s = 5.0 ppth.

If the determinations had been stopped after the first three values were obtained, the precision would suggest much greater reliability than is suggested by the whole set of six. As in Example 1, the weighings and titrations can only account for about 1 ppth uncertainty. In this case, the chemical difficulties in dissolving the ore and in the redox titration lead the chemist to report 45.9% ± 0.3% Sb, where the range of results is given (about 7 ppth). A simple report that the ore is 46.86% antimony would suggest a precision that the method does not possess. Whatever the method of stating results, the meaning of the range value *must* be given because there is no standard unit assumed. He should report 45.9% ± 0.3% (range), $n = 6$, signifying that this is the total range of six results. Alternatively, from the s value, he could report 45.86% ± 0.28% (95% confidence limit, $n = 6$) or 45.86% ± 0.41% (99% confidence limit, $n = 6$). These limits were found from Table 2–1.

A combination of these statistical methods with chemical and mechanical considerations allows one to assign reliabilities to experimental results. In a complicated calculation, uncertainties should be attached to each figure and followed through the calculation.

3) What reliability range should be expected for a gravimetric chloride determination using a 1 g sample about 50% Cl^-?

The sample can be weighed to ±0.2 mg, 2 parts in 10,000. The AgCl produced will weigh about 2 g, so that its weight should be known to about 1 part in 10,000. The calculation is

$$\frac{(\text{Cl})(\text{weight AgCl})100}{(\text{AgCl})(\text{weight sample})} = \%\text{Cl}^-.$$

Small relative errors can be added algebraically to approximate their effects on products and quotients. Proceed to get the relative uncertainties of the four terms in the equation. It will be convenient to use parts in 10^4 here.

Let the sample weight be known to ±0.2 mg, 2 parts in 10^4.
The product AgCl will weigh about 2 g, ±0.2 mg is 1 part in 10^4.
The atomic weight of Cl is 35.453 ± 0.001, 0.3 parts in 10^4.
The atomic weight of Ag is 107.870 ± 0.003, 0.3 parts in 10^4.

The aggregate effect of these errors is found by combining them in the most unfavorable ways to get a maximum possible error.

a) Take the Ag atomic-weight error as positive and the Cl as negative. Combine these with the weighing errors:

$$\frac{\{-0.3\}\ \{-1\}}{\{+0.14\}\ \{+2\}}.$$

The AgCl figure is

$$\frac{0.003 - 0.001}{143} = 0.14 \times 10^{-4}.$$

Combining the errors gives -3.4 parts in 10^4.

b) Taking the reverse signs for errors gives $+3.4$ parts in 10^4.

c) Taking Ag and Cl atomic-weight errors both of the same sign partially cancels the error and gives a result smaller than 3.4 parts in 10^4, which is thus the maximum possible resultant error.

Clearly, if we take a sample weighing 10 g, the weighing uncertainty would be on the same order as that of the atomic weights. Further improvement, by increased sample weights, is not possible for the same reason that the atomic weights are uncertain in parts per 100,000. That is, uncertainty in chemical purification on this level limited the original atomic-weight work.

This suggests the important conclusion that chemical purity of precipitates limits the precision of gravimetric work. A student can easily weigh out 100 g of material to almost a part per million, but he will be unable to find or make most substances in a similarly high degree of purity. (Distilled water is a possible exception).

Estimation of reliability has two important values for the investigator. First, it shows clearly the precision of his determinations and the results calculated from them. Second, it may allow him to change the magnitude of the figures in which there is the largest uncertainty, so that his result will have greater precision (smaller uncertainty limits). This kind of analysis of errors can teach the student clear and logical use of numerical data and results.

2.4 GRAPHICAL USE OF DATA

The process of transforming a small collection of numerical data in two variables into a curve on graph paper may mystify the beginner in science. It cannot be done without using several assumptions which are commonly made (intuitively!).

1) The two variables are assumed to be related by a continuous function. Thus a smooth curve, not straight-line segments, should be used to join the points. (One straight line is a smooth curve.)

2) The simplest curve coming within reasonable distance (say $\pm$ the standard deviation or the experimental reliability) of the points should be taken, since an infinite number of curves can be made to fit a finite number of points. "Simple" here means having the fewest possible inflections. For example, ten evenly spaced points in a straight line can be perfectly fitted by a sine-wave curve, but a straight line is simpler.

3) If the functional relation between the variables is known or suspected, appropriate coordinates to give a linear plot are often chosen instead of plotting one variable versus the other. For example, if $x^2 = ay + b$, a plot of x^2 versus y should give a straight line of slope a and intercept b. The great value of this technique stems from two considerations:

a) A well-fitting line can be drawn with a straightedge if errors in the data are not large, or it can be fitted to the points by the least-squares procedure more easily than with other functions.

b) The slope and intercept yield constants of the system.

4) When it is impossible or impracticable to use a linear plot (most titration curves, for example), plots having least curvature can be drawn with least error from limited data.

Curve Fitting

Only straight-line plots are discussed here since most data used for equilibrium investigation can be cast into this form. First, plot the data on coordinates of scale appropriate to the reliability of the data and the result desired. The uncertainty in the data (or result, if greater) must not be less than that in plotting: for example, 3.558 cannot be properly expressed on a coordinate having 10 one-mm spaces between 3.0 and 4.0. It would have to be placed at 3.5_6. Three methods may then be used to draw the best straight line for the set of points.

1) Use a straightedge and visually estimate. If the errors are small, this method can be quite satisfactory.

2) *Method of averages.* If there is enough scatter to make method 1 uncertain, plot the grand mean of all x_i and y_i values. Here x_i and y_i are the functions of the data being plotted to give a straight line of equation

$$y = mx + b.$$

Next, plot two more points, the averages of the x_i and y_i values of the top and bottom thirds of the data (or halves if there are fewer than six points). Draw the line through the grand mean and parallel to a line joining the upper and lower means.

3) *Method of least squares.* The principle is derived from the error function and states: The best straight line is that having the minimum value of the sum of the squares of the deviations of observed points from the line. Thus we need an equation for the deviations which we can square, differentiate, and set equal to zero to find the minimum. The deviation can usually be taken for one coordinate of the point. That is, we are asking: What is the difference between the experimental y_i value and the y on the line at x_i? Here, $y = mx_i + b$. The deviation is

$$d_i = y_i - y = y_i - mx_i - b.$$

The sum, S, of the squared deviations, d^2, is

$$S = \sum d_i^2 = \sum (y_i - mx_i - b)^2.$$

The summation is over i. The slope, m, and the intercept, b, are to be adjusted to make S a minimum:

$$\frac{\partial S}{\partial m} = 0 = -2\sum (y_i - mx_i - b)x_i,$$

$$\frac{\partial S}{\partial b} = 0 = -2\sum (y_i - mx_i - b).$$

With a total of n points of data, these equations rearrange to

$$m\sum x_i^2 = \sum x_i y_i - b\sum x_i,$$

$$nb = \sum y_i - m\sum x_i.$$

We solve these equations for m and b to get the condition for the best line,

$$m = \frac{n\sum x_i y_i - \sum x_i \sum y_i}{n\sum x_i^2 - (\sum x_i)^2},$$

$$b = \frac{\sum x_i^2 \sum y_i - \sum x_i y_i \sum x_i}{n\sum x_i^2 - (\sum x_i)^2}.$$

In the following example, it would be difficult to choose a line visually. The method of averages and the least-squares lines serve better in such cases. Slight changes in slope greatly affect the intercept. A tabular calculation speeds the work. Because the sums to be subtracted are, by their nature, close to each other, one finds that four to six significant figures must be carried to obtain two to four figures in m and b. A calculator is useful. Standard computer programs are routinely used for such calculations. Application of this method in cases of class results as described in the following example may be useful.

Example. Fit lines to the class data for equilibrium constants, K, determined at six ionic strengths, I; $\log K$ is expected to vary directly with $\sqrt{I}/(1 + 2.3\sqrt{I})$. Find the intercept, $\log K^0$ at $I = 0$. The needed functions and sums are indicated in terms of x_i and y_i.

Data					
I	$-y_i = -\log K$	$\sqrt{I}$	$x_i = \sqrt{I}/(1 + 2.3\sqrt{I})$	$-x_i y_i$	x_i^2
0.01	4.79	0.1000	0.08130	0.3894	0.006610
0.02	4.72	0.1414	0.1067	0.5036	0.011385
0.03	4.67	0.1732	0.1239	0.5786	0.015351
0.04	4.68	0.2000	0.1370	0.6411	0.018769
0.05	4.69	0.2236	0.1477	0.6925	0.021800
0.06	4.60	0.2449	0.1567	0.7208	0.024555
Sum	28.15		0.7533	3.5260	0.098470
Mean	4.69		0.1258		

$$m = \frac{6(-3.5260) - (0.7533)(-28.15)}{6(0.098470) - (0.7533)^2} = \frac{-21.1560 + 21.2054}{0.59082 - 0.56746} = 2.12,$$

$$b = \frac{(0.098470)(-28.15) - (-3.526)(0.7533)}{0.02336} = -4.95_7.$$

We have achieved the objective of finding the intercept, -4.96. The data as x_i and y_i are plotted in Fig. 2–2 along with the line obtained by the method of averages and two least-square lines, the one just given and another omitting the fifth point which is farthest from the line.

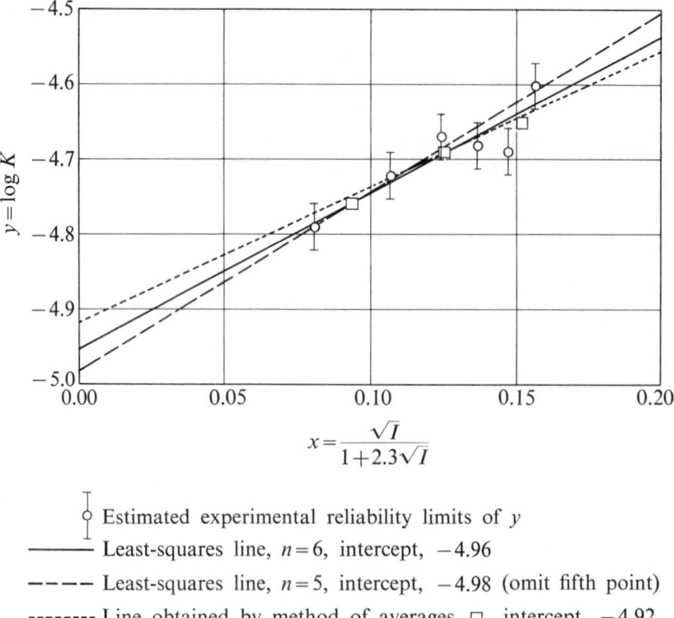

Fig. 2–2. Fitting a line to six points of class data.

SUMMARY

The student should become familiar with the following ideas and calculations and use them where applicable in his laboratory work.

- Determinate and indeterminate errors
- Deviation from the mean
- Standard deviation
- Confidence limits
- Reliability limits, estimated from limitations of data
- Rule for rejection of results
- Expression of results only to the precision justified
- Use of best line, slope, and intercept from data

SUGGESTIONS FOR FURTHER READING

DEAN, R. B., and W. J. DIXON, *Anal. Chem.* **23,** 636 (1951). A brief article on the statistics of small sets.

LAITINEN, H. A., *Chemical Analysis*, New York: McGraw-Hill, 1960, Chapter 26.

WILSON, E. B., JR., *An Introduction to Scientific Research*, New York: McGraw-Hill, 1952, Chapters 8 and 9.

YOUDEN, W. J., *Statistical Methods for Chemists*, New York: John Wiley, 1951.

PROBLEMS

1. What are the usual limiting factors determining the precision of volumetric and of gravimetric laboratory work?
2. Find the mean, the median, and the Q values of the extremes of the set of figures: 64.92, 65.05, 65.09, 65.11, 65.20, and 65.22. Should any be omitted by the Q test?
3. Express the averages of the following sets of replicates to a sensible number of significant figures (reason?). Calculate $\bar{d}$ and s. Circle the values that may be omitted by the Q test.

6.55	25.80	25.80	25.50
7.54	25.81	25.82	25.62
8.45	25.84	25.83	25.70
	25.90	25.98	25.83
			25.90

4. What is the effect in pH units of a 50% error in (H^+)?
5. For an error of +10% in I, what is the change in f at $I = 0.1$, if $\log f = -0.51\sqrt{I}$?
6. For an error of +10% in (H^+), what is the percent error in K_{eq}? At $(H^+) = 2.0 \times 10^{-4}$,

$$K_{eq} = \frac{0.0825(H^+)^3}{773.9}.$$

7. Consider starting the reaction $A + B \rightleftharpoons C + D$ with 20 units of each substance present. (It is similar to esterification study). At equilibrium, it was found that x units = 10.0 ± 0.5 had reversed so that

$$K_{eq} = \frac{(20 - x)^2}{(20 + x)^2}.$$

Calculate K and its limits.

8. Sometimes small amounts must be determined by an indirect back titration. If an ion determination of this type required 19.51 ml of a standard metal ion solution to back titrate an aliquot of EDTA, and a blank took 20.00 ml, what percent error would be introduced in the net volume (0.49 ml) by a 2° temperature difference between the two titrations? Approximately what percent error is due to the usual uncertainty in buret readings?
9. A sample of NaCl seemed to be 99.72% NaCl based on a chloride determination. If the only other material present to account for this composition is KCl, calculate the percentage of it that must be present. [*Hint:* Formulate an equation for the number of moles of each substance.] What could be present in NaCl to account for an apparent percentage of 100.8% NaCl?
10. Use the t test to find out if there is any difference significant at 95% or 99% levels between the second and third sets in Problem 3.
11. Natural boron contains only B-10 and B-11 of masses 10.0129 (19.6%) and 11.0093 (80.4%). Assume that the fractions, which are difficult to determine, have reliability ± 0.1 in % units. Prove that the proper atomic weight calculated from *these data* is 10.814 ± 0.001 and not 10.8 or 10.81.

CHAPTER 3

LABORATORY WORK

In his laboratory work the experimenter confronts chemical nature and develops his sense of its behavior, his chemical intuition. If he is interested and skeptical, he may see more than the expected. If he is also honest and brave, he may not be blind to behavior which is unexpected or even contrary to his notions. There are unknown facets of any laboratory operation. No one need be oppressed by ennui at certain routines when there are so many aspects of the work to wonder about. Good research projects have begun with undergraduate laboratory curiosities.

3.1 ORGANIZATION

Quantitative investigation includes frequent routine operations that take time but do not require constant attention, such as oven drying, evaporations, digestions, and dissolutions. During this time one should work on other phases of the experiment or on another experiment. A preliminary listing of the steps required and the times necessary to complete them will greatly increase the student's efficiency and save him time. This often means doing second or third things first.

For example, in volumetric determinations one is usually told to make and compare two solutions, then to dry and weigh a primary standard to be titrated with one of the solutions, then to dry and weigh an unknown material also to be titrated. The student who plods dutifully through each step in the order given will probably take two or three afternoons to complete the work. With planning, it might be done in one, if the determination is performed as outlined below.

1. Get the two solids and dry them for one hour in the oven.
2. Meanwhile prepare the solutions and compare them by titration.
3. Cool and weigh out both solids in one trip to the balance.
4. Titrate all the samples weighed, both known and unknown.
5. Calculate the results and report them.
6. Clean up.

In other cases, a long operation allows one to prepare solutions (if stable), crucibles, or other special apparatus for the next experiment. In these ways, experienced workers learn to use their time efficiently. The beginner who spends all his days in the laboratory is probably neither careful nor thoughtful in planning his time.

3.2 REAGENTS

An absolutely pure chemical has yet to be made in visible amounts. What is required for chemical determinations is that the impurities in the materials used either be inert for the purpose at hand, or be known and corrected for if they are large enough. Laboratory chemicals are commonly found in these grades:

Primary standard. These materials are of precisely known and stated composition and can be used to standardize. Examples are: Na_2CO_3 certified as 99.95% to 100.05% as a base toward strong acid and constant boiling HCl certified as 20.33% ± 0.01% by weight. Note that high purity is not required, only *known* purity.

Analytical reagent. Materials labeled with the maximum limits of likely impurities. The percentage purity or assay is not usually given for these. (*Note:* The producer is not telling you about other impurities that he does not expect and has not tested for. Be skeptical.)

USP and NF (United States Pharmacopoeia, and National Formulary). These have standards for impurities of physiological significance.

Practical, Technical, C.P. These are indefinite terms for materials of widely varying purity which are not for analytical work.

Only analytical-reagent grade chemicals can be used with safety for accurate work. Lower-grade materials require testing and blanks.*

Liquids and solutions commonly available are listed in Table 3–1 in the "concentrated" form usually supplied by manufacturers. Their labels give percentage by weight and density so that other designations must be calculated. They are given here for convenience.

Table 3–1

	HCl	HNO_3	H_2SO_4	$HC_2H_3O_2$	NH_3	NaOH
Density, g/ml	1.19	1.42	1.84	1.05	0.90	1.53
Percent by weight	37	70	96	100	28	50
Molarity	12	16	18	17.5	15	19
ml/mole	82	63	56	58	68	52

It is the duty of each worker to keep all reagents covered and free of contamination. Liquids evaporate, and both liquids and solids absorb moisture and other gases from the air. Good results are far more likely from the worker who keeps his chemicals and equipment clean and orderly than from one who does not.

* For a more detailed discussion of chemical reagents see J. Rosin, *Reagent Chemicals and Standards*, 5th ed. Princeton, N.J.: D. Van Nostrand, 1966.

3.3 CLEANING GLASSWARE

There is no ideal method of cleaning laboratory glassware. A method adequate for one use may leave a residue in trace amounts that will disturb another experiment. Recall that glass has a silicate surface which will have some attraction for acid materials: cations in general and hydrogen-bonded molecules. For instance, even prolonged baking of glass under vacuum may not remove the last trace of surface water.

For flasks, beakers, weighing bottles, etc., it is often enough to brush them with a warm detergent solution* and rinse with tap water followed by two small portions of pure water (deionized or distilled). If flasks are stored upright with a clean beaker inverted over each, both will be dust-free and ready for use. Keep the fingers away from the openings of cleaned glassware.

In volumetric pipets and burets, a very clean surface is needed to maintain a smooth film of liquid that does not break up into patches or droplets. The breakup signifies dirty spots which will cause erratic variations in delivered volume. Often brushing with a detergent solution will clean the burets, especially greaseless types. For more stubborn cases, and for pipets which cannot be reached by brush, a more active cleaning solution is needed. Some are listed below. Do *not* suck them by mouth. Do *not* brush with them. Work down *in a sink.*

"*Chromic acid.*" Pour sulfuric acid onto saturated $Na_2Cr_2O_7$ solution in the proportion 100 ml acid to 5 ml $Na_2Cr_2O_7$. ($K_2Cr_2O_7$ is not soluble enough in the acid to work.) This can be stored in a glass container and reused as long as it is red-brown. It works well hot (100°C) and slowly when cool. It is very hard on clothes, furniture, and books. Use only when other solutions do not work. Keep water out of the solution.

Alcoholic KOH. A solution of about 10% KOH in 95% ethanol or 20 ml saturated KOH solution in 80 ml ethanol is good for grease and carbonized matter. Since it attacks glass slowly, do not leave it in volumetric ware more than 5 min, then cool. Store in polyethylene containers. It can be reused even when dark colored.

Acid peroxide. A 1:1 mixture of 3% H_2O_2 and 6 *M* HCl loosens many residues on glass, especially brown stains of MnO_2 and iron compounds. Do not store in tightly stoppered containers.

For stubborn organic stains, try to remove the bulk with acetone, hexane, etc., and steel wool, if accessible. Next try 6 *M* NaOH or the KOH solution described above. Hot 2:1 HNO_3-H_2SO_4 mixture is next in order. For small trouble spots, the following oxidant can be tried:

Mn(VII) oxidant. Place one small crystal of $KMnO_4$ on the spot of wet glass. Allow a few drops of H_2SO_4 to run over it. Hold it away from you in the sink

* A mixture of about 1% laundry detergent (not soap) and 1% Na_2CO_3 makes a good general cleaning solution. Store in a bottle with a rubber stopper. Reuse it.

and rinse it off after a few minutes. Mn_2O_7 may be formed here. (*Caution:* Do not make any larger quantity, since it is a dangerous explosive.)

For iodine or silver nitrate spills on clothes or skin, put on a solution of $Na_2S_2O_3$ and wash off. This must be done right away for $AgNO_3$. For silver compound stains which have set on clothes, tables, tops of benches, floor tile, etc., the following method oxidizes, then dissolves the silver which has been reduced by organic materials. Soak the spot with dilute (0.1 *N*) I_2 in KI solution. This forms AgI. After a few minutes, wash out the I_2 and AgI with a concentrated solution of hypo, low-grade $Na_2S_2O_3$. Wash any cloth with hot water after this treatment. Badly blacked cotton lab coats have come out pure white by this treatment.

Acid or Base Spills

Add water and blot up with waste paper. Then wet the spot with saturated $NaHCO_3$ solution (technical, kept for this purpose by the acids). Solid $NaHCO_3$ may be used if the solution is not ready. The sodium bicarbonate is a cheap, safe material to put on clothes and skin, when spills occur. Keep in mind where it is and use it right away when you have an accident.

3.4 APPARATUS

Details of techniques will be given in the laboratory section at the end of the book. Only general ideas are mentioned here.

Drying

The consequences of the water vapor in our atmosphere are an important problem in chemical and much other laboratory work. Weighable amounts of water are absorbed on most surfaces except for polished metal. It can rarely be completely removed. Therefore we strive for *reproducible dryness* in weighing equipment and samples. Oven-dried and desiccated materials quickly take up water from the air at room temperature increasing their weight. To test this, a 100 ml beaker was washed, oven dried three times for 30, 40, and 130 min, respectively, at 110°C, and then weighed. Successive weighings were made on a one-pan semiautomatic balance at the times given in Table 3–2 from removal from a larger covered beaker in which it just reached room temperature. (The first weighing in each case shows the erratic behavior usually found if slightly warm items are put on a balance.)

These weighings were done at 23°C in a room of 55% relative humidity. Thus the partial pressure of water vapor was about 12 mm of Hg. Different variations can be expected for different humidities and methods of heating and cooling. How then can one get weights reliable to less than 1 mg for samples contained in glass? Clearly, a sample of 500 mg in the beaker of this experiment could have an apparent weight varying over 9 mg, or 18 ppth, depending on the time of weighing.

Table 3–2

After first heating		After second heating		After third heating	
t, min	Weight, g	*t*, min	Weight, g	*t*, min	Weight, g
1	43.9965	1	43.9900	1	43.9950
3	43.9982	3	43.9980	2	43.9977
5	44.0030	5	44.0025	5	44.0029
12	44.0057	12	44.0053	12	44.0054
14	44.0058	14	44.0054	14	44.0055
				34	44.0056

A tightly closed weighing bottle can prevent rapid absorption of water by the sample, but the outer glass surface still creates a problem. A practical solution is to time the weighings so that the same times can be used in subtracting the empty from the full beaker weight, and the absorbed water weight will largely cancel. In the experiment given, the error in a 500 mg sample weight could be reduced to 1 ppth or less by consistently weighing after 3, 5, 12, etc., minutes. It should be pointed out that this experiment presents an unfavorable case with larger glass surface than is commonly used. A small weighing bottle with only the outside exposed to air will change proportionately less. It may also dramatize to the student why we do not weigh dry titration flasks, add the sample, and weigh again. The large glass surface could introduce terrible error for small samples.

A further problem arises from the speed of semiautomatic balances. Few persons can weigh to 0.1 mg on a standard two-pan balance in less than 10 min. Thus the weight is taken after the rapid changes of the first few minutes the item spends in the moist air. With the rapid balances, one should wait a definite time before weighing after placing the object in the balance case. If a series of samples from the same weighing bottle is to be taken by difference, the bottle should stand in the balance case for 10 min before the series is begun. The absorbed water on the outside will have reached a nearly constant value. Workers must be especially observant of this error during warm humid weather. Without such care, no matter how good the balance, weighing will be reliable only to within milligrams rather than to within the tenths of milligrams required for many procedures.

Desiccators and Desiccants

The simple atmospheric-pressure desiccator can preserve materials in low-humidity air for long periods. However, because of slow circulation, the chamber takes one hour or more to recover from the moist air introduced with each opening. Therefore desiccators do not dry items put in them for short cooling times prior to weighing. They only protect from fresh moist air and dust. Vacuum desiccators permit rapid removal of the air and speed drying through faster diffusion. Circulation in ordinary desiccators can be improved with magnetic stirring. The

Table 3–3

Name	Capacity (approximate) g H_2O/g desiccant	Minimum P of H_2O reached, mm	Approximate cost, \$/lb
P_2O_5	0.2	$\ll 10^{-4}$	2.00
$CaSO_4$ (Drierite)	0.1	0.005	1.20
$CaCl_2$ (desiccator grade)	1	1.5	1.00
Silica gel (alumina)	0.2	0.002	2.00
KOH (flake)	—	0.002	0.80
H_2SO_4 (concentrated)	0.2	0.003	0.50

magnetic bar can be placed in a shallow dish on the bottom. A cardboard vane can be attached with a rubber band. A few minutes stirring serves to bring all the air in contact with the desiccant, a small dish of which may also be placed on the upper level of the chamber.

Red-hot items should be cooled to under 200°C before going into the desiccator. The desiccator top should be greased to slide easily. A thin (half-inch) layer of desiccant changed often is more reliable than a deep pile, of which only the top is in good contact with the air. A few pieces of indicating Drierite® can be placed in one side of the desiccant to warn of saturation.

Some common desiccants are listed in Table 3–3. Their capacity and cost are more important than ultimate lowering of humidity for general use.

Calcium sulfate can be treated for 1 to 2 hrs at 200°C and silica at 175°C to regenerate used desiccant many times. This can greatly reduce their cost. Anhydrous calcium sulfate can be easily tested for activity: fill a small crucible nearly full and put a thermometer in it. Barely cover with water. A 10° to 20°C temperature rise signifies active $CaSO_4$.

Since P_2O_5 is a very acidic powder which glazes over with HPO_3 as it reacts with water thus stopping further drying action, it is not recommended for general use. Sulfuric acid, a very corrosive liquid, has obvious difficulties in use. Potassium hydroxide gets wet and forms a powder of K_2CO_3. It can remove water, CO_2, and other acidic gases.

The capacities in Table 3–3 can be used as illustrated in the following example:

Example. Find the volume of air that can be dried by 100 g of Drierite.

Assume a temperature of 25°C, 50% humidity air, which thus has a water vapor pressure of 12 mm. From the table, 100 g Drierite can take up 10 g water. One liter of the air contains (by the ideal gas law):

$$\text{weight} = MPV/RT = (18)(\tfrac{12}{760})(1)/(0.082)(298) = 0.012 \text{ g.}$$

® Drierite is a registered trademark of W. A. Hammond Drierite Co.

Note that 1-mm water vapor pressure around room temperature happens to be 1 mg/liter

$$10\ \text{g}/0.012\ \text{g/liter} \cong 830\ \text{liters of air.}$$

A desiccator could be opened for brief periods about 800 times assuming 1 liter of air exchange. Probably 100 g is not needed. Naturally, forgetting to return the top as soon as possible would greatly shorten the time to exhaust the desiccant. The high capacity and low cost of $CaCl_2$ make it a favorite for student use.

3.5 NOTEBOOKS AND REPORTS

A true scientific notebook contains the original record of all the experimental data and observations made. A report may be condensed and rearranged as required. The notebook stays with the worker at balance and buret to receive the first record of his work. Use of bits of paper and memory are to be strictly denied for very good reasons. The possibilities for loss and for error in recopying are simply unnecessary risks to take. There are recorded cases of important discoveries missed because of foolish practices about notes.* Good notebook use saves time and misery over chance methods. It is not supposed to be a perfectly neat final report. But, it must be an intelligible record. Some self-discipline toward proper use of his notebook is a primary skill to be attained by every aspirant to scientific laboratory work.

There are some general rules on which scientists agree from long experience. Each instructor may have some special points for his students to follow. Some rules and examples follow.

1. Data should be recorded in ink as they are taken. Pencil smudges and is less legible.
2. The work on each page should be dated and clearly labeled so that a glance will tell what the page is about.
3. Each item should be sufficiently labeled to show what it is. A page full of numbers alone rapidly becomes meaningless to everyone. Units as well as descriptive words should be given.

The briefest descriptive notes that are still clear are best. Writing in the notebook should not take much time. Many achieve clarity and neatness by using the left page for preliminary readings, calculation, etc., and the right page for main data and results. On the left might go several readings of balance weights (and its swings if used) and buret readings around a difficult endpoint. Even these should have a designation, for example, "1st wt. of no. 1," or "titr. of no. 1" so that later rechecking is possible.

---

* E. Bright Wilson, Jr., *An Introduction to Scientific Research*, New York: McGraw-Hill, 1952. p. 130ff.

An experiment should begin with a reference to the method, if it is in print, and especially any changes to be made. Paper is cheap. Don't crowd. Spread the data so it is easy to find and later comments can be added. A sample page follows to illustrate these ideas. Extensive abbreviation is useful.

Sample notebook page for determination of an unknown

10–18–67 Soda ash (sample no. 73) John Smith

The method is given in Ayres, p. 640, no. 1. Use bromcresol green instead of methyl purple. Boil. By aliquots. Get % Na_2CO_3.

Wt. bottle before	24.8710 g	
Wt. bottle after	18.6739 g	(dried one hour, 112°)
Wt. soda ash taken	6.1971 g	sample → 500.0 ml

Titration of 50.00 ml aliquots

	I	II	III	IV	V
Final HCl buret rdg.	37.72	37.49	37.70	37.48	40.49
Initial	0.80	0.69	0.90	0.68	3.68
Net vol. HCl	36.92	36.80	36.80	36.80	36.81
	(overrun, omit)				
log (ml HCl)*		1.56585	1.56585	1.56585	1.56597
log (0.1872 N_a)		$\bar{1}$.27231	$\bar{1}$.27231	$\bar{1}$.27231	$\bar{1}$.27231
log (53.00 meq weight)		1.72428	1.72428	1.72428	1.72428
colog (619.71 mg)		$\bar{3}$.20781	$\bar{3}$.20781	$\bar{3}$.20781	$\bar{3}$.20781
log (100)		2.00000	2.00000	2.00000	2.00000
log (%Na_2CO_3)		1.77025	1.77025	1.77025	1.77037
% Na_2CO_3		58.92	58.92	58.92	58.93
Average		58.92			
Deviation, ppth		0	0	0	0.2
Std deviation, *s*, ppth		0.1			
Estimated experimental uncertainty		±0.10%			

* The formula used is %Na_2CO_3 = (ml HCl)(N_a)(meq weight)100/sample weight.

If calculations are done with logarithms, the use of the cologarithm for divisions saves space since the whole column may be added to get the result (colog $x = \log x^{-1}$).

For small numbers of results, especially those from titrations of aliquots of a single weighed sample, deviations and confidence limits are less meaningful than an estimated error limit obtained by combining the uncertainties in each quantity used in the calculation. (See Section 2.3.) In this report, the relative uncertainties in parts per thousand are: sample (0.03 in weight + 0.2 in pipet), titration volume, 0.5, acid normality, 1, milliequivalent weight, negligible. Adding gives 1.7_3 ppth.

So, the report should be: 58.92 ± 0.10 (estimated experimental uncertainty) $\%Na_2CO_3$. This is clearly more realistic than the limit ±0.006% (or 0.1 ppth) from the titration deviation alone.

Reporting forms vary among schools, industrial, and research laboratories. One, for the above determination, is given here. It is contained on a small card and has only the data needed to allow a recalculation of the results as a check. It has been found useful for grading and filing purposes.

Sample report card for determination of an unknown

10–18–67			Soda ash (sample no. 73)	John Smith	
Sample weight per aliquot =	619.71 mg				
Net vol. 0.1872 *N* HCl	36.92 (overrun, omit)	36.80	36.80	36.80	36.81
% Na_2CO_3		58.92	58.92	58.92	58.93
Average	58.92				
Deviation, ppth		0	0	0	0.2
Std. deviation, *s* ppth	0.1				
Report	58.92 ±0.10 $\%Na_2CO_3$				

For experiments requiring more detailed reports, the form of articles in the American Chemical Society journals is suggested. They would usually include:

1) *Introduction.* State the object and, very briefly, the methods of the work.

2) *Experimental.* Discuss in some detail techniques and instruments that were new to you. Include notes on any difficulties, changes, and unexpected behavior noted.

3) *Results.* A sheet of tables of the data obtained and results calculated from it, graphs, and recorder traces should be included.

4) *Discussion of errors and reliability limits of results.* Give a quantitative treatment of the effects of reasonable errors on the calculated results. Compare results with published values whenever they can be found. Try to account for differences. Give references to all published material found valuable.

The content of each part will vary with the experiment. The briefest report which covers the subject is the best report. If you love to write, work for the newspaper; don't pad the report. Read articles which appeal to you in the journals and you will find examples of clear, as well as unclear, reporting and discussion.

PROBLEMS

1. Look over the laboratory directions for the first three laboratory periods. List the steps in the order you should do them to make most economical use of time. Estimate the time required by each step. Do not leave long intervals of waiting. (Allow yourself no more than one coffee break per day.)
2. Thoroughly clean and dry a weighing bottle in air. Weigh to 0.1 mg. Oven dry for 30 min, cool, and reweigh after several intervals during which the bottle stands in air. Read the room temperature and humidity. This will give some idea of the precision and reliability you may expect from your subsequent laboratory procedures using the weighing bottle.

CHAPTER 4

ACIDS AND BASES

4.1 ACIDS AND BASES IN THE SCHEME OF CHEMICAL REACTIONS

It is convenient to consider ionic reactions in solution as falling into two categories: (1) association and dissociation, including conventional acid-base reactions, and (2) oxidation-reduction reactions. Chapters 4 through 10 and Chapter 25 treat the first, and Chapters 12 through 14, the second type.

Since the days of alchemy, acidic and basic properties have been recognized by their effect on the color of certain vegetable materials and by neutralization which discharges both properties. Lavoisier and early nineteenth century chemists identified acidity with the oxygen content of a substance. This was logical in view of the predominant number of oxy-acids. Svanté Arrhenius, in 1887, made a great step forward with a theory of ions and proposed hydrogen and hydroxide ions as the fundamental acidic and basic species. This idea was so successful in elucidating chemical behavior in water solutions that, although outmoded, it is still stressed, often to the exclusion of the broader and more fruitful theories of the twentieth century. It should become clear that the presence of hydrogen and hydroxide ions in water solutions, like the presence of oxygen of the earlier theory, is often a symptom and not a cause of the acidic or basic character of some other species. The examples to follow should help impress this on the student.

J. N. Brønsted and J. M. Lowry, in 1923, formulated the proton donor-acceptor theory, still the most frequently used by chemists to explain proton-transfer reactions in water solutions. A theory not tied to any definite chemical species was also developed about 1923 when G. N. Lewis proposed that electrophilic species are acidic and nucleophilic ones are basic. Electron-pair acceptors are acids, and electron-pair donors are bases. A few examples will illustrate these concepts.

The only neutralization in the Arrhenius theory was:

$$H^+ + OH^- \rightarrow H_2O.$$

In Brønsted-Lowry terms, many more species can be treated as acids and bases, as in these proton-transfer reactions:

$$\begin{aligned} \text{acid } x + \text{base } y &\rightleftharpoons \text{acid } y + \text{base } x, \\ HA + H_2O &\rightleftharpoons H_3O^+ + A^- \quad \text{(HA is any weak acid)}, \\ H_2O + NH_3 &\rightleftharpoons NH_4{}^+ + OH^-, \\ H_2O + A^- &\rightleftharpoons HA \quad + OH^-, \\ Fe(H_2O)_6{}^{3+} + H_2O &\rightleftharpoons H_3O^+ + Fe(H_2O)_5(OH)^{++}. \end{aligned} \qquad (4\text{–}1)$$

Lewis theory, the electronic theory, includes all of the above reactions, while nonprotonic reactions can be added (only one electron pair is shown):

$$\begin{aligned}
&\text{acid} + \text{base} &&\rightarrow \text{neutralized product(s)},\\
&BF_3 + {:}NH_3 &&\rightarrow H_3N{:}BF_3,\\
&Ag^+ + 2{:}NH_3 &&\rightarrow H_3N{:}Ag{:}NH_3{}^+,\\
&AlCl_3 + 3H_2O{:} &&\rightarrow Al({:}OH)_3 + 3HCl,\\
&Ag^+ + {:}Cl^- &&\rightarrow Ag{:}Cl.
\end{aligned}$$

4.2 THE EQUILIBRIUM CONSTANT

The true or thermodynamic equilibrium constant, K^0_{eq}, must be expressed in terms of activities, indicated by parentheses, for reaction (4–1):

$$K^0_{eq} = \frac{(\text{acid } y)(\text{base } x)}{(\text{acid } x)(\text{base } y)}. \tag{4–2}$$

For a general monoprotic weak acid or one step of a polyprotic acid,

$$K^0_{eq} = \frac{(H^+)(A^-)}{(HA)(H_2O)}.$$

Here, (H^+) stands for the activity of the aquated proton without regard to how many waters of hydration it holds. The relation of activity to molar concentration will be discussed in detail in Chapters 6 and 9. Activities must be used in calculations for solutions having ionic materials present in concentrations greater than about 0.01 *M*, if greater accuracy than the nearest power of ten is wanted in calculated equilibrium concentrations. For the purposes of Chapters 4 and 5, one need only accept that activities are defined so that they approach molarity more closely as the solution is diluted. However, for water, and solvents generally, the pure liquid is defined as having unit activity. For dilute solutions, it is assumed that the water activity is constantly *one*. By convention, the (H_2O) term is not written in K^0_{eq} expressions. However, for accurate work in concentrated solutions (above 0.1 *M*), a correction for the changed water activity may be added.

For the other species in the equilibrium, using molarities, indicated by square brackets, will be a good approximation to activities only below 10^{-3} *M* for ions. Molarities used with K^0 give results reliable to only one significant figure in the 0.1 *M* region. Errors are much greater for ions of charge greater than *one*. For molecular species like the uncharged acetic acid molecule, activity differs from molarity much less than for ionic species. In this text, (HA) will be assumed to be equal to [HA].

Within the restrictions outlined, an acid K_a, effectively constant for one temperature, pressure, and ionic strength, can be written

$$K_a = \frac{[H^+][A^-]}{[HA]}. \tag{4–3}$$

4.3 TITRATIONS

Titrations were first used in the eighteenth century, and the method was refined by Gay-Lussac and Mohr in the nineteenth century. An early recorded titration, preformed in 1756, measures the carbonate base content of pearl ash by addition of dilute nitric acid; the analyst counted the spoonfuls until effervescence stopped. A weight titration was performed in 1729 when the acidity of vinegar was found with a weighed portion of K_2CO_3, which was added gradually until CO_2 evolution stopped.

Volumetric measurement is rapid, and the calculations are simple, as given in the following section. With rapid balances, weight titrations could be used almost as easily. A plastic dropping bottle containing the standard titrant can be weighed before and after titration to get the weight of solution used. The standardization can be made the same way and expressed in milliequivalents per gram of solution, the weight normality. Then, (weight used)(weight N) = milliequivalents.

The advantages of weight titrations over volumetric titration are:

1. temperature change of the titrant does not affect the result by expansion as it does in a buret titration;
2. calibration of a buret, which would be required for comparable reliability volumetrically, is not needed;
3. small volumes can be used with high precision. For example, 10 ml which could have an uncertainty of 0.04 ml or 4 ppth volumetrically, can be weighed to 1 mg or 0.1 ppth. (Here the drop size will be a limiting factor, about 0.01 ml for a fine tip.)

The student may wish to standardize and use his solutions by both methods to compare the time and results for weight and volume titrations.*

Titration Calculations

When a volume of solution which just completes reaction with another material is measured, the two reacting species are equivalent. That is, for acid-base titrations, the number of equivalents of acid equals the number of equivalents of base, where the number of equivalents is:

$$\text{number of equivalents} = (\text{number of moles}) \times n,$$

where n is the number of protons gained or lost (Brønsted) or the number of electron pairs accepted or donated (Lewis). The equivalent weight is defined as =(formula weight or the mole)/n. The molar weight of H_2SO_4 is 98, and the equivalent weight is 49. For much laboratory work gram-liter units are too large and instead we use milligrams (mg), milliliters (ml), millimoles (mmole), and

---

* Good results in student hands are reported by S. W. Gaddis, *J. Chem. Educ.*, **40,** 324 (1963).

milliequivalents (meq). Concentration units to be used can be defined,

$$M = \text{molarity} = \text{moles/liter} = \text{mmole/ml},$$
$$N = \text{normality} = \text{eq/liter} = \text{meq/ml}.$$

From these come the useful relations, at equivalence in a titration,

$$\text{meq of acid}_a = \text{meq of base}_b, \quad (4\text{–}4)$$
$$\text{ml}_a \times N_a = \text{ml}_b \times N_b, \quad (4\text{–}5)$$
$$\text{ml}_{(a \text{ or } b)} \times N_{(a \text{ or } b)} = \text{meq}_{(b \text{ or } a)} = \text{mg}_{(b \text{ or } a)}/\text{equivalent weight}_{(b \text{ or } a)}. \quad (4\text{–}6)$$

With these equations, titration calculations are easily made.

Examples

1. A chemist prepares a stock of about 0.1 N HCl. If 38.83 ml of it react with 0.2206 g of pure Na_2CO_3, find N_a.

   Using the relation in Eq. (4–6), we have

$$(38.83\ \text{ml})\ (N_a) = 220.6\ \text{mg}/53.00\ \text{mg/meq},$$
$$N_a = 0.1072.$$

2. Given that 26.09 ml of his base stock titrate against a 25.00 ml portion of the above acid, find N_b.

   Using the relation in Eq. (4–5), we have

$$(26.09\ \text{ml})\ (N_b) = (25.00\ \text{ml})\ (0.1072\ N),$$
$$N_b = 0.1027.$$

3. If 40.06 ml of the acid were then used to titrate a 0.8088 g sample of soda ash of unknown purity, find the percentage Na_2CO_3.

   Using the relation in Eq. (4–6), we have

$$(40.06\ \text{ml})(0.1072\ N) = (\text{mg of } b)/53.00\ \text{mg/meq},$$
$$(\text{mg of } b) = 227.6\ \text{mg pure } Na_2CO_3,$$
$$\%\ Na_2CO_3 = (227.6\ \text{mg}/808.8\ \text{mg})(100) = 28.14\%.$$

   Examples 4 and 5 are dilution problems.

4. Find N_a if 40 ml of water are added to 1000.0 ml of 0.1005 N HCl.

   In dilution, meq before = meq after:

$$(1000\ \text{ml})(0.1005\ N) = (1040\ \text{ml})(N_a),$$
$$N_a = 0.0966.$$

5. Find the volume of 1.000 N HCl that must be added to the previous solution to correct it to 0.1000 N.

Let x = ml of 1 N HCl added and use the definition, N = meq/ml,

$$0.1000 \text{ meq/ml} = \frac{(1040 \text{ ml})(0.0966\ N) + (x \text{ ml})(1.000\ N)}{(1040 + x) \text{ ml}},$$

$$x = 3.9 \text{ ml}.$$

One further practical laboratory calculation is the preparation of a solution of specific weight relation.

6. To what normality should acid be made so that twice its titration volume is numerically equal to the percentage of Na_2CO_3 in 1.000 g samples of soda ash?

   Consider a 100% sample and substitute in Eq. (4–6)

$$(50.00 \text{ ml})(N_a) = 1000 \text{ mg}/53.00 \text{ mg/meq}, \qquad N_a = 0.3774.$$

This acid has a *titer* of 20.00 mg of Na_2CO_3/ml. That is, (1 ml)(0.3774)(53) = 20.00 mg. Titer, then, expresses the milligrams of a substance which react with one milliliter of the standard solution. Titer factors may be used to simplify calculations when many of the same type are to be done.

4.4 REAGENTS AND STANDARDS

Solutions

Hydrochloric acid is the most commonly used acid for strong-acid solutions, because it is inexpensive and precipitates few cations. Perchloric acid may be used if freedom from the more complexing anions is required. Hydrochloric acid is not volatilized even from boiling dilute solutions, under 1 M HCl.

Sodium hydroxide is available as reagent grade 50% solution which cannot dissolve more than about 0.1% Na_2CO_3. This greatly simplifies preparation of dilute NaOH of low $CO_3^=$ content. Freshly distilled or boiled water adds a negligible amount of CO_2 in preparing the solution, but it must be kept from much air contact. Rapid pouring and restoppering is safe for short use, but for more extended use, a CO_2 absorption tube can be arranged, or a 250 ml plastic bottle can be filled for small uses to preserve the large stock from so many openings.

Solid, reagent-grade NaOH contains 1 to 2% Na_2CO_3. When it must be used, the 50% saturated solution can be prepared and allowed to stand until the Na_2CO_3 settles. This is quite slow in the viscous solution. Alternatively, the diluted NaOH solution can be passed through a strongly basic anion exchange resin in the hydroxide form. Each $CO_3^=$ ion is replaced by 2 OH^- ions. A known weight of pure NaCl can be converted to NaOH by the same means and diluted to volume for a known normality NaOH solution.

Barium hydroxide can be used for a low-carbonate solution, since $BaCO_3$ is quite insoluble. However, air CO_2 changes its normality by the reaction,

$$Ba^{++} + CO_2 + 2OH^- \rightarrow \underline{BaCO_3} + H_2O.$$

The best ion-exchange method for producing very low carbonate base seems to be by treating a sodium or potassium hydroxide solution with $Ba(OH)_2$ in slight excess to precipitate $BaCO_3$. This solution is then put through a cation-exchange resin in the K^+ or Na^+ form to replace any Ba^{++} with the appropriate alkali ions.*

Absorption of CO_2 by NaOH does not change the total base normality if it is to be titrated by a strong acid to pH 4, or if acid strong enough to decompose H_2CO_3 is titrated by the base. But titration with phenolphthalein (to pH 8) by acids and titration by weak acids will give incorrect results if much $CO_3^{=}$ is present. (See Chapter 7.)

Standards

Azeotropic, constant boiling (CB) HCl can be used as a primary standard in making accurately known solutions of HCl. The azeotrope has been thoroughly investigated and found to be about 20% HCl, a composition slightly dependent on the pressure during distillation. It can be purchased or made, and the composition obtained from published tables is reliable to better than one part in 10,000. (See Table L-1 in the laboratory section.) It is about 6.1 *M*, so that this concentration can be used to start. The boiling mixture reaches constant composition slowly so that the first half, or more, must be discarded unless a fractionating column is used.

Potassium hydrogen phthalate (KHP) (equivalent weight 204.22, rational weight 204.14) is an excellent primary standard for use in standardizing low $CO_3^{=}$ strong base solutions. It may be dried at 110°C (over 125°C, phthalic anhydride is lost) and titrated to pH 8, using phenolphthalein indicator.

Other solid acids sometimes used are benzoic acid, oxalic acid 2-hydrate, $KH(IO_3)_2$, and sulfamic acid. The last two are strong acids.

Sodium carbonate (Na_2CO_3) (equivalent weight 53.00, rational weight 52.99) is the most frequently used primary standard base. It is reliable if well dried and kept from contact with moist air. It forms a series of hydrates up to $Na_2CO_3 \cdot 10H_2O$. The last water is lost slowly at 100°, but drying at 200 to 300°C is required to get water below 0.05%. With the available primary standard-grade anhydrous Na_2CO_3, drying one hour at 120° to 200°C probably will get the water content below 0.1%. Weighing must be rapid to avoid water absorption. It is better to make a stock solution for aliquots than to weigh small samples for each titration, which increases the water error. The means of titrating it completely (decomposing the H_2CO_3 formed) are discussed in Chapter 7 and in the laboratory section.

Tris(hydroxymethyl)aminomethane (equivalent weight 121.13, rational weight 121.04) is a more recently introduced base now available in primary standard grade. It can be dried at 100°C. (There is some decomposition above 110°C.) It is stable in air and seems to absorb very little CO_2. Its equivalence point with strong acid occurs at pH 4.7 so that bromcresol green is a suitable indicator.

---

* See J. E. Powell and M. A. Hiller, *J. Chem. Educ.* **34,** 330 (1957).

Other bases sometimes used are borax, $Na_2B_4O_7 \cdot 10H_2O$, Tl_2CO_3, and HgO, which is added to excess KBr (or KI, more expensive) to produce an equivalent strong base solution:

$$\underline{HgO} + 4Br^- + H_2O \rightarrow 2OH^- + HgBr_4^{=}.$$

HgO may be dried in a desiccator, but heating over 40°C is not recommended.

SUMMARY

This chapter covers the following topics.

1. Acid-base definitions and aqueous equilibrium constants
2. The equivalence-point condition and titration calculations
3. Reagents and primary standards for acid-base titrations

SUGGESTIONS FOR FURTHER READING

Luder, W. F., and S. Zuffanti, *The Electronic Theory of Acids and Bases*, 2nd ed. New York, Dover, 1961.

VanderWerf, C. A., *Acids, Bases, and the Chemistry of the Covalent Bond*, New York: Reinhold, 1961.

PROBLEMS

1. Indicate whether 0.1 *M* solutions of the following are acidic, basic, or neutral (pH 7 ± 0.1). State the appropriate *K* values and give reasons for your answers. Calculations should not be required in most cases.

   HBO_2, NH_4CN, NH_4Cl, K_2CO_3, $Ba(C_2H_3O_2)_2$,

   $NaBO_2$, KHC_2O_4, trimethylammonium acetate

2. A wicked laboratory instructor gives a freshman the project of making pure crystals of $(NH_4)_3PO_4$. The poor student keeps adding ammonia to H_3PO_4 and evaporating to get crystals. But his product always has less than 3 NH_4^+ to 1 PO_4^{3-}. Use K_a values to explain why the solid cannot be made. What happens when he evaporates it?
3. Given that 0.3400 g $Ca(OH)_2$ was dissolved in 500 ml water, find the base normality of the solution. How many ml of 0.1000 *N* HCl are required to neutralize 100 ml of the solution?
4. Sodium hydroxide is now available as a solution, 50% by weight, which has density 1.53 g/ml. Find its molarity. What volume should be taken to prepare 4 liters of 0.12 *N* NaOH?

5. What molarity HCl should you make to titrate 1.000 g samples of soda ash so that each milliliter is equivalent to 1.000% Na_2CO_3?

6. Given that 6.035 g pure NaCl is washed through an excess of anion-exchange resin in the OH^- form and diluted to 1000.0 ml, find the base normality of the resulting solution.

7. Constant boiling HCl at a certain pressure is given in tables as 20.34% HCl of density 1.096 g/ml. Find its normality to four figures. How many grams weighed in air should be taken to make a liter of 0.2000 *N* HCl?

8. a) Determine the range of weights of pure Na_2CO_3 that may be taken to make 10 aliquots of solution each one of which is to be titrated by about 40 ml of HCl whose concentration is within 10% of 0.1 *M*.
   b) Find the smallest titration volume possible in part (a).

CHAPTER 5

SURVEY OF ACID-BASE EQUILIBRIUM CALCULATIONS

The relative acidity of water solutions can be estimated from a knowledge of the concentrations of acidic and basic materials present and their quantitative strengths as given by their equilibrium constants. The calculations can be organized according to the types of materials exchanging protons as follows:

I. strong acids or bases alone,
II. weak acids or bases alone,
III. mixtures of conjugate weak acids and bases (buffers),
IV. the ion of a weak acid or base alone,
V. polyprotic weak acids and their ions,
VI. mixtures of the above.

Although these are traditional and fairly convenient ways of categorizing these solutions, the reader may find it easier to see most of these cases as variations of the one controlling equilibrium of Brønsted acids and bases:

$$\text{acid } x + \text{base } y \rightleftharpoons \text{acid } y + \text{base } x.$$

For example, for 0.1 M acetic acid,

$$\begin{matrix} HA & + & H_2O & \rightleftharpoons & H_3O^+ & + & A^-, \\ 0.1 & & 55 & & x & & x \end{matrix}$$

where the *approximate* molarities are written under the formulas. At equilibrium, x is small for weak acids and fits case II.

But for 0.1 M HA with 0.1 M NaA, also present,

$$\begin{matrix} HA & + & H_2O & \rightleftharpoons & H_3O^+ & + & A^-, \\ 0.1 & & 55 & & y & & 0.1 \end{matrix}$$

which fits case III. In both examples, the same species are present but in such different proportions that the degree of the equation and pH are different. However, it should be stressed that there are no fundamental differences among the equilibria of the six cases above.

The pH is of primary importance in the study of solution reactions in chemistry, biology, and geology.

5.1 REVIEW OF APPROXIMATE METHODS OF pH CALCULATION

The major task in finding the pH of a solution is to identify the equilibria (often only one) that control the $[H^+]$. First we review the approximate methods for the cases listed above. Later we examine the equations to see when the approximations will not serve.

CASE I (*Strong acids and bases*). Materials which contain and/or are leveled entirely to free $H^+(H_3O^+)$ or OH^- in dilute water solution such as

$$HCl + H_2O \rightarrow H_3O^+ + Cl^-$$

[and $HClO_4$, HBr, HI, HNO_3, H_2SO_4 (first H^+)] and

$$NH_2{}^- + H_2O \rightarrow NH_3 + OH^-$$

(and the usual KOH, etc.) are strong acids and bases, respectively.

The concentration of strong electrolyte here gives the $[H^+]$ or $[OH^-]$, and at room temperature, they are related easily by

$$[H^+][OH^-] = 1.0 \times 10^{-14}. \tag{5–1}$$

Example. For 0.1 M NaOH, $[OH^-] = 0.1\ M$ and $[H^+] = 10^{-13}$; pH = 13.

CASE II (*Weak acid or base alone in water*). The equilibria are (5–1) and (for acid)

$$HA \rightleftharpoons H^+ + A^-. \tag{5–2}$$

Assume that $[H^+]$ from the acid (or $[OH^-]$ from a base) is so much greater than that from H_2O by (5–1) that it may be taken as the total $[H^+]$ (or $[OH^-]$).

Example. For 0.1 M acetic acid, x moles dissociate by (5–2) to give x of H^+ and A^-. By Eq. (4–2) and (4–3),

$$K_a = \frac{[H^+][A^-]}{[HA]} = \frac{(x)^2}{0.1 - x},$$

where x is usually small enough to omit in the denominator. We then get $K_a = 1.75 \times 10^{-5}$, so $x = \sqrt{1.75 \times 10^{-5}(0.10)} = 1.3 \times 10^{-3}$ and pH = $-\log(1.3) + 3 = 2.88$. The algebra is analogous for a weak base.

CASE III (*Mixtures of conjugate weak acids and bases (buffers)*). The same equilibria apply as for case II, but $[H^+]$ is not at all equal to $[A^-]$.

Example. For 0.10 M HA with 0.10 M NaA also present,

$$K_a = \frac{(y)(0.10 + y)}{(0.10 - y)},$$

as above, $y \ll 0.1$, so $y = 1.75 \times 10^{-5}$ and pH = 4.76.

CASE IV (*The ion of a weak acid or base alone in water*). This is given as a separate case only because K is usually found for the conjugate species, the uncharged one. Once this is seen, the calculation is no longer mysterious. (Traditionally it is called, "the salt of a weak acid or base.")

Example 1. Let us consider 0.10 M sodium acetate.

a) If we know K_b for the weak base A^-, this is really just case II. The equilibrium is $A^- + H_2O \rightleftharpoons HA + OH^-$. From Table A–3, $pK_b = 9.24$. Then, with $x = [OH^-] = [HA]$,

$$K_b = 10^{-9.24} = \frac{[HA][OH^-]}{[A^-]} = \frac{x^2}{0.1 - x},$$

$$x = 10^{-5.12}, \qquad pH = 8.88.$$

b) If only K_a for the conjugate acid is given [Eq. (5–2) above],

$$K_a = \frac{[H^+][A^-]}{[HA]},$$

$$K_w = [H^+][OH^-].$$

Divide to get

$$\frac{K_w}{K_a} = \frac{[HA][OH^-]}{[A^-]} = \frac{10^{-14}}{10^{-4.76}} = 10^{-9.24}$$

to use as in part (a) above.

Example 2. Now let us consider 0.10 M NH_4NO_3.

The active species is the weak acid, NH_4^+, ($pK_a = 9.24 = 14 - pK_b$). The solution is analogous to that of HA, and pH = 5.12.

CASE V (*Polyprotic acids*). We shall use H_3PO_4 as an example and divide the solutions into three types which then can be described by cases II through IV.

$$H_3PO_4 \rightleftharpoons H^+ + H_2PO_4^-, \qquad pK_1 = 2.15,$$
$$H_2PO_4^- \rightleftharpoons H^+ + HPO_4^=, \qquad pK_2 = 7.21,$$
$$HPO_4^= \rightleftharpoons H^+ + PO_4^{3-}, \qquad pK_3 = 12.32.$$

a) First let us consider either "end species" alone:

1) the acid, which is like case II, and

2) PO_4^{3-}, which is like case IV.

Example 1. For 0.10 M H_3PO_4 we see from the pK values that most of the $[H^+]$ comes from ionization step one. So, as in case II,

$$K_1 = 10^{-2.15} = \frac{x^2}{0.1} \qquad \text{and} \qquad x = \sqrt{10^{-3.15}} = 10^{-1.58},$$

$$pH = 1.58 \qquad \text{and} \qquad [H^+] = 0.026.$$

(*Note:* Because of the large K_a, the use of $(0.1 - x)$ term for (H_3PO_4) is fairly important here and gives $[H^+] = 0.023$.)

Example 2. For the end ion, $PO_4{}^{3-}$ (0.10 M),

$$PO_4{}^{3-} + H_2O \rightleftharpoons HPO_4{}^{=} + OH^-,$$

which is much like case IV. Thus

$$\frac{K_w}{K_3} = \frac{[H^+][OH^-]}{\left[\dfrac{[PO_4{}^{3-}][H^+]}{[HPO_4{}^{=}]}\right]} = \frac{x^2}{0.1} = \frac{10^{-14}}{10^{-12.32}} = 10^{-1.68}.$$

Then $x = \sqrt{10^{-2.68}} = 10^{-1.34}$, pOH = 1.34, $[OH^-] = 0.046\ M$, and pH = 12.66. (Again, $[PO_4{}^{3-}] = 0.1 - x$ would be significantly better than 0.1.)

b) Now consider two conjugate species.

Example. Take any of the pairs in the three equations for H_3PO_4. Each of these pairs is then analogous to the HA-NaA buffer of case III, and can be treated mathematically in the same way for approximate purposes. Equimolar mixtures, for example, of these three pairs would then give solutions of pH 2.15, 7.21, and 12.32, respectively.

c) Now consider an ampholyte alone. Such ions as $H_2PO_4{}^-$, $HPO_4{}^{=}$, and $HCO_3{}^-$, as well as molecules like the amino acids, can either accept or donate a proton:

$$HCO_3{}^- + H_2O \rightleftharpoons OH^- + H_2CO_3.$$

or

$$HCO_3{}^- + H_2O \rightleftharpoons H_3O^+ + CO_3{}^{=},$$

Both equilibria must be used to calculate pH, and all the ampholytes are treated with identical algebra.

Example. Find the pH of 0.10 M $NaHCO_3$. For H_2CO_3, $pK_1 = 6.35$, $pK_2 = 10.33$. The two equations using the two K values will work here, but simpler algebra is obtained by another approach (which is applicable to all cases as well), that of material and charge balance.* A useful equation can be obtained in two ways:

i) Use 0.10 M $NaHCO_3$ for our example:

plus ions = minus ions	$[Na^+] + [H^+] = [OH^-] + [HCO_3{}^-] + 2[CO_3{}^{=}]$
moles C = moles Na	$[Na^+] = [H_2CO_3] + [HCO_3{}^-] + [CO_3{}^{=}]$
subtract	$[H^+] - [OH^-] = [CO_3{}^{=}] - [H_2CO_3]$

* The object to keep in mind is to obtain an equation in terms of $[H^+]$, equilibrium constants, and known concentrations of *major* species. With this method one achieves rapid elimination of minor species to arrive at a useful result like Eq. (5–3).

ii) This equation may be obvious on inspection of the two reactions of the ampholyte above. It states the equality of the gain and loss of protons, if rearranged with acids and bases on opposite sides. This is the proton-balance condition. Further uses of it will follow.

Now, solve for $[H^+]$ and substitute from the K expressions K_1, K_2, and K_w:

$$[H^+] = [CO_3^{=}] - [H_2CO_3] + [OH^-]$$
$$= K_2 \frac{[HCO_3^-]}{[H^+]} - \frac{[HCO_3^-][H^+]}{K_1} + \frac{K_w}{[H^+]}.$$

This eliminates the minor, unknown species, $[CO_3^{=}]$ and $[H_2CO_3]$. Then solve for $[H^+]$

$$[H^+] = \left[\frac{K_1K_2[HCO_3^-] + K_1K_w}{K_1 + [HCO_3^-]}\right]^{1/2}. \tag{5-3}$$

Then, putting in the K values and $[HCO_3^-]$ about 0.1 M, one can see that K_1 is negligible in the denominator and so is the second term in the numerator. Thus, approximately,

$$[H^+] = \sqrt{K_1K_2} = \sqrt{10^{-16.68}} = 10^{-8.34},$$
$$pH = 8.34. \tag{5-4}$$

This approximate equation thus predicts that the pH of the ampholyte solution is independent of concentration. But, this approximate treatment breaks down for some K and molarity values of some materials, so watch closely. (See later sections.)

Convince yourself that no other combinations of H_3PO_4 species are chemically possible. For example, $H_3PO_4 + Na_3PO_4$ would react to give some $HPO_4^{=}$ and $H_2PO_4^-$, or other pairs (or single species) depending on proportions. All mixtures must react to form (a), (b), or (c) above.

Examples. The following examples should help the student to do the arithmetic for mixtures more quickly.

i) Mix 25 ml 0.10 M H_3PO_4 and 10 ml 0.10 M Na_3PO_4. For bookkeeping, separate (mentally) the available H^+ and bases. Here we have a total of 3.5 mmole PO_4^{3-} and 7.5 mmole H^+. In general, add the protons to the strongest base first, to the next strongest base second, and so on, until all the protons have been used (or strong acid is left). Then put the resulting species in the appropriate K expressions.

In this example, first make 3.5 mmole $HPO_4^{=}$ leaving 4.0 mmole H^+. Then, make 3.5 mmole $H_2PO_4^-$ leaving 0.5 mmole H^+. Then, make 0.5 mmole H_3PO_4 leaving 3.0 mmole $H_2PO_4^-$. (Check the material balance at this point to see that you can account for all the H^+ and PO_4^{3-} you started with.) The final species fit the K_1 expression to give an approximate result:

$$[H^+] = K_1 \frac{[H_3PO_4]}{[H_2PO_4^-]} = 10^{-2.15} \frac{0.5}{3.0} = 10^{-2.93}.$$

ii) Mix 25 ml 0.10 M NaH_2PO_4 and 10 ml 0.10 M NaOH. In this example we have 2.5 mmole PO_4^{3-} and (5.0 − 1.0) mmole H^+. First, make 2.5 mmole $HPO_4^=$ leaving 1.5 mmole H^+. Then, make 1.5 mmole $H_2PO_4^-$ leaving 1.0 mmole $HPO_4^=$ to put into K_2:

$$[H^+] = K_2 \frac{[H_2PO_4^-]}{[HPO_4^=]} = 10^{-7.21} \frac{1.5}{1.0} = 10^{-7.03}.$$

iii) Try the reverse: How much 0.10 M NaOH should be added to 25 ml of 0.10 M H_3PO_4 to produce a buffer of pH 7.00? The closest pK value is pK_2 which means that $H_2PO_4^-$ and $HPO_4^=$ will be the major species at pH 7. Their ratio is then,

$$\frac{H_2PO_4^-}{HPO_4^=} = \frac{10^{-7.00}}{10^{-7.21}} = 1.62.$$

If x ml of NaOH are added, (7.5 − 0.1x) H^+ mmole remain to use as before. Material and proton balances lead easily to useful equations (in mmoles):

$$\text{material balance} \qquad H_2PO_4^- + HPO_4^= = 2.5,$$
$$\text{proton balance} \qquad 2H_2PO_4^- + HPO_4^= = (7.5 - 0.1x).$$

Eliminate the mmole of $HPO_4^=$ between these two equations to get

$$H_2PO_4^- = 5.0 - 0.1x \qquad \text{and} \qquad HPO_4^= = 0.1x - 2.5.$$

So, from the ratio above, one can find,

$$1.62 = \frac{5.0 - 0.1x}{0.1x - 2.5},$$

which yields x = 34.5 ml NaOH. [This approximate answer demonstrates the method. Introduction of activity coefficients allows us to get a value of pH as −log (H^+ activity) which agrees very well with experimental readings. This is detailed in Chapters 6 and 9.]

CASE VI (*Mixtures of various acidic and basic species*)

a) In a mixture of acids (or of bases), the strongest can usually be seen to prevail in establishing the pH, to good approximation.

Example 1. In a mixture of 0.1 M HCl and 0.1 M acetic acid, the HCl gives 0.1 M $[H^+]$ and the HA gives x. As usual in HA,

$$1.8 \times 10^{-5} = \frac{(0.1 + x)(x)}{(0.1 - x)},$$

so $x = 1.8 \times 10^{-5}$ *M*, which is negligible compared to the 0.1 *M* from the HCl. The $[H^+]$ comes entirely from the HCl for most purposes.

Example 2. Consider a mixture of acetic and formic acids, each 0.10 *M*.

Two equations in two unknowns will work, but, as in case V(c), the summation of charges (or sources of H^+) is simpler. Consider:

$$HA \rightleftharpoons H^+ + A^- \qquad \text{and} \qquad HCHO_2 \rightleftharpoons H^+ + CHO_2^-$$

and neglect the ionization of water as usual in acidic solution. Thus,

$$[H^+] = [A^-] + [CHO_2^-]$$

(in more nearly neutral solutions the added $[OH^-]$ term would be needed). Then multiplying by $[H^+]$,

$$[H^+]^2 = [H^+][A^-] + [H^+][CHO_2^-]$$

and

$$[H^+]^2 = K_{\text{acetic}}[HA] + K_{\text{formic}}[HCHO_2]$$

from the usual K_a expressions. Thus

$$[H^+]^2 = 1.75 \times 10^{-5}(0.1) + 1.76 \times 10^{-4}(0.1) = 19.4 \times 10^{-6},$$
$$[H^+] = 4.4 \times 10^{-3}.$$

From the formic acid alone one would get $x^2/0.1 = 1.76 \times 10^{-4}$, or $[H^+] = 4.2 \times 10^{-3}$ *M*. So, even here, with two acids of similar strength, the stronger supplies most of the $[H^+]$. The ionization of the weaker (acetic) is repressed by the common ion effect, the higher $[H^+]$ of the formic acid.

b) Now let us consider stoichiometric weak acid-base mixtures ("salt of a weak acid and a weak base").

Example 1. Consider a 0.10 *M* NH_4CHO_2 solution.

The equilibria expected are

$$NH_4^+ \rightleftharpoons H^+ + NH_3 \qquad \text{and} \qquad CHO_2^- + H_2O \rightleftharpoons HCHO_2 + OH^-.$$

Balance material and charge and subtract:

$$\begin{array}{ll} \text{balance material} & [NH_4^+] + [NH_3] = [CHO_2^-] + [HCHO_2] \\ \text{balance charge} & [NH_4^+] + [H^+] = [CHO_2^-] + [OH^-] \\ \hline \text{subtract} & [H^+] - [OH^-] = [NH_3] - [HCHO_2] \end{array}$$

[Note the clear analogy with case V(c), the ampholyte.] Now, we proceed just as in case V(c), solving for $[H^+]$ and substituting from the *K* expressions to get an equation in terms of known quantities. First multiply through by $[H^+]$:

$$[H^+]^2 - [H^+][OH^-] = [H^+][NH_3] - [H^+][HCHO_2],$$
$$[H^+]^2 - K_w = K_w[NH_4^+]/K_b - [H^+]^2[CHO_2^-]/K_a.$$

Then rearrange and take square roots:

$$[H^+] = [K_w K_a(K_b + [NH_4^+])/K_b(K_a + [CHO_2^-])]^{1/2}. \qquad (5\text{–}5)$$

For approximate calculations, look at the numerical values to see what simplifications can be made. Here, $K_a = 1.76 \times 10^{-4}$ and $K_b = 1.8 \times 10^{-5}$ so with $[NH_4^+]$ and $[CHO_2^-]$ = about 0.1 *M*, the additive K_a and K_b terms are negligible in Eq. (5–5). So Eq. (5–5) reduces to:

$$[H^+] = \sqrt{K_w K_a/K_b} = \sqrt{K_{a1}K_{a2}},$$

where K_{a1} and K_{a2} are the K_a's for formic and for ammonium ion acids. (See case IV(b): any $K_a K_b = K_w$.) The analogy with the ampholyte cases, Eqs. (5–3) and (5–4), is complete.

Numerically, here, $pH = \frac{1}{2}(pK_{a1} + pK_{a2}) = (3.75 + 9.24) = 6.50$. Qualitatively, formic acid is a stronger acid than NH_4^+ ion or formate ion is a weaker base than NH_3, so the solution is acidic.

Example 2. For 0.10 *M* $NH_4H_2PO_4$ (a weak acid ion and an ampholyte ion)

$$NH_4^+ \rightleftharpoons H^+ + NH_3, \qquad K_a = 10^{-9.24},$$
$$H_2PO_4^- \rightleftharpoons H^+ + HPO_4^=, \qquad K_2 = 10^{-7.2},$$
$$H_2PO_4^- + H_2O \rightleftharpoons H_3PO_4 + OH^-, \qquad K_b = K_w/K_1 = 10^{-14}/10^{-2.15}.$$

As above the summations of matter and charge give:

$$\begin{aligned} [NH_4^+] + [H^+] &= [H_2PO_4^-] + 2[HPO_4^=] + [OH^-] \\ [NH_4^+] + [NH_3] &= [H_2PO_4^-] + [H_3PO_4] + [HPO_4^=] \\ \hline [H^+] - [NH_3] &= [HPO_4^=] + [OH^-] - [H_3PO_4] \quad \text{by subtraction.} \end{aligned}$$

(The proton gain-loss balance here can be seen as follows: Consider the original species to be H_2O, NH_4^+, and $H_2PO_4^-$,

$$\text{proton gainers} = H_3O^+ + H_3PO_4,$$
$$\text{proton losers} = OH^- + NH_3 + HPO_4^=.$$

Setting these equal to each other yields the same equation obtained by material and charge balancing above.)

Then, just as before, the student can find that

$$[H^+] = \left[\frac{K_a[NH_4^+] + K_2[H_2PO_4^-] + K_w}{1 + [H_2PO_4^-]/K_1}\right]^{1/2} \quad \text{and} \quad pH = 4.69.$$

Example 3. For 0.10 *M* $(NH_4)_2HPO_4$, as above show that

$$[H^+] = \left[\frac{K_a[NH_4^+] + K_3[HPO_4^=] + K_w}{1 + [HPO_4^=]/K_2}\right]^{1/2} \quad \text{and} \quad pH = 8.1.$$

Examples 2 and 3 were solved through the approximation that the concentrations of the original major ions can be taken as unchanged by the equilibrium reactions. (The use of uncorrected K values at these ionic strengths also introduces large error. This will be shown and corrections made in Chapters 6 and 9.) Let us check this.

In Example 2 above, solve for $[PO_4^{3-}]$, $[HPO_4^{=}]$, $[H_3PO_4]$, and $[NH_3]$ using the K expressions and the pH found, 4.69:

$$[PO_4^{3-}] = \frac{K_2K_3[H_2PO_4^-]}{[H^+]^2} = 10^{-11},$$

$$[HPO_4^{=}] = \frac{K_2[H_2PO_4^-]}{[H^+]} = 10^{-3.5},$$

$$[H_3PO_4] = \frac{[H^+][H_2PO_4^-]}{K_1} = 10^{-3.5},$$

$$[NH_3] = \frac{K_a[NH_4^+]}{[H^+]} = 10^{-5.6}.$$

All species which can change the value 0.1 M for $[NH_4^+]$ or $[H_2PO_4^-]$ are under 1% of 0.1 M, and the approximations are valid.

In contrast to the previous case, in Example 3 appreciable amounts of NH_4^+ and $HPO_4^{=}$ react to produce the equilibrium pH. The constant expressions, as before, will show that $[NH_3]$ is about 0.01 M and $[H_2PO_4^-]$ is about 0.03 M at pH 8. Therefore successive approximations or higher-degree equations should be applied to get more accurate solutions. (Both $[H_3PO_4]$ and $[PO_4^{3-}]$ are negligible at pH 8.)

Amino Acids

For convenience, amino acids may be considered to be ampholytes or polyprotic acids. For example, glycine is listed with its equilibria expressed as the acid constants for the protonated form, the glycinium ion:

$$^+NH_3CH_2COOH,\ (H_2Gly^+), \qquad pK_1^0 = 2.35, \qquad pK_2^0 = 9.78;$$

$$K_1 = \frac{[H^+][HGly]}{[H_2Gly^+]}, \qquad K_2 = \frac{[H^+][Gly^-]}{[HGly]}.$$

The zwitterion form, HGly, is an ampholyte. Some older literature expresses the equilibria as K_a and K_b, where K_a is the same as K_2 above, and K_b is equal to K_w/K_1. The first method will be used in this book.

Since these acids are so important in biochemical studies, we will present several examples even though they are similar to previous polyprotic cases.

Example 1. Find the pH of 0.050 M glycine in water.

Charge balance requires that:

$$[H^+] + [H_2Gly^+] = [OH^-] + [Gly^-].$$

Substitute from the K_a and K_w expressions to get an equation similar to the equation for HCO_3^- (5–3) in terms of $[H^+]$ and [HGly] only:

$$[H^+] = \left[\frac{K_1K_2[\text{HGly}] + K_1K_w}{K_1 + [\text{HGly}]}\right]^{1/2} = 10^{-6.59}.$$

The pH of 6.59 is obtained by assuming that [HGly] is 0.050 *M* and very little forms any H_2Gly^+ or Gly^-. Returning this pH to the K_1 and K_2 expressions shows that the assumption is justified

$$[H_2Gly^+] = 2.9 \times 10^{-6}, \qquad [Gly^-] = 3.3 \times 10^{-5}.$$

But, they are *not* equal. An acid, like HCl, must be added to reach what is called the isoelectric point, the pH at which $[H_2Gly^+] = [Gly^-]$. Here the fraction in the zwitterion form is at a maximum, and the migration of amino acid in an electric field is at a minimum. This pH is easily calculated:

$$K_1K_2 = \frac{[H^+]^2[Gly^-]}{[H_2Gly^+]} = [H^+]^2, \qquad \text{at the isoelectric point}$$

$$\text{pH} = 12.13/2 = 6.06.$$

Alanine, CH_3CHNH_2COOH, with $pK_1 = 2.34$ and $pK_2 = 9.87$ differs little from glycine. However, there are other important amino acids having unequal numbers of carboxyl and amino groups.

Example 2. For aspartic acid, $HOOCCH_2CHNH_2COOH$, $pK_1^0 = 1.91$, $pK_2^0 = 3.63$, and $pK_3^0 = 9.47$. Here the pH is calculated like that for the first ampholyte (H_2A^-) of a triprotic acid (H_3A):

$$[H^+] = \left[\frac{K_1K_2[H_2Asp] + K_1K_w}{K_1 + [H_2Asp]}\right]^{1/2} = 10^{-2.82} \qquad \text{for 0.050 } M \text{ aspartic acid.}$$

The approximation for slight fraction dissociation is not so good here. The isoelectric pH calculated the same way as before is 2.77.

Lysine, $NH_2(CH_2)_4CHNH_2COOH$, is one of the essential amino acids and has $pK_1 = 2.18$, $pK_2 = 9.18$, and $pK_3 = 10.72$ at 20°C. Since there are two amino groups, the charges on the species differ from the examples above. If the zwitterion is abbreviated HLys, the four species are H_3Lys^{++}, H_2Lys^+, HLys, and Lys^-. Now the isoelectric condition is $K_2K_3 = [H^+]^2$ assuming that $[H_3Lys^{++}]$ is negligible. This pH is 9.95. For 0.050 *M* lysine, we use the second ampholyte equation with K_2 and K_3 terms corresponding to those above for the other cases to find a pH of 9.95.

The methods presented here can be applied to other polyfunctional acids and bases including polypeptides and proteins. Much useful information about the groups can be obtained by analysis of titration curves. (See Chapters 7 and 8.)

These examples illustrate the general method for attacking pH problems. Only experience will give the student facility in recognizing a complex mixture as an example of one of these six cases and then choosing an appropriate numerical method for solving the problem. In theory, multiple equations in many unknowns will work, but the algebra rapidly becomes intractable with increasing numbers of variables. Such systems of equations can be solved with computers (which apply numerical successive approximations very rapidly), and complex equilibrium data are now appearing in the literature from these calculations. An example and references are given in the next chapter.

SUMMARY

This chapter describes the way to approach a pH calculation:

1. Write the acid-base reactive species and their initial amounts.
2. Assume that possible neutralizations go to completion if stronger acids and bases can form weaker acids and bases and write the amounts of new materials present.
3. Write the controlling equilibria involving these species.
4. Then it should be possible to see into which of the six cases described in this chapter the solution may be fitted.
5. In cases calling for two or more equilibrium constants, a combination of material, proton, and charge balancing provides a rapid method for reaching a usable equation in terms of $[H^+]$, constants, and known concentrations of major species.

PROBLEMS

(For these problems assume that the activity coefficient is 1 in all cases so that K^0 values can be used.)

1. Calculate the pH of 1.00×10^{-7} *M* HCl.
2. Texts used to say that mixing equal volumes of strong acid and strong base of equal concentrations would produce a solution of pH 7. Calculate the pH obtained by two students who do this as carefully as possible with burets. The first one gets actually 9.99 ml of 0.10000 *M* HCl and 10.01 ml of 0.10000 *M* NaOH. The second gets 10.01 ml of 0.10000 *M* HCl and 9.99 ml of 0.10000 *M* NaOH. Repeat the calculations for 9.999 ml and 10.001 ml of each and the reverse.
3. Repeat Problem 2 using acetic acid instead of HCl. The endpoint pH expected is 8.9 (see Example 1(a) in case IV).
4. How many milliliters of 0.10 *M* sodium acetate should be added to 10 ml of 0.10 *M* acetic acid to give a buffer of pH 5.00?
5. How many milliliters of 0.10 *M* NaOH would be needed in Problem 4 in place of NaA? Why is this so much less than the base NaA in Problem 4? Would the answer be different for 0.10 *M* NH_3? Why?

6. You need a physiological buffer of pH 6.40. Find the ratio of moles of NaOH to citric acid that should be taken by approximate methods.

7. Test your ability to pick out the controlling equilibria in the mixtures of 0.10 *M* solutions listed below.

   a) Write the number of millimoles of each reactive substance added.
   b) Write any reactions that go to a large extent.
   c) Write the number of millimoles of products assuming complete reaction in (b).
   d) Set up the equations and solve for the approximate [H$^+$] and pH in each case. (Neglect activity effects here.)

10 ml HCl + 20 ml NaOH	30 ml $HC_2H_3O_2$ + 20 ml NaOH
10 ml HCl + 30 ml NH_3	10 ml $HC_2H_3O_2$ + 20 ml NaOH
10 ml $HC_2H_3O_2$ + 20 ml NH_3	10 ml H_3PO_4 + 21 ml NaOH

8. Derive the equation and calculate the pH of 0.050 *M* potassium acid phthalate.

9. Find the number of milliliters each of 0.10 *M* NaOH and H_3PO_4 that you should mix to make 100 ml of a buffer of pH 7.00, neglecting activity corrections.

10. Derive an equation for the [H$^+$] of 0.10 *M* NH_4HCO_3 and solve.

11. Repeat Problem 10 for 0.10 *M* NH_4BO_2.

12. Repeat Problem 10 for 0.10 *M* $NH_2(C_2H_4)NH_3^+, Cl^-$ (the monohydrochloride of ethylenediamine).

13. What is the approximate pH of 0.001 *M* $Fe(NO_3)_3$ solution? The pK_a for the Fe(III) aquo ion is 2.2. If K_{sp} for $Fe(OH)_3$ is about 10^{-38}, should the solution keep? Why?

14. Find the number of milliliters of 0.20 *M* NaOH that should be mixed with 80 ml of a solution which is 0.10 *M* in both acetic and formic acids to make the $[H^+] = 2.0 \times 10^{-5}$.

15. Amino acid buffers are suitable for some applications. One reference states that glycine + HCl buffers in the pH range 1.0 to 3.7 and glycine + NaOH in the range 8.2 to 10.1. Does this seem possible? Why? What are pH values of good (1:1) buffers in each case?

16. Find the pH of 0.0010 *M* lysine.

17. What are the predominant forms of glycine, alanine, aspartic acid, and lysine in normal blood which has pH 7.4?

CHAPTER 6

MORE EXACT TREATMENT OF ACID-BASE CALCULATIONS

Two factors render the preceding treatment inexact, in some solutions grossly inexact. These are (1) the omission of terms to avoid higher-degree equations and (2) neglecting to consider the effect of the inhibition of motion of ions and dipoles by the concentration of ionic materials and the viscosity of the medium—*activity effects*. The latter once known can be easily incorporated in calculations by a simple multiplied correction factor on K^0. The methods of finding that factor will be discussed in Chapter 9. Only the use of the correction factor is discussed here.

6.1 USE OF ACTIVITY COEFFICIENTS

First let us consider the size of the effect we are discussing. Table 6–1 gives the apparent acid "constant" for acetic acid in several solutions. We see that the acidity is increased about 40% as KCl is increased from 0 *M* KCl to 0.51 *M* KCl. Any attempt at accurate calculation of pH using $K_a = 1.754 \times 10^{-5}$ for all solutions of acetic acid is in vain. When the concentration of inert ions is not known, calculation to one significant figure with $K_a \cong 2 \times 10^{-5}$ is all that can be justified.

Table 6–1. Ionization Reaction of Acetic Acid in the Presence of the Inert Ions K^+ and Cl^-

Molarity of KCl	0	0.02	0.11	0.51	1.01
$K_a = [H^+]^2/[HA], \times 10^5$	1.754	2.302	2.891	3.340	3.071
$[H^+]$ in 0.1 *M* HA, $\times 10^3$	1.32	1.52	1.70	1.83	1.75

By inert ions here, we mean those having negligible effect on the neutrality of water and no ion in common with the material in question, HA. They are sometimes called indifferent ions.

The K_{sp} equilibria of slightly soluble electrolytes are also affected by the ionic atmosphere of the solution. For example, materials of ionic charges 1:1, 2:2, and 3:3 become, respectively, 12%, 77%, and 126% more soluble in 0.01 *M* KNO_3 than in water alone.

Corrections good to about two significant figures can be applied to improve calculations made with equilibrium constants obtained for pure water, zero ionic strength. They depend on the ionic strength of the solution and on the charge of the ion considered. Ionic strength, I, is defined:

$$I = \tfrac{1}{2} \sum_i c_i z_i^2,$$

where c_i is the concentration of ion i, z_i is the charge of ion i, and the summation is made over all the ions in the solution.

Examples. For 0.01 M NaCl, $I = \tfrac{1}{2}(0.01 \times 1^2 + 0.01 \times 1^2) = 0.01$ M and for 0.01 M $CaCl_2$, $I = \tfrac{1}{2}(0.01 \times 2^2 + 0.02 \times 1^2) = 0.03$ M. Knowing the ionic strength and the charge, one can find the correction factor, the *ionic activity coefficient*, in the Kielland table (Table 9–2) and in the Appendix. They are applied to the ionic concentrations to correct them to their "effective concentrations," or *activities*. These activities are then the correct terms to use in the K^0 expressions:

$$\text{activity} = a_+ = f_+ c_+$$

and similarly for the negative ion. For acetic acid,

$$K_a^0 = \frac{f_+[H^+]f_-[A^-]}{[HA]}.$$

The neutral species, like HA, can be taken as having $f = 1$. As ionic strength approaches zero, K^0 is the limiting value of K. For acetic acid we may write,

$$\frac{K_a^0}{f_+ f_-} = \frac{[H^+][A^-]}{[HA]} = K_a \quad \text{(at the given } I\text{)}.$$

Thus we can derive the corrected K_a for use at one ionic strength and do calculations just as before for K^0. For 0.10 M HA with 0.10 M KCl present, the table gives f_+ for H^+ as 0.83 and f_- for A^- as 0.77 so that the corrected K_a and $[H^+]$ can be found as follows:

$$K_a = 1.754 \times 10^{-5}/(0.83)(0.77) = 2.7_5 \times 10^{-5},$$

$$[H^+] = \sqrt{K_a c_a} = 1.6_6 \times 10^{-3}.$$

Both are in fair agreement with the experimental values for acetic acid in Table 6–1. Using them is certainly far better than just hoping the f values are not too far from unity.

6.2 COMPLETE EQUATION FOR MONOPROTIC WEAK ACIDS AND BASES

Let us define C_a and C_b as the *name* or *analytical* concentrations of a weak acid and its conjugate base. These are the amounts that should be weighed out to make one liter of solution named C_a M HA and C_b M NaA (or KA, etc.). These are not the amounts left after equilibrium is reached. The equilibrium concentrations are designated by square brackets as usual. The ionic compound, say NaA, for example, is completely dissociated so that $C_b = [Na^+]$.

The HA gives some H^+ and A^-, and

$$K_a = \frac{[H^+][A^-]}{[HA]}.$$

In addition, H_2O gives some H^+ and OH^-, and

$$K_w = [H^+][OH^-].$$

Electrical neutrality, charge balancing, requires that

$$[H^+] + [Na^+] = [A^-] + [OH^-]$$

or

$$C_b = [A^-] - [H^+] + [OH^-]$$

and

$$[A^-] = C_b + [H^+] - [OH^-]. \tag{6–1}$$

Material balancing requires that

$$C_a + C_b = [HA] + [A^-],$$

which, combined with (6–1), gives the equilibrium concentration of HA,

$$[HA] = C_a - [H^+] + [OH^-]. \tag{6–2}$$

We now have the complete terms for [HA] and $[A^-]$ at equilibrium to enter in the K_a expression for the weak acid:

$$[H^+] = K_a \frac{[HA]}{[A^-]} = K_a \frac{(C_a - [H^+] + [OH^-])}{(C_b + [H^+] - [OH^-])}. \tag{6–3}$$

Using K_w, we get an equation in terms of $[H^+]$ and name concentrations:

$$[H^+] = K_a \frac{(C_a - [H^+] + K_w/[H^+])}{(C_b + [H^+] - K_w/[H^+])}. \tag{6–4}$$

This is a cubic equation in $[H^+]$ which can give exact solutions for cases II, III, and IV of the previous chapter: HA alone, buffers, and A^- alone. That is, when $C_b = 0$, we have case II, a weak acid alone. When $C_a = 0$, it becomes case IV, the base alone. For neither C_a nor $C_b = 0$, it becomes case III, the buffer. Look at Eq. (6–4) with the proper terms for a 0.10 M acetic acid solution. Both the $[H^+]$ and $[OH^-]$ terms are very small, and the equation reduces to the usual approximate one, (with $C_b = 0$).

However, our interest here is to see when (6–4) is needed, and the approximate methods will not serve.

Example 1. In (6–4), find the $[H^+]$ of 1.00×10^{-7} M acetic acid solution where

$$[H^+] = 1.75 \times 10^{-5} \left[\frac{10^{-7} - [H^+] + K_w/[H^+]}{[H^+] - K_w/[H^+]}\right].$$

For this dilute solution, the pH cannot be far from 7, so no term here is obviously negligible. How, then, does one solve this cubic? For two or three significant figures, numerical successive approximation seems quickest, although some like to do it graphically to see where the function is going.* As an illustration, this equation will be solved both ways.

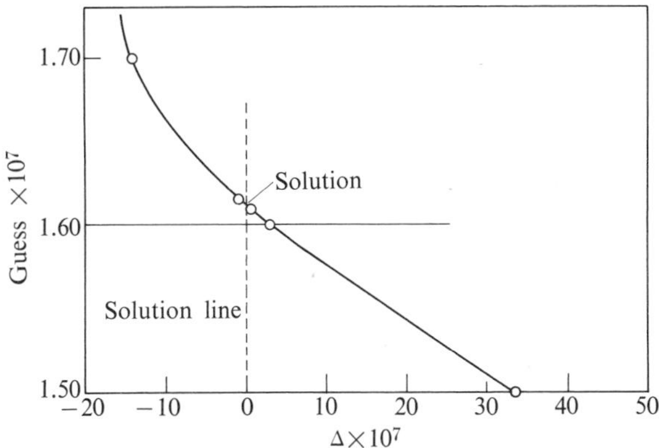

Fig. 6–1. Graphical solution of the cubic equation.

Method. Prepare a table of the values of $[H^+]$ tried and the values they give when put into the right side of the equation above. First, note that $[H^+]$ must be between 10^{-7} (no ionization of HA) and 2×10^{-7} (100% ionization of HA added to that of H_2O as a limit). As neither gives usable values in the equation, let us start by guessing 1.5×10^{-7}. Put this and other guesses into the right side of the equation to get (all $\times\ 10^{+7}$):†

Guess	1.5	1.6	1.7	1.61	1.615	(then to check the graph)	1.612
Equation	35	4.5	−14	1.94	0.7		1.59
Difference	34	2.9	−16	0.33	−0.9		−0.02

The reader should try the calculations on a slide rule to see how the successive values were chosen. The graph (Fig. 6–1) reflects what you will notice, that the function is steep—very sensitive to the changes in guessed values of $[H^+]$. Figure 6–1 shows about 1.612×10^{-7}, as solution. Note that the approximate method here gives $[H^+] = \sqrt{K_aC} = 1.3 \times 10^{-6}$ or 13 times the concentration of the HA added!

---

* Newton's method is also useful. It is used in the next section, on computer solutions.

† By convention, this notation means that the numbers shown *have been* multiplied by 10^7, thus the original numbers are obtained by multiplying by 10^{-7}.

Example 2. For 0.100 M bromoacetic acid, $K_a = 1.38 \times 10^{-3}$. By the usual approximate equation, $[H^+] = \sqrt{K_a C} = 0.012\ M$. Since this is 12% of the original acid, the approximation that the [HA] = 0.10 is not too good. So, trying Eq. (6–4), with $C_b = 0$, we get

$$[H^+] = 1.38 \times 10^{-3} \frac{(0.100 - [H^+])}{[H^+]},$$

since the $[OH^-] = 10^{-12}$, which is negligible here. This quadratic equation can be solved by the quadratic formula or faster by successive approximations when one has the approximate value to start with. (Answer: $[H^+] = 1.11 \times 10^{-2}$.)

Example 3. For a very weak acid, for example, $1.00 \times 10^{-4}\ M$ HCN, $K_a = 7.2 \times 10^{-10}$ and $C_b = 0$. The approximate solution $\sqrt{K_a C_a} = 2.7 \times 10^{-7}$ so (6–4) becomes:

$$[H^+] = 7.2 \times 10^{-10} \frac{(1.00 \times 10^{-4})}{[H^+] - K_w/[H^+]}.$$

Solving for $[H^+]$ gives

$$[H^+] = \sqrt{K_w + K_a C_a} = 2.9 \times 10^{-7}.$$

Example 4. Compare methods for acetate buffers for C_a and C_b, 0.100 M in one case and $1.000 \times 10^{-4}\ M$ in another.

For both, the approximate method gives $[H^+] = K_a = 1.75 \times 10^{-5}$. Putting this value in (6–4), one sees that the $[OH^-]$ term is negligible (10^{-9}). For the 0.100 M solution, the $[H^+]$ term is also negligible so that the approximate answer is algebraically correct to the number of significant figures warranted. However, this is not true for the $10^{-4}\ M$ solution. To check, substitute the approximate value in the right side of Eq. (6–4),

$$[H^+] = 1.75 \times 10^{-5} \frac{(10^{-4} - 1.75 \times 10^{-5})}{(10^{-4} + 1.75 \times 10^{-5})} = 1.22 \times 10^{-5}.$$

So the $[H^+]$ terms are not negligible here and the approximate $[H^+]$ does not check in the equation. The correct answer is not 1.22×10^{-5}! Further approximations or the quadratic formula give $1.34 \times 10^{-5}\ M\ [H^+]$. So, there is a 23% decrease in $[H^+]$ in the dilution from 0.1 to 0.0001 M, and the pH changes from 4.76 to 4.87. Here one sees the degree of approximation in the statement that buffer pH is insensitive to dilution. (Note that activity effects have not been included in these values yet. They will be even farther apart then, and will agree with values read on the pH meter for these buffers.)

Computer solutions of cubic equations. Equation (6–4) can be arranged into the standard cubic form in descending powers of $[H^+] = x$ to give

$$x^3 + (C_b + K_a)x^2 - (K_a C_a + K_w)x - K_a K_w = 0. \qquad (6\text{–}5)$$

Numerical methods* and electronic computers can be used for solution. Results from the computer solution of this cubic are plotted in Fig. 6–2 showing the pH as a function of the molarity of acetic acid and sodium acetate, each alone and in 1:1 buffers. The K_a and K_w values were corrected for activity effects above 10^{-3} ionic strength. The values in Table 6–2 give an idea of the validity of the approximate methods (values in italics).

Table 6–2. pH Values from the Computer Solution of the Exact Equation for Acetic Acid Mixtures, Using $pK_a^0 = 4.756$ and $pK_w^0 = 14.00$

Molarity of HA and NaA	HA alone	Approximate $p\sqrt{K_a^0 C_a}$	$[HA] = [A^-]$ buffer	Approximate pK_a^0	NaA alone	Approximate $14 - p\sqrt{C_b K_w^0/K_a^0}$
0.1000	2.86	*2.88*	4.56	*4.756*	8.68	*8.88*
10^{-2}	3.40	*3.38*	4.67	*4.756*	8.34	*8.38*
10^{-3}	3.91	*3.88*	4.74	*4.756*	7.85	*7.88*
10^{-4}	4.468	*4.38*	4.873	*4.756*	7.409	*7.38*
10^{-5}	5.148	*4.88*	5.273	*4.756*	7.098	*6.88*
10^{-6}	6.019	*5.38*	6.040	*4.756*	7.012	*6.38*
10^{-7}	6.791	*5.88*	6.795	*4.756*	7.001	*5.88*
10^{-8}	6.978	*6.38*	6.978	*4.756*	7.000_1	*5.38*

Table 6–3 shows the agreement of laboratory measurements on a pH meter with the pH and p (activity of H^+) obtained above and from the Kielland table of activities (Table 9–2). The mean activity was used.

Table 6–3. pH, p*a*, and Experimental pH for 1:1 HA-NaA Buffers

Molarity of HA and NaA	pH by exact equation	pa_{H^+} mean	pH measured (reliability, ±0.02)
10^{-1}	4.56	4.66	4.66
10^{-2}	4.67	4.71	4.71
10^{-3}	4.74	4.76	4.74

* A detailed discussion of numerical methods of solution of chemical problems is given by J. G. Eberhart and T. R. Sweet, *J. Chem. Educ.*, **37**, 422–30 (1960).

A brief description of approximations and Newton's method is given by J. N. Butler, *Ionic Equilibrium* (Reading, Mass.: Addison-Wesley, 1964), pp. 79ff. Newton's method is used in programming the computer and could have been used instead of the simple successive approximations to the cubic equation in the previous section.

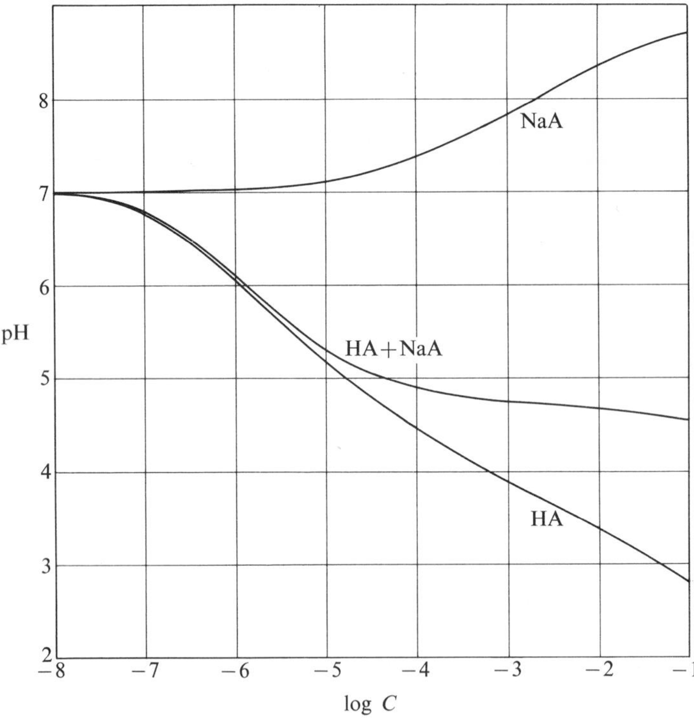

Fig. 6–2. Curves from exact equation (6–5) by IBM 1620, showing the pH at concentrations, C, 10^{-1} to 10^{-8} M of acetate solutions, HA alone, HA + NaA buffers 1:1, and NaA alone.

6.3 EQUATIONS FOR DIPROTIC AND POLYPROTIC ACIDS

Material- and charge-balance equations can be applied to polyprotic acids and buffers made with combinations of their ions. The complete equations for $[H^+]$ derived in this way can be solved by successive approximations and appropriate simplifications. First, however, let us show how the method is applied to a solution which is C molar in the diprotic acid alone (As before, C is the name, or analytical, concentration.):

$$\text{material balance,} \qquad C = [H_2A] + [HA^-] + [A^=],$$

$$\text{charge balance,} \qquad [H^+] = [OH^-] + [HA^-] + 2[A^=].$$

Double the first equation and eliminate $[A^=]$ between the two to get:

$$[H^+] = [OH^-] + 2C - 2[H_2A] - [HA^-]. \tag{6–6}$$

The equilibrium-constant expressions we need are:

$$K_1 = \frac{[H^+][HA^-]}{[H_2A]}, \qquad K_2 = \frac{[H^+][A^=]}{[HA^-]}, \qquad K_w = [H^+][OH^-].$$

With these, we convert (6–6) into an equation in $[H^+]$ and $[H_2A]$:

$$[H^+] = K_w/[H^+] + 2C - 2[H_2A] - K_1[H_2A]/[H^+], \tag{6–7}$$

which is useful for some cases. For others, we eliminate C with the material-balance equation to get:

$$[H^+] = K_w/[H^+] + K_1[H_2A]/[H^+] + 2[A^=]. \tag{6–8a}$$

Or, substituting for $A^=$ from the K expressions we have:

$$[H^+]^2 = K_w + K_1[H_2A](1 + 2K_2/[H^+]). \tag{6–8b}$$

Let us examine possible solutions for various situations.

a) If K_1 is large and K_2 is small, most of the H^+ comes from the first ionization step, the approximation used in Chapter 5, case V. For H_2A about 0.1 M, with $K_1 = 10^{-3}$ and $K_2 = 10^{-8}$, Eq. (6–8b) becomes

$$[H^+]^2 = K_1[H_2A] \qquad \text{and} \qquad [H^+] = 10^{-2}.$$

Here we make about 10% error in taking the $[H_2A]$ equal to C, since our result shows that about 10% of it is ionized. Using $[H_2A] = C - [H^+]$ would give a much better approximation.

b) As the K_1 and K_2 values become closer together, the first approximation is less useful. Return to Eq. (6–8a) and omit the $K_w/[H^+]$ term again and use the material-balance equation,

$$[H_2A] = C - [HA^-] - [A^=],$$

and the approximations (for pure H_2A solutions):

$$[HA^-] = [H^+] \qquad \text{and thus} \qquad [A^=] = K_2.$$

Then,

$$[H_2A] = C - [H^+] - K_2.$$

Now, (6–8a) has become (using x for $[H^+]$):

$$x^2 = K_1(C - x - K_2) + 2K_2x$$

or

$$x^2 + (K_1 - 2K_2)x + K_1(K_2 - C) = 0. \tag{6–9}$$

This equation is now limited by the approximations just introduced. It can be solved for specific materials by use of the quadratic formula.

Example. Find the $[H^+]$ in 0.050 M oxalic acid, where $pK_1^0 = 1.25$ and $pK_2^0 =$ 4.28.

For Eq. (6–9), we calculate

$$K_1 - 2K_2 \cong K_1 = 0.056,$$
$$K_1(K_2 - C) \cong -K_1C = -2.8 \times 10^{-3}.$$

Then, in the quadratic formula we get,

$$x = \frac{-0.056 \pm \sqrt{0.00316 + 0.0112}}{2} = 0.032\ M = [H^+].$$

The reader may see that the approximations here had the effect of using only the K_1 expression for oxalic acid with $[H_2A] = C - x$. Activity corrections on K_1 change this result to 0.034 (pH = 1.47).

For buffers, recall (Chapter 5) that all mixtures can be resolved to those resulting from mixing no more than two species. (For example, a solution made 0.1 M in H_2A and NaHA and 0.05 M in Na_2A is identical with one having 0.05 M H_2A and 0.20 M NaHA.) Thus our equations need never have more than two analytical concentration terms.

CASE A. For mixtures of H_2A and MHA at analytical concentrations C_a and C_{b1} ($C_{b1} = [M^+]$):

material balance, $C_a + C_{b1} = [H_2A] + [HA^-] + [A^=]$,

charge balance, $C_{b1} + [H^+] = [OH^-] + [HA^-] + 2[A^=]$.

The reader can show, just as we did for HA, Eq. (6–3), that inserting these into the K_1 expression gives:

$$[H^+] = K_1\frac{[H_2A]}{[HA^-]} = K_1\frac{(C_a - [H^+] + [OH^-] + [A^=])}{(C_{b1} + [H^+] - [OH^-] - 2[A^=])}. \qquad (6\text{–}10)$$

CASE B. For mixtures of MHA and M_2A at analytical concentrations C_{b1} and C_{b2}, corresponding equations give:

$$[H^+] = K_2\frac{[HA]}{[A^=]} = K_2\frac{(C_{b1} - [H^+] + [OH^-] - 2[H_2A])}{(C_{b2} + [H^+] - [OH^-] + [H_2A])}. \qquad (6\text{–}11)$$

Approximate solutions for specific cases can be obtained as above. Some examples in titration curves are found in the next chapter.

For polyprotic acids, similar treatments can be given. Good approximations can be made by taking two constants at a time, treating them effectively as diprotic acids in certain pH intervals.

SUMMARY

1. Interionic effects on activities of ions in equilibria can be found approximately at a given ionic strength and a corrected, or effective, K_{eq} can then be used in calculations.
2. Complete equations for monoprotic acid-base equilibria were obtained through use of material- and charge-balancing principles. The complete equation covers all cases of Chapter 5 involving any combinations of HA and A^- (or B and HB^+), conjugate pairs, without any reference to "hydrolysis."
3. The methods were extended to consideration of diprotic acids.

PROBLEMS

1. Derive exact equations for the $[H^+]$ of monoprotic weak acid solutions alone and with conjugate base added. Show clearly how and under what conditions they reduce to simple approximate equations. Give a clear numerical example of a case when all terms in the exact equation for the buffer are required. Put in the figures to demonstrate this.
2. Find the ionic strengths of 0.010 *M* solutions of KCl, K_2CO_3, and $La_2(SO_4)_3$.
3. a) Calculate first by the most approximate equation, and then by the exact equation, the $[H^+]$ of 1.00×10^{-3} *M* acetic acid and then of 1.00×10^{-6} *M* acetic acid.
   b) Recalculate the exact values with 0.100 *M* NaCl also present in the solution.
4. Derive the exact equation for the $[H^+]$ of a diprotic acid solution. Show which terms are needed to get the $[H^+]$ to two significant figures for 0.010 *M* solutions of oxalic acid, and of H_2S (separately).
5. a) Calculate the $[H^+]$ in 0.0100 *M* bromoacetic acid by the first approximation and by the more exact equations.
   b) Repeat for a 1:1 buffer, 0.0100 *M* in both the acid and sodium bromoacetate.
6. Set up equilibrium conditions for
   a) a triprotic acid solution alone and
   b) the various buffer mixtures possible with a triprotic acid.

   Derive equations for $[H^+]$ in each case and discuss methods for their approximate solution for various values of K_1, K_2, and K_3.

CHAPTER 7

APPLICATIONS OF ACID-BASE CALCULATIONS: TITRATIONS, INDICATORS, AND BUFFERS

Detection of titration endpoints usually depends on large changes in the relative concentrations of the reacting species. For example, in strong acid-base titrations, with tenth normal solutions, the pH changes from about pH = 5 one drop before the equivalence point to pH = 9 one drop past the equivalence point. This is a factor of 10^4 in $[H^+]$.

7.1 TITRATION CURVES

A titration curve is a graph of pH versus the amount of titrant added. Figure 7–1 shows examples of titration curves. The values for the curves can be calculated if the equilibrium-constant values are known for weak acids or bases. For the strong acid-base titration, the points are easily calculated as shown below for 50 ml of 0.1 *N* HCl being titrated by 0.1 *N* NaOH.

ml 0.1 *N* NaOH added	meq OH^- added	meq OH^-	meq H^+	Solution volume, ml	$[H^+]$	pH
0	0		5.00	50	0.1	1
10.0	1.00		4.00	60	0.067	1.17
20.0	2.00		3.00	70	0.043	1.37
40.0	4.00		1.00	90	0.011	1.96
49.0	4.90		0.10	99	0.0010	3.0
49.9	4.99		0.01	99.9	0.0001	4.0
50.0	5.00		0.00	100.0	(10^{-7})	(7)
50.1	5.01	0.01		100.1	10^{-10}	10
51.0	5.10	0.10		101	10^{-11}	11
60.0	6.00	1.00		110	10^{-12}	12

Note that the pH rises 2 units during the addition of the first 49 ml, while it jumps 8 units in the interval from 49 to 51 ml. The reader should examine this titration well for it presents the common features of all titrations including precipitation, redox, and complexing titrations. He should also understand clearly why the 50 ml point in the table is probably not pH 7: note the precision that would be required to be sure that it is 7. (See Problem 2 at the end of Chapter 5.)

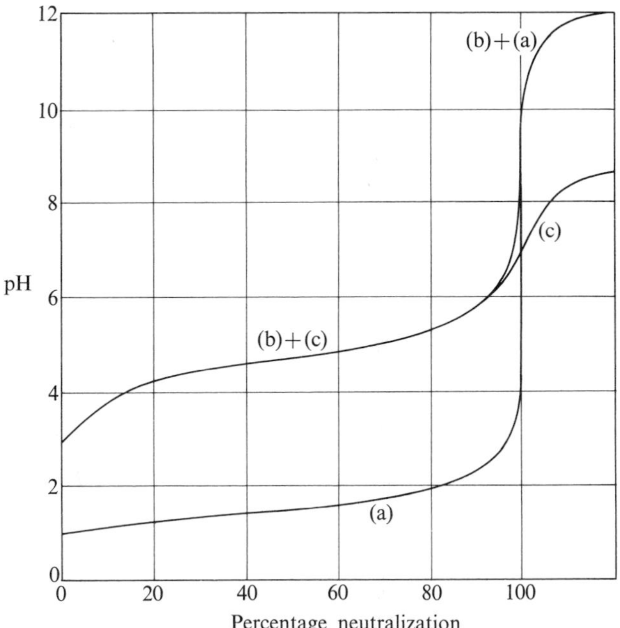

Fig. 7–1. Neutralization titration curves, 0.1 M solutions: (a) HCl by NaOH, (b) acetic acid by NaOH, (c) acetic acid by NH_3.

A somewhat different curve can be derived for the titration of a weak acid by sodium hydroxide. For example, titrate 50.00 ml of 0.1000 M acetic acid, HA, by 0.1000 M NaOH. During titration, a buffered solution obtains. The following pH equation can be derived from the approximate equations already discussed. At $I = 0$,*

$$\mathrm{pH} = \mathrm{p}K_a^0 + \log R, \tag{7–1}$$

which comes from,

$$\mathrm{p}K_a^0 = -\log \frac{[\mathrm{H}^+][\mathrm{A}^-]}{[\mathrm{HA}]} = \mathrm{pH} - \log \frac{[\mathrm{A}^-]}{[\mathrm{HA}]}, \tag{7–2}$$

where $R = [\mathrm{A}^-]/[\mathrm{HA}]$. For acetic acid, $\mathrm{pH} = 4.756 + \log R$. We can sketch the titration curve by first obtaining several points along it.

1. Initially,

$$[\mathrm{H}^+] = \sqrt{K_a C_a},$$

$$\mathrm{pH} = \tfrac{1}{2}(\mathrm{p}K_a - \log C_a) = \tfrac{1}{2}(4.756 + 1) = 2.88.$$

* The constant $I = 0$ calculation shows us the general features of the curve. For 1:1 charged weak acid HA, constant ionic strength during this titration can be achieved by starting with 0.1 M NaCl present. Added ions then balance the dilution during titration, so that $\mathrm{pH} = 4.56 + \log R$.

2. After 9% of the acid has been titrated; that is, when $R \cong 0.1$,

$$\mathrm{pH} = 4.756 - 1 = 3.76.$$

3. Half-way to the equivalence point, when $R = 1$,

$$\mathrm{pH} = 4.756 + 0.$$

4. At 1% before the equivalence point, when $R \cong 100$,

$$\mathrm{pH} = 4.756 + 2 = 6.76.$$

5. At the equivalence point, 0.050 M NaA, we see from Chapter 5, case IV that

$$[\mathrm{OH^-}] = \sqrt{K_b C_b} = \sqrt{(10^{-9.24})10^{-2}(5)} = 10^{-5.27}, \qquad K_b K_a = K_w,$$

$$\mathrm{pH} = 14 - 5.27 = 8.73.$$

After the equivalence point has been reached, there is no HA buffering, so that the pH change is the same as in the previous case as NaOH is added (see Fig. 7–1). We can summarize the HA titration as follows:

ml NaOH	0	4.5	25	49.5	50.0	50.1	51.0
pH	2.88	3.76	4.76	6.76	8.73	10	11

If more points are needed on the curve, they can be obtained by using the procedure illustrated in (3) and (4) above: for example, at 45.5 ml NaOH added, $R = 10$, pH $= 4.756 + 1 = 5.756$. At 49.95 ml NaOH, pH $= 7.76$. Close to the equivalence point, these approximations are not valid and the exact equation (6–4) must be used.

These curves can be used as an aid in choosing the proper indicator by indicating the range of rapid pH change. For example, either phenolphthalein or bromcresol green would serve for the first case, but with acetic acid bromcresol green would not be used, since it would change slowly from about the middle of the titration to the end. In this case phenolphthalein would change sharply at the equivalence point. On the other hand, phenolphthalein would not work in titration of ammonia by HCl, where the equivalence point is near pH 5.2. In this case, bromcresol green would serve well.

For negligible titration error in most cases where either the acid or base is strong, the range of the indicator (Table 7–1) should include the pH at the equivalence point. That is, the pH at equivalence should be within about ± 1 pH unit of $\mathrm{p}K_{\mathrm{In}}$. Furthermore, depending on the charges of the acid and base forms of the indicator, ionic strength may not affect $\mathrm{p}K_{\mathrm{In}}$ in the same way that it affects the pH of equivalence. This may lead to errors at high ionic strength. (See Chapter 9.)

Complete Equation for Monoprotic Titration Curves

Rather than calculating the points step-by-step, it is more efficient to derive an equation for the whole curve. To do this as an explicit function of volume of base added in titration leads to a rather cumbersome expression. Fortunately, a simpler function results if one uses the concept of the fraction of acid titrated, t. This is the ratio of moles of OH^- added to moles of H^+ taken, both from analytical concentrations. Clearly t runs from *zero* to *one*, from the start to the equivalence point of titration. A simple function results if we disguise the increasing volume during titration in this way:

a = the analytical concentration the weak acid HA would have if the original number of mmoles were present in the volume, V.
b = the analytical concentration of added base in the total volume, V.

Thus b is also the $[Na^+]$ in titrations by NaOH, and $a = C_a + b$. Now, substitute these terms into the complete weak acid equation (6–4),

$$[H^+] = K_a \frac{(a - b - [H^+] + [OH^-])}{(b - [OH^-] + [H^+])}.$$

Multiply through by the right-hand denominator, divide by a, and collect terms to get

$$t - \frac{([OH^-] - [H^+])}{a} = \frac{K_a}{[H^+]}\left(1 - t - \frac{[H^+]}{a} + \frac{[OH^-]}{a}\right),$$

where $t = b/a$. Then solve for t to get:

$$t = \frac{([OH^-] - [H^+])}{a} + \left(\frac{[H^+]}{K_a} + 1\right)^{-1}. \tag{7–3}$$

For given molarities of acid and base solutions, the added volume will be easily calculated from t. To get the titration curve, we choose $[H^+]$ values, insert them in the equation, and calculate t. The reason for keeping the terms separated, as they are, is to show the dependence on volume and K_a more clearly. This becomes apparent in the calculation of a curve. The idea is from the article by Waser cited at the end of the chapter.

Example. Use the t equation to find the curve for 0.1 M acetic acid titrated by 0.1 M NaOH. Take 50.00 ml as the starting volume. Assume an ionic strength such that K_a is 2.0×10^{-5} throughout. (It will be seen that adjustment of K_w^0 for ionic strength has negligible effect.)

At pH 4

$$t = -10^{-4}/0.1 + (5 + 1)^{-1} = 0.166.$$

(Here, we assumed that $a = 0.1$. Since the acid is found 16.6% titrated, we have added 8.3 ml NaOH for a total volume of 58.3 ml. The small change in a makes no difference at this pH where the first term is quite small.)

At pH 6

$$t = -10^{-6}/0.1 + (0.05 + 1)^{-1} = 0.95.$$

(Here, the first term is truly negligible. For a well-defined curve one should get some points at pH values between 4 and 6.)

At pH 8

$$t = 10^{-6}/0.1 + (0.0005 + 1)^{-1} = 0.9995.$$

(This is quantitatively on the equivalence point. Note that the first term is still negligible, but it has changed sign.)

At pH 10

$$t = 10^{-4}/0.05 + (0 + 1)^{-1} = 1.002.$$

(Here, we have passed the equivalence point by 0.002(50) ml = 0.1 ml. The $[OH^-]$, or $K_w/[H^+]$, term of the complete equation is taking care of giving the correct pH for addition of NaOH to the solution.)

At pH 12

$$t = 10^{-2}/0.05 + (0 + 1)^{-1} = 1.20.$$

(Here, we are 0.20(50) = 10 ml of NaOH beyond the equivalence point. The corrected a value is thus 5 mmole/110 ml = 0.0455, which changes t to 1.22.)

Thus we see that the first term expresses the effects of H^+ and OH^- outside the HA-A^- buffering system. See what happens if we choose pH = 2:

$$t = -10^{-2}/0.1 + (500 + 1)^{-1} \cong -0.1.$$

The negative t value is correctly interpreted as 0.1(50) = 5 ml of strong *acid*, 0.1 M, needed to give pH 2.

The t equation predicts that the shape of titration curves depends only on K_a and the a value, concentration, taken. A family of curves at integral pK_a values and 0.1 M weak acid can easily be constructed as in Fig. 7–2. Further, it makes no difference which species is considered the conjugate acid or base. The titration of a weak base by strong acid exhibits the same t behavior as the corresponding reverse case if the pH scale is inverted. Note that the curve calculated earlier for acetic acid, using the approximate equation, amounts to use of the second term of the t equation which is α_0, the fraction in the A^- form.

Slope of the Titration Curve: Feasibility, Error, and Buffer Index

The slope of the titration curve is small where good buffering obtains and large at the equivalence point. A more exact treatment is required to get an equation for this slope valid at all points on the curve. We shall derive it because, in addition to an index of buffering, it will tell the feasibility of titration, that is, whether the pH change near the equivalence point is rapid enough to allow the use of a change in a visible indicator.

Charge balance requires that $[H^+] + [Na^+] = [OH^-] + [A^-]$ for a solution of HA being titrated by NaOH. If C is the total acetate species concentration, $[HA] = C - [A^-]$, and the K_a expression gives

$$K_a = \frac{[H^+][A^-]}{C - [A^-]}$$

and

$$[A^-] = K_a C/([H^+] + K_a).$$

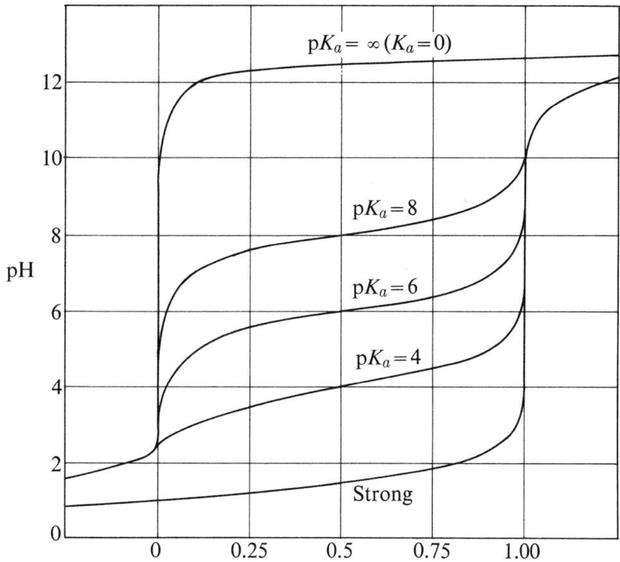

Fig. 7–2. Titration curves for various strength acids, 0.1 M acids, by 0.1 M NaOH (for constant ionic strength).

Solving the first equation for added base, $[Na^+]$, gives

$$[Na^+] = K_w/[H^+] - [H^+] + K_aC/([H^+] + K_a).$$

Differentiating with respect to $[H^+]$ at constant solution volume,

$$\frac{d[Na^+]}{d[H^+]} = -K_w/[H^+]^2 - 1 - K_aC/([H^+] + K_a)^2.$$

Multiplying by $[H^+]$, and making the substitution,

$$d(\text{pH}) = \frac{-d[H^+]}{2.303[H^+]},$$

since $\ln [H^+] = 2.303 \log [H^+]$, gives us the desired slope equation,

$$\frac{d[Na^+]}{d\text{pH}} = \beta = 2.303\left[[H^+] + K_w/[H^+] + \frac{K_aC[H^+]}{([H^+] + K_a)^2}\right], \tag{7–4}$$

where β is a buffer index, or capacity, the added moles per liter of base (or acid) to make a unit pH change at that point on the titration curve. By adding the N_b and volume for a particular case, $1/\beta$, the slope of the titration curve, can be expressed as change in pH per ml of titrant added.

These ideas can be illustrated using the acetic-acid titration described above.

Half-way to the equivalence point (point 3, p. 68), pH = 4.76 and the volume is 75 ml. Then

$$\beta = 2.3\left[10^{-4.76} + 10^{-9.24} + \frac{10^{-4.76}(0.0667\ M)10^{-4.76}}{(2 \times 10^{-4.76})^2}\right]$$
$$= 0.038\ M/\text{pH}.$$

Since 10^4 ml of 0.1 M base contain one mole and we have 0.075 liter of solution, β can be converted to new units,

$$(0.038)(10^4)(0.075) = 28 \text{ ml base/pH unit.}$$

The curve is relatively flat half-way through the titration.

After 99% of titration is completed (point 4), pH = 6.76 and the volume is 99.5 ml. As above, $\beta = 0.0012\ M/\text{pH}$, or 1.2 ml base/pH unit.

At the equivalence point (point 5), pH = 8.73 and the volume is 100 ml. As before, $\beta = 2.5 \times 10^{-5}\ M/\text{pH}$, or 0.025 ml base/pH unit. Here the curve is steep: $1/\beta = 40$ pH units/ml base.

Since one pH unit is very roughly the change required for visual indication of endpoints with colored acid-base indicators, the value of β in milliliters per pH unit at the equivalence point gives the value of the precision that can be expected. For this case, (0.025 ml/50 ml)(1000) = 0.5 ppth, and the 0.025 ml is less than 1 drop (about 0.05 ml) so that four-figure precision is expected for the 50 ml titration.

However, with both solutions at concentrations of 0.01 M, the equivalence-point (point 5) calculation gives pH = 8.23; then $\beta = 7.8 \times 10^{-6}$, or 0.078 ml base/pH. Now the precision is, (0.078 ml/50 ml)(1000) = 1.6 ppth. High dilution and small K_a reduce the precision available in titrations.

For example, let us look at the very weak acid, NH_4^+, with $pK_a = 9.24$. In a titration of 0.1 M NH_4Cl by 0.1 M NaOH, the pH at the endpoint (0.05 M NH_3 solution) is 10.97 by the usual approximate method. As before, $\beta = 9 \times 10^{-4}$ or 0.9 ml/pH unit, so that the indicator will be changing over 0.9 ml giving an uncertainty of 0.9 ml/50 ml, which is about 18 ppth.

The slope permits estimation of the error expected if the visual change of the indicator does not correspond to the equivalence point. If, for the acetic-acid titration described above, the endpoint were taken at pH 8.2, the error would be $\beta \times (8.7 - 8.2) = 0.01$ ml of base, which agrees with our previous statement that indicators whose change occurs over about 1 pH unit (± 0.5) give satisfactory precision for such titrations.

Titration Curves for Polyprotic Acids and Bases

The approximate equations in Chapter 5 give good results for some parts of the titration curve for sodium carbonate by a strong acid. The reason is that H_2CO_3 is a rather weak acid, and its K_1 is much greater than its K_2 ($pK_1^0 = 6.35$ and $pK_2^0 = 10.33$). Therefore there will be little proton binding by the HCO_3^- ion during most of the first half of the titration and little dissociation of H_2CO_3

during most of the second half of the titration. However, near the first equivalence point, we shall find that both steps of the H_2CO_3 ionization must be considered to get even approximate results from the calculation of pH. These effects will be even more pronounced in acids and bases of which the successive ionization constants are closer together, for example oxalic acid, $pK_1^0 = 1.27$ and $pK_2^0 = 4.27$.

Let us consider the titration of 0.05000 *M* Na_2CO_3 by 0.1000 *M* HCl. At the start, 0.05 *M* Na_2CO_3 has ionic strength 0.15. Using the Kielland table, Table 9–2, values for activity coefficients, we can get the correction factor 1.68 for the K_b of the carbonate ion:

$$\frac{K_w^0}{K_2^0} = K_b^0 = \frac{[HCO_3^-][OH^-]}{[CO_3^=]}(1.68).$$

Solving, we have $[OH^-] = 10^{-2.60}$ and pH = 11.40. Half-way to the first equivalence point, the ionic strength is 0.1, and the K_2 solution gives pH = K_2 = 9.93.

From Eqs. (5–3) and (5–4), we can find the pH at the first equivalence point as $\frac{1}{2}(pK_1^0 + pK_2^0) = 8.34$, assuming that the ionic strength is zero. More exactly, using $pK_1 = 6.19$ and $pK_2 = 9.98$ at ionic strength 0.066, we get pH = 8.09. To see the difficulty, look at the approximate methods for finding the pH just to each side of the first equivalence point. When 99.9% of the HCl required to add one proton to $CO_3^=$ is added, the approximate method predicts pH = 10.0 − 3 = 7.0. This value comes from the expression for K_2 using the ratio $[CO_3^=]/[HCO_3^-] = \frac{1}{999}$. But the pH should be above 8.09. So, it is reasonable to deduce that some HCO_3^- ion is raising the pH by forming some H_2CO_3. This can be shown clearly if one tries the K_1 expression at pH 7.0:

$$\begin{aligned} K_1 &= [H^+][HCO_3^-]/[H_2CO_3], \\ \log [HCO_3^-]/[H_2CO_3] &= 7.0 - 6.19 = 0.8, \\ [HCO_3^-]/[H_2CO_3] &= 6.3/1. \end{aligned}$$

Thus about 14% of the HCO_3^- must be converted to H_2CO_3 to maintain a pH of 7.0.

Hence, we cannot escape the complication of using both steps in the equilibrium for calculations near the first equivalence point. Attempting to solve for pH after the addition of known portions of HCl leads to cumbersome algebra in polyprotic cases, Eqs. (6–10) and (6–11). Instead, we can choose pH values on the curve and solve for the proportions of H_2CO_3, HCO_3^-, and $CO_3^=$ present. From these, it is easy to deduce the amount of HCl added to reach that pH.

Examples

1. Find the number of milliliters of 0.1000 *M* HCl needed to reach a pH of 8.50 in the titration of 50 ml 0.05000 *M* Na_2CO_3. This occurs a little before the first equivalence point at 8.1.

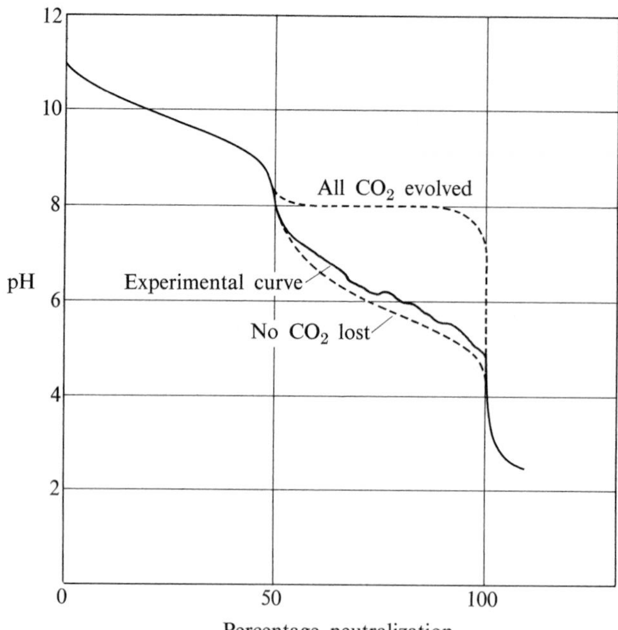

Fig. 7–3. Titration of 0.05 *M* Na_2CO_3 by 0.1 *M* HCl.

There were 2.500 mmoles of $CO_3^{=}$ to start. Let x = millimoles of HCO_3^-, and y = millimoles H_2CO_3. (In both equations the solution volumes cancel in *this particular calculation.*)

Using activity coefficients from the Kielland table to adjust the K values to those for ionic strength 0.066 *M* we can put

$$K_1 = 10^{-6.19} = 10^{-8.50}x/y, \qquad K_2 = 10^{-9.98} = 10^{-8.50}(2.5 - x - y)/x.$$

From the first step, $x = 204y$ and substitution in K_2 gives $x = 2.41$. Thus at pH 8.50, $HCO_3^- = 2.41$ mmoles, $H_2CO_3 = 0.01$ mmole, and $CO_3^{=} = 0.08$ mmole. The amount of HCl added must be $2.41 + 2(0.01) = 2.43$ mmoles, or 24.3 ml.

2. Repeat the calculation for a pH of 8.00, which occurs just after the first equivalence point. By the same algebra as in Example 1 we get $HCO_3^- = 2.44$ mmoles, $H_2CO_3 = 0.04$ mmole, and $CO_3^{=} = 0.02$ mmole. The amount of HCl is then $2.44 + 2(0.04) = 2.52$ mmoles, or 25.2 ml of the 0.1 *M* acid.

In this way, a titration curve can be calculated which is in good agreement with the experimental one, shown in Fig. 7–3. From this point, however, variable amounts of the carbonic acid formed will break up to H_2O and CO_2 so that the actual pH cannot be calculated. If this reaction were complete, the pH would remain near 8 until close to the second equivalence point because only HCO_3^-

ion is present to determine the pH. If the H_2CO_3 remained in solution, the pH would decrease in the usual way to approximately $\sqrt{K_a C}$, pH 4, at the endpoint. In practice, one may titrate to about pH 4 to 5 and boil out the CO_2 before reaching a final, accurate endpoint.

Oxalic acid. For a contrasting example, with larger K values, we can look at the titration of 50 ml of 0.05 M oxalic acid by 0.1000 M NaOH. Near the first equivalence point, the ionic strength is about 0.033 M, and the effective K values become (from the Kielland table):

$$K_1 = 1.35\,(10^{-1.27}) = 10^{-1.14}, \qquad K_2 = 1.88(10^{-4.27}) = 10^{-4.00}.$$

Also, as above, we can calculate the pH at the first equivalence point from Eq. (5–3), where now both terms in the denominator are needed. We get pH 2.82 for this ionic strength. At the start, the pH is 1.47 and the $[H^+]$ and the $[HC_2O_4{}^-]$, approximately, are 0.034 M. The ionic strength remains about the same during the first half of the titration, and the K values above can be used without adjustment. This starting pH was calculated on p. 63.

Let us then begin finding points on the titration curve at pH 2.00. The reader can verify that the method just used for H_2CO_3 gives inaccurate results here because of the much greater strength of oxalic acid. That is, the oxalic acid forms more anions than just those equivalent to the NaOH added. So, we must use a complete equation. Summation of charges gives

$$[Na^+] + [H^+] = [HA^-] + 2[A^=] + [OH^-],$$

where $A^=$ is the oxalate ion. Since we want to find the numbers of milliliters of NaOH added, it will prove simpler to recast the equation into millimoles:

$$\text{mmole NaOH added} = [Na^+]V = x + 2y + [OH^-]V - [H^+]V,$$

where V is the total volume of the solution, x is the number of millimoles of HA^-, and y is the number of millimoles of $A^=$. Next, letting n = the number of millimoles of oxalic acid taken, we can use the acid K expressions to eliminate x and y to get an equation for mmoles of NaOH as a function of $[H^+]$:

$$K_1 = [H^+]x/(n - x - y), \qquad K_2 = [H^+]y/x,$$

where $n - x - y = [H_2A]V$, and $x = [HA^-]V$, $y = [A^=]V$. (The solution volumes happen to cancel here.) Thus

$$\begin{aligned}\text{mmole NaOH added} &= n(1 + K_2/[H^+] + [H^+]/K_1)^{-1} \\ &\quad \times (1 + 2K_2/[H^+]) + V([OH^-] - [H^+]).\end{aligned}$$

Now, putting in pH 2.00, $[H^+] = 10^{-2}$, one finds that only the $[OH^-]$ term can be neglected. Thus

$$\begin{aligned}\text{mmole NaOH} &= (0.1000\ M)(V - 50) \\ &= 2.500(1 + 0.01 + 0.138)^{-1}(1.02) - 0.01V.\end{aligned}$$

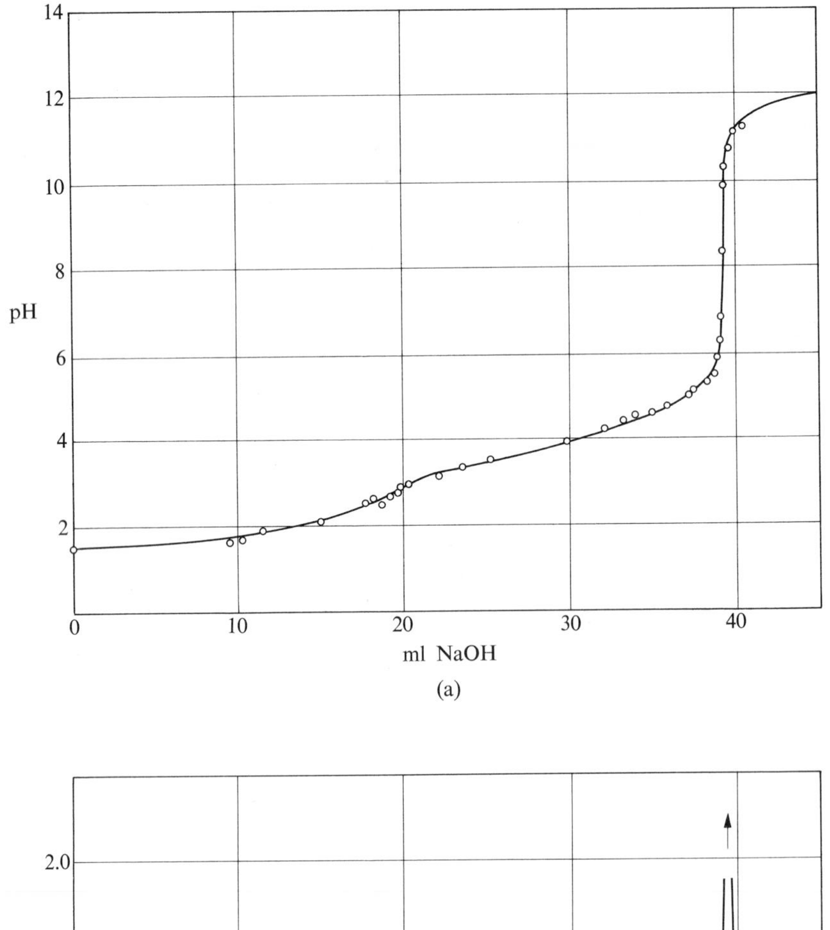

(a)

2.0
1.5
ΔpH/Δml
1.0
0.5
0
10
20
30
40
ml NaOH

(b)

Fig. 7.4. (a) Titration of 0.0500 *M* oxalic acid with 0.2020 *M* NaOH (pH vs. ml). The line was calculated on an IBM 1620 computer by a student, Alan Darlington. The points represent experimental data. (b) First derivative curve (ΔpH/Δml vs. ml).

Solving for V gives

$$V = 65.65 \text{ ml} \quad \text{or} \quad V - 50 = 15.65 \text{ ml of the NaOH added.}$$

One can continue in this way to get sufficient points to plot the titration curve. One finds that the $[H^+]$ term becomes negligible above pH 5. The reader can check these points and plot them. The curve for 0.0500 M oxalic acid titrated against 0.202 M NaOH is shown in Fig. 7–4(a). The first derivative curve is illustrated in Fig. 7–4(b).

We can summarize the titration of 50.00 ml of 0.05000 M oxalic acid by 0.1000 N NaOH as follows.

ml NaOH	0	15.65	22.5	25.0	26.16	30.68	47.7	49.7	49.97	50.0
pH	1.47	2.00	2.50	2.82	3.00	3.50	5.00	6.00	7.00	8.20

For simplicity in presenting the methods, in all the calculations just given, pH is left as $-\log [H^+]$. To compare the readings on a pH meter with the calculated curves, we must add (usually 0.1 to 0.2) to the pH calculated to get $-\log (a_{H^+})$. That is we add $-\log (f_+)$ for the hydrogen ion.

7.2 INDICATORS

Visual acid-base indicators are weak acids or bases of which one or both of the conjugate forms are highly colored. The addition of a very small amount of the indicator will show a color change without adding to the measurable amount of acid or base present. If the indicator is symbolized by HIn, the usual weak acid-base equilibrium shows:

$$HIn + H_2O \rightleftharpoons H_3O^+ + In^-.$$

Writing the usual shortened forms, we have

$$K_{In} = \frac{[H^+][In^-]}{[HIn]}.$$

Thus

$$R_{a/b} = [HIn]/[In^-] = [H^+]/K_{In}. \tag{7–4}$$

So, the ratio, R, of acid-to-base color is controlled by the $[H^+]$. If, as is roughly the case, the human eye can detect a color gradation between ratios of $\frac{10}{1}$ and $\frac{1}{10}$, the $[H^+]$ must change 100-fold to bring about these extremes of ratio. This pH change of two units is called the *range* of the indicator. It varies somewhat with the colors involved. Table 7–1 lists some useful indicators at various pH values.

Bromthymol blue should show an intermediate green color about pH 6.8, where equal amounts of the two forms, yellow and blue, are present. When $R = 1$, pH $= -\log K_{In} = pK_{In}$. Some tables record pK_{In} values rather than the ranges for the indicators.

Table 7–1

Common name	Chemical name	Color change, acid to base	pH transition range
Thymol blue	Thymolsulfonephthalein	Red to yellow	1.2 to 2.8
Methyl orange	*p*-dimethylaminazo-benzenesulfonic acid	Red to yellow	3.1 to 4.4
Bromcresol green	Tetrabromo-*m*-cresol-sulfonephthalein	Yellow to blue	3.8 to 5.4
Bromthymol blue	Dibromothymol-sulfonephthalein	Yellow to blue	6.0 to 7.6
Thymol blue	Thymolsulfonephthalein	Yellow to blue	8.0 to 9.6
Phenolphthalein	Phenolphthalein	Colorless to red	8.0 to 9.8
Thymolphthalein	Thymolphthalein	Colorless to blue	9.3 to 10.5

Hundreds of acid-base indicators are known. Handbooks list others that may be needed for special purposes.

Indicators are usually used in solutions from 0.1 to 1.0 mg/ml. Using a few drops of this stock adds only about 10^{-4} mmole of the indicator to the solution being titrated.

Mixed Indicators (The Carbonate-Hydroxide Problem)

So far, we have taken about one pH unit change as the minimum needed to give a visual indicator color change. By mixing two indicators whose ranges overlap and whose colors are appropriate, the useful change can be reduced to a few tenths of a pH unit. This can be understood by examining a practical example, finding the HCO_3^- endpoint in a titration of $CO_3^=$ by HCl. The rather small inflection occurs at pH 8.1. The mixed indicator, one part cresol red, three parts thymol blue, is used. The ranges of color are: cresol red 7.2 to 8.8, and thymol blue, 8.0 to 9.6. The overlap region is shown diagrammatically in Fig. 7–5. During the titration of $CO_3^=$, down to about pH 9, the color mixture of the red plus the blue of both basic forms of the indicators produces a violet color. This violet color begins to change as the pH falls, and some of the yellow color of the thymol blue is formed giving a salmon pink until just below pH 8, where both indicators show yellow colors. A definite change can be observed with only about 0.2 pH unit change, which is a much smaller change than can be seen with either indicator alone. If one makes a color comparison solution of $NaHCO_3$, it is possible to titrate $CO_3^=$ to the same color, HCO_3^- solution with fair precision, about ± 0.2 ml of 0.1 *N* HCl. This allows an estimation of $CO_3^=$ in mixtures of $CO_3^=$ and OH^-. At the HCO_3^- endpoint, all the OH^- and half the $CO_3^=$ have been titrated. Another titration to pH 4 gives the total $OH^- + CO_3^=$.

Another method used for these mixtures is to precipitate all the $CO_3^=$ as $BaCO_3$ and titrate the OH^- to about pH 9.

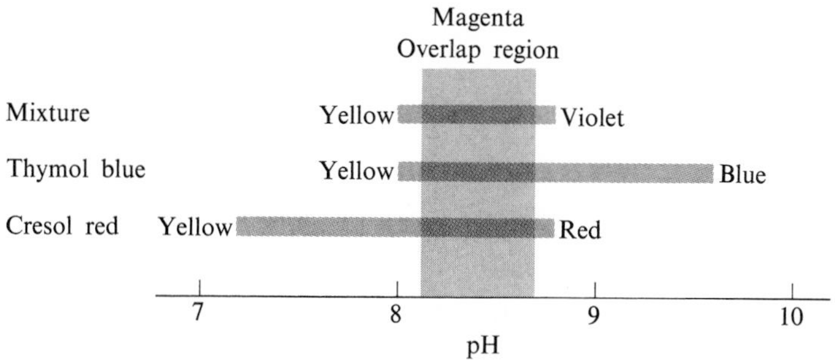

Figure 7–5

For a numerical example illustrating these two methods, consider a mixed base of OH^- and $CO_3^=$ which took 6.0 meq of acid to titrate to the pH 4 endpoint (by the usual method for $CO_3^=$). An indicator titration to pH 8.1 as described above gave 5.0 meq for the sum of $OH^- + \frac{1}{2}CO_3^=$. Thus there are

$$2(6.0 - 5.0) = 2.0 \text{ meq of } CO_3^= \qquad \text{and } 4.0 \text{ meq of } OH^-.$$

In the second method, excess $BaCl_2$ would be added to an aliquot, and 4.0 meq of acid would be required to titrate the remaining OH^-. Thus the original mixture contained such materials as NaOH and Na_2CO_3 in the ratio $\frac{4}{1}$ by moles ($\frac{4}{2}$ by meq).

Other Indicator Methods

Addition of a colored material to an indicator may improve the visibility of the change and sometimes even sharpen it a little. For example, a modified methyl orange is made by addition of a blue dye, xylene cyanol, which happens to be nearly complementary to the orange midpoint color of the indicator, thus producing a gray. The difficult red-to-yellow transition of methyl orange then becomes violet to green with the gray between. The commercially prepared "methyl purple" is another much-used example consisting of methyl red and alphazurine dye.

The range of indicators can be affected by ionic material, temperature, and nonaqueous solvents. For titration in other than dilute aqueous solution at room temperature, this must be considered.*

7.3 pH STANDARDS

With the development of pH meters reading to 0.001 unit, and the acceptance of a convention for the activity corrections of reference HCl solutions, it has been possible to set up tables of standard buffer solutions with the pH given to three decimal places in pH units.† The work done by Bates at the National Bureau of

* See H. A. Laitinen, *Chemical Analysis*, McGraw-Hill, 1960, pp. 50–55.

† R. G. Bates, *J. Res. Nat. Bur. Std.* **66A,** 179 (1962). (See also the book by Bates cited at the end of the chapter.)

Standards gives the pH of seven standard buffers from 0° to 95°C. With reasonable assumptions about activities and liquid junction potential, this standard, pH_s, represents very closely the negative log of the hydrogen-ion activity, $-\log (a_{H^+})$. Some room-temperature values for these standards are given in Table 7–2.

Table 7–2. Standard Buffer Solutions

Buffer	20°	25°	30°	dpH_s/dt
A Tetraoxalate, 0.05 *m*, 12.61g/l of $KH_3(C_2O_4)_2 \cdot 2H_2O$	1.675	1.679	1.683	+0.001
B Tartrate, 0.034 *m* (saturated at 25°C) $KHC_4H_4O_6$	—	3.557	3.552	−0.0014
C Phthalate, 0.05 *m* 10.12 g/l of $KHC_8H_4O_4$	4.002	4.008	4.015	+0.0012
D Phosphate, 0.025 *m* 3.39 g/l of KH_2PO_4 + 3.53 g/l of Na_2HPO_4	6.881	6.865	6.853	−0.0028
E Phosphate, 1.179 g/l of KH_2PO_4 + 4.30 g/l of Na_2HPO_4	7.429	7.413	7.400	−0.0028
F Borax, 0.01 *m* 3.80 g/l of $Na_2B_4O_7{\cdot}10H_2O$	9.225	9.180	9.139	−0.0082
G Calcium hydroxide (saturated at 25°C)	12.627	12.454	12.289	−0.033

Solids for buffers *A* through *F* are available as certified standard samples from the National Bureau of Standards. Reagent grade chemicals would be suitable for standard solutions for ±0.01 pH unit use. Buffers *D* through *F* must be made with CO_2-free water and protected from the CO_2 in air. The last column of the table shows the change in pH per degree. Appropriate temperature control can be adopted for 0.1, 0.01, or 0.001 pH unit precision desired. Further discussion of pH measurement appears in Chapter 24.

Carbonate buffers. Because of the possibility of CO_2 loss the carbonate buffers are of unique importance in biochemistry. Other important buffers in the human blood plasma and other fluids are phosphates, amino acids and proteins, citrates, and lactates. All of these must use added protons to alter the ratios of the buffer species and the pH. The bicarbonate ion, however, can form H_2CO_3, and some CO_2 which is lost from the lungs. This can effect complete removal of the added acidity, corresponding to the flat portion of the titration curve, as acid is added to HCO_3^-. In certain diseases, like diabetes mellitus, larger than normal quantities of acids are produced in metabolic oxidations. Fatal acidosis would result if large amounts of CO_2 were not rapidly exhaled. The pH of normal blood is near 7.4. This fixes the buffer ratios of all species. The predominant species in the carbonate and phosphate systems must be (from the appropriate K_a expressions for each acid):

$$[H^+] = 10^{-7.4} = K_1 \frac{[H_2CO_3]}{[HCO_3^-]} = K_2 \frac{[H_2PO_4^-]}{[HPO_4^=]}.$$

[A log or pH form of these equations is often given in biological texts and called the Henderson-Hasselbalch equation (Eq. 7–2).] The zero-ionic strength approximation yields ratios at pH 7.4:

$$[H_2PO_4^-]/[HPO_4^=] = 1/1.6$$

and

$$[H_2CO_3]/[HCO_3^-] = 1/10.$$

Carbonates are actually present in blood plasma in much higher concentration than phosphates so that any added acidity goes to form H_2CO_3. Normally, acids are removed slowly in the kidneys as $H_2PO_4^-$ and NH_4^+ excreted in the urine, which has pH 4 to 8. The CO_2 exhalation is useful for more rapid adjustment of pH. Fast breathing after exercise occurs because decomposition of sugars in the muscles forms lactic and pyruvic acids, which increase the $[H_2CO_3]$ and stimulate faster breathing to remove CO_2.

SUMMARY

A titration curve, in general, is a plot of some property proportional to a log (concentration) (ordinate) versus the amount of titrant added (abscissa). Its calculation brings into play all the acid-base equilibrium situations. Acids, buffers, ampholytes, and bases may become important at stages of a titration curve. Often, rapid approximate calculations serve to show the general features of the curve, its feasibility, and the indicator requirements.

The buffer index, feasibility of titration, and error due to any difference between the true equivalence point and the indicated endpoint are all related to the slope of the curve. The slope can be found by the usual first-derivative method.

SUGGESTIONS FOR FURTHER READING

BATES, R. G., *Determination of pH*, New York: John Wiley and Sons, 1964. Chapter 4 gives details of pH standards. A standard phosphate buffer of pH 7.4 for reference in blood measurements is described on p. 86.

FLECK, G. M., *Equilibria in Solution*, New York: Holt, Rinehart and Winston, 1966. Chapter 4 gives detailed consideration of the full equations for points along the titration curves.

WASER, J., "Acid-Base Titration Curves," *J. Chem. Educ.* **44**, 274 (1967).

WEST, E. S., *Textbook of Biophysical Chemistry*, 3rd ed. New York: Macmillan, 1963. Chapters 8 and 9 discuss the mechanisms of acid-base balance in the body.

PROBLEMS

1. Sketch roughly (do not perform extensive point calculation) the titration curves (pH vs. ml added) for the following to well past the final endpoint.
   a) 0.1 *M* NH_3 adding 0.1 *M* HCl
   b) 0.1 *M* H_3PO_4 adding 0.1 *M* NaOH
   c) 0.1 *M* citric acid adding 0.1 *M* NaOH.
2. Sketch a titration curve (pH vs. ml 0.1000 *M* HCl) for 1.000 mmole of Na_2CO_3 dissolved in 50 ml water. Calculate the approximate pH (no activity corrections) after adding 0, 1, 5, 9, 9.9, 10, 11, 15, 19.9, 20, and 21 ml of HCl. After the addition of 10 ml, plot two lines:
   a) for all H_2CO_3 remaining in solution and
   b) for all H_2CO_3 reacted to H_2O and CO_2 (lost) as formed.
3. Use the approximate equation (Chapter 5, case IV) to find the equivalence point pH and then calculate the slope of the titration curve at equivalence, in pH/ml base, if 25 ml of 0.100 *M* solution of each is titrated with 0.100 *M* NaOH:
   a) acetic acid [Use $\beta = 2.5 \times 10^{-5}$ *M*/pH calculated in the example in this chapter. However, the slope is greater in this smaller volume of solution (50 ml).]
   b) potassium acid phthalate,
   c) HCN.

   Indicate which titrations are feasible and list suitable indicators.
4. If pK_{In} for bromthymol blue is 6.8, what fraction is in the blue form at pH 7.1?
5. An unknown solution gave the curve shown in Fig. 7–6 when 10.00 ml of the solution was titrated with 0.2000 *M* NaOH. A pH meter was used. What information can be deduced about the kinds and amounts of materials in the solution? Show the calculations and the reasoning behind your answer.

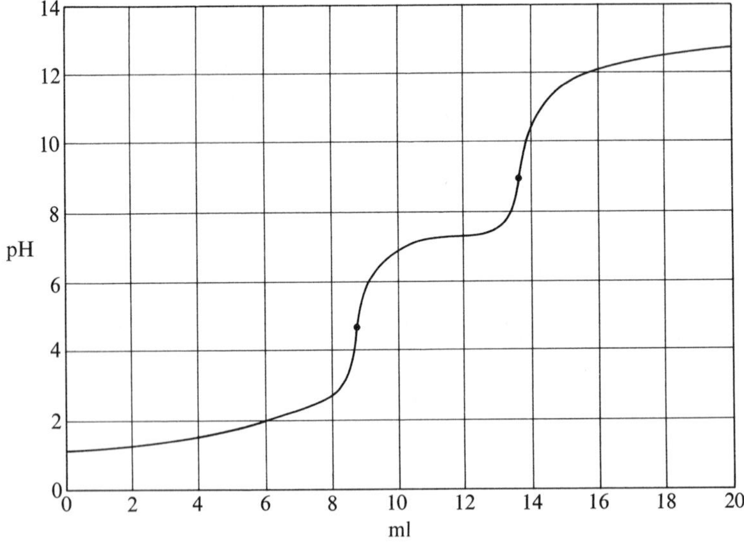

Figure 7–6

6. Given that a Winkler-type analysis is made on 200.0 mg of solid Na_2CO_3-NaOH mixture, 40.00 ± 0.02 ml of 0.10000 M HCl were needed to reach pH 4.0, a total base titration. To reach pH 9.0 on another sample of the same weight with excess $BaCl_2$ present, 12.00 ± 0.02 ml HCl were needed. Calculate the percentages of Na_2CO_3 and NaOH with widest possible reliability limits from the figures as given.
7. Calculate the pH of 0.100 M glycine solution. (For glycine hydrochloride, $pK_1 =$ 2.35, and $pK_2 = 9.78$.) Derive your equation for $[H^+]$.
8. Calculate pH values at five or more crucial points on the titration curve of the polyprotic acid you titrated using the pH meter in laboratory. Explain any lack of agreement.
9. The ratios $H_2PO_4^-/HPO_4^=$ and H_2CO_3/HCO_3^- were given in the text for pH 7.4 assuming zero ionic strength. What are more realistic values at the normal ionic strength of blood 0.15 M, if pH 7.40 is taken to mean the meter reading, $p(a_{H^+})$?
10. Look up the formulas and K_a values of lactic and pyruvic acids. Should they donate their protons to HCO_3^- in solution? Demonstrate numerically.
11. Citrate buffers are used in preserving blood. What volumes of 0.100 M Na_3C and Na_2HC should be mixed to make 100 ml of $p(a_{H^+})$ 7.40, if pK_3 at the conditions used is 5.62 and f_+ for H^+ is 0.70?
12. Use the t-fraction equation to sketch titration curves for 0.1 M weak acids of pK_a 3, 4, 5, and 9 by 0.1 M NaOH.

CHAPTER 8

DIAGRAMMATIC REPRESENTATIONS OF IONIC EQUILIBRIA

Three kinds of diagram are commonly used to illustrate the concentrations and proportions of the species in equilibrium as a function of one of the variables. (For acid-base equilibria one of the variables is usually the pH.) The diagrams are: plots of the fractions, α, of each species, plotted in two different ways, and log-concentration diagrams; all three have the pH as abscissa. The methods are applicable to equilibrium systems generally and are not limited to acid-base systems. The first two have many uses in coordination complex equilibrium discussions as well. (See Chapter 19.)

8.1 ABUNDANCE AND DISTRIBUTION DIAGRAMS

For a very simple example, let us consider acetic acid. Various pH values can be obtained by adding strong acid or base to prepare buffers or stronger acid solutions. The original acetate can only be present in two forms: HA and A^-. (The very strong acid form, H_2A^+ is ignored here.) Therefore the fraction of each is

$$\alpha_1 = \frac{[\mathrm{HA}]}{[\mathrm{HA}] + [\mathrm{A}^-]} \quad \text{and} \quad \alpha_0 = \frac{[\mathrm{A}^-]}{[\mathrm{HA}] + [\mathrm{A}^-]}. \tag{8-1}$$

Throughout, the subscripts on alphas indicate the number of protons on the base form. Now, one can substitute from the K_a expression for the acid to eliminate the [HA] and $[A^-]$ terms:

$$K_a = \frac{[\mathrm{H}^+][\mathrm{A}^-]}{[\mathrm{HA}]}, \qquad \alpha_1 = \frac{[\mathrm{H}^+]}{K_a + [\mathrm{H}^+]}, \qquad \alpha_0 = \frac{K_a}{K_a + [\mathrm{H}^+]}. \tag{8-2}$$

Clearly, we always have $\alpha_1 + \alpha_0 = 1$. Using $pK_a = 4.76$, we can calculate α values for plotting by substituting any desired $[H^+]$ values in the α equations.
The values in the table below are plotted in Fig. 8–1.

pH	α_1	α_0
0	"1"	$10^{-4.76}$
2	0.998	0.002
4	0.848	0.152
5	0.357	0.643
6	0.053	0.947
8	0.0005	0.9995

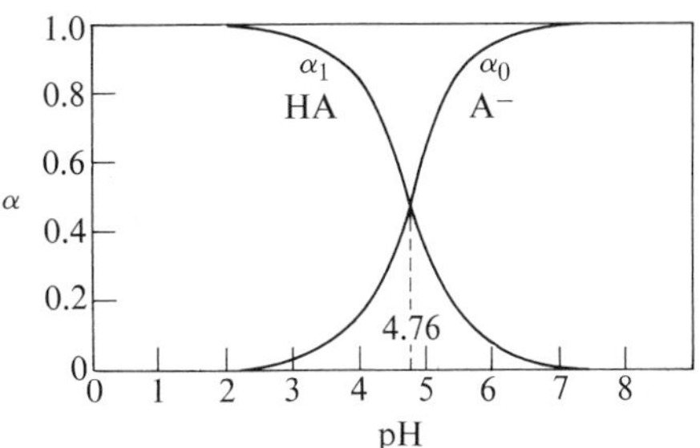

Fig. 8–1. Representation of the acetic acid-acetate equilibrium, with an α, fractional abundance, diagram.

This figure shows a symmetrical pair of curves, as must be the case for only two species since $\alpha_1 = 1 - \alpha_0$. Indeed, one of the lines gives all the information. The two lines intersect at pH 4.76, where $[HA] = [A^-]$. This is approximately the situation at the half-way point in titration which thus provides an estimate of the pK_a of a monoprotic acid.

8.2 LOG-CONCENTRATION DIAGRAMS

Figure 8–2 shows the logarithmic-concentration diagram for 0.10 *M* acetic acid. The logarithm of the concentration of any species of interest is plotted on the ordinate versus pH on the abscissa. At each chosen pH value, all species can be found since $[HA] = 0.1 - [A^-]$, and pH + pOH = 14. The numbered intersections have these significances:

1. $[HA] = [A^-]$ (at pH 4.76). Each concentration is 0.05 *M*, $\log(0.05) = -1.3$.
2. $[A^-] = [H^+]$. In pure HA solution, the pH is about 2.88.
3. $[HA] = [OH^-]$. In pure NaA solution, the pH is about 8.8.
4. $[H^+] = [OH^-]$ at pH 7.

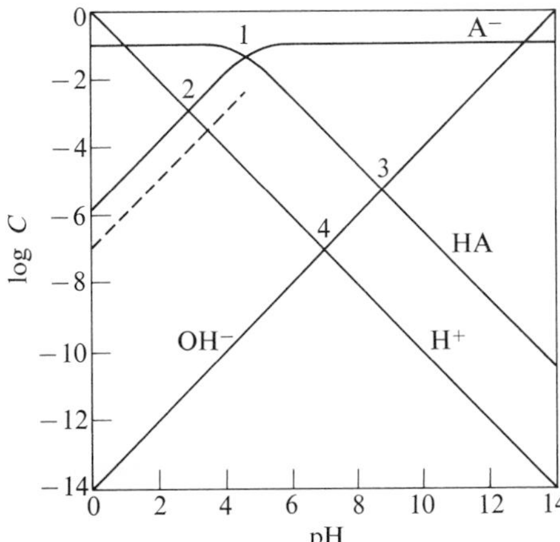

Fig. 8–2. Representation of the acetic acid-acetate equilibrium with a log-concentration diagram.

The advantage of log C diagrams is that they can be constructed rapidly with no computation. The acetic acid 0.1 M example is done as follows:

1. Enter the "system point" at pH = pK_a (4.76) and log C_a (−1).
2. Place the 1:1 buffer point −0.30 units below it, since log $\frac{1}{2}$ = −0.30. Draw lines downward from this point with slopes +1 and −1 for A^- and HA.
3. Draw H^+ and OH^- lines of slopes +1 and −1 through −7,7.
4. Connect the buffer point with short curves, with lines along log C = −1 for the HA and A^- limiting values at low and high pH.

Thus the diagram is drawn for a given C_a from knowledge of only pK_a and pK_w. From it one can read values of pH of a pure 0.1 M HA solution and the values of other species at this, or any other chosen pH. The pH of 0.1 M HA is seen at intersection (2) as 2.9. Other concentrations of HA can now be easily added: For 0.01 M the A^- line (dashed) is added 1 log unit below the 0.1 M case to give pH = 3.4 for pure 0.01 M HA. This suggests putting the HA and A^- lines on transparent paper to slide up or down over the H^+, OH^- plot to determine pH of any HA, NaA combination or pure solution of one alone. (See the article by Freiser and Fernando.)

8.3 DIAGRAMS FOR POLYPROTIC ACIDS

For equilibria containing several steps, more complex curves are obtained. They clarify the relation of the several species present at various pH values. To show this, let us take citric acid for our example. This is instructive because several species can be present in measurable amounts at certain pH values, and there is much overlapping of the α curves. This overlap does not occur so extensively with H_3PO_4, where the pK values are widely separated, a rather uncommon situation.

For citric acid,

```
                OH
                |
HOOC—CH2—C—CH2—COOH,
                |
               COOH
```

$$pK_1 = 3.13, \qquad pK_2 = 4.76, \qquad pK_3 = 6.40, \qquad pK_4 = 16.$$

The pK values are given for 25°C and zero ionic strength. The pK_4 value may be ignored below pH 12. We treat this as effectively a triprotic acid. The α calculations proceed as with acetic acid. Let A^{3-} stand for the citrate −3 ion and C for the total citrate concentration taken. Four citrate species are possible so that

$$C = [H_3A] + [H_2A^-] + [HA^=] + [A^{3-}].$$

Algebraic simplifications result if one calculates first the reciprocal of α_3, the fraction of H_3A* ($\alpha_3 = [H_3A]/C$):

$$1/\alpha_3 = C/[H_3A] = 1 + [H_2A^-]/[H_3A] + [HA^=]/[H_3A] + [A^{3-}]/[H_3A].$$

Now, write the K expressions for the acid and substitute them to eliminate all citric acid species terms as was done for acetic acid:

$$K_1 = \frac{[H^+][H_2A^-]}{[H_3A]}, \quad K_2 = \frac{[H^+][HA^=]}{[H_2A^-]}, \quad K_3 = \frac{[H^+][A^{3-}]}{[HA^=]},$$

$$\frac{1}{\alpha_3} = 1 + \frac{K_1}{[H^+]} + \frac{K_1K_2}{[H^+]^2} + \frac{K_1K_2K_3}{[H^+]^3}.$$

The other α values are more easily found from α_3 because

$$\alpha_2 = [H_2A^-]/C = ([H_2A^-]/C)([H_3A]/[H_3A]) = \alpha_3([H_2A^-]/[H_3A]) = \alpha_3 K_1/[H^+].$$

Similarly,

$$\alpha_1 = \alpha_3K_1K_2/[H^+]^2 \quad \text{and} \quad \alpha_0 = \alpha_3K_1K_2K_3/[H^+]^3.$$

Now, one may insert any chosen $[H^+]$ values in the α expressions to see how the relative abundances of species change with pH (see the table below).

pH	α_3	α_2	α_1	α_0	$\alpha_3 + \alpha_2$	$\alpha_3 + \alpha_2 + \alpha_1$
1	0.993	0.007	0	0	1	1
3	0.572	0.422	0.007	0	0.994	1
4	0.103	0.761	0.133	0.003	0.864	0.997
5	0.005	0.354	0.617	0.024	0.359	0.976
7	10^{-7}	0.001	0.201	0.798	0.001	0.202

A diagram of the alpha values from this table, Fig. 8–3, should clarify the rise and fall of the various species as base is added to citric acid. Another often-used plot, Fig. 8–4, is called a *distribution diagram.* Three lines, α_3, $\alpha_3 + \alpha_2$, and $\alpha_3 + \alpha_2 + \alpha_1$, are plotted versus pH. These lines contain all the information of the first plot. An explanatory vertical is given.

The α diagram, Fig. 8–3, reveals interesting correlations with the K_n values and titration curves for the acid by NaOH.

1) The intersection of α_3 and α_2, that is, the point at which $\alpha_3 = \alpha_2$, occurs where $[H_3A] = [H_2A^-]$. In the K_1 expression this means that $K_1 = [H^+] = 10^{-3.13}$. This would occur in titration when half the protons on H_3A were removed by NaOH so that $[H_2A^-] = [H_3A]$ (activity coefficients unity). In a real case, the corrected K_1 at the ionic strength used can be calculated, or the observed pH can be corrected to yield an estimate of K_1^0. Consider the following example.

* See the discussion on nomenclature in the Appendix.

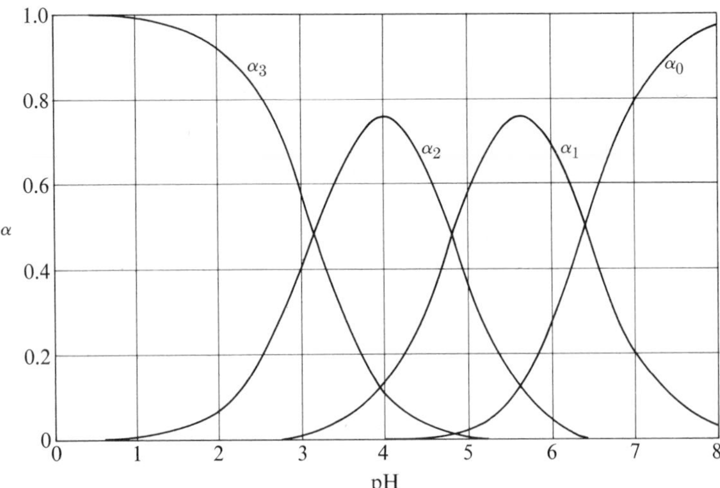

Fig. 8–3. Alpha diagram for citric acid showing fractions of species, $H_3A(\alpha_3)$, $H_2A^-(\alpha_2)$, $HA^=(\alpha_1)$, and $A^{3-}(\alpha_0)$. (The A signifies citrate -3 ion.) (K values are for zero ionic strength.)

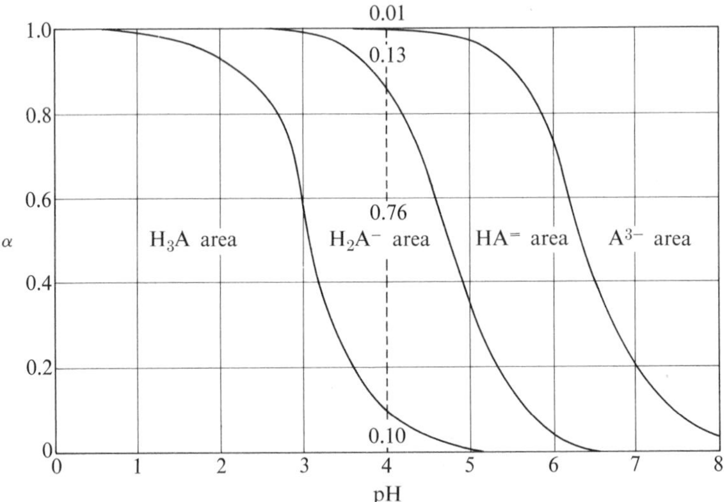

Fig. 8–4. Distribution diagram for citric acid. Distances between curves give α values for each species present at a given pH. The example shown is at pH 4, where $\alpha_3 = 0.10$, $\alpha_2 = 0.76$, $\alpha_1 = 0.13$, and $\alpha_0 = 0.01$. (K values for zero ionic strength.)

Example 1. A student dissolves 3.000 mmole citric acid in 90 ml of 0.100 M NaCl and titrates at the pH meter with 0.2000 M NaOH. The pH reading when 7.50 ml of NaOH were added was 3.01. Estimate the K_1^0 for citric acid.

The total volume is 97.5 ml which contains, approximately,

9 mmole NaCl	(at 0.0924 M),	
1.5 mmole H_3A	(at 0.0154 M),	
1.5 mmole H_2A^-	(at 0.0154 M),	
1.5 mmole Na^+	(at 0.0154 M)	added by titration.

Omitting H^+ and $HA^=$ as small, we have ionic strength, $I = 0.108\ M$. Assume that the pH meter reads $-\log$ (activity H^+), 3.01, so that we need only the activity coefficient for the H_2A^- to correct the K_1 to K_1^0. From the Kielland table or the Debye-Hückel extended equation, we get a value of about 0.80, so that

$$K_1^0 = \frac{[H^+]f_+(0.0154)(0.80)}{(0.0154)} = 10^{-3.11}.$$

More exactly, the pH tells us that $[H_2A^-]$ and $[H_3A]$ cannot be equal here because so much of the relatively strong acid, H_3A, ionizes. The observed $[H^+]$ comes from $H_3A \rightarrow H_2A^- + H^+$. It is

$$[H^+] = \frac{10^{-3.01}}{0.83} = 9.8 \times 10^{-4}.$$

This 0.00098 M should be added to the 0.0154 M H_2A^- formed by reaction with the added OH^-, and subtracted from the 0.0154 M H_3A to get a more accurate estimate of K_1^0:

$$K_1^0 = \frac{10^{-3.01}(0.0164)(0.80)}{(0.0144)} = 10^{-3.05}.$$

2) The intersection of α_2 and α_1 must occur where $[H_2A^-] = [HA^=]$, at pH 4.76, corrected to zero ionic strength.

3) The intersection of α_1 and α_0 must occur where $[HA^=] = [A^{3-}]$ at pH 6.40, with zero ionic strength. Consider the following example.

Example 2. Estimate K_3^0, if the titration curve in Example 1 above shows pH 5.80 when 37.5 ml NaOH were added.

The total volume is now 127.5 ml containing

9 mmole NaCl	(at 0.0706 M),	
1.5 mmole $HA^=$	(at 0.0118 M),	
1.5 mmole A^{3-}	(at 0.0118 M),	
7.5 mmole Na^+	(at 0.0588 M)	added.

These give the ionic strength as 0.177. The extended Debye-Hückel equation as shown in the Kielland table, taking ionic diameters about 6 Å, gives f values

0.34 and 0.091 for $HA^{=}$ and A^{3-}. Thus

$$K_3^0 = \frac{10^{-5.80}(0.091)}{(0.34)} = 10^{-6.37}.$$

4) Other intersections of help in interpreting or plotting the curves are:

α_3 and α_1, where $[H_3A] = [HA^{=}]$ at $[H^+] = \sqrt{K_1K_2} = 10^{-3.94}$;

α_2 and α_0, where $[H_2A] = [A^{3-}]$ at $[H^+] = \sqrt{K_2K_3} = 10^{-5.58}$;

α_3 and α_0, where $[H_3A] = [A^{3-}]$ at $[H^+] = \sqrt[3]{K_1K_2K_3} = 10^{-4.76}$.

The proof of these is left to the student as an exercise at the end of the chapter.

Note that the high symmetry of the α_2 and α_1 curves results from equal spacing of pK_1^0, pK_2^0, and pK_3^0 which happens to occur. Published values of the three pK's at $I = 0.15$ M (25°C) are 2.94, 4.34, and 5.62. Plots of α from these would not be so nearly symmetrical.

Maxima Calculations

The maxima of curves such as α_2 and α_1 may be found by standard methods: taking the derivative with respect to $[H^+]$ and setting it equal to zero. It is easier to use the reciprocal, for example:

$$\frac{1}{\alpha_2} = \frac{[H^+]}{K_1\alpha_3} = \frac{[H^+]}{K_1} + 1 + \frac{K_2}{[H^+]} + \frac{K_2K_3}{[H^+]^2},$$

$$\frac{\partial(1/\alpha_2)}{\partial[H^+]} = \frac{1}{K_1} + 0 - \frac{K_2}{[H^+]^2} - \frac{2K_2K_3}{[H^+]^3}.$$

Setting equal to zero, we find that it is easy to solve by successive approximations because the diagram, or tabular calculations, suggests a maximum near pH 4. We see that pH 3.94 satisfies the equation. The α values can then be calculated at pH 3.94 and found to be $\alpha_3 = 0.119$, $\alpha_2 = 0.765$, $\alpha_1 = 0.116$, and $\alpha_0 = 0.0004$.

SUMMARY

This chapter discusses the interpretation of distribution and abundance-of-species diagrams and logarithmic-concentration diagrams. We note that as with titration curves, important features can be deduced from simple calculations at a few key points.

SUGGESTIONS FOR FURTHER READING

See the references for Chapter 7 and the following:

ALBERT, A., and E. P. SERJEANT, *Ionization Constants of Acids and Bases*, New York: John Wiley, 1962. This text gives details of experimental methods of determining equilibrium constants and a brief chapter on stepwise formation constants of coordination compounds.

FREISER, H., and Q. FERNANDO, *J. Chem. Educ.* **42,** 35 (1965). Freiser and Fernando describe graphical methods for the solution of problems on mixtures. They suggest a transparent chart of log (α) versus pH for the rapid solution of problems that can be expressed with log C diagrams.

RINGBOM, A., *Complexation in Analytical Chemistry*, New York: Interscience, 1963. Ringbom suggests the use of identical equations for metal complexing and acid-base equilibria by considering H^+ the ligand and A^{n-} the central group analogous to the metal ion. This unified treatment allows him to make a single diagram for titration errors for all types of titrations (pp. 77ff and 160ff). The reader may well note the formal mathematical parallel between our α equations for polyprotic acids and for polyligand metal complexes in Chapter 19.

SILLEN, L. G., "Graphic Presentation of Equilibrium Data," in *Treatise on Analytical Chemistry*, ed. I. M. Kolthoff and P. J. Elving, Part I, Vol. 1. New York: Interscience, 1959, Chapter 8. (Reprinted in paperback as *Chemical Equilibrium in Analytical Chemistry.*)

PROBLEMS

1. Plot α versus pH for bromoacetic acid. Plot the log-concentration diagram for 0.10 M total bromoacetate concentration. From this diagram find the pH of pure 0.1 M bromoacetic acid.
2. For oxalic acid, derive the α expressions and plot the α-versus-pH diagram and a distribution diagram.
3. Prove the relations for the intersections of α diagrams of triprotic acids as stated in Part 4 of Section 8.3.
4. Find the pH of the maximum of the α_1 curve of citric acid and check the α_1 value at that point against that shown in Fig. 8–3. Find all the α values at the pH of the maximum.
5. Derive the α equations and construct both abundance and distribution diagrams for H_3PO_4. Point out reasons for the very obvious differences from the citric acid case given in the chapter.
6. Derive equations for the maxima of the α-versus-pH curves for H_3PO_4. Calculate the maxima and check against your plot in Problem 5.
7. From α or distribution diagrams available to you, find the compositions of some feasible buffers to obtain pH 4.00, 5.00, 6.00, and 7.00 with ionic strengths less than 0.1 M.
8. Prove that the slopes are $+1$ or -1 on log C-versus-pH diagrams for H^+, OH^-, and the lower parts of HA and A^-.
9. Use a straightedge to read off the pH of pure acetic acid solutions of concentrations 0.01, 0.001, 0.0001, etc. Where does this method break down and why? Use Fig. 8–2. Repeat for NaA.

CHAPTER 9

INTERIONIC EFFECTS IN CHEMICAL EQUILIBRIA

9.1 ACTIVITIES

Use of activity corrections was introduced in Chapter 6. Now we shall discuss them in more detail.

Table 6–1 shows the increase in $[H^+]$ of acetic acid solutions as inert ("neutral") ionic material is added. The solubility of ionic solids also increases as shown in Table 9–1. Note that this occurrence is opposite to the salting out of nonelectrolytes, where the salt removes water. These three materials in the table each give two ions in water.

Table 9–1. Solubilities of 1:1, 2:2, and 3:3 Electrolytes with Increasing Ionic Strength

	Solubility, $M \times 10^5$				Increase at 0.01 M, percent
	Pure water	0.001 M KNO_3	0.005 M KNO_3	0.01 M KNO_3	
AgCl	1.28	1.32	1.38	1.43	12
$BaSO_4$	0.96	1.16	1.42	1.70	77
$[Co(NH_3)_6][Co(CN)_6]$	1.38	1.71	2.45	3.12	126

The effect on the more highly charged ions is greater than on the singly charged ions. This points up the fallacy in the common statement that interionic effects can be ignored for student calculations. If they are ignored, calculations from equilibrium constants can be justified in being given only to the nearest power of ten. If the concentrations of other ions are not given, one can only say that the solubility of AgCl is about 10^{-5} M. (Of course, the common-ion effect must not be overlooked when it is present.)

A quantitative theoretical treatment of the interionic forces in solution was made by Debye and Hückel in 1923. Their analysis produced an equation relating the activity coefficient to the size and charge of the ion in question and to the ionic strength of the solution around it. This means that, at sufficient dilution, the activity correction does not depend on any other property of the individual ion. The ionic strength, I, as previously defined is

$$I = \frac{1}{2} \sum_i c_i z_i^2,$$

where c_i and z_i are the concentration and charge of ion i. Illustrations were given in Chapter 6.

Activity coefficients cannot be measured for single ions, so we deal with the mean activity coefficients of electrolytes. These are defined, for a 1:1 electrolyte, as

$$f_{\pm} = \sqrt{f_+ f_-},$$

or more generally, for electrolyte A_xB_y, as

$$f_{\pm} = [f_+^x f_-^y]^{1/(x+y)}.$$

One form of the Debye-Hückel equation is

$$\log f_{\pm} = \frac{-0.51 z_+ z_- \sqrt{I}}{1 + a\sqrt{I}}.$$

The a factor contains a size parameter and turns out to be about one for a size of 3 Å. Thus for small ions, the Debye-Hückel equation is often used in the form

$$\log f_{\pm} = \frac{-0.51 z_+ z_- \sqrt{I}}{1 + \sqrt{I}}. \tag{9–1}$$

This gives results within about 5% of experimental values at 0.1 M and within about 1% at 0.01 M for 1:1 electrolytes. A briefer form may be used at lower I, since $1 + \sqrt{I} \rightarrow 1$, and

$$\log f_{\pm} = -0.51 z_+ z_- \sqrt{I}. \tag{9–2}$$

This is called the Debye-Hückel limiting equation. It is good to about 10% at 0.1 M and about 2% at 0.01 M for 1:1 electrolytes.

The extended Debye-Hückel equation was used by Kielland in 1937 to derive the values listed in Table 9–2.

The size can also be accommodated by an added factor as in the Davies equation,

$$\log f_{\pm} = -0.51 z_+ z_- \left(\frac{\sqrt{I}}{1 + \sqrt{I}} - \alpha I\right).$$

All of these equations may be used to calculate single ionic activity coefficients by using z^2 for z_+z_-. Ionic f values can be read from the alignment chart (Fig. 9–1) constructed from this equation. In the absence of specific data, the α of the Davies equation is usually taken as 0.2.

Table 9–3 compares f values from the Debye-Hückel equations and the Kielland table (the Davies equation is almost the same) with experimentally determined values. (Cell voltage, vapor pressure, and freezing points depend on activities and can be used to evaluate them.) Certainly these values are significantly different from unity for many solutions and use of Debye-Hückel f values will be far better than an assumption that $f = 1$. Tables of experimental values are compiled in H. S. Harned and B. B. Owen, *The Physical Chemistry of Electrolytic Solutions* (New York: Reinhold, 1958).

Table 9–2. Kielland Table of Ionic Activity Coefficients Arranged by the Sizes of Ions

Charge	Size* a	Ions	$I = 0.0005$	0.001	0.0025	0.005	0.01	0.025	0.05	0.1
1	2.5	Rb^+, Cs^+, Ag^+, NH_4^+, Tl^+	0.975	0.964	0.945	0.924	0.898	0.85	0.80	0.75
	3	K^+, Cl^-, Br^-, I^-, CN^-, NO_3^-, NO_2^-, OH^-, F^-, ClO_4^-	0.975	0.964	0.945	0.925	0.899	0.85	0.805	0.755
	4	Na^+, IO_3^-, HCO_3^-, HSO_3^-, $H_2PO_4^-$, ClO_2^-, $C_2H_3O_2^-$	0.975	0.964	0.947	0.928	0.902	0.86	0.82	0.775
	6	Li^+, $C_6H_5COO^-$	0.975	0.965	0.948	0.929	0.907	0.87	0.835	0.80
	9	H^+	0.975	0.967	0.950	0.933	0.914	0.88	0.86	0.83
2	4.5	Pb^{++}, Hg_2^{++}, $SO_4^{=}$, $CrO_4^{=}$, $CO_3^{=}$, $SO_3^{=}$, $C_2O_4^{=}$, $S_2O_3^{=}$, H citrate$^{=}$	0.903	0.867	0.805	0.742	0.665	0.55	0.455	0.37
	5	Sr^{++}, Ba^{++}, Cd^{++}, Hg^{++}, $S^{=}$, $WO_4^{=}$	0.903	0.868	0.805	0.744	0.67	0.555	0.465	0.38
	6	Ca^{++}, Cu^{++}, Zn^{++}, Sn^{++}, Mn^{++}, Fe^{++}, Ni^{++}, Co^{++}, Phthalate$^{=}$	0.905	0.870	0.809	0.749	0.675	0.57	0.485	0.405
	8	Mg^{++}, Be^{++}	0.906	0.872	0.813	0.755	0.69	0.595	0.52	0.45
3	4	PO_4^{3-}, $Fe(CN)_6^{3-}$, $Cr(NH_3)_6^{3+}$	0.796	0.725	0.612	0.505	0.395	0.25	0.16	0.095
	9	Al^{3+}, Fe^{3+}, Cr^{3+}, Sc^{3+}, In^{3+}, and rare earths	0.802	0.738	0.632	0.54	0.445	0.325	0.245	0.18

* Note that these sizes are rounded values for the *effective* size in water solution and are not the size of the simple ions, unhydrated. For a more detailed discussion see the original paper from which these values are taken [J. Kielland, *J. Am. Chem. Soc.* **59,** 1675 (1937)]. Calculated from

$$\log f = \frac{-0.509\, z^2\sqrt{I}}{1 + 0.328\, a\sqrt{I}}$$

at 25°C, where a is the effective diameter in angstroms. Note I is not M for 2 and 3 charge ions.

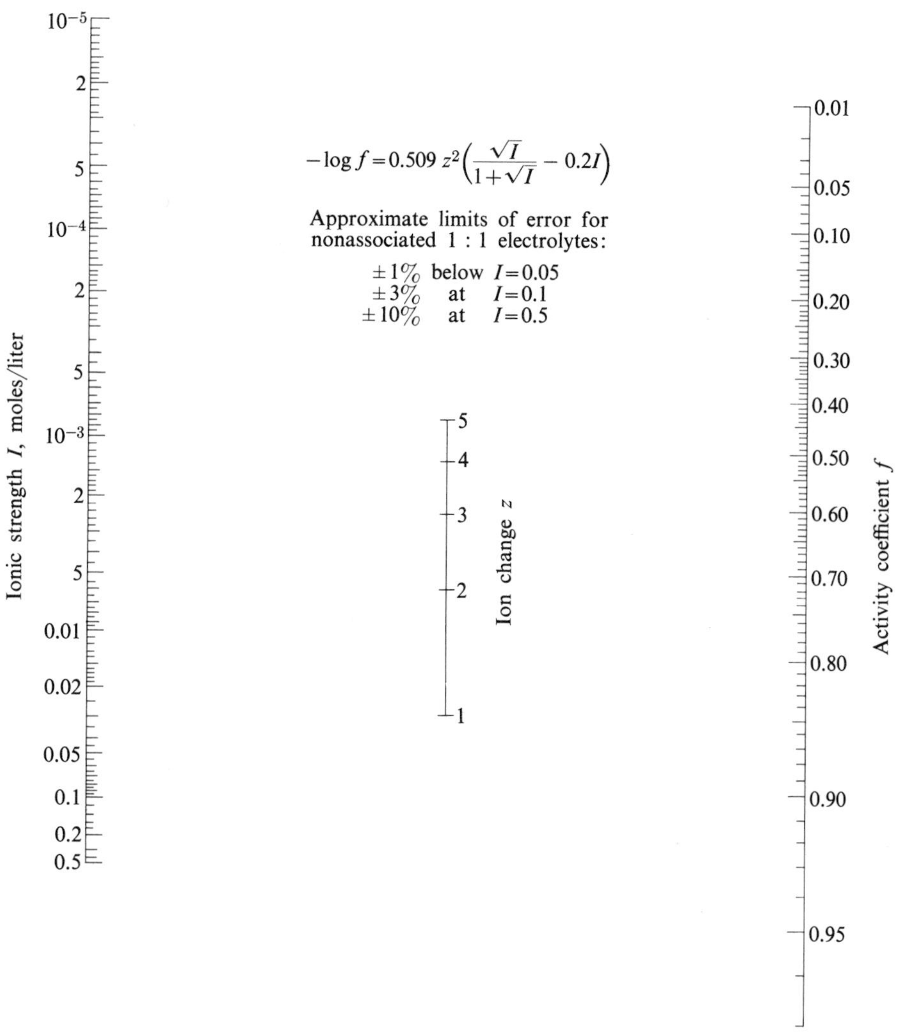

Fig. 9–1. Alignment chart for calculating activity coefficients, based on the Davies equation. Put a straightedge on I and z to read f at right. (From J. N. Butler, *Ionic Equilibrium*, Reading, Mass.: Addison-Wesley, 1964.)

In discussions of activities, the reader may be puzzled by the meaning of "very dilute solutions" in which $a \longrightarrow M$ and $f \longrightarrow 1$. The following values may help clarify this. (The $f_{\pm}$ values are for charge 1 : 1 electrolytes.)

I	10^{-2}	10^{-3}	10^{-4}	10^{-5}
$f_{\pm}$	0.90	0.97	0.988	0.996

Table 9–3. Experimental and Calculated Mean Activity Coefficients, $f_\pm$

	Experimental	Debye-Hückel long form (9–1)	Debye-Hückel limiting equation (9–2)	Kielland table values (Table 9–2)
		0.001 m*		
HCl	0.966	0.96	0.96	0.97
NaCl	0.966	0.96	0.96	0.96
$CuSO_4$	0.74	0.76	0.74	0.75
$LaCl_3$	0.788	0.78	0.76	0.80
$In_2(SO_4)_3$	—	0.46	0.42	0.52
		0.01 m		
HCl	0.904	0.90	0.89	0.91
NaCl	0.904	0.90	0.89	0.90
$CuSO_4$	0.41	0.46	0.39	0.5
$LaCl_3$	0.559	0.50	0.42	0.58
$In_2(SO_4)_3$	0.142	0.14	0.07	0.2
		0.1 m		
HCl	0.796	0.75	0.69	0.79
NaCl	0.780	0.75	0.69	0.77
$CuSO_4$	0.16	0.16	0.05	—
$LaCl_3$	0.336	0.21	0.06	—
$In_2(SO_4)_3$	0.035	0.02	0.00	—

* The difference between molality, m, and molarity, M, is negligible below 0.01 m and about 1 to 2% at 0.1 m.

Only for I less than 10^{-4} can we assume $f = 1$ with 1% accuracy for 1:1 electrolytes. With ions of higher charge, the coefficients are lower. For a charge-three ion of size 4 Å, the longer form Debye-Hückel equation gives $f = 0.901$ at $I = 10^{-4}$.

In more concentrated solutions, the activity coefficients depend on the natures of the individual ions. A general rule for all ions of one charge is not available. Experimental values can sometimes be found, but they may be very different in mixtures of electrolytes. For this reason, only approximate calculations are possible for equilibrium concentrations in solutions of high ionic strength. Some experimental values are listed in Table 9–4. These values and the graphs (Figs. 9–2, 9–3, and 9–4) illustrate the variety of behavior which occurs.

The Debye-Hückel limiting equation can be rearranged to

$$\frac{\log f_\pm}{z_+z_-} = -0.51\sqrt{I}.$$

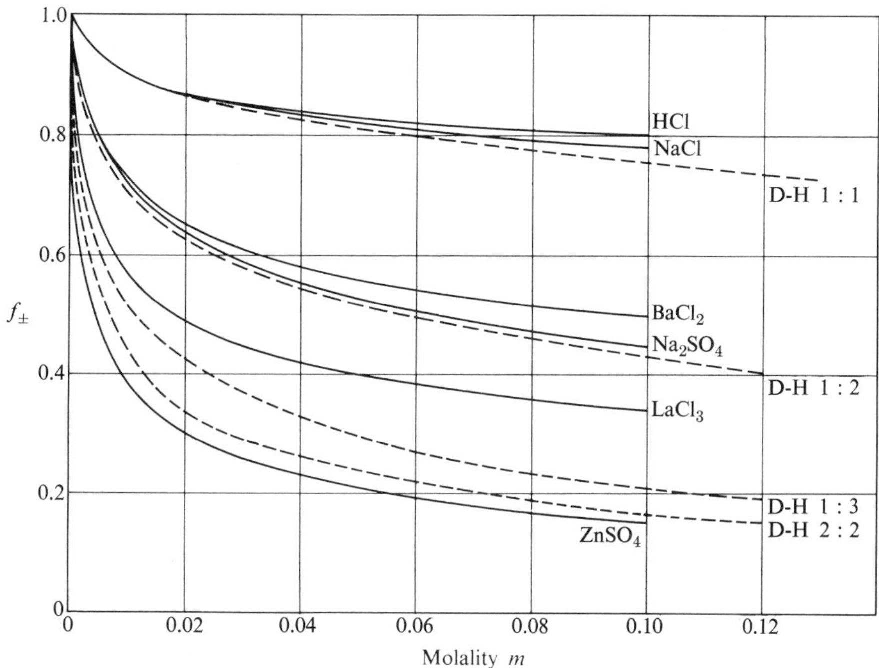

Fig. 9–2. Experimental mean activity coefficients compared with Debye-Hückel theory, Eq. (9–1) (for low-concentration data). (D-H is used to represent Debye-Hückel.)

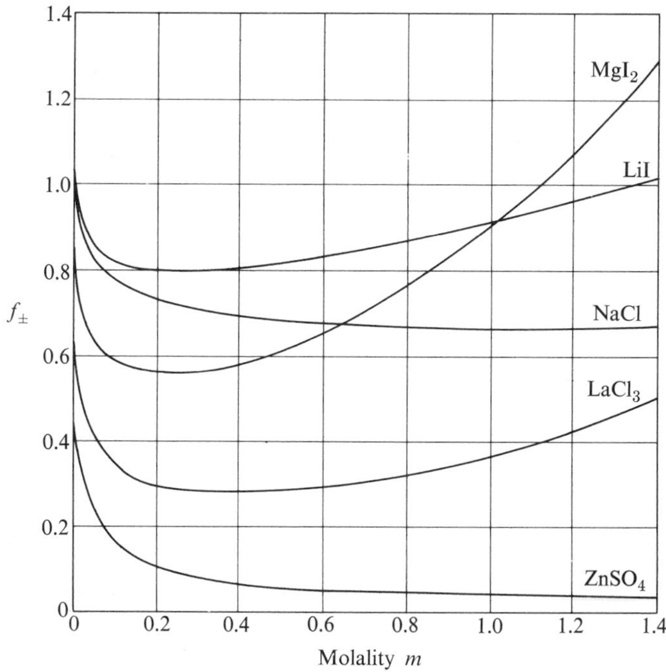

Fig. 9–3. Experimental mean activity coefficients for various electrolytes (extending to higher concentrations).

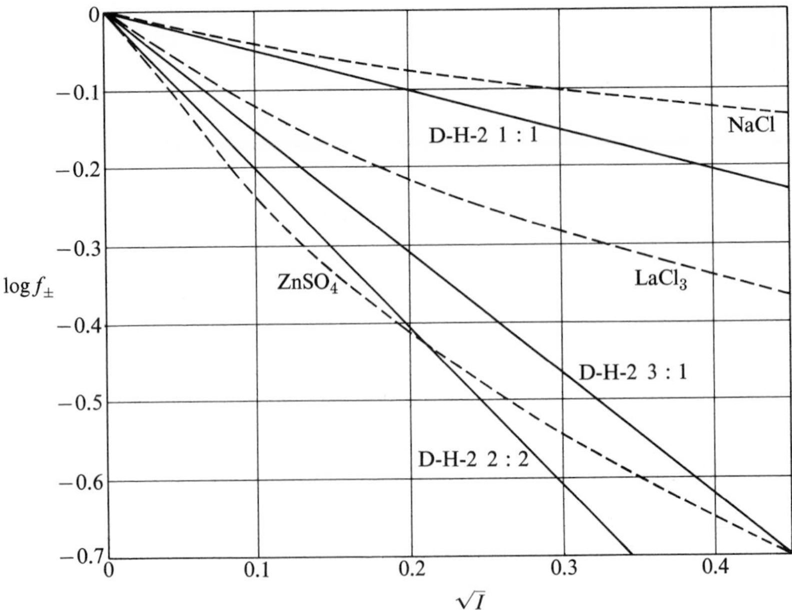

Fig. 9–4. Solid lines represent the Debye-Hückel (D-H) limiting equation predictions.

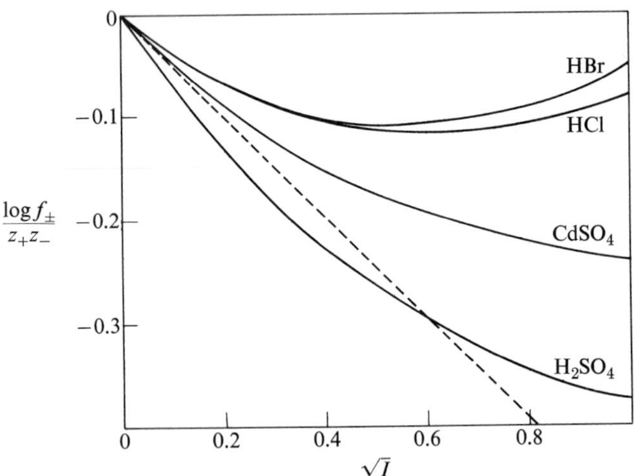

Fig. 9–5. After W. M. Latimer, *Oxidation Potentials*, 2nd ed. Englewood Cliffs, N.J.: Prentice-Hall, 1952, p. 351.

Thus, for all electrolytes, a plot of the left side versus $\sqrt{I}$ should give a straight line of slope -0.51 in the region where the equation applies. In Fig. 9–5 are plotted the experimental data for several electrolytes to illustrate the approach to this slope at low ionic strength. The dashed line is this limiting slope.

Table 9–4. Mean Activity Coefficients at 25°C*

Molality	NaCl	LiI	CsI	$MgCl_2$	MgI_2	$LaCl_3$	$MnSO_4$
1	0.658	0.907	0.532	0.570	0.892	0.366	0.044
2	0.671	1.196	0.470	1.053	2.43	0.883	0.035
4	0.792	—	—	5.54	29.0	—	0.048

* Values from Harned and Owen, *The Physical Chemistry of Electrolytic Solutions.*

9.2 THE SOLUBILITY PRODUCT

The thermodynamic equilibrium constant for weak acid reaction in water, K_a^0, was defined in Chapter 4. The concept of the solubility product for slightly soluble ionic compounds derives from the equilibrium, for a 1:1 example, M^+X^-:

$$M^+X^- \text{ (solid)} \rightleftharpoons M^+ + X^-, \qquad K^0 = \frac{(M^+)(X^-)}{(\underline{MX})}.$$

Here, the parentheses indicate activities, and the underline, a solid. The activity of a pure solid is defined as *one*. It is clearly not *in* the solution as are M^+ and X^- in moles per liter. The unit activity of the solid is included in the constant to give the constant termed the *solubility-product constant*, K_{sp}^0. It can be related to practical constants, K_{sp}, which are approximately constant at given ionic strengths:

$$K_{sp}^0 = (M^+)(X^-) = [M^+][X^-]f_+f_- = K_{sp}f_+f_-.$$

Literature values for solubility products may be found for specific ionic strengths, K_{sp}, or extrapolated to zero ionic strength, K_{sp}^0. For other formula compounds M_aX_b, appropriate exponents are used as usual in equilibrium expressions. Naturally, these constants can be used only for equilibrium situations, which means saturated solutions of the compound. Further refinements for side reactions and interfering equilibria are discussed in Chapter 10.

9.3 EXAMPLE CALCULATIONS WITH ACTIVITIES

The following examples illustrate the use of activity coefficients in simple equilibrium calculations.

Example 1. Compare the solubility of AgCl in pure water and in 0.030 *M* HNO_3, using $K_{sp}^0 = 1.7 \times 10^{-10}$. The approximate solubility is $\sqrt{K_{sp}} = 10^{-5}$.

Since I will be about 10^{-5} M, we can use $f = 1$ in the pure water. At $I = 0.030$, $f_\pm$ is 0.84 and $K_{sp}^0 = (Ag^+)(Cl^-)f_\pm^2$. Since there is no common ion, the molar solubility, M, is

$$M = \sqrt{K^0}/f_\pm,$$

which is 1.3×10^{-5} in water and $1.5_6 \times 10^{-5}$ in the 0.030 *M* HNO_3, an increase of about 19%.

Example 2. Repeat Example 1 for the 3:3 solid of Table 9–1. The water solubility given is 1.38×10^{-5} *M*.

Here, $f = 1$ is not valid, since the ionic strength is $\frac{1}{2}(1.38 \times 10^{-5} \times 3^2 \times 2) = 1.17 \times 10^{-4}$. This makes the $f_{\pm}$ about 0.90 and

$$K^0_{\text{sp}} = (1.38 \times 10^{-5})^2(0.90)^2.$$

The solubility in 0.030 *M* HNO_3, with $I = 0.030$, is

$$M_{.03} = \sqrt{K^0}/f = 5.4 \times 10^{-5}.$$

(At $I = 0.03$, $f_{\pm}$ is 0.23 from the Kielland table.) This represents a fourfold increase in solubility, which is typical behavior for these highly charged ionic solids.

Example 3. Calculate the pH of an acetate buffer made of equal, 0.100 *M*, concentrations of acetic acid and sodium acetate. (The experimental value of 4.66 was obtained on a pH meter and $\text{p}K^0_a = 4.76$.)

The approximate method without activity correction gives pH = 4.76. Taking f values from the Kielland table gives

$$K^0_a = 10^{-4.76} = \frac{0.83[\text{H}^+] \times 0.77(0.1)}{(0.1)},$$

$$[\text{H}^+] = 2.74 \times 10^{-5}, \qquad \text{pH} = 4.56.$$

However, if the pH meter is giving $-\log$ (activity of H^+),

$$a_{\text{H}^+} = 0.83 \times 2.74 \times 10^{-5}, \qquad \text{p}a_{\text{H}^+} = 4.64.$$

In fact, if one takes the mean activity coefficient as 0.80, one gets $\text{p}a_{\text{H}^+} = 4.66$, in agreement with the measurement. The difficulty in defining pH rigorously is mentioned in Chapters 7 and 24 in the section on pH standards and measurements.

Example 4. One of the pH standards suggested by the National Bureau of Standards is 0.0500 *M* KHP (potassium acid phthalate) which they set at a pH-meter reading of 4.008 (Chapter 7). What is the expected reading if we take $\text{p}K^0_1$ as 2.95 and $\text{p}K^0_2$ as 5.41?

For a first approximation, ionic strength, $I = 0.05$ *M*. The ampholyte equation [Eq. (5–3), for HCO_3^-] is

$$[\text{H}^+] = \left[\frac{K_1K_2[\text{HP}^-] + K_1K_w}{K_1 + [\text{HP}^-]}\right]^{1/2}.$$

Now, find the corrected, or effective, K values at this ionic strength from the K^0 expressions (for H^+, find f_+, for HP^-, find f_-, and for $P^=$, find $f_=$):

$$K^0_1 = K_1f_+f_-, \qquad K^0_2 = K_2f_+f_=/f_- \qquad \text{and} \qquad K_1K_2 = K^0_1K^0_2/f^2_+f_=.$$

In the ampholyte equation given, the K_1K_w term is much smaller than the other term in the numerator, so it may be omitted to get

$$[H^+]f_+ = a_{H^+} = \left[\frac{K_1^0 K_2^0}{(f_=)(K_1^0/f_+ f_-[HP^-] + 1)}\right]^{1/2}.$$

Since the term added to 1 in the denominator is small, only the $f_=$ term is important to the calculation of a_{H^+}. The Kielland table gives 0.48 for $f_=$ and about 0.85 for the other two, at $I = 0.050$. Thus

$$a_{H^+} = \left[\frac{10^{-8.36}}{(0.48)(1.03)}\right]^{1/2} = 10^{-4.03}.$$

We may now check the species present and adjust $f_=$ if required. Use the K^0 expressions with $[HP^-]$ about 0.05 to find $[H_2P]$ and $[P^=]$:

$$K_1^0 = 10^{-2.95} = \frac{10^{-4.03}(0.05)(0.85)}{[H_2P]} \quad \text{and} \quad [H_2P] = 0.0035\ M,$$

$$K_2^0 = 10^{-5.41} = \frac{10^{-4.03}[P^=](0.48)}{(0.05)(0.85)} \quad \text{and} \quad [P^=] = 0.0036\ M.$$

Now, $I = \frac{1}{2}[0.043 + 0.0500 + 0.0036(4)] = 0.054$, since $[HP^-]$ has been reduced to $0.0500 - 0.0035 - 0.0036 = 0.043$. The new $f_=$ from the Kielland table is now 0.42 which changes pa_{H^+} to 4.00, which is quite satisfactory agreement considering the uncertainty in activity coefficients and K^0 values. By straining a bit with K^0 values and the Davies equation for f's, Butler (*Ionic Equilibrium*, pp. 441–443) is able to get 4.008. He points out that such agreement is probably lucky and is not quite so perfect in a neighboring example on the phosphate buffer. See Problem 8 at the end of this chapter.

SUMMARY

The magnitudes of calculated and observed activity coefficients are presented. The range of usefulness of calculation from theory is discussed. The Debye-Hückel equations allow calculation of pH and solubilities reliable within about $\pm 1\%$ below ionic strength 0.1 *M*. Errors may be as great as tenfold for multiply-charged ions if activity coefficients are assumed to be *one*.

PROBLEMS

1. a) Find the ionic strengths of the following solutions.

   i) 0.020 *M* KNO_3 ii) 0.020 *M* K_2SO_4

   iii) 0.020 *M* each KNO_3, K_2SO_4, and $ZnSO_4$ (all in the same solution)

   b) Find the mean ionic activity coefficients calculated from the Debye-Hückel limiting equation, and from the long form, for AgCl, $CaSO_4$, and $La_2(SO_4)_3$ when a trace dissolves in each of the three solutions in (a). Compare with values from Fig. 9–1 and Table 9–2.

2. Calculate the solubility in moles/liter with, and without, activity corrections (use the long form Debye-Hückel equation or the Kielland table) for each of the following (for $CaSO_4$, $pK^0_{sp} = 5.04$).

   a) $CaSO_4$ in 0.0050 *M* $ZnCl_2$
   b) $CaSO_4$ in 0.0050 *M* $ZnSO_4$
   c) $Co(NH_3)_6Co(CN)_6$ in 0.050 *M* NaCl
   d) $Co(NH_3)_6Co(CN)_6$ in 0.010 *M* $K_3Co(CN)_6$

3. Find the percentage increase in $[H^+]$ when 10.0 g NaCl are added to 1 liter of 0.0100 *M* acetic acid according to the Debye-Hückel limiting law and also the more extended equation.

4. Repeat Problem 3 for the acid $HC_2O_4^-$. Explain the difference.

5. Distinguish between the uses of K_{sp} and K^0_{sp}. What is the relation between the two for a general electrolyte X_aY_b?

6. Find experimental activity coefficients for HCl solutions up to 1 *M*. Plot $\log f_\pm$ versus $\sqrt{M}$ for these and also for those calculated from the extended Debye-Hückel equation. If possible compare HBr, HI, and $HClO_4$. Can you draw any general conclusions?

7. From the K^0_a expression demonstrate the plausibility of the experimental observation that on addition of NaCl to dilute acetic acid, the $[H^+]$ increases, but the pH-meter reading is unchanged.

8. The NBS certifies (Chapter 7) that a buffer composed of KH_2PO_4 and Na_2HPO_4 each 0.025 *M* will produce a pH of 6.865 at 25°C. Try to rationalize this with the best K^0 values for H_3PO_4.

CHAPTER 10

PRECIPITATION EQUILIBRIUM CALCULATIONS

So far, we have considered titrations whose endpoint occurs through the sudden change of $[H^+]$. In this chapter we discuss titrations which depend on precipitation to produce a sudden change in the concentration of some measurable species. Precipitation is also used in gravimetric analyses in which the solid is collected quantitatively and weighed. We must look into the equilibria involved and the effects of conditions of temperature, concentration, and perhaps pressure (for reactions of a gas like H_2S) on equilibria. These can affect the purity and completeness of precipitation.

The most widely used reaction for precipitation titration and gravimetric work is

$$Ag^+ + Cl^- \rightarrow \underline{AgCl}.$$

(Underlining is used here to indicate materials which are present mainly in solid form rather than in solution.) For titration of chloride ion by standard $AgNO_3$ solution, an indicator for Cl^- or Ag^+ is needed. Karl Mohr (1806–1879) discovered the use of red Ag_2CrO_4 as the indicator for excess silver ion. In the Mohr titration, a carefully determined amount of $CrO_4^=$ is present. After all the AgCl precipitates, the next drop of Ag^+ added causes red Ag_2CrO_4 to form. The presence of too much, or too little, $CrO_4^=$ will bring the color indication too soon or too late. Calculation from the equilibrium constants and laboratory testing are required to find a proper concentration of chromate.

Another method, a modified Volhard (1834–1910) titration, is also used. A small known amount of thiocyanate and an excess of Fe(III) solutions are added to the chloride sample. Titration with standard $AgNO_3$ proceeds through precipitation of the AgCl and then the AgSCN. The SCN^- had been coordinated with the Fe(III) as the red $FeSCN^{++}$ which disappears at the endpoint. The known SCN^- can be subtracted from the total milliequivalents of $AgNO_3$ to give the Cl^-. The endpoint is somewhat easier to see than that of the Mohr titration and the method is especially useful for solutions which are intended for both chloride and silver determinations. The Volhard titration for silver is simple and direct: SCN^- solution is the titrant for Ag^+ with Fe(III) as the indicator. The red complex appears at the endpoint.

10.1 HETEROGENEOUS EQUILIBRIUM

For precipitates in equilibrium with only two ions, the simple hyperbolic relation holds, for X^+Y^- at constant ionic strength:

$$\underline{X^+Y^-} \leftrightarrows X^+ + Y^-, \qquad K_{sp} = [X^+][Y^-].$$

For those with more than two ions, X_2Y_3, for example, higher powers are required,

$$\underline{X_2Y_3} \leftrightarrows 2X^{3+} + 3Y^{=}, \qquad K_{sp} = [X^{3+}]^2[Y^{=}]^3.$$

Remember, in all these cases, the amount of precipitate present has no effect on the concentrations in the saturated solutions. Its activity is constant and defined as *one*. This is equivalent to saying it is constant and absorbed into the K_{eq} to make K_{sp}.

Unfortunately, it is rare that the simple K_{sp} relations given above give correct results in solubility calculations. Some considerations which enter a case so simple looking as the AgCl expression,

$$\underline{AgCl} \rightleftharpoons Ag^+ + Cl^-, \qquad K^0_{sp} = 1.8 \times 10^{-10} \quad \text{at } 25°C, \qquad (10\text{–}1)$$

are:

a) activity corrections,
b) common-ion effects,
c) other possible reactions of the ions and the solid.

Activity-coefficient calculations were given in Chapter 9. Common-ion effects are treated in elementary courses, and many examples occur in the problems of this chapter. Other reactions occurring in the AgCl case are:

$$Ag^+ + H_2O \rightleftharpoons Ag(OH) + H^+, \qquad K_a = 10^{-12}, \qquad (10\text{–}2)$$

$$\underline{AgCl} \rightleftharpoons AgCl \text{ (molecules)}, \qquad K_s = 10^{-6.70}, \qquad (10\text{–}3)$$

$$\underline{AgCl} + Cl^- \rightleftharpoons AgCl_2^-, \qquad K_2 = 10^{-4.70}, \qquad (10\text{–}4)$$

$$AgCl_2^- + Cl^- \rightleftharpoons AgCl_3^{=}, \qquad K_3 = 1, \qquad (10\text{–}5)$$

$$AgCl_3^{=} + Cl^- \rightleftharpoons AgCl_4^{3-}, \qquad K_4 = 1.7, \qquad (10\text{–}6)$$

$$\underline{AgCl} + Ag^+ \rightleftharpoons Ag_2Cl^+, \qquad K = 10^{-4.5}. \qquad (10\text{–}7)$$

We shall see that the values given allow one to ignore all but the conventional K_{sp} only in pure water solutions of AgCl, or in solutions with small excess of common ions. Equation (10–3) means that AgCl is a weak electrolyte.*

Example. Let us try to calculate the solubility of AgCl in 0.0010 *M* HCl. For $I = 0.0010$, $f_\pm = 0.96$, so from (10–1), the molar solubility, *S*, is

$$[Ag^+][Cl^-] = [S][S + 0.0010](0.96)^2 = 1.8 \times 10^{-10}, \qquad S = 1.9_6 \times 10^{-7}.$$

---

* This whole question is discussed in detail by R. W. Ramette, *J. Chem. Educ.* **37,** 348 (1960).

(The approximation that S is negligible with respect to addition to 0.0010 is justified.) Now we must check to see whether any appreciable amount of Ag^+ is removed in steps (10–2) to (10–7). From (10–2),

$$\frac{[AgOH][H^+]}{[Ag^+]} = \frac{[AgOH](10^{-3})}{(10^{-7})} = 10^{-12},$$

$$[AgOH] = 10^{-16} \quad \text{or} \quad 1/10^9 \text{ of the } [Ag^+].$$

This is clearly a negligible fraction of the dissolved silver. Equation (10–3) tells us that all saturated solutions contain $10^{-6.70}$ molar AgCl molecules, or 2.0×10^{-7} M, in addition to the K_{sp} amounts of ionic materials. So far our total solubility is

$$(1.9_6 + 2.0)10^{-7} = 4.0 \times 10^{-7}\ M.$$

The experimental value is about 5×10^{-7} M.

Next we see what Eq. (10–4) contributes:

$$\frac{[AgCl_2^-]\cancel{f_-}}{[Cl^-]\cancel{f_-}} = 10^{-4.70} \quad (\text{taking } Cl^- = 0.0010),$$

$$[AgCl_2^-] = 2 \times 10^{-8}.$$

From steps (10–5), (10–6), and (10–7), we get $[AgCl_3^{=}] = 2 \times 10^{-11}$, with $[AgCl_4^{3-}]$ and $[Ag_2Cl^+]$ even smaller so that they are negligible in calculating total solubility, which now adds up to 4.2×10^{-7}.

The example just given shows the kind of thinking that must be applied to solubility calculations. When values of the various equilibrium constants are lacking, only a lower limit of the solubility can be made from K^0_{sp}. However, if complexing ions are absent, accurate calculations may be possible. In Example 1 in Chapter 9 for AgCl in 0.030 M HNO_3, a good result was obtained. The acidity made the [AgOH] negligible, as in the example given above, and the NO_3^- ion complexes most cations very weakly in water solution. With no added chloride ion, the higher Cl^- complexes of AgCl are negligible compared to the 10^{-5} M solubility and the AgCl molecule content is only about 1% of the ion solubility, in that case.

Only when complexing is negligible, can simple K_{sp} calculations give reliable results for solubility. This is the case for pure water solutions of AgCl, $BaSO_4$, $AgBrO_3$, and a few others.* But, even these, with complexing materials present, and other precipitates in pure water if they have acidic cations or basic anions, will have actual solubilities far greater than K_{sp} calculations give. For instance, HgS with $K^0_{sp} = 10^{-51}$ is actually 100 million times more soluble in water than expected from K_{sp} alone. This is because it dissolves mainly as $HgS_2^{=}$, $Hg(OH)_2$, HS^-, and H_2S.*

---

* Discussed in detail by J. N. Butler, *J. Chem. Educ.* **38,** 460 (1961).

Equilibrium of the Ag^+-SCN^- System

The equilibria of the Ag^+-SCN^- system are of interest in connection with the Volhard titration and as a more complex example of the phenomena seen with AgCl in excess Cl^-. Cave and Hume [*J. Am. Chem. Soc.* **75**, 2893 (1953)] report determinations of the solubility of AgSCN in solutions of KSCN, at total ionic strength 2.2 *m* (with added KNO_3). Dissolved silver was determined by colorimetric, polarographic, or gravimetric means depending on its concentration. Some of their data follow:

Table 10–1. Solubility of AgSCN in KSCN Solutions ($I = 2.2\ m$)

$S \times 10^6$	KSCN	$\dfrac{S \times 10^4}{[SCN^-]}$	$\left(\dfrac{S \times 10^4}{[SCN^-]} - 2.5\right)[SCN^-]^{-1}$
1.62	0.00548	2.96	84
3.65	0.01033	3.53	100
30.0	0.04133	7.27	116
33.6	0.04440	7.58	115
79.9	0.06662	12.0	143
139.	0.08885	15.7	149
238.	0.1111	21.5	171
356.	0.1334	26.7	182
724.	0.1779	40.6	214
1280.	0.2224	57.6	248

Obviously, a simple K_{sp} treatment cannot account for these data, since solubility would be expected to decrease as $[SCN^-]$ increases. Figure 10–1 illustrates the great increase in solubility, which points to extensive reaction with SCN^- drawing AgSCN into solution. The reason for computing the third and fourth columns of Table 10–1 will become clear in the following discussion.

The equilibria suggested to account for the observed solubility are:

$$K_{sp} = [Ag^+][SCN^-],$$

$$K_s = [AgSCN] \quad \text{molecules (weak electrolyte)},$$

$$\beta_2 = \frac{[Ag(SCN)_2^-]}{[Ag^+][SCN^-]^2}, \qquad \beta_3 = \frac{[Ag(SCN)_3^=]}{[Ag^+][SCN^-]^3}, \qquad \beta_4 = \frac{[Ag(SCN)_4^{3-}]}{[Ag^+][SCN^-]^4}.$$

HSCN is a strong electrolyte so no K_a is needed. The overall constants, β, are used instead of stepwise constants, K, for algebraic convenience in the following derivations. Evaluation of the constants proceeds as follows: If the equilibria shown are the ones operating, the solubility, S, of AgSCN must be given by the silver material balance,

$$S = [Ag^+] + [AgSCN] + [Ag(SCN)_2^-] + [Ag(SCN)_3^=] + [Ag(SCN)_4^{3-}].$$

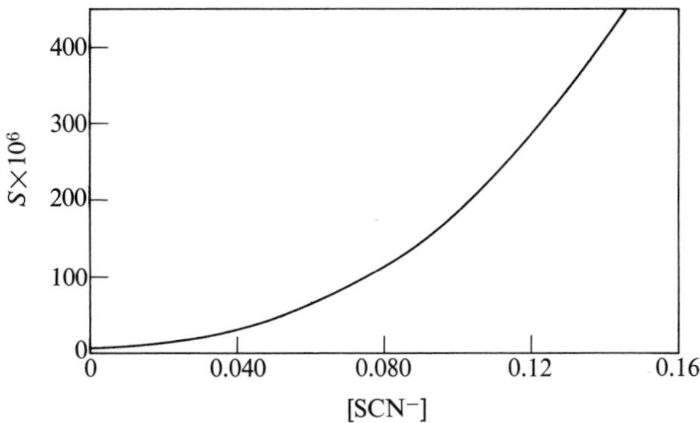

Figure 10–1

Now, let us abbreviate $[SCN^-]$ as X and substitute throughout $[Ag^+] = K_{sp}/X$. Thus

$$S = K_{sp}/X + K_s + \beta_2 K_{sp} X + \beta_3 K_{sp} X^2 + \beta_4 K_{sp} X^3.$$

We now have an equation for the solubility of AgSCN as a function of the thiocyanate concentration at constant ionic strength. If one had five independent sets of solubility data, one should be able to solve for the five unknown constants in the equation by inserting the measured S and $[SCN^-]$. The attempt to do so may be instructive as to the limitations of such methods. It turns out that K_{sp} and K_s are so small that experimental uncertainty in the data make it impossible to determine them with precision. Fortunately, this does not rule out determination of the β values. Other data in pure water and extrapolation of the solubility curve tell us that K_{sp} is on the order of 10^{-12}, and K_s, about 10^{-7}. The first datum in the table then suggests that Ag^+ is about $K_{sp}/X = 10^{-9.7}$. Thus, even at the lowest solubility in the table, Ag^+ and AgSCN molecules are a negligible part of the measured solubility, 10^{-6} M. (The AgSCN is about 10% of this, but this fraction decreases as KSCN increases, so that the approximation is justified.)

Next we see where this assumption leads. If the first two terms are omitted, the solubility equation becomes

$$S = AX + BX^2 + CX^3,$$

where A, B, and C stand for the combined constants in the last three terms of the original equation. Now, to evaluate the constants, a graphical method is preferable to algebraic solution of simultaneous equations to smooth out errors in individual points. Divide by X to get

$$S/X = A + BX + CX^2.$$

A plot of S/X versus X should be the positive half of a parabola going through $X = 0$ at $S/X = A$. This is shown in curve a of Fig. 10–2. From the graph, A is 2.5×10^{-4}.

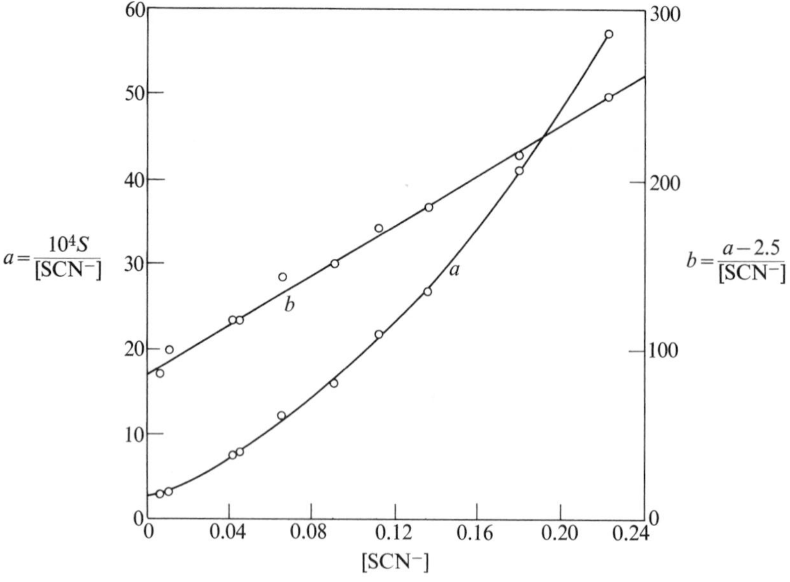

Figure 10–2

Next, rearrange the previous equation to get

$$\frac{(S/X) - A}{X} = B + CX.$$

So a plot of the left term versus X should produce a straight line of intercept B and slope C. Curve b of Fig. 10–2 shows this, and the values are $B = 0.0083$ and $C = 0.075$.

The solubility of AgSCN in pure 2.2 m KNO_3 gave them a value of 6.75×10^{-12} for the K_{sp} at the ionic strength of their experiments. The β values can now be found:

$$\beta_2 K_{sp} = A, \qquad \beta_2 = (2.5 \times 10^{-4})/(6.75 \times 10^{-12}) = 3.7 \times 10^7,$$
$$\beta_3 K_{sp} = B, \qquad \beta_3 = 0.0083/(6.75 \times 10^{-12}) = 1.2 \times 10^9,$$
$$\beta_4 K_{sp} = C, \qquad \beta_4 = 0.075/(6.75 \times 10^{-12}) = 1.1 \times 10^{10}.$$

As we had expected from the solubility behavior, these are much larger than the corresponding values in the Ag^+-Cl^- system. They vary slightly from the literature values for which corrections were made for the reduced activity of water in 2.2 m solutions, and for the SCN^- complexed. Mathematically, one should be able to return A, B, and C to the full S equation to get K_{sp} and K_s. The student may wish to see why it is impracticable in this case.

Next let us turn to the equilibria involved in the titrations mentioned above, since they will illustrate many facets of multiple equilibrium calculations which are of wide importance also in geochemistry and biochemistry.

The Mohr Titration

The Mohr titration requires the use of K values for the following steps:

$$\underline{AgCl} \rightleftharpoons Ag^+ + Cl^-, \qquad K^0_{sp} = 1.8 \times 10^{-10}, \qquad (10\text{–}8)$$

$$\underline{Ag_2CrO_4} \rightleftharpoons 2Ag^+ + CrO_4^=, \qquad K^0_{sp} = 2.4 \times 10^{-12}, \qquad (10\text{–}9)$$

$$CrO_4^= + H_2O \rightleftharpoons HCrO_4^- + OH^-, \qquad K^0_b = 3.3 \times 10^{-8}, \qquad (10\text{–}10)$$

$$2HCrO_4^- \rightleftharpoons Cr_2O_7^= + H_2O, \qquad K = 43. \qquad (10\text{–}11)$$

Near the endpoint, the higher chloro complexes of Ag^+ are negligible, as is AgOH in neutral or acid solution. Acid solution may remove much $CrO_4^=$ to prevent precipitation in (10–9), so that the effect of pH on (10–10) and (10–11) is critical.

Examples

1) Find the $[CrO_4^=]$ required to saturate the solution with respect to Ag_2CrO_4 at the equivalence point of a titration of Cl^- by Ag^+, both 0.1 M solutions.

At the equivalence point,

$$[Ag^+] = [Cl^-] \cong \sqrt{K^0_{sp}} = 1.3 \times 10^{-5}\ M.$$

To saturate this solution with Ag_2CrO_4, the $[CrO_4^=]$ must be

$$[CrO_4^=] \cong K^0_{sp}/[Ag^+]^2 = 0.013\ M.$$

But, the activity correction will be important for the -2 ions at this ionic strength, and further calculation gives ($I = 0.09$), with f values from the Kielland table,

$$K_{sp(AgCl)} = K^0/(0.76)^2 = 3.1 \times 10^{-10}$$

and

$$K_{sp(Ag_2CrO_4)} = K^0/(0.76)^2(0.39) = 11. \times 10^{-12},$$

which leads, as before, to $[CrO_4^=] = 0.035\ M$. Further approximation with the new ionic strength leads to about 0.04 M needed for the added K_2CrO_4. However, this is so deeply yellow that it is difficult to see the first bit of red Ag_2CrO_4 formed, and considerable overtitration results. Laboratory testing leads to a compromise with 0.005 M K_2CrO_4. As a result some excess Ag^+ must be added to signal an endpoint.

2) Find the error this excess $AgNO_3$ introduces at ionic strength 0.075.

From (10–9), we find that to saturate the solution with Ag_2CrO_4 requires

$$[Ag^+] = \sqrt{9.5 \times 10^{-12}/(0.005)} = 4.2 \times 10^{-5}\ M.$$

At equivalence, from AgCl, we had

$$[Ag^+] = \sqrt{3 \times 10^{-10}} = 1.7 \times 10^{-5}.$$

In moving to the higher $[Ag^+]$, some AgCl had to precipitate. The remaining silver ion from AgCl equals the Cl^-:

$$(Cl^-) = 3 \times 10^{-10}/(4.2 \times 10^{-5}) = 0.7 \times 10^{-5}.$$

The difference must come from added $AgNO_3$ $(4.2 - 0.7)10^{-5} = 3.5 \times 10^{-5}$ *M*. In 100 ml, this is 3.5×10^{-3} mmole or 0.035 ml of 0.1 *M* $AgNO_3$ solution. Beyond this error, a finite amount of solid Ag_2CrO_4 must form to be visible. Standardization by the same method helps to cancel the error. (An accounting, with paper and pencil, of Ag^+ present, precipitated, and added helps clarify the previous calculation for the reader.)

3) Consider the effects of pH. For pH 7, steps (10–10) and (10–11) give

$$\frac{[HCrO_4^-](10^{-7})}{[CrO_4^=]} = 3.3 \times 10^{-8},$$

and the ratio

$$[CrO_4^=]/[HCrO_4^-] = \tfrac{3}{1}.$$

That is, about one-fourth of the $CrO_4^=$ is converted to $HCrO_4^-$, and

$$[Cr_2O_7^=]/[HCrO_4^-]^2 = 43,$$

and with $[HCrO_4^-] = 0.005/4$,

$$[Cr_2O_7^=] = 7 \times 10^{-5}\ M.$$

Less than one-tenth of the K_2CrO_4 has formed dichromate. (In these calculations only rough values are needed, and activity coefficients are not used.)

Now, at pH 3,

$$[CrO_4^=][HCrO_4^-] = 3 \times 10^{-4},$$

over 99.9% of the $CrO_4^=$ has gone to $HCrO_4^-$, and with $[HCrO_4^-] = 0.005$,

$$[Cr_2O_7^=] = 43(0.005)^2 = 0.0011\ M.$$

About one-fifth of the $HCrO_4^-$ has formed dichromate ion. In practice, it is found that nearly neutral solutions are required for the Mohr method. Acid samples of Cl^- can be neutralized with $NaHCO_3$ to the end of effervescence. A slight excess usually does no harm. Very basic solution may precipitate Ag_2O or form NH_3 complexes. The solutions must be cool.

The Volhard Method

The Volhard method involves the equilibria (near the endpoint):

$$\underline{AgSCN} \rightleftharpoons Ag^+ + SCN^-, \qquad K^0_{sp} = 1.0 \times 10^{-12}, \qquad (10\text{–}12)$$

$$\underline{AgCl} \rightleftharpoons Ag^+ + Cl^-, \qquad K^0_{sp} = 1.8 \times 10^{-10}, \qquad (10\text{–}13)$$

$$FeSCN^{++} \rightleftharpoons Fe^{3+} + SCN^-, \qquad K_d = 0.01 \text{ (approximately)}. \qquad (10\text{–}14)$$

(As always, ions are understood to be aquated.) Acid solutions are used to repress the reaction,

$$Fe(H_2O)_6{}^{3+} \rightleftharpoons Fe(H_2O)_5OH^{++} + H^+,$$

because the hydroxopentaquo ion is deep yellow-brown.

Example. If experiment shows that 6×10^{-6} *M* is the minimum visible concentration of $FeSCN^{++}$, find the $[Fe^{3+}]$ needed to give the red color at the equivalence point of the Swift modification of the Volhard method for Cl^-.

As described above, the chloride plus a small known amount of SCN^- are titrated by standard $AgNO_3$ with Fe^{3+} as indicator to the disappearance of the red color. At the equivalence point, it follows that Ag^+ equals total Cl^- and SCN^-:

$$[Ag^+] = [Cl^-] + [SCN^-] + [FeSCN^{++}].$$

Upon division, K^0_{sp} values in (10–12) and (10–13) give $[SCN^-] = 0.0056\,[Cl^-]$, so that the equivalence condition becomes

$$\frac{1.8 \times 10^{-10}}{[Cl^-]} = [Cl^-] + 0.0056[Cl^-] + 6 \times 10^{-6},$$

from which $[Cl^-] = 1.1 \times 10^{-5}$ *M* and $[SCN^-] = 6 \times 10^{-8}$ *M*, which in (10–14) gives

$$\frac{[Fe^{3+}][SCN^-]}{[FeSCN^{++}]} = 0.01 \qquad \text{and} \qquad [Fe^{3+}] = \frac{0.01(6 \times 10^{-6})}{(6 \times 10^{-8})} = 1\ M.$$

As with the Mohr method, it is found that a compromise with less indicator gives acceptable accuracy, 1 ppth. A final concentration of 0.2 *M* Fe^{3+} suffices. The undertitration caused can be found from the excess of the right side over the left side of the equivalence equation:

Eq. (10–14) gives

$$[SCN^-] = \frac{K_d[FeSCN^{++}]}{[Fe^{3+}]} = \frac{(0.01)(6 \times 10^{-6})}{(0.2)} = 3 \times 10^{-7},$$

Eq. (10–12) gives

$$[Ag^+] \cong K^0_{sp}/[SCN^-] = 3 \times 10^{-6},$$

Eq. (10–13) gives

$$[Cl^-] \cong K^0_{sp}/[Ag^+] = 6 \times 10^{-5}.$$

Then, the right-hand side of the equivalence condition is

$$[Cl^-] + [SCN^-] + [FeSCN^{++}] = 6.6 \times 10^{-5}.$$

Subtracting the $[Ag^+]$ leaves 6.3×10^{-5} *M* excess. For 100 ml total volume and 0.1 *M* $AgNO_3$, this gives 0.06 ml undertitration. This approximate calculation illustrates the method. Activity effects could change the result appreciably. [At $I = 0.05$, $K_d = 0.0072$, and at $I = 1.8$, $K_d = 0.011$. These are experimental values for (10–14).]

However, it should be noted that the result, 0.06 ml, is the point at which the red color is just visible. One more drop, about 0.04 ml, would cause the disappearance of the color and would be taken as the endpoint.

Earlier Volhard methods for Cl^- involved adding excess $AgNO_3$ and back titrating with standard SCN^- solution to the red $FeSCN^{++}$ endpoint. Since AgSCN is less soluble than AgCl, the reaction,

$$\underline{AgCl} + SCN^- \rightarrow \underline{AgSCN} + Cl^-,$$

caused the red endpoint to fade as the SCN^- was removed. Removal of the precipitated AgCl, either by filtration or by physical coating with an oil like nitrobenzene, before the back titration made it work. For determination of Br^-, I^-, or SCN^-, the fading problem does not occur because of the lower K_{sp} values of the precipitates. With I^-, the AgI must be precipitated before the addition of indicator, since Fe^{3+} oxidizes I^-.

10.2 GRAPHICAL REPRESENTATIONS OF PRECIPITATION EQUILIBRIA

If [X] is plotted against [Y] for the ideal electrolyte, XY, which has $K_{sp} = [X][Y]$, a right hyperbola asymptotic to the axes is made at constant ionic strength. However, a more obvious test of data can be made with a straight-line relationship, $[X] = K_{sp}/[Y]$, a plot of [X] versus $1/[Y]$ should give a line of slope K_{sp} and intercept zero. For solutions in which activity coefficients are not *one*, we must use

$$[X][Y]f_\pm^2 = K_{sp}^0,$$

plotting [X] versus $1/[Y]f_\pm^2$ to get a straight line of slope K_{sp}^0 and intercept zero. Two plots, one which includes and one which does not include the activity coefficients, are shown in Fig. 10–3 for $CaSO_4$ in the presence of added K_2SO_4. At low $[SO_4^=]$ where reliable f values can be calculated, the data corrected with $f_\pm$ do give a straight-line plot of intercept zero and slope 5×10^{-5}, the K_{sp}^0 for $CaSO_4$.

(Although the data used for the graph do not show it clearly, the $CaSO_4$ case also is complicated by ion-pair formation, or weak electrolyte behavior,* which is seen clearly in the graph for AgCl in Fig. 10–4.)

In the plot of the experimental total solubility of AgCl versus $1/[Cl^-]f_\pm^2$ (Fig. 10–4), the intercept is not zero, but the molarity of AgCl molecules, about 2×10^{-7}. The slope is 1.8×10^{-10}, the K_{sp}^0. This should be clear from the following equation for the total solubility, S,†

$$S = [Ag^+] + [AgCl] = K_{sp}^0/[Cl^-]f_\pm^2 + K_s.$$

* The detailed treatment of $CaSO_4$ is discussed by L. Meites, J. Pode, and H. Thomas, *J. Chem. Educ.* **43,** 667 (1966). New results using a specific ion electrode for Ca^{++} activity are reported by F. S. Nakayama and B. A. Rasnick, *Anal. Chem.* **39,** 1022 (1967).

† See R. W. Ramette, *J. Chem. Educ.* **37,** 348 (1960).

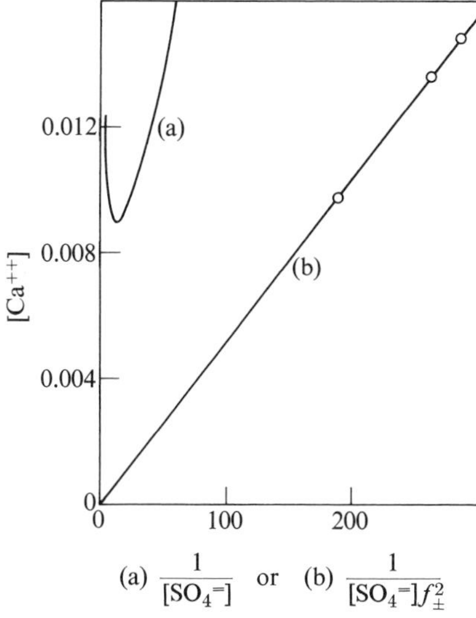

Fig. 10–3. Solubility of $CaSO_4$.

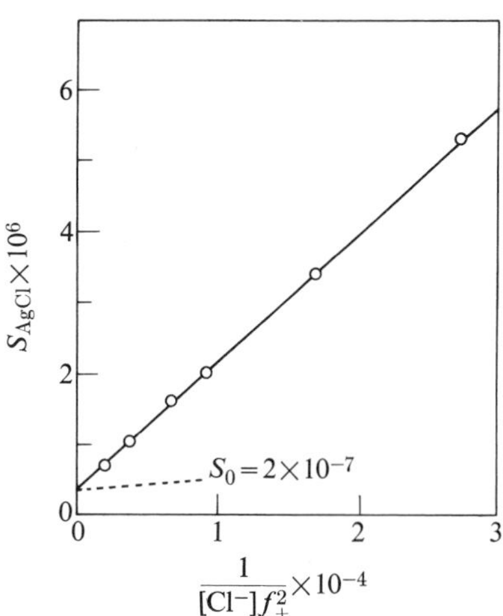

Fig. 10–4. Solubility of AgCl.

This relation holds only for $[Cl^-]$ up to about 5×10^{-4} *M*, below which the higher chloro complexes are negligible. At higher $[Cl^-]$, a straight line is not obtained, indicating that other equilibria must be considered.

Another way of treating solubility data, one used originally as a test of the Debye-Hückel theory, can be explained with the equation for a general electrolyte, X_aY_b, for which the constant expression is:

$$K^0_{sp} = [X]^a f_+^a [Y]^b f_-^b.$$

Neglecting hydrolysis, valid only for a few materials, and in the absence of common ions, we find that if S moles per liter dissolve, then

$$K^0_{sp} = (aSf_+)^a (bSf_-)^b = a^a b^b f_\pm^{a+b} S^{a+b}. \tag{10–15}$$

[For example, for Bi_2S_3, $K^0_{sp} = 4(27)f_\pm^5 S^5$.] Take logs to get a form suitable for applying the Debye-Hückel limiting equation:

$$\log K^0_{sp} = \log a^a b^b + (a + b)\log f_\pm + (a + b)\log S.$$

Inserting the term from the Debye-Hückel limiting equation and rearranging gives

$$\log S = 0.51 z_+ z_- \sqrt{I} + C,$$

where C stands for all the remaining constant terms. This predicts that a plot of $\log S$ versus $\sqrt{I}$ will give a straight line of slope 0.51 z_+z_-. A test of this is shown in Fig. 10–5 where the data of Table 9–1 are plotted. The agreement is fair.

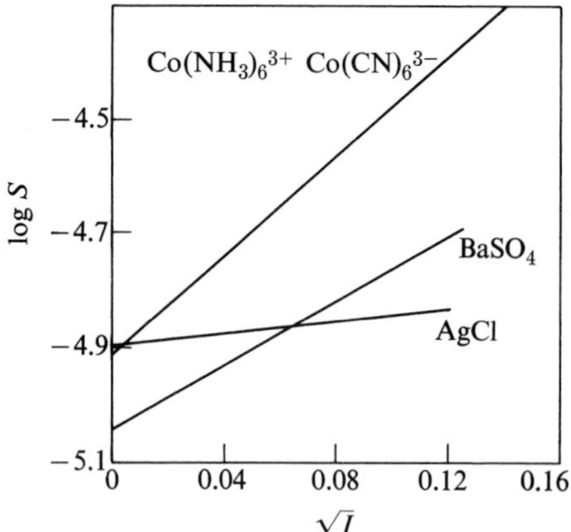

Fig. 10–5. Debye-Hückel test plot for 1:1, 2:2, 3:3 cases.

The slopes are:

	Debye-Hückel	Graph, experimental
1:1 AgCl	0.51	0.46
2:2 $BaSO_4$	2.0	2.5
3:3 $[Co(NH_3)_6]$ $[Co(CN)_6]$	4.6	4.3

Note that relatively unhydrolyzed ions were chosen. This is a problem for the higher charges. For instance, $AlPO_4$ would be a bad choice for 3:3 ions, while the much larger $Co(NH_3)_6{}^{3+}$ and $Co(CN)_6{}^{3-}$ have very low acid and base strengths.

Equation (10–15) can be rearranged with all the variables collected:

$$(Sf_{\pm})^{a+b} = K^0_{sp}/a^a b^b \qquad \text{or} \qquad Sf_{\pm} = \text{constant.}$$

This remarkable result says that electrolytes dissolve up to the same value of their mean ionic activity in all solutions. When one takes into account that the activity is a measure of the chemical potential, or free energy, and that the chemical potential of the pure solid is constant, it is clear from thermodynamics that the activity in the solution must also be constant.

10.3 THE pH DEPENDENCE OF SOLUBILITY

Unlike AgCl, AgSCN, $BaSO_4$, and a few others, for most slightly soluble ionic compounds solubility depends strongly on $[H^+]$. In general, for the ionic compounds with m metal ions and x anions,

$$\underline{M_mX_x} \rightleftharpoons m\text{M} + x\text{X},$$

where the M and X ions have charges which are multiples of $+x$ and $-m$. (For example, in $LaPO_4$, m and x are *one*, while the charges are +3 and −3.) If one uses α_0 to represent the fraction of each ion left in the simple (aquo) form, not complexed by OH^-, H^+, or other ligands, and if C stands for the total of all forms of the ion in solution,

$$[M] = \alpha_{0M}C_M, \qquad [X] = \alpha_{0X}C_X, \tag{10–16}$$

$$K_{sp} = [M]^m[X]^x = C_M^m C_X^x \alpha_{0M}^m \alpha_{0X}^x. \tag{10–17}$$

As usual, K_{sp} is an effective constant at one temperature and ionic strength. The fraction of uncomplexed metal ion in the presence of various ligands can be calculated by methods given in Chapter 19. Here, consider only cases with $\alpha_{0M} = 1$, that is, with the cation uncomplexed. This is a good approximation for many metal ions below pH 7 and for alkaline earth ions up to pH 10.

Here we are considering the increased solubility of ionic compounds due to reaction of the basic anion with H^+. In Chapter 8 the equations needed for the α fractions of acids were derived.

Example 1 (*A monoprotic anion*). Find the function for the solubility of silver acetate at various pH values at 25°C and constant ionic strength, 0.10 M, and with no common ions added.

From (10–17) with $\alpha_{0M} = 1$, the K_{sp} function is

$$K_{sp} = C_M C_A \alpha_{0A} = S^2\left(1 + \frac{[H^+]}{K_a}\right)^{-1}, \tag{10–18}$$

where $C_M = [Ag^+] = S = C_A$ and C_A is the *total* of $[HA] + [A^-]$. The α_0 expression for acetic acid was derived in Chapter 8. From (10–18), the desired function is

$$S = \left[K_{sp}\left(1 + \frac{[H^+]}{K_a}\right)\right]^{1/2}. \tag{10–19}$$

To proceed to calculation, one needs the effective constants. Using the activity coefficients at $I = 0.10\ M$ from Table 9–2, we get

$$K_{sp} = K_{sp}^0/f_+f_- = \frac{10^{-2.40}}{(0.75)(0.76)} = 10^{-2.16},$$

$$K_a = K_a^0/f_+f_- = \frac{10^{-4.76}}{(0.83)(0.77)} = 10^{-4.57}.$$

Putting these into Eq. (10–19) yields

$$S = (10^{-2.16} + 10^{2.41}[H^+])^{1/2}.$$

This shows that at high $[H^+]$, S is proportional to $\sqrt{[H+]}$, and the limiting solubility as $[H^+]$ decreases is $\sqrt{K_{sp}}$, as expected. Complications due to weak electrolyte behavior, AgA molecules, and other complexing are assumed to be negligible here. This is not the case if excess acetate ions are added.* The log (S)-versus-pH

---

* See Butler, *Ionic Equilibrium*, p. 196ff.

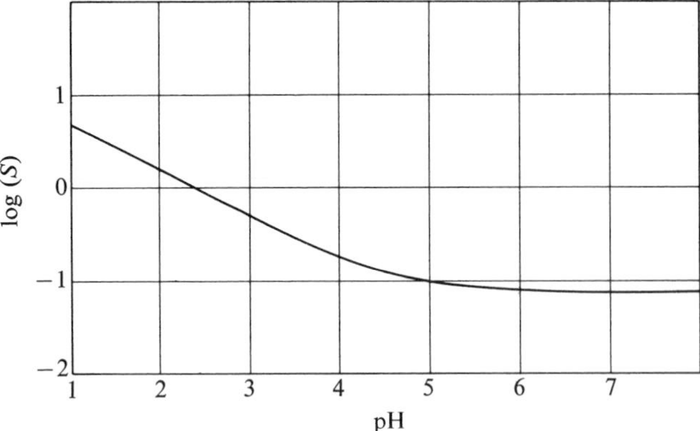

Fig. 10–6. Solubility of silver acetate as a function of pH at 25°C and ionic strength 0.10 *M*.

curve from this function is plotted in Fig. 10–6. Note that the solubility does decrease to the constant $\sqrt{K_{sp}}$ value at high pH. From Eq. (10–18) one predicts that a plot of S^2 versus $[H^+]$ should be a straight line of slope K_{sp}/K_a and intercept K_{sp}. Thus solubility data might be used to determine these constants. This is a method often used, and curvature of the line indicates other complexing must be taken into account.

Example 2 (*A diprotic acid anion*). Calculate the solubility of $CaCO_3$ as a function of $[H^+]$ at constant ionic strength 0.10 *M* and at 25°C, with no added common ions. Again, take $\alpha_{0M} = 1$ and $C_{Ca} = C_{CO_3} = S$.

From Eq. (10–14) and the α_0 expression (Chapter 8) for a diprotic acid, we get

$$K_{sp} = C_{Ca}C_{CO_3}\alpha_0 = S^2 \frac{K_1K_2}{[H^+]^2 + K_1[H^+] + K_1K_2}. \tag{10–20}$$

Again, looking up the activity coefficients for the appropriate ions, we get

$$K_{sp} = \frac{10^{-8.35}}{(0.405)(0.37)} = 10^{-7.53},$$

$$K_1 = \frac{10^{-6.35}}{(0.83)(0.77)} = 10^{-6.16},$$

$$K_2 = \frac{10^{-10.33}(0.77)}{(0.83)(0.37)} = 10^{-9.93}.$$

Putting these into (10–20) gives the solubility function,

$$S = \left[\frac{K_{sp}}{K_1K_2}([H^+]^2 + K_1[H^+] + K_1K_2)\right]^{1/2}. \tag{10–21}$$

This is a general equation for the solubility of any strong electrolyte, MX, where $X^=$ is the basic ion of a diprotic acid and $\alpha_{0M} = 1$. However, recent work has

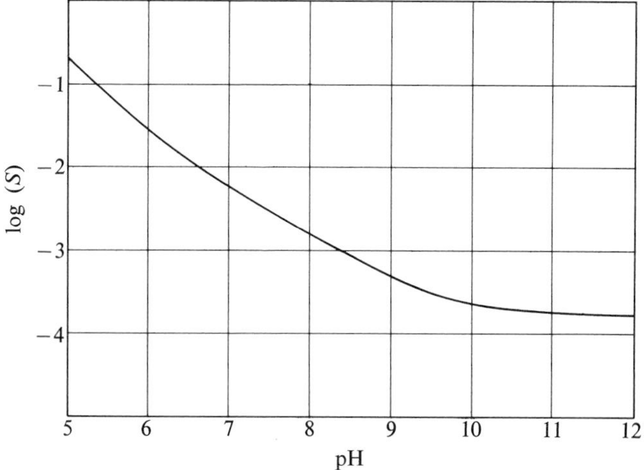

Fig. 10–7. Solubility of $CaCO_3$ as a function of pH at 25°C and ionic strength 0.10 *M* (closed system, no CO_2 loss).

shown that $CaCO_3$, like AgCl and many other slightly soluble compounds, is definitely associated to $CaCO_3$ units. (It makes no difference to the function whether this association is made by coordination, formation of ion pairs, or the formation of some other structure.) The K_{eq} for this process is

$$Ca^{++} + CO_3^{=} \rightleftharpoons CaCO_3 \text{ (dissolved)}, \qquad K_{eq\,1} = \frac{[CaCO_3]}{[Ca^{++}][CO_3^{=}]} = 10^{3.2}.$$

In a saturated solution, the denominator is simply K_{sp}, so

$$K_{eq\,1}K_{sp} = [CaCO_3] = 10^{-5.2}.$$

Therefore all saturated $CaCO_3$ solutions contain this constant molarity of $CaCO_3$ units at 25°C, in addition to the ionic S, Eq. (10–21). The complete solubility equation for $CaCO_3$ then becomes

$$S = [10^{8.56}([H^+]^2 + 10^{-6.16}[H^+] + 10^{-16.09})]^{1/2} + 10^{-5.2}. \qquad (10\text{–}22)$$

One may now calculate S at various values of $[H^+]$.

At pH 5 and below, the solubility predicted is so large that the ionic-strength condition, 0.1 *M*, is violated. This high solubility is, as qualitatively expected, due to

$$CaCO_3 + H^+ \rightleftharpoons Ca^{++} + HCO_3^-.$$

The $CO_3^{=}$ is made very low in acid solution, and $CaCO_3$ dissolves to make up for that. Remember that these solubilities mean that the given pH obtains at equilibrium, not that the $CaCO_3$ is dissolved in a solution initially at the given pH. The plot of log (S) versus pH is shown in Fig. 10–7. Again, it levels off to $\sqrt{K_{sp}}$ at sufficiently high pH.

The $CaCO_3$ example has assumed a constant amount of matter, no loss or gain of CO_2. If CO_2 can be dissolved from the atmosphere, Eq. (10–22) is no longer valid as it stands, and it proves fruitful to approach it through charge balance. Charge and/or material balancing conditions can also be used to derive all the equations needed above. Since the α-fraction expressions had already been derived, it was shorter to use them in the examples given.

Carbonate Rock Solubility

By far the most abundant carbon compound on the earth is $CaCO_3$, limestone, marble, calcite, aragonite, etc., which accounts for over 99% of the carbon present on the earth. The weathering effects of H_2O and CO_2 on these relatively soluble rocks are of primary importance in geochemical processes.* Here we consider one case, with another assigned as a problem.

The only new factor is the equilibrium for CO_2 gas:

$$CO_2\ (\text{gas}) + H_2O \rightleftharpoons H_2CO_3, \qquad K_P = 10^{-1.46},$$

where P is measured in atmospheres. This reaction occurs through the steps,

$$CO_2\ (\text{gas}) + H_2O \rightleftharpoons CO_2 \cdot H_2O,$$
$$CO_2{\cdot}H_2O \rightleftharpoons H_2CO_3,$$

because the conversion of dissolved CO_2, $(CO_2{\cdot}H_2O)$ to H_2CO_3 is quite slow due to need for bond-angle reorganization. However, the two steps can be combined by taking the product of the equilibrium constants as usual; the common term $CO_2{\cdot}H_2O$ cancels to give the same form as the overall process given first.

For example, let us calculate the solubility of pure $CaCO_3$ in water under a constant CO_2 partial pressure of 10^{-3} atm, approximately that in air, and compare it with the solubility in the absence of outside CO_2. (A material balance might be complicated here because carbonates come from two sources and are of unknown concentration.) Charge balance is straightforward and requires:

$$2[Ca^{++}] + [H^+] = [HCO_3^-] + 2[CO_3^=] + [OH^-]. \qquad (10\text{–}23)$$

The equilibrium constants needed are:

$$K_{sp}^0 = [Ca^{++}][CO_3^=] = 10^{-8.35},$$

$$K_1^0 = \frac{[H^+][HCO_3^-]}{[H_2CO_3]} = 10^{-6.35}, \qquad K_2^0 = \frac{[H^+][CO_3^=]}{[HCO_3^-]} = 10^{-10.33},$$

$$K_P^0 = \frac{[H_2CO_3]}{P_{CO_2}} = 10^{-1.46}, \qquad K_w^0 = [H^+][OH^-] = 10^{-14.00}.$$

These can be combined to get the terms needed for the charge-balance equation

* Chapter 3 of the book by R. M. Garrels, *Mineral Equilibria* (New York: Harper and Brothers, 1960) details the mathematics of many possible situations.

(omit ^{0} superscripts for clarity):

$$[H^+] = \left([Ca^{++}]\frac{K_1K_2K_PP_{CO_2}}{K_{sp}}\right)^{1/2},$$

$$[HCO_3^-] = \left(\frac{K_{sp}K_1K_PP_{CO_2}}{[Ca^{++}]K_2}\right)^{1/2},$$

$$[CO_3^=] = K_{sp}/[Ca^{++}],$$

$$[OH^-] = K_w/[H^+].$$

Substituting these into (10–23) yields (let $S = [Ca^{++}]$),

$$2S + \left(\frac{K_1K_2K_PP_{CO_2}}{K_{sp}}\right)^{1/2} S^{1/2} = \left(\frac{K_{sp}K_1K_PP_{CO_2}}{K_2}\right)^{1/2} S^{-1/2} + \frac{2K_{sp}}{S} + K_w\left(\frac{K_{sp}}{K_1K_2K_PP_{CO_2}}\right)^{1/2} S^{-1/2}. \tag{10–24}$$

Inserting the K^0 values and $P_{CO_2} = 10^{-3}$ gives, after multiplying by $S/2$ and rearranging,

$$S^2 + 10^{-6.70}S^{3/2} - (10^{-4.72} + 10^{-7.90})S^{1/2} - 10^{-8.35} = 0.$$

From Example (2) above, one might estimate that the solution will not be very acidic and the solubility might be about 10^{-2} to 10^{-3}. Trying such S values in the solubility equation quickly shows that only the first and third terms are significant and that $S = 10^{-3.15}$ satisfies the equation. (We use K^0 values here since ionic strength is low. A better approximation can then be obtained by adjusting K values to the I found.) Other P_{CO_2} pressures can be used and the following values obtained. (The pH is found by putting S into the $[H^+]$ equation.)

P_{CO_2}, atm	S	pH
10^{-3}	$10^{-3.15}$	7.97
0.10	$10^{-2.48}$	6.64
1.0	$10^{-2.14}$	5.97

Note that $10^{-5.2}$ M $CaCO_3$ associated units are always present as explained in Example 2. This is a very small fraction of S here.

This result is in good agreement with experimental tests described by Garrels. In water, without outside CO_2, the solubility is $10^{-3.9}$, only $\frac{1}{6}$ the solubility in the CO_2 saturated water. This occurs because H_2CO_3 converts $CO_3^=$ to HCO_3^- and changes the pH from 9.95 (for $CaCO_3$ in pure water) to 8.0.

Underground water can contain higher CO_2 content from the decay of organic matter and root respiration products so that larger amounts of $CaCO_3$ may be carried off to precipitate when exposure to fresh air removes some CO_2. This accounts for continuous formation of stalactites and stalagmites in caves and of beds of $CaCO_3$ on the floors of streams, lakes, and oceans.

Human blood plasma contains about 0.002 M Ca^{++} at pH 7.4. With $[CO_3^{=}]$ about 10^{-5} M and ionic strength about 0.15 M, one is close to saturation with respect to $CaCO_3$. Only a slight shift to higher pH increases the $[CO_3^{=}]$ enough to deposit $CaCO_3$ in bone. (The situation for $CaHPO_4$ is similar; phosphates form a larger fraction of the inorganic portion of bone.)

SUMMARY

Worked examples are given to demonstrate the mathematical handling of systems in which acid-base, precipitation, and complex-ion equilibria coexist. Graphical extrapolation methods are applied to K_{sp}^0 determination.

PROBLEMS

1. Calculate the ppth error in a Mohr titration of 4.000 meq of Cl^- with 0.1000 M $AgNO_3$ to a final volume of 100 ml in the presence of 0.0010 M K_2CrO_4, at the end-point.
2. Calculate the Volhard undertitration error in milliliters of 0.1000 M $AgNO_3$, if it is performed as described in the chapter but at $I = 1.8$, where the K_d for $FeSCN^{++}$ is 0.011. Estimate the f values for Ag^+, Cl^-, and SCN^- from a silver compound in the literature. (Give your assumptions in doing this.)
3. The molar solubilities of Ag_2SO_4 at 25°C are reported to be: in water, 0.0266 M, in 0.0100 M K_2SO_4, 0.0258 M, and in 0.0250 M $AgNO_3$, 0.0195 M. Make a table listing the concentration of each ion, its ionic strength, the activity coefficients of Ag^+ and $SO_4^{=}$, K_{sp}, and K_{sp}^0.
4. The solubility of Ag_2SO_4 in 0.0145 M H_2SO_4 is reported to be 0.0274 M at 25°C. Taking K_2^0 for H_2SO_4 as 0.0102, determine the activity coefficients and find the equilibrium concentration of $SO_4^{=}$ ion. Then calculate K_{sp} and K_{sp}^0 as in the previous problem.
5. A more desirable method for evaluating K_{sp}^0 is one not using any calculated f values. Prove that a plot of $\log K_{sp}$ versus $\sqrt{I}$ [or versus $\sqrt{I}/(1 + \sqrt{I})$ for higher ionic strength] should give a line of intercept $\log K_{sp}^0$ at $I = 0$. Plot the K_{sp} values from the previous problems on Ag_2SO_4 and find K_{sp}^0.
6. Given that the pH is found to be 9.95 when powdered calcite is equilibrated with pure water in the absence of air, calculate the concentrations of the species present and the K_{sp} of $CaCO_3$. Use the Debye-Hückel equation to calculate the K_{sp}^0 and compare with published values.

7. a) Make a table of concentrations of the ions, K_{sp}, I, $\sqrt{I}$, log K_{sp}, etc., as needed (for high ionic strength) and plot them as suggested in Problem 5 to get K^0_{sp} for $Co(IO_3)_2$. The molar solubilities at 30°C are:

$Co(IO_3)_2$	0.01165	0.0124	0.0131	0.0102	0.0050	0.0113	0.0107
Added electrolyte	0	0.0111 NaCl	0.0267 NaCl	0.0044 $NaIO_3$	0.0280 $NaIO_3$	0.0026 $CoSO_4$	0.0123 $CoSO_4$

(The first column is the solubility in pure water.)

b) Use f values from the Kielland table (or the Debye-Hückel equation) to calculate the K^0_{sp} values from K_{sp} in (a). Estimate the uncertainty in these and in the K^0_{sp} you got from the graph in (a). Is any difference you have in the K^0 values significant?

c) The K^0_a for HIO_3 is 0.16, and K^0_a for the Co(II) aquo ion is 7×10^{-13}. Demonstrate with rough calculations that formation of HIO_3 and $Co(OH)^+$ does not introduce error into your previous calculations.

d) The K_d for $CoCl^+$ is $10^{2.4}$. What fraction of the Co(II) is present as $CoCl^+$ in the highest $[Cl^-]$ solution of (a)?

8. Derive an equation for the solubility, S, of $BaCO_3$ in constant ionic strength, 0.05 M, solutions of pH 6 to 10. Calculate S at unit pH values of 6, 8, and 10. How does this check with the choice of indicator for the Winkler method for OH^- titration in the presence of carbonate? (pK_a for Ba^{++} is 13.2.)

9. A 340.0 mg sample of mixed NaCl and KCl took 48.20 ml of 0.1020 M $AgNO_3$ in a Mohr titration. Find the percent of KCl and NaCl. What is the effect on the percentages of an error of 0.05 ml?

10. What sample weight should be taken for chloride titration so that the ml of 0.1000 M $AgNO_3$ used will be numerically equal to (a) the percentage of Cl^-, (b) the percentage of NaCl?

11. What molarity $AgNO_3$ should be prepared so that, numerically, one may take half the number of milliliters used to get the percentage Cl^- in 500 mg samples?

12. Calculate the solubility of silver acetate at pH 2 and 7 by Eq. (10–19), for $I = 0.1\ M$. Compare with Fig. 10–6. What do the calculations show about the relative importance of terms in Eq. (10–19)?

13. Calculate the solubility of $CaCO_3$ at pH 6, 10, and 12 at $I = 0.1\ M$ in a closed system. See Eq. (10–22) and compare with Fig. 10–7. What do these calculations show about the relative importance of the terms in the equation?

14. Using the values given in this chapter, plus two others you calculate, plot log (S $CaCO_3$), in water in equilibrium with CO_2 gas, versus log (P_{CO_2}) from 10^{-4} to 10 atm pressure of CO_2.

15. Derive the solubility function of $Ca(IO_3)_2$ with respect to $[H^+]$ and calculate S at pH 0, 1, 2, 3. Take ionic strength, 0.10 M and point out where the results are only hypothetical [$pK^0_{sp} = 6.15$, $pK^0_a(HIO_3) = 0.78$].

16. Find the solubility of calcium oxalate at zero ionic strength at pH 3 and 6. [(pK_{sp}^0 = 8.68, pK_{sat}^0 = 5.7 (associated CaC_2O_4)]. For oxalic acid, pK_1^0 = 1.25 and pK_2^0 = 4.28.

17. Discuss the reason that the K_{sp} concept is not applied to alkali metal ionic compounds. Do some calculation and plotting to show how well, or how poorly, K_{sp} calculation interprets the following data on saturated solutions of $KClO_4$ with a common ion present.

Solubility of $KClO_4$ in $HClO_4$ Solutions, Molarity at 25°C

Molarity $HClO_4$	0	0.0100	0.100	1.00
Molarity $KClO_4$	0.151	0.144	0.107	0.038

CHAPTER 11

GRAVIMETRIC METHODS

We have shown why titration methods are practically limited to a precision of four significant figures. Gravimetric work, in which only weights are measured, is limited by the impurities in the materials and the amounts that can be handled and weighed. The weighings themselves can be made to seven significant figures (100 g to 0.1 mg). When precipitates can be produced in a comparable purity, gravimetric analysis can far surpass volumetric in accuracy and precision. Examples from historic atomic-weight determinations emphasize this.

The difficulty in obtaining pure solids together with the mechanical problems of handling them (especially without much experience) greatly limit the number of gravimetric methods that can be pushed beyond a precision of five significant figures. Add to this the time usually required in digestion, manipulation, and weighing to constant weights, and we are not surprised that chemists choose a volumetric method whenever possible. Some common gravimetric determinations are listed in Table 11–1.

11.1 GRAVIMETRIC USE OF AgCl

The gravimetric use of AgCl depends on its fortunate and rare property of forming quite pure precipitates under easily arranged conditions. Indeed, much classical chemical atomic-weight determination has depended on converting pure chlorides of elements to AgCl, which was believed to be pure to better than one part in 10^5. The element in question was being compared with silver, which then becomes an important secondary standard of atomic weight. Six-figure precision in the atomic weights of silver and many other elements was obtained by T. W. Richards and coworkers at Harvard during the first two decades of this century. Richards and Forbes, in a paper recommended for student reading,* describe the formation of $AgNO_3$ from highly purified silver and nitric acid. Taking the atomic weights of oxygen and nitrogen as known, they could calculate the relative weight of silver. Their average value was 107.876† (the old-scale value was 107.880). This stood until 1962 when it was revised to 107.870† from physical mass and electrodeposition results.‡ This change of 0.06 ppth indicates the reliability possible in careful

* *J. Am. Chem. Soc.* **29**, 808 (1907).

† On the ^{12}C scale.

‡ See Cameron and Wichers.

Table 11–1. Some Common Precipitation Separations and Determinations

Determination of	Reagent	Comments
Cl^-, Br^-, I^-(Ag^+)	Ag^+, (Cl^-)	High purity precipitates
Fe(III)	OH^-	Weighed as Fe_2O_3
Ba(II), Pb(II) or ($SO_4^=$)	$SO_4^=$ or (Ba^{++})	Best method for some mixtures
Sn	HNO_3	SnO_2 formed in alloy reaction with HNO_3 (not pure)
K^+	$NaB(C_6H_5)_4$	Best reagent for K^+ (Rb^+, Cs^+, Ag^+, NH_4^+ also precipitate); adaptable to titration (See laboratory section.)
Ni(II)	Dimethylglyoxime	Highly specific for Ni^{++} (Pd^{++} only other element to precipitate)
Al(III)	"Oxine" (8-hydroxyquinoline)	At pH 5, separated from Mg^{++}
Mg^{++}	"Oxine"	At pH 10, separated from Ca^{++}, Na^+, and K^+
Fe(III)	"Cupferron" (*N*-nitrosophenyl-hydroxylamine)	In 4 *M* strong acid, separated from Ni(II), Co(II), Cu(II), Pb(II), Cr(III)
Co(II)	1-Nitroso-2-napthol	In acid, separated from Ni(II), Zn(II), Al(III), Mn(II); ignite to Co_3O_4
Cu(II)	Anthranilic acid	At pH 3, separated from Pb(II), Cd(II), and Mn(II)
Cu and Pb (as PbO_2)	By electrodeposition	(See Chapter 24 and the laboratory section on brass.)

gravimetric work with silver compounds. Silver nitrate can be melted at 212°C which drives out traces of water. It is a reliable primary standard.

A photochemically induced error peculiar to AgCl should be mentioned. In strong light, especially blue light (sky or fluorescent), AgCl decomposes slowly to its elements. This only becomes measurable upon long exposure or when the AgCl particles have just formed so that they are small with large surface area exposed to the light. This gives high results since the Cl_2 formed produces more AgCl in the usual chloride determination, where excess $AgNO_3$ is present in solution:

$$2AgCl \xrightarrow{h\nu} 2Ag + Cl_2,$$

$$Cl_2 + H_2O + 2Ag^+ \rightarrow 2AgCl + \tfrac{1}{2}O_2 + 2H^+.$$

Thus, in effect, one extra atom of Ag is weighed for each AgCl photolyzed. There is no net loss of AgCl. Of course, if photolysis occurs during drying of the AgCl, Cl_2 can be lost and low results ensue.

An extension of the AgCl method used to find the atomic weight of fluorine is reported by A. F. Scott and W. R. Ware of Reed College.* This painstaking work was performed in a series of senior research projects carried out by undergraduates under the direction of Dr. Scott, a student of T. W. Richards. Highly purified Ag was dissolved in HNO_3 and combined with perfluorobutyryl chloride, the Ag and C_4F_7OCl having been weighed to six significant figures. The ratio C_4F_7OCl/Ag was found to be 2.15512 ± 0.00002 (standard deviation). This fixed F at 18.999 on the old scale instead of 19.00, the earlier and less precisely known value. The high percentage F in the starting compound prevents loss of significant figures in the calculations. The atomic weights of C, O, Cl, and Ag were, of course, taken as known well enough to permit calculation of F to five or six figures. This paper should interest the student. The details of purification of the Ag and C_4F_7OCl are crucial to the reliability of the result.

11.2 CRYSTAL GROWTH AND THE PURITY OF PRECIPITATES

The mechanism of precipitation is complicated and controversial. One can show quite rigorously and in agreement with experiment that thermodynamics requires an increase in the vapor pressure (escaping tendency) of liquid drops with decreasing drop radius. The Becker-Doering theory (1935) extends this concept to solubility and *solid* particle size. The logarithm of the solubility should vary directly with the surface tension of the solid and inversely with the density and particle radius. However, Gibbs (1878) pointed out that crystal growth is not of the same random continuous nature as liquid condensation from a gas. Furthermore, experimental testing is difficult. Complete exclusion of rough surfaces, dust, and other sources of minute particles serving to start nucleation of precipitate is practically impossible. The relation between solubility and particle size turns out to require higher solubility only for very small crystals, with radius under 1 micron (10^4 Å). However, it raises the question of how precipitation can get started. A chance agglomeration of ions will still require significant supersaturation in the surrounding solution to grow further. Experimentally it is found that an induction period does follow mixing of reagents for precipitation. Once some nuclei form, crystal-growth rate accelerates. But, final equilibrium may be reached slowly requiring some digestion time for good results.

It should be clarified that higher solubility of tiny crystals cannot be an equilibrium condition for macroscopic amounts of solid. Therefore K_{sp} values always refer to equilibrium conditions with crystals of mixed sizes present. Clearly this will mean the attainment of the minimum solubility.

Coprecipitation of other substances is the major source of inaccuracy in gravimetric work. When a precipitate forms rapidly from supersaturated solution, it is not surprising that weighable amounts of other components of the solution

---

* *J. Am. Chem. Soc.* **79,** 4253 (1957).

can be entrapped or occluded in the solid. In specific cases there may also be solid-solution formation and surface adsorption of impurities. For example, AgCl precipitated from NaCl solution by excess $AgNO_3$ can adsorb excess Ag^+ at Cl^- sites on the crystal surface. Upon coagulation, some NO_3^- will be carried along to neutralize this charge. Digestion and washing may help purify precipitates. Much empirical labor has been expended in finding conditions for preparation of pure solids by precipitation.

The long digestions often directed after precipitation may allow trapped and coprecipitated impurities to escape from the solid. Studies of the mechanisms of purification and growth of the crystals have been extensive. (See Laitinen and Walton for a more complete discussion.)

Digestion does not remove all impurity. The washings of the precipitate are important. However, water washing often removes the counter ion (NO_3^- in the above AgCl case) so that the particles become charged and peptize, returning to colloidal dispersion. Washing with an electrolyte prevents this. In the AgCl case, dilute HNO_3 can replace the $AgNO_3$ between the AgCl crystals. This trace of HNO_3 can later be volatilized in drying.

With gelatinous precipitates which have very tiny crystals and much water loosely clumped together, the pH is important in determining adsorption of ions. Iron, aluminum, and chromium plus-three hydroxides are examples. The ion-exchange properties of such materials are well known. In acid solution these solids pick up extra protons and attract anions strongly, coprecipitating sulfate, nitrate, etc. At high pH, they lose protons and then attract and carry down cations.

Reprecipitation is sometimes required to purify these materials. The precipitate, say $Fe(OH)_3$, is washed and dissolved in dilute acid whereupon the impurities are highly diluted. With addition of excess NH_3, the reprecipitated solid will contain much less impurity than the first one.

Postprecipitation refers to a distressing phenomenon by which a precipitate initially clean builds up layers of other substances on standing in contact with the solution. It is common with sulfides. For example, one experiment* reported the following percentages of NiS adding to CuS when H_2S was added to a solution originally holding 0.05 *M* each of $CuCl_2$ and $NiCl_2$ and 0.01 *M* HCl. (NiS is not expected to form at this acidity.)

Hours after precipitation	3	12	24	36	60
Percent NiS in the CuS	0	3.0	6.5	13.5	37.0

Control of pH and addition of complexing ions can prevent some postprecipitation. This demonstrates why sulfide methods are not used for quantitative separations when other ways can be found.

* I. M. Kolthoff and F. S. Griffith, *J. Phys. Chem.* **42,** 541 (1938).

11.3 HOMOGENEOUS PRECIPITATION

Since a high degree of supersaturation and rapid crystal growth traps much impurity in precipitation, it is natural to try for conditions of slight supersaturation. The use of high temperatures and diluted reagents are steps in this direction used in regular precipitation methods. However, it is even more clever to find a slow chemical reaction to generate one of the precipitating species in the solution. Thus there should be no regions of high concentration. This technique is called *precipitation from homogeneous solution.* During regular precipitation, solutions of different reagents must be mixed, and the whole is not homogeneous. (A single true solution is, of course, homogeneous.) The examples in Table 11–2 will make clear the principle.

Table 11–2

Ions to be precipitated	By reagent B	Reaction producing B
Fe(III)	OH^-	Hydrolysis of urea at 90° $(NH_2)_2CO + H_2O \rightarrow 2NH_3 + CO_2$
Ni(II)	DMG	Oximation of biacetyl
Halides	Ag^+	$Ag(NH_3)_2{}^+$, by evaporation of NH_3 or ester hydrolysis to make acid
Metal sulfides	$S^=$	Hydrolysis of thioacetamide in hot water to give H_2S and acetamide

The urea hydrolysis can be used to raise pH slowly and effect precipitations by many basic anions. For example, $PbCrO_4$ can be formed slowly in large crystals by boiling a solution with acid and urea so that $HCrO_4{}^-$ is converted slowly to $CrO_4{}^=$.

The slow crystal growth makes more perfect and purer solids. Coprecipitation is greatly reduced. The larger crystals are more easily handled. For example, the standard DMG method for Ni produces a very bulky precipitate so that only about 50 mg of Ni are usually taken. The homogeneous method gives long needle-like crystals which permit nickel samples up to 200 mg to be taken. With Fe(III) the homogeneous precipitate appears to have about $\frac{1}{20}$ the volume of the gelatinous solid formed in the direct ammonia precipitation. Procedures for Ni and Fe are given in the laboratory section.

SUMMARY

The relatively high accuracy of gravimetric methods and historical atomic-weight determinations involving silver compounds is discussed. Factors affecting the purity of precipitates are presented. The special advantage of slow precipitation from homogeneous solution is pointed out.

SUGGESTIONS FOR FURTHER READING

CAMERON, A. E., and E. WICHERS, *J. Am. Chem. Soc.* **84,** 4175 (1962) is a report of the International Commission on Atomic Weights on the ^{12}C scale.

LAITINEN, H. A., *Chemical Analysis*, New York: McGraw-Hill, 1960. Chapters 7 through 10 treat the theories of precipitation and contamination in detail.

RICHARDS, T. W., *Chem. Rev.* **1,** 1 (1924) describes his methods.

SCOTT, A. F., and M. BETTMAN, *Chem. Rev.* **50,** 363 (1952) describes atomic-weight determinations of the monoisotopic elements.

WALTON, H. F., *Principles and Methods of Chemical Analysis*, 2nd ed. Englewood Cliffs, N.J.: Prentice-Hall, 1964, Chapters 2, 3, 4, 5.

WICHERS, E., *Anal. Chem.* **35,** 23A (1963) discusses the history of atomic-weight determinations and the ^{12}C scale.

Homogeneous precipitations

GORDON, L., M. L. SALUTSKY, and H. H. WILLARD, *Precipitation from Homogeneous Solution*, New York: John Wiley, 1959.

SWIFT, E. H., and F. C. ANSON, "Analytical Chemistry of Thioacetamide," in *Advances in Analytical Chemistry and Instrumentation*, ed. by C. N. Reilley. Vol. I. New York: Interscience Publishers, 1960.

PROBLEMS

1. Richards and Forbes [*J. Am. Chem. Soc.* **29,** 808(1907)] obtained the weight ratio $AgNO_3/Ag = 1.574800$ (uncorrected). Determine their atomic weight of Ag, taking $O = 16.0000$ and $N = 14.008$. Repeat for ^{12}C scale values. Justify the number of significant figures you retain.
2. In Richards' atomic-weight experiments, Ag and $AgNO_3$ were the only materials weighed, to get the ratio $Ag/AgNO_3$ to seven significant figures. What figures of the ratio are affected by buoyancy corrections on the air weights? What is the total change in the ratio due to these corrections? (Assume weights of density 8.80 g/ml.)
3. Richards [*J. Am. Chem. Soc.* **32,** 4, (1910)] compared Ag to O by an indirect method, since silver oxides of high purity could not be made. First he converted LiCl to AgCl to Ag getting the ratio LiCl/Ag as 0.392997 ($\pm 4 \times 10^{-6}$). Second he converted LiCl to $LiClO_4$ to get $4(O)/LiCl = 1.50962$ ($\pm 6 \times 10^{-5}$). Calculate the ratio Ag/O and the atomic weight of silver on the $O = 16$ scale. Atomic weights of Cl and Li must not be used in the calculations. Show the $\pm$ uncertainty in the answer.
4. Given that the experimental ratio $C_4F_7OCl/Ag = 2.15512$, calculate the atomic weight of F on the old and ^{12}C scales with C, O, Cl, and Ag as known. Find the ppth and ppm difference between the calculated ^{12}C scale value and that in tables (taken from mass spectrometry).
5. What weight samples should be taken so that the number of milligrams of AgCl weighed in gravimetric determination may be divided by 8 to give the percentage of NaCl in the original sample?

6. A 340.0 mg sample containing only KCl and NaCl gave 706.2 mg AgCl by a standard gravimetric method. Calculate the percentage of each compound to the proper number of significant figures. Show where you lose the fourth figure.

7. A solubility of 1.8×10^{-4} *M* is reported for potassium tetraphenylborate at 25°. What could be the ppth loss in washing 200 mg of precipitated $KB(C_6H_5)_4$ with

   a) 100 ml water,
   b) 100 ml 0.01 *M* $NaB(C_6H_5)_4$ solution?

8. What size sample of a clay containing about 1% K should be taken for gravimetric *K* determination as tetraphenylborate so that the final weighing uncertainty (±0.2 mg) will be 1 ppth?

CHAPTER 12

OXIDATION-REDUCTION EQUILIBRIA

Applications of electrochemistry to quantitative measurements and the calculation of equilibrium constants are discussed in Chapters 12 and 13. Potentiometric methods are treated in Chapter 24. Basic ideas about voltaic cells and electrolysis are presented in general chemistry texts.

12.1 ELECTROCHEMISTRY

There are many quantitatively useful reactions in which electron transfer, or at least a change of formal oxidation state, occurs. The free-energy drive of such reactions, if they achieve rapid equilibrium (are reversible), is easily measured by standard potentiometric means and furnishes one of the easiest methods for determining equilibrium constants and thermodynamic data.

Consider the following two reactions as examples of the application of electrochemistry to solution reactions:

$$\underline{Cu^0} + 2Ag^+ \rightleftharpoons Cu^{++} + \underline{2Ag^0}, \qquad (12\text{–}1a)$$

$$2Fe^{3+} + Hg_2{}^{++} \rightleftharpoons 2Fe^{++} + 2Hg^{++}. \qquad (12\text{–}1b)$$

The unit-activity standard states are: solids in their stable crystalline form at 25°C and 1 atm, liquids in the pure compound at 25°C and 1 atm, gases at 1 atm partial pressure as ideal gas, solutes at unit activity on the molar scale, as explained in Chapter 9.

The equilibrium constants for these reactions can be written:

for (12–1a),

$$K_{eq} = \frac{[Cu^{++}]}{[Ag^+]^2}, \qquad (12\text{–}2a)$$

and for (12–1b),

$$K_{eq} = \frac{[Fe^{++}]^2[Hg^{++}]^2}{[Fe^{3+}]^2[Hg_2{}^{++}]}, \qquad (12\text{–}2b)$$

where, as usual, thermodynamic equilibrium constants, K^0, are indicated if the brackets enclose activities, or formal or conditional constants are indicated if the brackets are filled with concentrations.

The numerical value of the K_{eq} can vary with the multiple used in balancing the chemical equation. Note that a factor of 2 or $\frac{1}{2}$ in balancing would not, however, change the functional relationship. Doubling the reaction squares both sides of the K_{eq} expression.

The interrelations of the important quantities, standard free energy change, ΔG^0, standard cell voltage, $\mathcal{E}^0$, and K_{eq}^0 are:

$$\Delta G^0 = -RT \ln K_{eq}^0 = -n\mathfrak{F}\mathcal{E}^0, \tag{12–3}$$

where R is the ideal gas constant, T, the absolute temperature, n, the number of electrons exchanged in the balanced equation, and $\mathfrak{F}$ is the faraday, 96,500 coul, one mole of electrons (Chapter 26).

Equation (12–3) says that the free energy push for reaction of the number of moles shown in the balanced chemical equation going from reactants to products, all in their standard states, is directly related to $\mathcal{E}^0$, or to the logarithm of the thermodynamic equilibrium constant. Each of these is then a measure of the "distance" (in free energy) from the standard states to equilibrium conditions.

A relation deduced from experimental measurements in the 1890's by Nernst and logically derivable from thermodynamics gives the value of $\mathcal{E}$ at conditions different from unit activity (for reversible redox couples):

$$\mathcal{E} = \mathcal{E}^0 - \frac{0.0592}{n} \log Q \quad \text{(at 25°C)}, \tag{12–4}$$

where Q is the quotient, which has the form of the equilibrium constant, with the given conditions instead of the equilibrium ones. Note that (12–3) can be rearranged to show

$$\mathcal{E}^0 = \frac{0.0592}{n} \log K_{eq}^0, \tag{12–5}$$

where all the constants and 25°C, 298°K, have been combined. If other temperatures are needed, appropriate values of the Nernst constant can be derived. Note that, as must be the case, at equilibrium, Q has the value K_{eq}^0, and $\mathcal{E} = 0$. Also, when all activities in Q are one, log Q is zero, and $\mathcal{E} = \mathcal{E}^0$ as defined.

To make correct use of these equations and the cell-voltage values in Table 12–1, we must know the conventions used. Note that the ΔG^0 and $\mathcal{E}^0$ refer to *differences* in free energy or voltage (chemical or electrical potential) so that half-reactions can be expressed in relation to any reference standard without affecting these values. (That is, the difference between a standard taken as zero volts and a metal couple at 1.00 V is still 1.00 V if the standard is taken to be 10.00 V and the metal thus set at 11.00 V.)

12.2 HALF-CELL REACTIONS

The concept of dividing redox reactions into half-cell reactions will be reviewed using the examples given above. We can write the oxidation and the reduction halves for each:

from (12–1a),

$$Cu^0 \rightarrow Cu^{++} + 2e^-, \qquad Ag^+ + e^- \rightarrow Ag^0, \tag{12–6}$$

Table 12–1

Half-reaction	Electrode potential, volts
$Li^+ + e^- \rightleftharpoons Li(s)$	−3.045
$Na^+ + e^- \rightleftharpoons Na(s)$	−2.714
$Zn^{++} + 2e^- \rightleftharpoons Zn(s)$	−0.763
$Fe^{++} + 2e^- \rightleftharpoons Fe(s)$	−0.440
$Cr^{3+} + e^- \rightleftharpoons Cr^{++}$	−0.41
$2H^+ + 2e^- \rightleftharpoons H_2(g)$	0.000
$S(s) + 2H^+ + 2e^- \rightleftharpoons H_2S(g)$	+0.141
$Cu^{++} + e^- \rightleftharpoons Cu^+$	+0.153
$AgCl(s) + e^- \rightleftharpoons Ag(s) + Cl^-$	+0.222
$Cu^{++} + 2e^- \rightleftharpoons Cu(s)$	+0.337
$I_2(s) + 2e^- \rightleftharpoons 2I^-$	+0.5355
$H_3AsO_4 + 2H^+ + 2e^- \rightleftharpoons HAsO_2 + 2H_2O$	+0.56
$O_2(g) + 2H^+ + 2e^- \rightleftharpoons H_2O_2$	+0.682
$Fe^{3+} + e^- \rightleftharpoons Fe^{++}$	+0.771
$Hg_2{}^{++} + 2e^- \rightleftharpoons 2Hg(l)$	+0.789
$Ag^+ + e^- \rightleftharpoons Ag(s)$	+0.7991
$Hg^{++} + e^- \rightleftharpoons \frac{1}{2}Hg_2{}^{++}$	+0.920
$Br_2(l) + 2e \rightleftharpoons 2Br^-$	+1.0652
$MnO_2(s) + 4H^+ + 2e^- \rightleftharpoons Mn^{++} + 2H_2O$	+1.23
$Cr_2O_7{}^{=} + 14H^+ + 6e^- \rightleftharpoons 2Cr^{3+} + 7H_2O$	+1.33
$Cl_2(g) + 2e^- \rightleftharpoons 2Cl^-$	+1.3595
$Mn^{3+} + e^- \rightleftharpoons Mn^{++}$	+1.51
$MnO_4{}^- + 8H^+ + 5e^- \rightleftharpoons Mn^{++} + 4H_2O$	+1.51
$H_2O_2 + 2H^+ + 2e^- \rightleftharpoons 2H_2O$	+1.77
$F_2(g) + 2e^- \rightleftharpoons 2F^-$	+2.65

Data from Latimer's *Oxidation Potentials* (Englewood Cliffs, N.J.: Prentice-Hall, 1952). Because the reactions in this table are written as reductions, in accordance with the IUPAC convention, the signs of the electrode potentials are opposite from the signs of the oxidation potentials given in Latimer's tables.

and from (12–1b),

$$Fe^{3+} + e^- \rightarrow Fe^{++}, \qquad Hg_2{}^{++} \rightarrow 2Hg^{++} + 2e^-.$$

Putting the Q expression for these into the Nernst equation (12–4) gives, for (12–1a),

$$\mathcal{E} = \mathcal{E}^0 - \frac{0.0592}{n} \log \frac{[Cu^{++}]}{[Ag^+]^2}, \tag{12–7}$$

which can be divided into

$$\mathcal{E}_1 - \mathcal{E}_2 = \mathcal{E}_1^0 - \mathcal{E}_2^0 - \frac{0.0592}{2} \log [Cu^{++}] + 0.0592 \log [Ag^+], \tag{12–8}$$

where $\mathcal{E}_1$ and $\mathcal{E}_2$ are to be associated with the half-reactions:

$$\mathcal{E}_1 = \mathcal{E}_1^0 - 0.0592 \log [Ag^+]^{-1}, \qquad \mathcal{E}_2 = \mathcal{E}_2^0 - \frac{0.0592}{2} \log [Cu^{++}]^{-1}. \qquad (12\text{–}9)$$

Equations (12–7) and (12–8) would also result from the alternative approach from the tabulated $\mathcal{E}^0$ values. The standard $\mathcal{E}^0$ half-cell values (for reduction) are referred to the standard hydrogen electrode (SHE) taken as zero. Thus, as explained above, in all combinations of two half-cells, the SHE value is canceled by subtraction. Since its value is immaterial, the arbitrary choice of zero is made for convenience. For the Ag couple, the tabulated value actually means that the $\mathcal{E}^0$ cell is 0.799 V for the reaction $2Ag^+ + H_2 \rightarrow 2Ag^0 + 2H^+$, which by (12–4) gives

$$\mathcal{E} = \mathcal{E}_1^0 - \mathcal{E}_{H_2}^0 - \frac{0.0592}{2} \log \frac{[H^+]^2}{[Ag^+]^2[H_2]}.$$

Inserting the values $\mathcal{E}_{H_2}^0 = 0$ at $[H^+] = 1$ and $[H_2] = 1$ atm, we have

$$\mathcal{E} = \mathcal{E}_1^0 - 0.0592 \log [Ag^+]^{-1},$$

which is the usual abbreviated expression for the concentration-dependence of a simple metal couple. The reader should remember that the SHE is understood in all the so-called half-cell potential tables.

12.3 CELL VOLTAGE, K_{eq}, AND REACTION DIRECTION

Returning to the Ag-Cu example, we find that the $\mathcal{E}^0$ values can be inserted in (12–8) to give ($\mathcal{E}_1^0 = 0.799$ V, $\mathcal{E}_2^0 = 0.337$ V)

$$\mathcal{E} = 0.462 - \frac{0.0592}{2} \log \frac{[Cu^{++}]}{[Ag^+]^2}. \qquad (12\text{–}10)$$

At equilibrium, the $[Ag^+]$ and $[Cu^{++}]$ will have attained values such that $\mathcal{E}_1 = \mathcal{E}_2$ [*note:* not $\mathcal{E}^0$'s] so that $\mathcal{E} = 0$, and Q is K_{eq}^0:

$$0 = 0.462 - \frac{0.0592}{2} \log K_{eq}^0, \qquad K_{eq}^0 = \log^{-1} \frac{2(0.462)}{0.0592} = 10^{15.6}.$$

Thus the original reaction goes far to completion.

Note that in (12–9) the use of standard values for oxidation rather than reduction potentials would not change the result provided one recognizes that the Q term must correspond to the $\mathcal{E}^0$ reaction *as written* in the table used. For example,

$$Ag^0 \rightarrow Ag^+ + e^-, \qquad \mathcal{E}_{ox}^0 = -0.799 \text{ V},$$

$$Cu^0 \rightarrow Cu^{++} + 2e^-, \qquad \mathcal{E}_{ox}^0 = -0.337 \text{ V},$$

$$\mathcal{E}' = -0.462 - \frac{0.0592}{2} \log \frac{[Ag^+]^2}{[Cu^{++}]},$$

which is the same result as (12–10), where $\mathcal{E}' = -\mathcal{E}$, since it is for the reverse reaction. The reader should be sure to get a clear view of the correlation of these signs, since confusing the signs is a frequent source of student error.

Effect of Concentration

Let us look at some simple examples of the concentration effect on $\mathcal{E}$ values. For the silver couple, (12–9), $\mathcal{E}$ varies 0.0592 V for each tenfold change in $[Ag^+]$ at 25°C. For example, a cell using 0.010 *M* $AgNO_3$ versus SHE should give a potential of

$$\mathcal{E} = 0.799 - 0.0592(2) = 0.681 \text{ V} \qquad (12\text{–}11)$$

(assuming activity equals molarity.)

The push toward free Ag is less after dilution from the standard unit activity to 0.010 *M*, as one expects (Le Chatelier principle). Let us find the effect of a similar dilution on the Cu potential:

$$\mathcal{E} = 0.337 - \frac{0.0592}{2}(2) = 0.337 - 0.0592 = 0.278 \text{ V}. \qquad (12\text{–}12)$$

Thus, in general, voltage changes by $(0.0592/n) \log (a)$, where n is the number of electrons transferred in the half-cell reaction. This means that the dilution effects will not cancel in our Ag-Cu cell (12–10):

$$\mathcal{E} = 0.462 - \frac{0.0592}{2} \log \frac{(0.01)}{(0.01)^2} = 0.403 \text{ V}.$$

The same result can be seen from (12–11) and (12–12):

$$\mathcal{E} = 0.681 - 0.278 = 0.403 \text{ V}.$$

For two half-cells of equal n, $\mathcal{E}$ would be insensitive to concentration if the activity coefficients also would cancel (for simple metal couples).

Effect of Complexing

Now let us look at a more complicated example, reaction (12–1b). Here as in the SHE, the oxidized and reduced species of each half-reaction are conceived as undergoing their electron exchanges at an inert (Pt) electrode. With the simple metal couples, the reduced species, the free metal, can be the electrode. For our Fe-Hg system,

$$\mathcal{E}^0 = 0.771 - 0.920 = -0.149 \text{ V},$$
$$K^0_{eq} = \log^{-1} \frac{(2)(-0.149)}{(0.0592)} = 10^{-5.04}. \qquad (12\text{–}13)$$

Thus the reduction of Fe(III) by Hg_2^{++} is not favored at standard conditions. (The proper $\mathcal{E}^0$ signs were chosen by paying attention to the directions of the half-reactions as written. For Fe(III) reduction, $\mathcal{E}^0 = +0.771$ V and for Hg_2^{++} oxidation, $\mathcal{E}^0_{ox} = -0.920$ V.)

Now, the result in (12–13) may be surprising if one remembers that there is a titration method for Fe(III) by reduction with Hg_2^{++}. It is done, however, in a solution about 1 M in SCN^- ion. Let us calculate the effect of this on $\mathcal{E}$ from the Nernst equation. Let us take all four ions of reaction (12–1b) initially at 0.010 M* and assume that Fe(III) and Hg(II) react "completely" with SCN^-. We shall have to use K_{eq} for these complex formations to find the remaining Fe(III) and Hg(II) concentrations for use in the Nernst equation:

$$K_{eq} = 200 = \frac{[FeSCN^{++}]}{[Fe^{3+}][SCN^-]} \quad \text{from which} \quad [Fe^{3+}] = \frac{(0.01)}{200(1)} = 5 \times 10^{-5},$$

$$\beta_4 = 10^{20} = \frac{[Hg(SCN)_4^{=}]}{[Hg^{++}][SCN^-]^4} \quad \text{from which} \quad [Hg^{++}] = \frac{(0.01)}{(10^{20})(1)^4} = 10^{-22}.$$

Since we omit activity correction, let us round to the nearest power of ten and insert these values in the Nernst equation to get $\mathcal{E}$, approximately,

$$\mathcal{E} = -0.149 - \frac{0.0592}{2} \log \frac{[Fe^{++}]^2[Hg^{++}]^2}{[Fe^{3+}]^2[Hg_2^{++}]} = -0.149 + 1.09 = +0.94 \text{ V}. \tag{12–14}$$

So the reaction is now favored as written. This dramatically illustrates the great effect complexing agents can have on the direction of chemical reactions. Complexing is frequently used to increase completeness of a reaction for quantitative use. There are many examples met in qualitative inorganic analysis. One may recall that HgS is a most difficultly soluble precipitate. It dissolves easily in acidic KI solution,

$$\underline{HgS} + 4I^- + 2H^+ \rightarrow HgI_4^{=} + H_2S.$$

The foregoing calculations are approximate also because further complexing was ignored. Reaction with SCN^- as well as with H_2O can be important. (Fe^{3+} and Hg^{++} are quite acidic.) The pH can have a large effect on oxy-ion potentials. For example, look at the concentration-dependence of the dichromate-ion reaction,

$$Cr_2O_7^{=} + 14H^+ + 6e^- \rightarrow 2Cr^{3+} + 7H_2O, \qquad \mathcal{E}^0 = 1.36 \text{ V},$$

$$\mathcal{E} = 1.36 - \frac{0.0592}{6} \log \frac{[Cr^{3+}]^2}{[Cr_2O_7^{=}][H^+]^{14}}, \tag{12–15}$$

assuming the activity of H_2O and e^- to be one as usual. This shows that each pH unit change in acidity changes $\mathcal{E}$ by $0.0592(\frac{14}{6}) = 0.138$ V, a very large effect. Changing from unit activity H^+ (pH = 0) to pH = 7 would lower the oxidation potential of dichromate to $1.36 - 7(0.138) = 0.39$ V. To lower it to zero requires pH = 1.36/0.138 = 9.85 in agreement with our chemical knowledge that oxidation of Cr(III) to Cr(VI) is easier in basic solution. This is true in general for oxidation of metal aquo ions. Note that this electrode reaction, and many others,

* The low solubility of $Hg_2(SCN)_2$ makes this unrealistic, but can only lower the voltage of (12–14) by 0.2 V.

are not easily reversible. The principle of pH shift of equilibrium is valid, nevertheless, for any reaction involving H^+ or OH^-. This dichromate case is discussed in Chapter 13.

Precipitation. Precipitation can also serve to alter $\mathcal{E}$ by lowering concentrations. For example let us calculate $\mathcal{E}$ for the Ag couple in the presence of unit activity chloride ion:

$$a_{Ag^+} = K^0_{sp}/1 = 1.69 \times 10^{-10},$$

$$\mathcal{E} = 0.799 - 0.0592 \log a^{-1}_{Ag^+} = 0.799 - 0.577 = 0.222 \text{ V}.$$

This $\mathcal{E}$ might be termed an $\mathcal{E}^0$ for the half-reaction

$$\underline{AgCl} + e^- \rightarrow \underline{Ag} + Cl^-.$$

(This is an ideal value for this single reaction not including any other possible complexing.) The $\mathcal{E}$ values of such systems can be measured easily and provide some of our most reliable K^0_{sp} values. For example, the $\mathcal{E}^0$ for the reaction,

$$\underline{AgBr} + e^- \rightarrow \underline{Ag} + Br^-,$$

is found to be 0.071 V. Find the K^0_{sp} for AgBr. Using the Nernst expression as above for AgCl, we have

$$\mathcal{E}^0 = 0.071 = 0.799 - 0.0592 \log (K^0_{sp})^{-1}, \qquad K^0_{sp} = 10^{-12.3}.$$

Formal Potentials

Because of the effects of complexing and ionic strength, which may be impossible to calculate owing to lack of activity coefficients and K_{eq} values, *formal potentials* are often reported and used in calculations. The formal potential is the measured $\mathcal{E}$ value under specific conditions for unit *concentrations* of the species in the cell equations. Some are given in the Appendix and used in the calculations of the Fe(II)-$Cr_2O_7^{=}$ titration curve in Chapter 13.

Experimental Determination of $\mathcal{E}^0$

We pointed out in the preceding chapter the difficulty in finding accurate ionic activity coefficients in concentrated solutions. The reader may well wonder how precise $\mathcal{E}^0$ values are obtained for this hypothetical concentration of unit activity. They are *not* measured at unit activity, but through an extrapolation device. For the general couple, $M^{n+} + ne^- \rightarrow M^0$,

$$\mathcal{E} = \mathcal{E}^0 + \frac{0.0592}{n} \log [M] f_{+n},$$

where M stands for M^{n+}. Dividing the log term into two parts and substituting the Debye-Hückel limiting equation for the log (f_{+n}) term gives (where $n = z$),

$$\mathcal{E} - \frac{0.0592}{n} \log [M] = \mathcal{E}^0 + 0.0592\,(0.51) n\sqrt{I}. \qquad (12\text{–}16)$$

The Debye-Hückel term becomes increasingly accurate as I decreases so that a plot of the left side of Eq. (12–16) (from experimental measurement of $\mathcal{E}$ and M) versus $\sqrt{I}$ will give a line with intercept $\mathcal{E}^0$ at $I = 0$. The $\mathcal{E}$ values can be measured at several concentrations against a known or standard half-cell.

For a general cell, the Nernst equation may be used and rearranged as above. The Q term is divided into its concentration and activity-coefficient parts, the latter quotient called **(F)** here:

$$\mathcal{E} + \frac{0.0592}{n} \log Q = \mathcal{E}^0 - \frac{0.0592}{n} \log \mathbf{(F)} = \mathcal{E}^{0\prime} \quad \text{(the formal potential).} \tag{12–17}$$

[*Note:* In (12–16), Q is $1/[\mathrm{M}]$, which gives the different sign.]

Combining Half-Cells To Get New Half-Cells

While we have simply done algebraic addition of half-cells to obtain $\mathcal{E}$ values for whole cells (e^- canceled out), new half-cells cannot often be so derived (e^- add up). To understand this, the analogy of voltage to pressure may help if not pushed too far. Both are intensity factors. Two opposing pistons will have a net force given by the difference between the pressures behind them, regardless of the amount of gas (whole-cell case). (Pressure is force per unit area.) However, if the two gases are mixed in one container, the pressure will not often be the sum of the two original ones. The mass and volume of each gas must be considered in the calculation (new half-cell case). The sum or difference of *molar* free energies must be considered for calculation of the new half-cell potential. From (12–3) for any stepwise process,

$$\Delta G_1^0 \pm \Delta G_2^0 = \Delta G_3^0$$

and

$$-n_1\mathcal{F}\mathcal{E}_1^0 \mp n_2\mathcal{F}\mathcal{E}_2^0 = -n_3\mathcal{F}\mathcal{E}_3^0 \quad (\mathcal{F} \text{ cancels}). \tag{12–18}$$

The algebraic sum of changes from states one to two and two to three gives the change from one to three.

Example. The gold(I) potential, $Au^+ + e^- \rightleftharpoons Au^0$, ($\mathcal{E}_3^0$) is difficult to measure. Calculate it from the known potentials,

$$Au^{3+} + 3e^- \rightleftharpoons Au^0, \qquad \mathcal{E}_1^0 = 1.50\ \mathrm{V},$$

$$Au^{3+} + 2e^- \rightleftharpoons Au^+, \qquad \mathcal{E}_2^0 = 1.41\ \mathrm{V}.$$

From (12–18) with $\mathcal{F}$ canceled, we have

$$3(1.50) - 2(1.41) = 1(\mathcal{E}_3^0) = 1.68\ \mathrm{V}. \tag{12–19}$$

It may seem at first that we have a contradiction in finding gold(I) with a higher reduction potential than gold(III). But, it is the free energy change that clarifies the picture. Convert (12–19) to ΔG^0 values as in (12–18) ($\mathfrak{F}$ = 23,090 cal/volt equivalents),

$$3\mathfrak{F}(1.50) - 2\mathfrak{F}(1.41) = \mathfrak{F}(1.68),$$
$$10\bar{3}.9 \text{ kcal/mole} - 65.1 \text{ kcal/mole} = 38.8 \text{ kcal/mole}.$$

Diagrammatically,

$$\Delta G^0 \text{ values, kcal/mole} \quad Au^0 \xrightarrow{38.8} Au^+ \xrightarrow{65.1} Au^{3+}.$$
$$\underbrace{\qquad\qquad\qquad}_{104}$$

SUMMARY

For all reactions, the thermodynamic equilibrium constant, K^0, is simply related to the standard free energy change. In redox cases, both are also simply related to the standard cell potential, $\mathcal{E}^0$. Extrapolation methods for determination of standard potential are presented. The Nernst equation relates actual cell potential to logarithms of concentrations (activities) of the species involved.

PROBLEMS

1. If you, instead of Nernst, had experimental values for some $\mathcal{E}$ values as a function of [M] for some simple metal couples versus SHE, describe how you could go about discovering the functional relationship between $\mathcal{E}$ and concentration. What difficulties might this method have?

2. Find $\mathcal{E}^0$ and K^0_{eq} values for the following oxidations by I_2 solution. Is each a likely candidate for I_2 titration?

$$Cr^{++} \rightarrow Cr^{3+} + e^-$$
$$Sn^{++} \rightarrow Sn^{4+} + 2e^- \quad \text{(in HCl)}$$
$$Fe^{++} \rightarrow Fe^{3+} + e^-$$
$$H_2S \rightarrow S^0 + 2H^+ + 2e^-$$

3. a) For one-electron transfer reactions, what values of $\mathcal{E}^0$ are required to give values for K^0_{eq} of 1, 10, 10^4, 10^{10}?
   b) Find K^0 for a one-electron reaction of $\mathcal{E}^0$ = 1.0 V.

4. For a redox reaction, A + B → C + D, find the $\mathcal{E}^0$ if the reaction is to be quantitative for a mixture initially 0.10 *M* in both A and B. (Here, quantitative means 99.9% yield.)
   a) Do it for a one-electron exchange reaction.
   b) Do the same for a five-electron reaction.

5. The $\mathcal{E}^0$ for the reaction

$$\underline{AgBrO_3} + e^- \rightarrow \underline{Ag^0} + BrO_3^-$$

has been found to be 0.55 V versus SHE. Derive the equation and calculate the K_{sp}^0 from the Nernst equation for the silver electrode.

6. For the reaction

$$H_2 + 2\underline{AgBr} \rightarrow 2H^+ + 2Br^- + 2\underline{Ag^0}$$

(an Ag: AgBr electrode versus SHE), $\mathcal{E}$ was measured as +0.200 V at [HBr] = 0.100 *M*, at a hydrogen pressure of 1 atm. Use the Nernst equation (12–4) and activity coefficient, $f_{\pm} = 0.79$ for HBr to get the value for $\mathcal{E}^0$. [*Note:* $n = 2$.]

7. For the reaction in Problem 6 the extrapolation method of Eq. (12–16) and (12–17) may be applied to get a better $\mathcal{E}^0$ value from this data:

Molarity of HBr	0.00100	0.00500	0.0100	0.0200	0.1000
$\mathcal{E}$, volts	0.4277	0.3470	0.3126	0.2786	0.2004

Discuss reasons for any deviation of your graph from a straight line.

CHAPTER 13

OXIDATION-REDUCTION TITRATIONS

Oxidation-reduction normality is defined, by analogy with acid-base usage, as molarity $\times$ n, where n is the number of electrons exchanged in the reaction. It cannot be stated without ambiguity for many solutions unless n is also stated. For example, $KMnO_4$ solution will have different normality values for reactions producing Mn(II), Mn(IV), and Mn(VI).

At any point during titration, it is important to realize that we assume that the reagents have mixed and come to equilibrium. Thus the whole-cell potential for the redox pair present is zero. That is, the concentrations reach values such that the two half-cells have equal and opposed potentials. Let us look at examples which clarify the application of the principles of Chapter 12 to titrations.

Examples

1) In the titration of 50.00 ml of 0.1000 N I_2 by 0.1000 N Cr^{++} the reaction is $2Cr^{++} + I_2 \rightarrow 2Cr^{3+} + 2I^-$. (Let us assume a constant ionic strength and neglect activity corrections to get an approximate titration curve.) The half-cell Nernst equations are (for the reaction directions needed here)

$$\mathcal{E}_{Cr} = 0.41 - 0.0592 \log \frac{[Cr^{3+}]}{[Cr^{++}]}, \qquad \mathcal{E}_I = 0.54 - \frac{0.0592}{2} \log \frac{[I^-]^2}{[I_2]}. \tag{13-1}$$

Solution

a) At the start of the titration we naively assume 0.1 N I_2 alone. This makes the $\mathcal{E}_I$ infinite: this is impossible, since I_2 can then oxidize water to form some I^-. In this case, however, I^- would always be added to keep I_2 in solution as I_3^- ion. So, let us take $[I^-]$ constant as 1 M throughout this titration. In general, the half-cell potential at the start of titrations will be indeterminate. Here it is 0.51 V.

b) After 1% of the total Cr^{++} needed has been added, we assume practically complete reaction; I_2 is then 99% of the original 5.000 meq. Thus

$$[I_2] = \frac{(0.99)(5 \text{ meq})}{(51 \text{ ml})(2 \text{ meq/mmole})} = 0.0485\ M,$$

$$\mathcal{E}_I = 0.54 - \frac{0.0592}{2} \log \frac{(1)^2}{0.0485} = 0.50 \text{ V}.$$

This 0.50 V must also be the negative half-cell potential for $\mathcal{E}_{Cr}$, otherwise further reaction would occur. This allows us to estimate the amount of Cr^{++} left unreacted (x):

$$[Cr^{3+}] = \frac{0.01(5\text{ mmole})}{(51\text{ ml})}, \qquad \mathcal{E}_{Cr} = -0.50 = 0.41 - 0.0592\log\frac{0.001 - x}{x}.$$

Try solving assuming x is small enough to omit from the 0.001 term:

$$\frac{0.91}{0.0592} = \log\frac{0.001}{x}, \qquad x \cong 10^{-18}.$$

The assumption is justified and the reaction does go far toward the right.

c) Half-way to the equivalence point, in many cases, $Q = 1$ just as $[HA] = [A^-]$ in weak acid titrations. If we were titrating Cr^{++}, half of it would be Cr^{3+} and from (13–1), $\mathcal{E}_{Cr} = \mathcal{E}^0 - 0.0592\log(1) = \mathcal{E}^0$.

However, the iodine stoichiometry changes the ratio, and furthermore we have added extra I^-. Thus

$$[I_2] = \frac{2.5\text{ meq}}{(75\text{ ml})(2\text{ meq/mmole})} = 0.0167\ M,$$

$$\mathcal{E}_I = \mathcal{E}^0 - \frac{0.0592}{2}\log\frac{1^2}{0.0167} = 0.54 - 0.05 = 0.49\text{ V}.$$

d) For 99% and 99.9% titration just as in (c), we can find the I_2 concentrations and get $\mathcal{E}_I$. For 99% titration:

$$\mathcal{E} = 0.54 - \frac{0.0592}{2}\log\frac{1^2}{0.0025} = 0.46\text{ V}.$$

For 99.9% titration:

$$\mathcal{E} = 0.54 - \frac{0.0592}{2}\log\frac{1^2}{0.00025} = 0.43\text{ V}.$$

e) At 0.1% past the equivalence point, we can use the $\mathcal{E}_{Cr}$, since its concentrations are calculable here more easily than $[I_2]$:

$$[Cr^{3+}] \cong 5\text{ mmole/100 ml} = 0.05\ M, \qquad [Cr^{++}] = 10^{-3}[Cr^{3+}] \cong 5 \times 10^{-5}\ M,$$

$$\mathcal{E}_{Cr} = 0.41 - 0.0592\log\frac{0.05}{5 \times 10^{-5}} = 0.23\text{ V}.$$

This is the oxidation potential of the Cr couple. So, -0.23 V is the reduction potential of the iodine couple to use in our curve.

f) At the equivalence point, the half-cell method used so far leaves us stranded because we now have no simple approximation for the small amount of I_2 or Cr^{++} remaining. It can be calculated from the K_{eq} or the whole-cell potential. The chemical equation allows us to say, at this point only,

$$[Cr^{3+}] = [I^-\text{ formed}] \quad \text{and} \quad [Cr^{++}] = 2[I_2] = 2x,$$

letting $[I_2] = x$ (very small). Now, from (12–5) and these values,

$$K^0_{eq} = 10^{32} = \frac{[Cr^{3+}]^2[I^-]^2}{[Cr^{++}]^2[I_2]} = \frac{0.05^2 1^2}{(2x)^2(x)}.$$

From which, $x = 2 \times 10^{-12}$. Put into either half-cell expression,

$$\mathcal{E}_I = 0.54 - \frac{0.0592}{2} \log \frac{1^2}{2 \times 10^{-12}} = 0.20 \text{ V},$$

$$\mathcal{E}_{Cr} = 0.41 - 0.0592 \log \frac{0.05}{4 \times 10^{-12}} = -0.23 \text{ V},$$

which are equal and opposed within the limitations of the approximate calculations being used here.

An alternative approach is to add the two Nernst expressions written in the same direction (let us use both *reduction*, *r*). Assume activity coefficients of unity. Double the iodine expression so that the log terms can be combined:

$$\mathcal{E}^r_{Cr} + 2\mathcal{E}^r_I = \mathcal{E}^{0r}_{Cr} + 2\mathcal{E}^{0r}_I - 0.0592 \log \frac{[Cr^{++}]}{[Cr^{3+}]} - 0.0592 \log \frac{[I^-]^2}{[I_2]}.$$

Inserting the above values at the equivalence point and assuming that $\mathcal{E}_{ep} = \mathcal{E}^r$ for either half-cell, we have

$$3\mathcal{E}_{ep} = -0.41 + 2(0.54) - 0.0592 \log \frac{(2x)1^2}{0.05x},$$

$$\mathcal{E}_{ep} = \frac{0.67}{3} - \frac{0.0592}{3} \log \frac{2}{0.05} = 0.19 \text{ V}.$$

(Note that the second term is small and the first is just the electron-weighted average of the two reduction potentials.)

We now have enough points to sketch the titration curve (Fig. 13–1).

Fraction reacted	0 to 0.01	0.5	0.99	0.999	1.000	1.01
$\mathcal{E}^r_I$, volts	0.50	0.49	0.46	0.43	0.21	−0.23

When oxidized and reduced forms of each half-reaction appear without change of coefficients (e.g., not $I_2 \rightarrow 2I^-$) in the balanced chemical equation and neither H^+ nor OH^- is involved, the log term in the equation for the potential at the equivalence point will be $\log(1) = 0$, so that the potential is

$$\mathcal{E}_{ep} = \frac{n_1\mathcal{E}^0_1 + n_2\mathcal{E}^0_2}{n_1 + n_2}.$$

For example, using the formal potentials, $\mathcal{E}^{0\prime}$, in 1 *M* HCl for

$$\text{Fe(II)} + \text{Ce(IV)} \rightarrow \text{Fe(III)} + \text{Ce(III)},$$

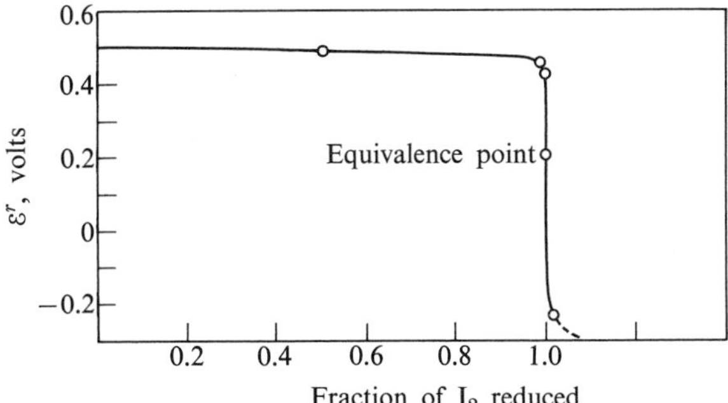

Fig. 13–1. Titration curve for 0.05 M I_2 by 0.1 M Cr^{++} solution (calculated points); reduction potential vs. fraction reacted, $[I^-] = 1\ M$.

we get

$$\mathcal{E}_{ep} = \frac{1.28 + 0.70}{1 + 1} = 0.99\text{ V}.$$

2) Calculate $\mathcal{E}_{ep}$ and sketch the titration curve for 0.02000 M Fe^{++} by 0.1000 N $K_2Cr_2O_7$ at unit H^+ activity as HCl. The reaction is

$$6Fe^{++} + Cr_2O_7^{=} + 14H^+ \rightarrow 6Fe^{3+} + 2Cr^{3+} + 7H_2O.$$

Let us assume quantitative reaction at the equivalence point and let x be the small concentration of $Cr_2O_7^{=}$ left at equilibrium. Then

$$[Fe^{3+}] = 3[Cr^{3+}] \qquad \text{and} \qquad [Fe^{++}] = 6[Cr_2O_7^{=}] = 6x.$$

The two Nernst expressions are (using the formal potentials in 1 M HCl):

$$\mathcal{E}_{Fe} = 0.70 - 0.0592 \log \frac{6x}{[Fe^{3+}]}$$

and

$$\mathcal{E}_{Cr} = 1.00 - \frac{0.0592}{6} \log \frac{[Cr^{3+}]^2}{\underset{x}{[Cr_2O_7^{=}]}[H^+]^{14}}\cdot$$

To combine, multiply the second equation by six, substitute the Fe terms equivalent to the Cr terms given just above, and add to get:

$$\mathcal{E}_{Fe} + 6\mathcal{E}_{Cr} = 7\mathcal{E}_{ep} = 0.70 + 6(1.00) - 0.0592 \log \tfrac{6}{9}\,[Fe^{3+}]\cdot$$

Then, assuming the Fe^{3+} is diluted to about 0.01 M by the end of titration, we have

$$\mathcal{E}_{ep} = \frac{6.70 + 0.18}{7} = 0.96\text{ V}.$$

(Taking the final Fe^{3+} concentration as 0.1 would only change $\mathcal{E}_{ep}$ to 0.98 V.) From $\mathcal{E}_{Fe}$ with this $\mathcal{E}_{ep}$ and $[Fe^{3+}]$, we find $[Fe^{++}] = 10^{-6.4}$ left at the equivalence point. So the reaction is barely quantitative. For this reason, H_3PO_4 is added in

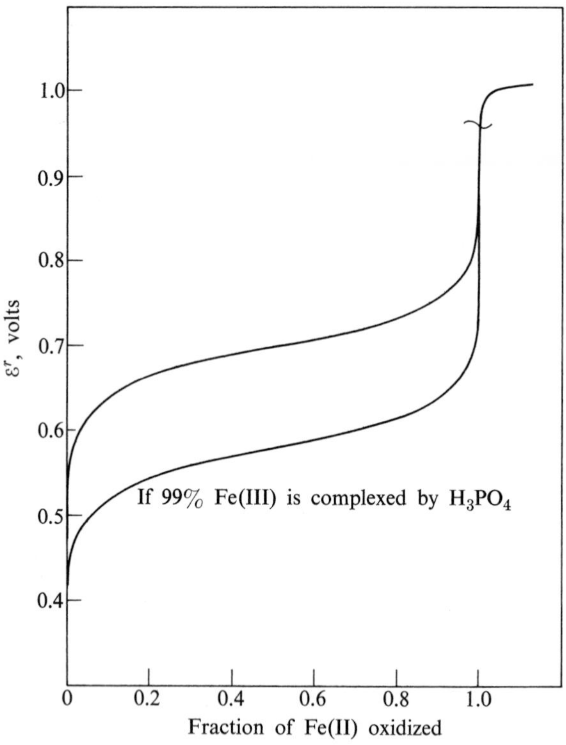

Fig. 13–2. Calculated titration curves for 0.02 *M* Fe(II) by 0.1 *N* $K_2Cr_2O_7$ in 1 *M* HCl.

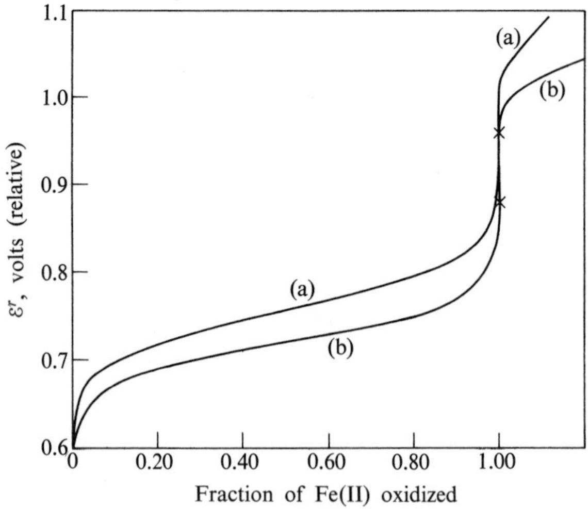

Fig. 13–3. Experimental titration curves for 0.02 *M* Fe(II) by 0.1 *N* $K_2Cr_2O_7$ in 1 *M* HCl (a) without, and (b) with 1 *M* H_3PO_4 present. (Platinum electrode on the pH meter. Starting voltage is set at 0.600 V.)

practice to complex Fe(III). One can easily deduce from $\mathcal{E}_{Fe}$ that if 99% of Fe^{3+} is complexed, the $\mathcal{E}_{Fe}$ will be lowered 0.12 V and the sharp rise at the endpoint will spread over about 0.2 instead of only 0.1 V.

One can now sketch the curve approximately, using ratios of Fe(II)/Fe(III) of 100, 1, 0.01 and a ratio of $\frac{20}{1}$ for Cr(III)/$Cr_2O_7^{=}$, corresponding to 1, 50, 99, and 110% of the needed dichromate added. One may easily check that these give $\mathcal{E}_{Fe}$ values 0.58, 0.70, 0.82, and 1.01 V. This is a very unsymmetrical curve. Only when $n_1 = n_2$ does the equivalence point occur at the inflection of the titration curve. The sketch in Fig. 13–2 also shows the rapid initial rise mentioned before (e.g., at 0.01% reaction, log(ratio) = 4, $\mathcal{E}_{Fe} = 0.46$ V).

The expected reversible behavior seems to occur for this electrode reaction until well past the equivalence point, in spite of the fact that such couples as $Cr_2O_7^{=}$-Cr(III) and MnO_4^{-}-Mn(II) are not, in general, reversible. Here, the presence of the reversible couple, Fe(III)-Fe(II), seems to establish equilibrium. This problem is discussed in detail for some important titrations in Chapter 17 of the book by Laitinen.

Indicators

Visible endpoint indication can be achieved in several ways:

1) The materials reacting give distinct color changes. Among common reagents having sufficiently intense color in one oxidation state to serve as indicators at some concentrations are:

MnO_4^- (deep purple) $\rightarrow$ Mn^{++} (colorless below 0.1 *M*),
I_3^- (brown) $\rightarrow$ I^- (colorless),
Ce(IV) (yellow-orange) $\rightarrow$ Ce(III) (colorless).

2) An added substance may react visibly with one of the reactants or products. The most common example is the deep blue starch-iodine complex. Another is the thiocyanate ion, which signals the appearance or disappearance of Fe(III).

3) An indicator can itself be oxidized or reduced at the endpoint of titration to produce a visible color change. The Nernst equation for the indicator reaction may be written

$$\mathrm{In_{ox}} + ne^- \rightleftharpoons \mathrm{In_{red}}, \qquad \mathcal{E} = \mathcal{E}^{0\prime}_{\mathrm{In}} - \frac{0.059}{n}\log\frac{[\mathrm{In_{red}}]}{[\mathrm{In_{ox}}]},$$

where $\mathcal{E}^{0\prime}_{\mathrm{In}}$ is the formal potential of the indicator. If its observed change is assumed to occur over a range of ratios $\mathrm{In_{red}}/\mathrm{In_{ox}}$ from $\frac{10}{1}$ to $\frac{1}{10}$, the $\mathcal{E}$ range must be $\mathcal{E}^{0\prime}_{\mathrm{In}} \pm 0.059/n$ V. The widest range (for $n = 1$) could lie within the steep portion of the slopes of the titration curves plotted in this chapter, if $\mathcal{E}^{0\prime}_{\mathrm{In}}$ is at the center of this region. In the case of the Fe(II)-$Cr_2O_7^{=}$ titration, it will be important to use an indicator of $\mathcal{E}^{0\prime}$ near 0.9 V (see Fig. 13–2). Diphenylamine was an early indicator used for this titration. It is oxidized in several steps to a violet product and has $\mathcal{E}^{0\prime}$ 0.76 V. The curves on p. 144 show that H_3PO_4 would have to be present to make this indicator useful. The color change would occur several percent too soon without phosphate complexing of Fe(III).

Diphenylaminesulfonate ion, $\mathcal{E}^{0\prime} = 0.85$ V, is a better indicator for this titration. Phosphoric acid is usually added to increase the sharpness of the end-point. The oxidation of these indicators seems to require the presence of the Fe(II)-$Cr_2O_7^{=}$ reaction to produce its rapid change. Addition of indicator to excess dichromate alone gives a different, slow, irreversible change. Therefore if an indicator blank is wanted, it must be determined with known solutions of Fe(II) and dichromate.

Indicators of higher $\mathcal{E}^{0\prime}$ may be required for titrations with Ce(IV). For example, the equivalence point of the Fe(II)-Ce(IV) titration in sulfuric acid solution occurs at 1.06 V. *Ortho*phenanthroline (1,10-phenanthroline) and some of its derivatives have been found suitable. It forms an intensely red tris complex with Fe(II), called ferroin. This changes sharply and reversibly at the equivalence point to a pale blue oxidized form. Its effective $\mathcal{E}^{0\prime}$ is about 1.1 V.

SUMMARY

The Nernst equation is applied to the calculation of redox titration curves. The important effects of complexing and pH are pointed out. The action of indicators is described.

SUGGESTIONS FOR FURTHER READING

LAITINEN, H. A., *Chemical Analysis*, New York: McGraw-Hill, 1960. Chapter 15 discusses electrode potentials, Chapter 17, titration curves.

PROBLEMS

1. Find the equilibrium constant for the reaction
   a) $I_2 + HAsO_2 + 2H_2O \rightarrow 2I^- + H_3AsO_4 + 2H^+$.
   b) If equal volumes of 0.10 M I_2 and $HAsO_2$ are mixed, what is $[HAsO_2]$ and the percent yield at equilibrium for (H^+) of 1.0 activity and of 10^{-5}? What is the pH usually recommended for the titration? [*Hint:* Use numerical approximation methods if you encounter a cubic equation.]
2. Calculate $\mathcal{E}$ values at 0.1, 1, 50, 90, 99, 99.9, 100 (equivalence point), 101, 110% of equivalence for the symmetrical titration, 0.1 M Fe^{++} by 0.1 M Ce(IV) in H_2SO_4 solution. Sketch the titration curve.
3. Sketch the titration curve, as in the previous problem, for 0.1 N As(III) by 0.1 N I_2 buffered at pH 8.
4. In bromate titrations, where Br_2 is an intermediate, Hg^{++} can be added to complex Br^- and increase the Br_2-Br^- oxidation potential. If a certain Hg^{++} addition increases $\mathcal{E}$ by 0.504 V, by what factor has the $[Br^-]$ been reduced?

CHAPTER 14

OXIDATION-REDUCTION CHEMISTRY OF SELECTED ELEMENTS

This chapter treats the chemistry of several elements most frequently used in quantitative oxidation-reduction titrations including Fe, Cr, Mn, Ce, U, the halogens, As, and Sb.

14.1 IRON

The abundance of iron and the stability and solubility of its complexes in two oxidation states make it the most important transition metal in geochemical, biochemical, and industrial reactions. Some $\mathcal{E}^0$ values for aquo ions are:

$$\mathrm{Fe(III)} \xrightarrow{0.77\ \mathrm{V}} \mathrm{Fe(II)} \xrightarrow{-0.44\ \mathrm{V}} \mathrm{Fe}^0.$$
$$\underbrace{\hspace{6cm}}_{-0.04\ \mathrm{V}}$$

The Fe(III) to (0) value cannot be measured because Fe(II) forms. It is calculated from the other two values as explained in Chapter 12:

$$\frac{0.77 + 2(-0.44)}{3} = -0.04\ \mathrm{V}.$$

Remember that complexing can alter and even reverse the sign of $\mathcal{E}$.

Since $\mathcal{E}^0$ for the Fe(III)-Fe(II) couple is 0.77 V, titration of Fe(II) requires an oxidizing agent of $\mathcal{E}^0$ above 1.0 V for quantitative results. Dichromate, permanganate, and cerium(IV) are commonly used for Fe(II) titration in acid solutions. Each is discussed later. The equilibrium constants and colors of some important species are listed in Table 14–1. Compounds of iron in higher oxidation states are known.

Historically, Fe(III) has been determined by quantitative reduction to Fe(II) followed by titration with a standard oxidizing solution. The problem is to get rid of the excess reducing agent before titration. The Fe(II) is oxidized by O_2 in the air, but slowly enough so that immediate titration gives good results.

Reduction Titrations

Clearly, it would be simpler to titrate Fe(III) with a reducing reagent. Unfortunately, few suitable ones have been found. Most solutions that are strongly reducing react rapidly with O_2 in air changing their normality. One fairly stable reductant is ascorbic acid, $C_6H_8O_6$, an enediol acid, easily oxidized to dehydroascorbic acid by Fe(III). Thiocyanate or other Fe(III) indicators can be used for

Table 14–1

Formula	K value	Color
Fe(III)		
$Fe(H_2O)_6{}^{3+}$	$K_{a1} = 10^{-2}$	Pale violet (seen only in very acid solutions and crystals)
$Fe(H_2O)_5OH^{++}$		Yellow: the form usually seen in dilute solutions
$Fe(H_2O)_5Cl^{++}$	$K_{f1} = 30$	Yellow-brown
$Fe(H_2O)_5SCN^{++}$	$K_{f1} = 10^2$	Deep red
$Fe(H_2O)_5F^{++}$	$K_{f1} = 10^5$	Colorless
$Fe(CN)_6{}^{3-}$	$\beta_6 = 10^{31}$	Red solid which becomes yellow in solution
FeY^- (EDTA complex)	$K_f = 10^{25}$	Yellow
Fe(II)		
$Fe(H_2O)_6{}^{++}$	$K_{a1} = 10^{-8}$	Pale green
$Fe(CN)_6{}^{4-}$	$\beta_6 = 10^{24}$	Yellow
$FeY^=$	$K_f = 10^{14}$	Green

the endpoint detection. The reagent solution should probably be standardized each day because of air oxidation.

More satisfactory are mercury(I) solutions, as the perchlorate or nitrate, which are stable in air. The reduction, aided by SCN^- complexing of Hg(II), was discussed in detail in Chapter 12, and methods of using it are given in the laboratory section.

Oxidation Titrations

Quantitative reduction of all Fe(III) to Fe(II) can be achieved by methods using (a) free metals and (b) $SnCl_2$ in hot HCl solution.

a) The solution to be titrated is slowly passed through a column of amalgamated zinc, a "Jones reductor." The reaction is

$$2Fe^{3+} + \underline{Zn^0} \rightarrow 2Fe^{++} + Zn^{++}.$$

It is then quickly titrated with a standard oxidizing solution. The Zn ion does not interfere. Other ions present such as Ti(IV), V(V), Cr(III), etc., are also reduced and titrated by this method.

A milder reductant is Ag. It will not reduce Cr(III) or Ti(IV) nor does it add new cations to the solution in the presence of the HCl needed to make $\mathcal{E}^0$ favorable by forming AgCl by the reaction

$$\underline{Ag^0} + Fe(III) + Cl^- \rightarrow Fe(II) + \underline{AgCl}.$$

Lead metal can be used ($\mathcal{E}^0 = -0.1$ V) and has advantages for U(VI) reduction.

b) Homogeneous reduction with $SnCl_2$ is rapid only in hot 6 *N* HCl solutions. Only a very small excess can be properly removed in the next step with cold $HgCl_2$:

$$2Cl^- + SnCl_2 + 2HgCl_2 \rightarrow SnCl_6^{=} + \underline{Hg_2Cl_2}.$$

Neither mercury compound reacts with the Fe(II) nor the oxidizing agent in titration. However, larger excesses of $SnCl_2$ will make some free mercury in this step, which then interferes.

For titration of the Fe(II), $KMnO_4$ is used in the venerable Zimmermann-Reinhardt method. It works well only if Mn(II) and H_3PO_4 are added to inhibit the reaction of Cl^- with MnO_4^- to form Cl_2. The Cl^- reaction with $K_2Cr_2O_7$ and Ce(IV) solutions is not fast enough to interfere at moderate acidity. The color of MnO_4^- is sufficiently deep to act as its own indicator in 0.1 *N* solution titrations. For the others, a diphenylamine sulfonate or *ortho*phenanthroline-Fe(II) complex (ferroin) act as indicators. The titration curve of Fe(II) by $K_2Cr_2O_7$ is discussed in detail in the second example of Chapter 13.

Standards

Pure *iron* is available for redox titration with reactivity stated as percentage Fe. Carbon is the major impurity present in iron.

Fe(II). Most Fe(II) compounds are relatively unstable in air. "Mohr's salt," $Fe(NH_4)_2(SO_4)_2 \cdot 6H_2O$ (formula weight, 392.16), when fresh and green usually has purity above 99.5%, but the purity is not reliable without a check. "Oesper's salt," $Fe(en)(SO_4)_2 \cdot 4H_2O$ (en = ethylenediammonium) (formula weight, 382.1), of stated purity (usually 99.9%) is more stable than Mohr's salt.

Fe(III). The recently suggested compound,* tetramethylammonium tetrachloroferrate(III) $(CH_3)_4NFeCl_4$ (formula weight, 271.8), seems reliable as 99.9% pure when properly prepared. It is easily made from tetramethylammonium chloride and $FeCl_3$, and recrystallized several times from methanol. It is useful for known solutions, for standardization of Hg(I) solutions, as well as for the other methods.

Ferric alum and other Fe(III) solids suffer from isomorphous impurities and are not reliable to better than about 99%.

14.2 CHROMIUM

Chromium, in oxidation states II, III, and VI, is of analytical importance. Some $\mathcal{E}^0$ values for aquo ions are:

$$\mathrm{Cr(VI)} \xrightarrow[-0.13\ \mathrm{V(basic)}]{+1.33\ \mathrm{V\ (acid)}} \mathrm{Cr(III)} \xrightarrow{-0.41\ \mathrm{V}} \mathrm{Cr(II)} \xrightarrow{-0.91\ \mathrm{V}} \mathrm{Cr}^0.$$
$$\mathrm{Cr(III)} \xrightarrow{-0.74\ \mathrm{V}} \mathrm{Cr}^0$$

Chromium(VI) is a strong oxidant in acid solution ($Cr_2O_7^{=}$) and quite weak in

* L. J. Sacks, *Anal. Chem.* **35,** 1299 (1963).

basic solution ($CrO_4^=$). Two acid-base equilibria control the distribution of species:

$$2CrO_4^= + 2H^+ \rightleftharpoons Cr_2O_7^= + H_2O, \qquad K = 4 \times 10^{14},$$
$$Cr_2O_7^= + H_2O \rightleftharpoons 2HCrO_4^-, \qquad K = 3 \times 10^{-2}.$$

The first is more important in very acidic or basic solutions. The red solid $K_2Cr_2O_7$ is available in high purity, is easily dried, and absorbs little moisture from air. Its water solutions are stable indefinitely. One patient chemist reported no change in a 0.1 *N* solution in 24 years. Its major use is in the titration of Fe(II) and thus, indirectly, of many reducing agents that produce equivalent amounts of Fe(II) when excess Fe(III) is added to them. The Fe(II) is more stable in air than many of the other reducing agents, thus permitting more accurate titration.

Determination of chromium is usually performed through oxidation to Cr(VI) followed by Fe(II) titration. The most complete oxidation, in the author's experience, is achieved with peroxydisulfate with Ag(I) catalyst. Boiling decomposes the excess $S_2O_8^=$. Oxidations by Na_2O_2 or $HClO_4$ seem hard to push above 99% completion.

As an indirect determination of these elements, Pb and Ba ions can be precipitated from nearly neutral $CrO_4^=$ solutions, and the solid $BaCrO_4$ or $PbCrO_4$ washed and dissolved in acid for Fe(II) titration.

Blue Cr(II) solutions result from the reaction of zinc with one of the higher oxidation states of chromium. They react so well with O_2 that they have been used to remove O_2 from other gases. It is the strongest reducing titrant easily available, but, of course, it must be stored and manipulated without contacting air. With its $\mathcal{E}^0$ of -0.4 V, it can reduce many transition metal ions to their lowest available oxidation states. It reduces nitrate to NH_4^+ and organic nitro and nitroso compounds to amines. Back titration of excess Cr(II) with Fe(III) solution permits determinations of these.

Cr(III) is of interest as a product of the previous reactions. The hexaquo ion is violet while the chloro, sulfato, etc., complexes are mostly green. The mutual interconversions are slow for these inert complexes. The colors can interfere with endpoint visibility at high concentrations. However, little trouble is experienced with 0.1 *N* solutions used to titrate large volumes of reductant. (0.1 *N* $K_2Cr_2O_7$ is 0.0167 *M*, or only 4.9 g/liter).

14.3 MANGANESE

Manganese presents a formidable array of oxidation states that are attainable in solution reactions. There is evidence for the existence of all the positive states from one to seven. Well known are:

Mn(II) pale pink aquo ion,
Mn(III) red complexes with F^-, Cl^-, $C_2O_4^=$, $SO_4^=$, CN^-,
Mn(IV) MnO_2 black solid,
Mn(VI) green $MnO_4^=$, in high (OH^-),
Mn(VII) purple MnO_4^-.

Some $\mathcal{E}^0$ values in acid solution for aquo ions are:

$$MnO_4^- \xrightarrow{+0.56\text{ V}} MnO_4^{=} \xrightarrow{+2.26\text{ V}} MnO_2 \xrightarrow{+0.95\text{ V}} Mn(III) \xrightarrow{+1.51\text{ V}} Mn(II) \xrightarrow{-1.18\text{ V}} Mn^0.$$

$$MnO_4^- \xrightarrow{+1.51\text{ V}} Mn(II)$$

This shows that all states above (II) are good oxidizing agents and that the favored product is always Mn(II) for reduction in acid solutions.

The early availability of $KMnO_4$ made from pyrolusite, an MnO_2 ore, provided chemists with a powerful oxidant solution of some stability, which acts as its own indicator giving a nearly colorless product in acid. It is not very soluble (0.4 *M* at 20°C) so that it can be crystallized easily if KOH is used in the production steps:

$$\underline{2MnO_2} + 4KOH + O_2 \xrightarrow{\Delta} 2K_2MnO_4 + 2H_2O,$$

$$3MnO_4^{=} + 2H_2O \rightarrow 2MnO_4^- + \underline{MnO_2} + 4OH^-.$$

The high oxidation potential of MnO_4^- is a clue to its major drawback. It reacts with any trace of organic matter (dust, grease) to give MnO_2 in neutral solutions. This, as well as light, catalyze the decomposition according to the equation,

$$4MnO_4^- + 2H_2O \rightarrow \underline{4MnO_2} + 3O_2 + 4OH^-.$$

Only very clean solutions keep well. Boiling and filtration through fritted glass can produce stable solutions. However, no special precautions are required if a solution is made and used the same day. Since solid $KMnO_4$ usually contains some MnO_2, it is not a primary standard. Its solutions can be standardized against As_2O_3, $Na_2C_2O_4$, or known Fe(II) solutions. The mechanisms of permanganate reactions have been extensively investigated.* In view of the many oxidation states, their complexity is not surprising. Proper control of conditions is required for quantitative results. Among reducing agents that can be titrated directly by permanganate are: As(III), Sb(III), Sn(II), Fe(II), Mn(II), U(IV), Cr(III), H_2O_2, and $C_2O_4^{=}$. Many other determinations are possible via indirect back-titration methods.

The Mn(II) titration is an interesting illustration of the effect of pH on extent of reaction. In the Volhard Mn method, quantitative conversion to MnO_2 occurs in nearly neutral solution with excess ZnO present to react with the acid formed:

$$3Mn^{++} + 2MnO_4^- + 2H_2O \rightarrow \underline{5MnO_2} + 4H^+.$$

14.4 CERIUM

By contrast, this fairly abundant rare earth has only two oxidation states in solution: Ce(III) is colorless and Ce(IV) is orange. The $\mathcal{E}^0$ for oxidation by Ce(IV) is about 1.7 V. This is enough to oxidize water, but complexing by $SO_4^{=}$ in the very acid solutions required to hold Ce(IV) lowers $\mathcal{E}$ to about 1.4 V. The H_2SO_4 solutions are quite stable. Since it is not affected by Cl^- and gives very sharp

* See H. A. Laitinen, *Chemical Analysis*, New York: McGraw-Hill, 1960, Chapter 19.

endpoints in titration, Ce(IV) has some advantages over $Cr_2O_7^{=}$ and MnO_4^- solutions. The reducing agents listed above for MnO_4^- titration can also be determined with Ce(IV); As_2O_3 is used for standardization, but a catalyst of Os(VIII) or ICl is required. For a primary standard, $(NH_4)_2Ce(NO_3)_6$ is used. Ce(IV) compounds are rather expensive, and the solutions must be carefully prepared starting in concentrated H_2SO_4 if they are not to develop precipitates.

High acidity is needed to hold Ce(IV) in solution. Hydroxy complexes, as well as OH^- and $O^=$ bridged polymeric ions are present even in acid media. This is a more complex example of the same phenomenon found in less acidic solutions of Cr(III), Fe(III), and Al(III).

The quantitative oxidation of many organic compounds such as glycols and sugars affords a method for their determination via back titration of Ce(IV) after oxidation with a measured excess.

14.5 URANIUM

From the actinide group, let us consider uranium which is of interest because of its use in nuclear reactors. Its major ores are pitchblende (contains UO_2) and carnotite, a complex UO_2^{++} compound. In 1 *M* HCl, some $\mathcal{E}$ values are:

$$UO_2^{++} \xrightarrow{+0.05\ V} UO_2^{+} \xrightarrow{+0.62\ V} U^{4+} \xrightarrow{-0.61\ V} U^{3+} \xrightarrow{-1.8\ V} U$$

$$UO_2^{++} \xrightarrow{+0.334\ V} U^{4+}$$

We see that U(IV) and U(VI) are the more stable states and, like the rare earths, uranium is a very reactive metal. It is usually determined by titration with a strong oxidant from U(IV), green, to U(VI), yellow. But the quantitative reduction to U(IV) is more complicated than reduction of Fe(III). Since the $\mathcal{E}^0$ for Zn is 0.76 V, it will reduce U(VI) to a mixture of (III) and (IV) oxidation states. The U(III) is red-brown. Bubbling air will take the U(III) to U(IV) in a few minutes without appreciably oxidizing U(IV). A milder reducing agent like Pb gives quantitative reduction to U(IV) in 3 *M* HCl. Details of procedure and interferences have been carefully studied by C. W. Sill and H. E. Peterson.* Directions for the determination are included in the laboratory section.

Uranium chemistry has been intensively investigated.† The strong bonding to $O^=$ and OH^- mentioned above for Ce ions is found with U(IV) and U(VI), which form polymeric species. Both oxidation states complex well with Cl^-, $SO_4^=$, SCN^-, etc. The metal and its oxides dissolve readily in HNO_3. The remarkably high solubility of $UO_2(NO_3)_2{\cdot}6H_2O$ in alcohols, ketones, and ethers has led to extraction-separation methods.

---

* *Anal. Chem.* **24,** 1175 (1952).

† See G. Booman and J. Rein, "Uranium" in *Treatise on Analytical Chemistry*, ed. by I. M. Kolthoff and P. J. Elving, Part II, Vol. 9. New York: Interscience, 1962, pp. 5–164.

14.6 HALOGEN COMPOUNDS

Some analytically useful halogen compounds are I_2, KI, KIO_3, $KH(IO_3)_2$, and $KBrO_3$. All are available as highly pure solids suitable for use as primary standards, although I_2 is not often so used because of its volatility.

Iodine solutions are valuable as mild oxidants, $\mathcal{E}^0 = 0.54$ V, because a very sharp indicator is available in starch solutions. Direct titration with I_2 (i.e., I_3^-) solutions is limited to reaction with $S_2O_3^=$, $SO_3^=$, As(III), Sb(III), and Sn(II). But many oxidizing agents react with KI to form an equivalent amount of I_2, which can be titrated with a standard reducing solution, usually $Na_2S_2O_3$. This is done because few of these oxidizing agents react directly with thiosulfate quantitatively. This indirect method is widely applicable to determination of the oxidizing power of solutions of Cl_2, Br_2, Cu^{++}, $CrO_4^=$, BrO_3^-, and many more. The Cu reaction is valuable and interesting because highly insoluble CuI makes the reaction favorable and quantitative:

$$2Cu^{++} + 4I^- \rightarrow 2\underline{CuI} + I_2.$$

Iodine solutions are prepared with excess KI to increase its solubility and decrease its volatility:

$$I_2 + I^- \rightleftharpoons I_3^-, \qquad K = \bar{8}00.$$

This affects the $\mathcal{E}$ only slightly. For 0.1 N I_2 solution, approximately 0.2 M KI is sufficient. (Iodine materials are expensive.) Clean neutral solutions of I_3^- are relatively stable if kept in all-glass bottles in a cool dark place. (Do not use plastic.)

An excellent primary standard for determining the normality of iodine solutions is As_2O_3. Its reaction

$$I_2 + HAsO_2 + 2H_2O \rightarrow 2I^- + H_3AsO_4 + 2H^+$$

requires a pH of 5 to 9 for quantitative results. Buffering with $NaHCO_3$ is commonly used to keep the pH about 8 while I_2 is added to the As(III) solution. The reverse titration can be used for neutral I_2 solutions, but it is difficult to manage for the more common situation of I_2 production in a strongly acid mixture. Here, adding $NaHCO_3$ removes much I_2 vapor with the CO_2 formed. For this reason, thiosulfate is the preferred reagent for I_2, since it requires a pH of 1 to 7.

Solutions are prepared from "hypo" crystals, $Na_2S_2O_3{\cdot}5H_2O$. For high accuracy, they must be standardized with known I_2 or a primary-standard oxidant through its $I^- \rightarrow I_2$ reaction. The titration reaction is

$$2S_2O_3^= + I_2 \rightarrow S_4O_6^= + 2I^-.$$

Unfortunately, it is decomposed, depositing sulfur by heat, light, acid, and bacteria. Sterile thiosulfate solutions with a trace of base added are stable for a week or two.

The reaction with strong acid is slow enough so that acid I_2 solutions can be titrated with thiosulfate, but the reverse is not true. In basic solution, oxidation to sulfate occurs

$$S_2O_3^{=} + 4I_2 + 10OH^- \rightarrow 2SO_4^{=} + 8I^- + 5H_2O.$$

Oxidizing agents other than I_2 give a mixture of products so that I_2 is the only satisfactory titrant for $S_2O_3^{=}$.

Starches, which contain a variety of chain lengths of hexose polymers, exhibit an unknown color reaction with I_2 which is extremely sensitive. An amylose starch fraction is sold as "soluble starch," but varies widely in behavior from sample to sample. It must be dissolved in hot water and should give a sky-blue color with a trace of I_2. Red-purple color materials are less sensitive. This superb indicator, however, does not function in hot, strongly acidic, or alcohol solutions.

Acetic acid is usually used for the thiosulfate-I_2 titration for the reasons given above and because strongly acidic I_2 is more rapidly oxidized by air.

The iodates, KIO_3 and $KH(IO_3)_2$, are good primary-standard solids which make stable solutions. They are easily made from the reaction of I_2 with warm base

$$3I_2 + 6OH^- \rightarrow IO_3^- + 5I^- + 3H_2O.$$

Adding excess KI to the standard solutions of iodate makes I_2 quantitatively at pH less than 4, the reverse of the above basic reaction. Direct titration of SCN^- is possible in HCl solutions by the reaction,

$$2SCN^- + 3IO_3^- + 4H^+ + 3Cl^- \rightarrow 2SO_4^{=} + 2HCN + 3ICl + H_2O.$$

This can be extended to a mercury method via the precipitate $ZnHg(SCN)_4$. (Note that 0.1 M IO_3^- would be 0.4 N for the above titration and 0.6 N for I_2 production. Here is a case where it is best to stay with molarity.)

Another good primary standard, $KBrO_3$, produces I_2 in strongly acid solution with KI, but also has direct uses. It reacts with As(III) and Sb(III) in acid solutions and is used for quantitative brominations. Phenols, aniline, etc., can be determined by:

$$BrO_3^- + 5Br^- + 6H^+ \rightarrow 3Br_2 + 3H_2O,$$
$$C_6H_5OH + 3Br_2 \rightarrow C_6H_2Br_3OH + 3H^+ + 3Br^-.$$

Bromination will serve to determine metals which precipitate with 8-hydroxyquinoline ("oxine"). Each oxine reacts with $2Br_2$. Excess BrO_3^- can be used and the excess determined by adding KI and back titrating the I_2 with thiosulfate.*

* For the details of the many applications of the halogen oxidation-reduction systems to determinations of both inorganic and organic materials, consult I. M. Kolthoff *et al.*, *Volumetric Analysis*, Vol. III. New York: Interscience Publishers, 1957.

14.7 ARSENIC AND ANTIMONY

The solution chemistry of these elements is governed by the very high acidity (small size) of the hypothetical +3 and +5 ions. In acids, the (III) states form such species as $AsCl_4^-$, $HAsO_2$, H_3AsO_3, $SbCl_4^-$, $SbOCl_2^-$, etc. There is no evidence for the occurrence of the As^{3+} aquo cation. Sb(III) may form some aquo ion in strongly acid solution. In basic solution, AsO_2^- and $Sb(OH)_4^-$ may exist. In the (V) state, H_3AsO_4 (acid) and $H_2AsO_4^-$, etc., (basic) are known. With Sb, in HCl, $SbCl_6^-$ forms, and in NaOH, $Sb(OH)_6^-$ forms.

Titration by I_2, $KMnO_4$, and $KBrO_3$ have been mentioned. The potential

$$H_3AsO_4 + 2H^+ + 2e^- \rightleftharpoons HAsO_2 + 2H_2O, \qquad \mathcal{E}^0 = +0.56 \text{ V}.$$

A powerful oxidant would not be necessary for As(III) if H^+ were removed by base as is certainly required for I_2 ($\mathcal{E}^0 = 0.54$ V) titration. Our main reason for interest in arsenic stems from the availability of As_2O_3 as a dry solid of high purity making an excellent primary standard for I_2 and $KMnO_4$ solutions.

In acid solution, As(V) is a sufficiently strong oxidant to reverse the usual reaction and produce I_2 from I^-. Arsenates can be determined from this reaction.

The antimony potential is about the same,

$$Sb_2O_5 + 6H^+ + 4e^- \rightleftharpoons 2SbO^+ + 3H_2O, \qquad \mathcal{E}^0 = +0.6 \text{ V}.$$

For I_2 titration of Sb(III) then, basic conditions will again be required. Tartrate complexing is used to hold Sb in solution as $(SbO)C_4H_4O_6^-$ and $(SbO_2)C_4H_4O_6^-$. This is not necessary in acid solutions where $KMnO_4$ or $KBrO_3$ are used for titration of Sb(III).

Small amounts of arsenic (or antimony) can be determined (as in forensic laboratories) via the volatile hydride, in acid,

$$H_3AsO_3 + 3Zn + 6H^+ \rightarrow AsH_3 + 3Zn^{++} + 3H_2O,$$

or in base (for As only),

$$H_2AsO_3^- + 2Al + 4H_2O + OH^- \rightarrow AsH_3 + 2Al(OH)_4^-.$$

SUGGESTIONS FOR FURTHER READING

LINGANE, J. L., *Analytical Chemistry of Selected Metallic Elements*, New York: Reinhold, 1966. This paperback gives brief outlines of the chemistry of important metals.

ZIELEN, A. J., *Anal. Chem.* **40,** 139 (1968), presents a critical study of the conditions needed for precision (5 to 6 figures) uses of the Ce(IV)-As(III) and the Cr_2O_7-Fe(II) titrations. The reader may enjoy the careful description of experimental procedure including the use of plastic bottles as weight burets.

PROBLEMS

1. Excess KI was added to 50.00 ml of 0.06633 *N* $K_2Cr_2O_7$ with HCl present. The I_2 formed required 39.47 ml $Na_2S_2O_3$ solution to reduce it to I^-. Find the normality of the thiosulfate.
2. In Problem 1 find the molarity of the $K_2Cr_2O_7$, the I_2 formed in 50 ml, and the $Na_2S_2O_3$.
3. A high-purity sample of magnetite, Fe_3O_4 (formula weight, 231.5), weighing 500.0 mg is to be titrated with Hg(I). Find the approximate volume of 0.1 *M* Hg(I) required if the sample is dissolved (a) in HCl under CO_2 and (b) in HCl with a slight excess of HNO_3.
4. Samples weighing 1.000 g of a pitchblende from Great Bear Lake were treated with HNO_3 and HCl to dissolve U and Fe. Sample (a) was made 7 *M* in HCl and shaken with ether to remove Fe(III). Sample (b) was not separated. Both were reduced by lead metal. Sample (a) required 4.81 ml and sample (b), 38.22 ml of 0.01000 *N* $K_2Cr_2O_7$ for oxidation. Find the percentages Fe and U.
5. A 1.000 g sample of limestone is dissolved in HCl. Tartrate is added to complex iron and aluminum, and NH_3 is added to make the pH 10. Then 8-hydroxyquinoline precipitates only $Mg(C_9H_6ON)_2$, which is filtered, washed, and dissolved in 2 *M* HCl. Excess KBr and 30.00 ml of 0.1000 *M* $KBrO_3$ are added. Excess KI forms I_2 from the unused Br_2 and requires 36.60 ml of 0.1000 *N* $Na_2S_2O_3$ to reach the starch endpoint. Find the percentage of magnesium in the limestone.
6. Devise a titration method for an investigation of the solubility of $Co(IO_3)_2$. (See Problem 7, Chapter 10 for data.) What concentration of what titrant should be used? What volume of the saturated $Co(IO_3)_2$ solutions should be used to obtain 3 to 4 significant figures in the results? Use the pure water solubility for your illustration. You might wish to try this in the laboratory. How was the published data obtained? (See the Linke-Seidell tables cited in the General References.)

CHAPTER 15

GAS BEHAVIOR AND MEASUREMENTS

Understanding the behavior of gases, liquids, and solutions will clarify many common laboratory operations. By understanding concepts introduced in fractional-distillation theory, we may come to understand several important methods, such as extractions, ion exchange, and chromatography, which also depend on multiple stages of successive equilibria.

Boyle's Law (1662) was formulated as a result of his experiments on the volume of air in the sealed side of a U-tube manometer containing Hg. He was able to change the pressure in the large vessel enclosing it with the newly invented air pump (1650). He found that the product PV, pressure times volume, was nearly constant at "room temperature." Accurate thermometers were not yet invented.

After the development of reliable sealed Hg thermometers, Charles (1787) was able to discover that several gases expanded the same amount for a given temperature rise at constant pressure. Gay-Lussac (1802) formulated the data in the straight-line relation

$$V_t = V_0 + \alpha V_0 t, \tag{15–1}$$

where V_t is the volume at Celsius temperature, t°C, and V_0 is the gas volume at 0°C, and α, the fractional volume expansion per degree at 0°C (the slope of V versus t). Alternative expressions for α are:

$$\alpha = \frac{(V_t - V_0)}{V_0 t} = \frac{1}{V_0}\left(\frac{dV}{dt}\right)_P. \tag{15–2}$$

A modern experimental value for He at 1 atm is $\alpha = 3.6591 \times 10^{-3}\ \text{deg}^{-1}$. We can use this in Eq. (15–1) to find the value of t at which V_t becomes zero:

$$V_t = 0 = V_0 + (3.6591 \times 10^{-3})\, V_0 t,$$

which gives $t = -273.29$°C. From data obtained at lower pressures, the best value of this "absolute zero" seems to lie between -273.1 and -273.2°C. Since the absolute zero cannot be reached, the ice point has been *defined* as 273.15°K. On this scale, the triple point, solid-liquid-gas in equilibrium with no air present, is 273.16°K for H_2O. Thus temperatures cannot be correctly expressed with precision beyond 0.01°K, but temperature differences can be more precisely known.

Graphical methods are so useful here that we mention again several ideas that may already have been used by the student. Using Boyle's Law, $PV = k$, as an

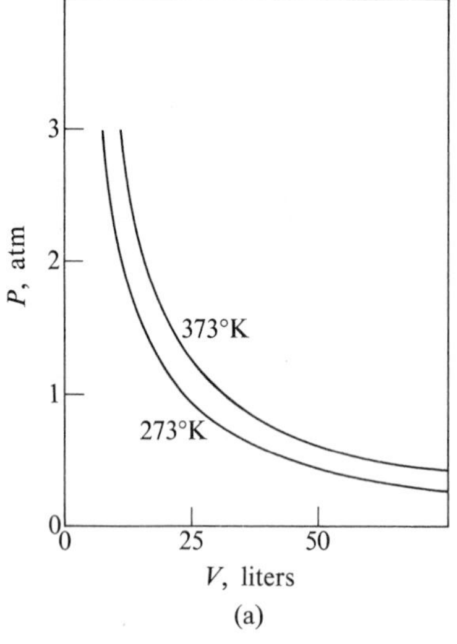

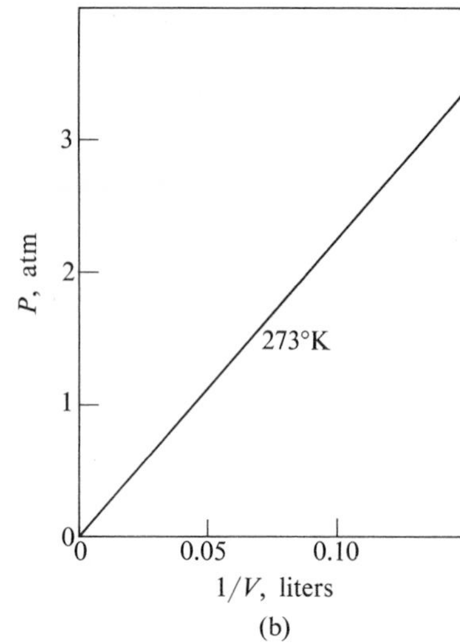

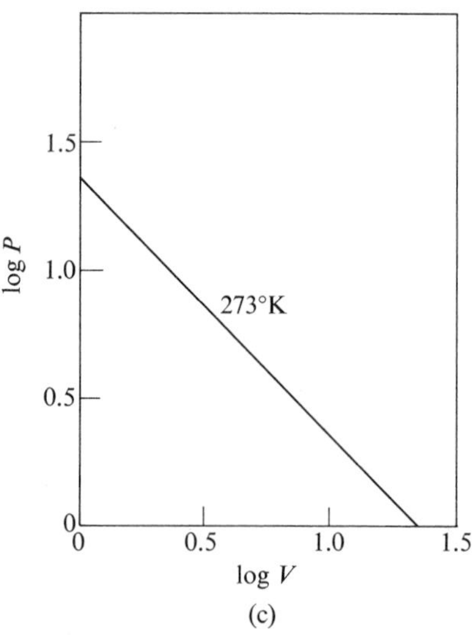

Fig. 15–1. Three plots of Boyle's Law: (a) the hyperbolic relation $PV = k$, (b) in straight-line form, $P = k(1/V) + 0$. The plot of P vs. $1/V$ has slope 22.4 and intercept 0. (c) From (a), $\log P = -\log V + \log k$; therefore the plot has slope -1 and intercept $\log k$.

example, one is tempted to say that this can be represented by a hyperbola. However, a straight line results from a plot of P versus $1/V$ or from $\log P$ versus $\log V$. You may have noted that scientists are devoted to straight-line plots. There is good reason for this. The slope and intercept are easily evaluated and are often desired constants in the equations. Three ways of displaying Boyle's Law data are shown in Fig. 15–1. Drawing the best straight line through a number of experimental points plotted as shown in (b) or (c) permits one to find the average k more easily than is possible from (a). Furthermore, use of graph (c) allows precise plotting of a wide range of data, say, 0.01 to 100 atm P, where the $\log P$ goes from -2 to $+2$.

Boyle's and Charles' Laws can be combined by imagining two sequential volume changes on a gas: one using Boyle's Law, constant T, and the second using Charles' Law, constant P. Only two variables can be independently chosen:

1) constant T_1, $P_1V_1 = P_2V'$,
2) constant P_2, $V'/T_1 = V_2/T_2$,

where V' is an intermediate volume which can now be eliminated between the two equations to give the ideal gas law:

$$P_1V_1/T_1 = P_2V_2/T_2 = c.$$

The constant for one mole is called the *molar gas constant*, R:

$$PV = RT, \quad \text{for one mole} \quad \text{or} \quad PV = nRT, \quad \text{for } n \text{ moles.} \tag{15–3}$$

Inserting the known experimental values for the best approximation to an ideal gas into Eq. (15–3) gives a value for the constant, R:

$$\begin{aligned} R = PV/nT &= (1 \text{ atm})(22.413 \text{ liters})/(1 \text{ mole})(273.15°\text{K}) \\ &= 0.082054 \text{ liter-atm/mole-deg.} \end{aligned}$$

The liter-atmosphere has dimensions of energy (work). Other energy units, which are convenient for certain calculations, can be used to express R:

1.9872 cal/mole-deg,
8.3143 joules/mole-deg,
8.3143×10^7 ergs/mole-deg.

15.1 KINETIC-MOLECULAR THEORY OF GASES

The fact that gases should follow so simple a law as $PV = nRT$ has long fascinated scientists. It seems too good to be true that three (or four, including mass in n) variables can be related in so uncomplicated a function. But it is true for all gases—at the limit of sufficiently low pressure and sufficiently high temperature. The rub is in the phrases, "sufficiently low pressure" and "sufficiently high temperature." We shall consider behavior of real gases in the next section.

A simple physical model, a theory, can account for the ideal gas law. The assumptions of this model, *the Kinetic-Molecular Theory of Gases* (KMT), are:

1) Gases are a collection of point particles.
2) The particles have no volume or the distances between the particles are immeasurably large compared to their size.
3) The particles have no attractive forces between them.
4) Their collisions are perfectly elastic. Total kinetic energy is unchanged by collisions.

5) Gas pressure is the result of the impacts of the particles on all the surfaces exposed to the gas.
6) The temperature of a gas is proportional to the kinetic energy of the gas particles: $T \propto E = \frac{1}{2}mu^2$, where m is mass and u is velocity.

Using this plausible mechanical model for a gas, we can derive an equation relating P, V, and T as follows: Since P is force per unit area, let us find the force exerted through collisions of the particles on a unit area of wall. Assume a cubic container for the gas sample. Let it have edge a cm. Let it contain n particles and let the particle velocity be u cm/sec. The force of a particle in a wall collision is

$$\text{force (dimensions } mlt^{-2}) = \text{mass} \times \text{acceleration}.$$

A particle of velocity $+u$ normal to the wall rebounds with velocity $-u$, a change of $2u$. The particle can cross the box and return to the same wall, a distance of $2a$ cm, in $(2a/u)$ sec. Thus it makes $u/2a$ collisions/sec with this wall. The product of the velocity change, the number of collisions/sec, and the mass gives the force per particle:

$$F = m(2u)u/2a = mu^2/a \text{ per particle.}$$

To find force per unit area divide by area, a^2,

$$P = F/A = mu^2/a^3 = mu^2/v,$$

where v = volume. Now, to consider all the particles moving in all directions and at many velocities, let us assume that the n particles have equal thirds of their velocity components in each of the three perpendicular directions and use the mean-square-velocity component in the equation above to get the total pressure on the wall ($\frac{1}{3}n$ acts on each wall)

$$P = (\tfrac{1}{3}n)m\overline{u^2}/v \qquad \text{or} \qquad Pv = \tfrac{1}{3}nm\overline{u^2}. \tag{15–4}$$

This is the fundamental equation of *KMT*. It relates the macroscopic variables, P and v, to the mass and velocities of the model particles. Note that $\overline{u^2}$ is the mean square velocity, which is not the same as the mean velocity squared [e.g., $(2 + 3)^2 = 25$, but $2^2 + 3^2 = 13$].

For one mole of gas, $n = N$, Avogadro's number, and $v = V$, the molar volume, so that (15–4) becomes

$$PV = \tfrac{1}{3}M\overline{u^2}, \qquad M = Nm. \tag{15–5}$$

As mentioned in postulate 6 above, we can say, for one mole, $E = \frac{1}{2}M\overline{u^2} \propto T$ and, thus, from Eq. (15–5), $PV = \frac{2}{3}E \propto T$. This result, that PV is proportional to T, is the Ideal Gas Law. So we have shown that the model chosen is consistent with observed gas behavior, at least for the limiting conditions where ideal behavior is approached. The postulates will help explain the deviations of real gases from ideality.

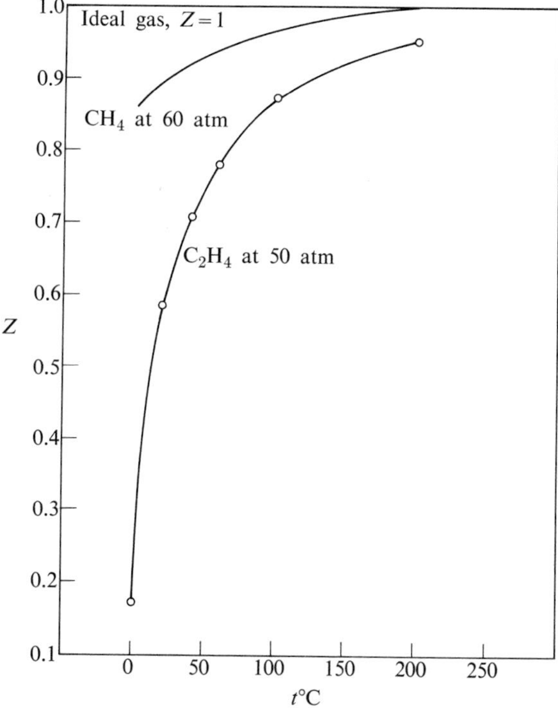

Fig. 15–2. Charles' Law deviations $Z = PV_{\text{obs}}/RT = V_{\text{obs}}/V_{\text{ideal}}$.

15.2 REAL GASES

The best value for the molar volume of an ideal gas at 0°C and 1 atm pressure (National Bureau of Standards, 1963) is 22.4130 liters. Some experimental values for actual gases are:

H_2,	22.432,	CO_2,	22.263,	SO_2,	21.889,	C_2H_4,	22.246,
He,	22.396,	HCl,	22.221,	CH_4,	22.377,	C_2H_2,	22.085.
O_2,	22.392,	NH_3,	22.094,	C_2H_6,	22.172,		

Thus one sees that the ideal-gas equation will give results within only a few percent of the observed values under these conditions. There are some structural correlations: CO_2 is linear, while SO_2 is bent and has a dipole moment. This increases intermolecular attraction, violating postulate 3 of the KMT. The other dipoles HCl and NH_3 also deviate.

Before trying to account for deviations in more detail, one should see how the deviations change with conditions. Figures 15–2 and 15–3 show experimentally determined deviations from Boyle's and Charles' Laws. Clearly the gases approach ideal-gas behavior at sufficiently high temperatures and sufficiently low pressures. The temperature effect looks like a simple function, but the pressure effect shows

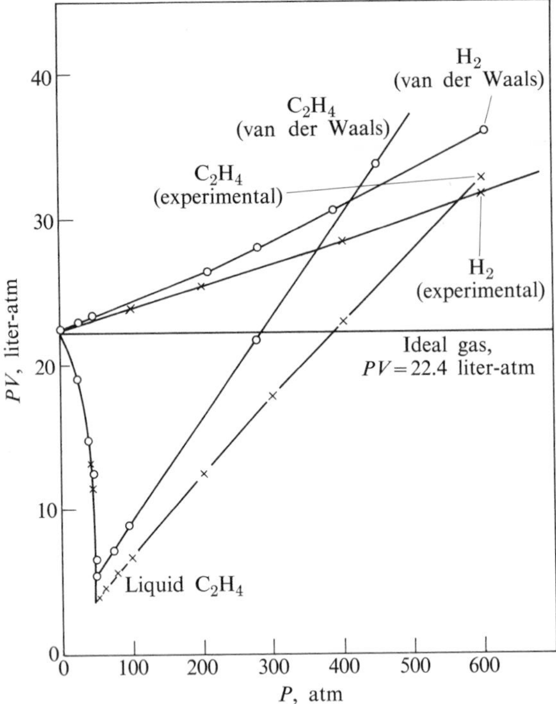

Fig. 15–3. Boyle's Law deviations at 0°C for H_2 and C_2H_4.

factors operating to reduce, and later to increase, the PV product as P increases, with temperature held constant.

To find a better gas equation, van der Waals, in 1873, introduced correction terms into the ideal-gas equation. He did this through a deft use of physical intuition about the mechanisms by which molecular motions produce the deviations. His equation can be deduced as follows:

a) *The volume correction.* The molecules actually do take up some space leaving less room for molecular motion. They hit the walls more often and make the pressure (or PV) higher than ideal. Van der Waals then corrected for this by reducing the observed volume to the empty (ideal) volume by subtracting a constant volume for the molecules themselves, b. So, $(V - b)$ is used in place of V.

b) *The pressure correction.* Attraction between molecules can reduce the observed pressure below the ideal value. An additive correction is needed. The function here is the crucial point of van der Waals' equation. The total attractive force depends on the number of molecules per volume acting on one molecule about to hit the wall, and also on the number of molecules about to hit the wall. Both of these depend on the density of the gas, mass/volume. The pressure reduction is thus proportional to M^2/V^2. Since M is constant for one gas, it can be

Table 15–1. Pressure (Atmospheres)

	1 mole CH_4 at 0°C		C_2H_4 at 0°C			C_2H_4 at 25°C	
Observed P	32.3	108	1.0000	38.0	200*	10.0	20.0
Calculated P (15–7)	31.8	103	1.0004	40.2	1720	10.9	21.8
Calculated P (ideal)	34.6	140	1.0075	64.2	356	11.6	24.9

* Note that at 200 atm and 0° ethene has liquified.

included in the proportionality constant to write a correction term, a/V^2. The pressure term becomes $(P_{\text{obs}} + a/V^2)$, and the ideal-gas equation is adjusted to read

$$(P + a/V^2)(V - b) = RT \quad \text{for one mole,} \tag{15–6}$$

or

$$(P + n^2a/V^2)(V - nb) = nRT \quad \text{for } n \text{ moles.} \tag{15–7}$$

This works surprisingly well at moderate pressures once a and b have been found from experimental data for each compound. In Table 15–1 the observed pressure is compared with the ideal pressure and that obtained from Eq. (15–7).

Further information on the validity of van der Waals' equation can be derived as follows. Rearrange Eq. (15–6) to

$$P = RT/(V - b) - a/V^2 \tag{15–8}$$

and

$$PV = RTV/(V - b) - a/V. \tag{15–9}$$

Examine Charles' Law deviations, Fig. 15–2, in the light of Eq. (15–9). At constant pressure, V increases with T. So as T becomes very large, a/V becomes very small, and $(V - b)$ approaches V; thus (15–9) reduces to $PV = RT$.

For the Boyle's Law deviations, Fig. 15–3, let us examine (15–9) at constant temperature with low P and with higher P. At low P and high V, a/V is again small and $(V - b) \rightarrow V$ so that $PV \rightarrow RT$ as $P \rightarrow 0$. At higher P, as P increases, the values of van der Waals a and b for the particular gas will determine whether PV is greater or less than RT. Note that in Eq. (15–9) $V/(V - b)$ is always greater than one, and a/V is always subtracted from the other term on the right side. Values for van der Waals constants for some gases are listed in Table 15–2.

Table 15–2. van der Waals Constants and Critical Data

Gas	T_c, °K	P_c, atm	V_c, ml/mole	a, liter^2-atm/mole^2	b, ml/mole
He	5.3	2.26	57.6	0.0341	23.7
H_2	33.3	12.8	65.0	0.244	26.6
O_2	153.4	49.7	74.4	1.36	31.8
CO_2	304.2	73.0	95.7	3.59	42.7
C_2H_4	282.9	50.9	127.5	4.47	57.1

Table 15–3. van der Waals Calculations for C_2H_4 at 0°C

V, liter/mole	$RT/(V-b)$	a/V^2	P	PV
1	23.8	4.47	19.3	19.3
0.4	65.4	27.9	37.5	15.0
0.2	156.8	111.8	45.0	9.0
0.122	345	301	44	5.5
0.1	520	447	73	7.3
0.0751	1244	794	450	33.8

We see from Table 15–2 that the a values for H_2 and He are so small that the b term predominates, and the PV-versus-P curves for these two gases at 0°C rise steadily. With ethene, the a term is relatively much larger, and the falling curve at low pressures is found. The terms in van der Waals' equation (15–8) are given in Table 15–3 to show how they behave with increasing pressure. The V is first chosen, then P and PV are calculated.

The van der Waals minimum at 0.122 liter and 5.5 liter-atm was derived as follows. Van der Waals' equation (15–6) can be multiplied out to give

$$PV = RT + Pb - a/V + ab/V^2. \qquad (15\text{–}10)$$

To find the minimum of the curve PV versus P, find the first derivative and set it equal to zero. Rearrange (15–10) and insert a new variable $x = PV$:

$$PV = RT + Pb - Pa/PV + abP^2/(PV)^2, \qquad (15\text{–}11)$$

$$x = RT + Pb - Pa/x + abP^2/x^2. \qquad (15\text{–}12)$$

We now have PV as a function of P (T constant). By taking $dx/dP = 0$ we have

$$dx/dP = b - a/x + 2abP/x^2.$$

Substituting this equation as $P = x/2b - x^2/2a$ into (15–12) gives

$$x^2 + 2ax/b - 4aRT/b + a^2/b^2 = 0.$$

With the a and b values for ethene this becomes

$$x^2 + 156.6x - 895 = 0.$$

The positive root, from the quadratic formula, is

$$x = 5.52 \text{ liter-atm}.$$

The P and then the V (from PV) can be calculated from the first derivative equation above. The experimental values are: minimum at 3.5 liter-atm at 42 atm, compared with van der Waals 5.5 liter-atm at 44 atm. When we realize that this is in the liquid region of ethene, we see that the agreement is remarkable. The graph (Fig. 15–3) shows that van der Waals' equation calculations behave like the experimental data even after this point. But the numerical agreement is poor.

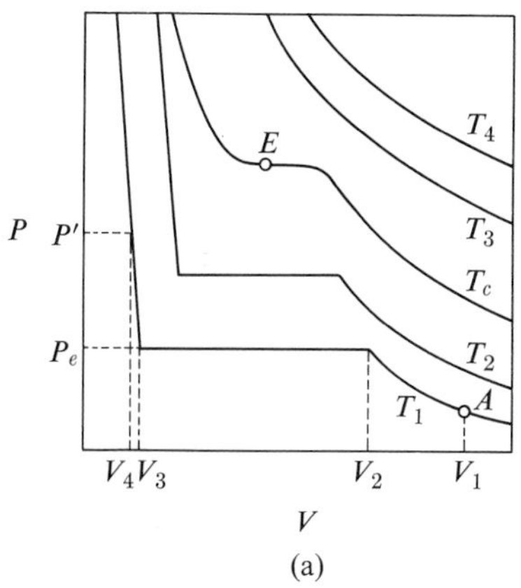

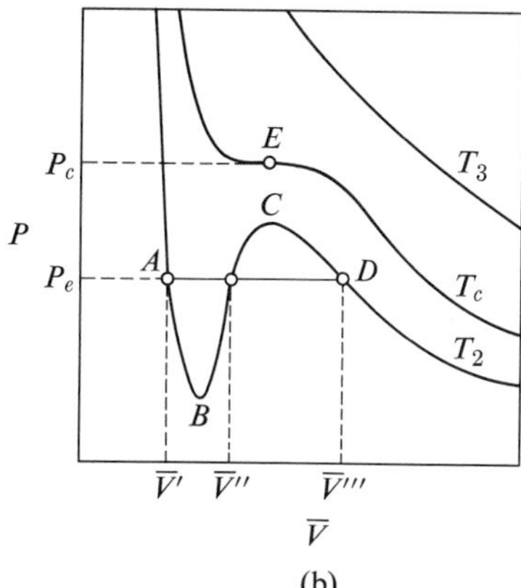

Fig. 15–4. Isotherms of a real gas and as predicted by van der Waals' equation: (a) real gas, showing inflection at the critical point; (b) van der Waals' gas showing correct critical point but cubic form below critical temperature. (After G. W. Castellan, *Physical Chemistry*, Reading, Mass.: Addison-Wesley, 1964.)

The value of van der Waals' equation lies in its demonstration of the nature of the factors that can account for the behavior of real gases. It also contributes to an understanding of the liquifaction of gases. Let us now look at what is called the *critical phenomenon*.

Figure 15–4(a) shows the experimental P-versus-V curves at constant temperature (isotherms) at a series of temperatures. The curve in Fig. 15–4(b) is typical of the cubic van der Waals function [from Eq. (15–10)]:

$$V^3 - (b + RT/P)V^2 + (a/P)V - ab/P = 0. \tag{15–13}$$

That is, at a chosen P and T, (15–13) will have three roots for V, V', V'', and V'''. These three roots become equal at the critical point E, but we shall use a different approach below. The critical pressure, P_c, critical temperature, T_c, and critical volume, V_c, are interpreted as follows. The highest temperature at which a gas can be liquified is T_c. The minimum pressure required to do this at T_c is the critical pressure. The molar volume of the liquid at P_c and T_c is the critical volume.

The maximum and minimum of (15–13) below the critical temperature become an inflection at T_c, P_c, V_c. Both the first and second derivatives are zero at this point. The student should show, from (15–8), that

$$\begin{aligned}(dP/dV)_T &= 0 = -RT_c/(V_c - b)^2 + 2a/V_c^3,\\ (d^2P/dV^2)_T &= 0 = 2RT_c/(V_c - b)^3 - 6a/V_c^4.\end{aligned} \tag{15–14}$$

Combining these two results gives

$$V_c = 3b, \tag{15–15}$$

which, in the first derivative equation, gives

$$T_c = 8a/27bR. \tag{15–16}$$

These inserted in the van der Waals equation at the critical point give

$$P_c = a/27b^2. \tag{15–17}$$

These can be combined to show that

$$a = 3P_cV_c^2, \qquad b = V_c/3, \qquad R = 8P_cV_c/3T_c. \tag{15–18}$$

Putting these into van der Waals' equation eliminates all three constants:

$$(P + 3P_cV_c^2/V^2)(V - V_c/3) = (8P_cV_c/3T_c)T. \tag{15–19}$$

This is a general gas equation. It can be written in terms of *reduced P, T,* and *V* defined:

$$P_r = P/P_c, \qquad T_r = T/T_c, \qquad V_r = V/V_c. \tag{15–20}$$

With these, (15–19) becomes

$$[P/P_c + 3(V_c/V)^2](3V/V_c - 1) = 8T/T_c \tag{15–21}$$

or

$$(P_r + 3/V_r^2)(3V_r - 1) = 8T_r. \tag{15–22}$$

This brings us to a much-investigated rule, The Law of Corresponding States. Equation (15–22) predicts that all gases behave alike at the same values of P_r, V_r, and T_r, that is, at the same "distance" from the critical point. This is a fair approximation. Looking at Fig. 15–3, we see that H_2 cooled to (273.15/282.8)33.3 = 32.2°K would behave the way C_2H_4 does at 273.15°K. Both are at $T_r = 0.966$.

Other equations have been devised to fit the behavior of real gases more closely, by use of more constants, more functional terms, or both.* Van der Waals *a* and *b* are not strictly constant so that values chosen to agree with experiment at one point will not necessarily give good results at other temperatures and pressures. Note that *b*, which was described in the derivation as the volume of the molecules, turns out to be $V_c/3$. It may not seem likely that the critical liquid is $\frac{2}{3}$ empty space, but the order of magnitude is right.

For gases, we may conclude:

1) Calculations with the ideal-gas equation will give results with less than 1% error for real gases which are well above their critical temperature and below about 2 atm pressure.

2) Van der Waals' equation extends the region of 1 to 2% reliability to slightly higher pressures and to lower temperatures, often below T_c.

---

* J. R. Partington, *Advanced Treatise on Physical Chemistry*, Vol. I. New York: John Wiley, 1949, pp. 703–745.

3) Van der Waals' equation gives a qualitative description of real gases, critical phenomena, and some aspects of the liquid state. It leads to the Law of Corresponding States.

15.3 SOME QUANTITATIVE MEASUREMENTS WITH GASES

Gas measurements are most widely used in gas chromatography and for volumetric-absorption determinations. In addition, measurement of gas density provides a means of determining apparent molecular weights and formulas of pure substances. Chromatography is discussed in a later chapter.

Gas Density

Apparent molecular weights, M, of pure substances available in the gas phase can be determined by weighing a sample of known P, T, and V. With $n = \text{mass}/M$, the ideal-gas equation gives

$$M = (\text{mass})RT/PV.$$

If the van der Waals constants are known, and precision warrants it, Eq. (15–7) can be solved for n, and then M can be calculated from it.

The experimental difficulties become clear if one considers a 500 ml glass bulb containing a sample at room temperature. The glass may weigh 50 g and the gas, for example, butane (formula weight, 58) may weigh 1 g. With so large a glass surface, great care is required in handling if weighing precision is to extend even to ± 1 mg (see Chapter 3). For six-figure precision (atomic-weight work) early chemists developed intricate weighing methods.* However, for such determinations as that of the molecular formula of a gas of empirical formula CH_2, for example, three figures are ample to distinguish among the possibilities 28, 42, 56, 70, etc.

The method is often useful for determining the molecular weights of liquids which can be vaporized at convenient temperatures where P and V can also be determined. The techniques of Dumas, Hofmann, and Victor Meyer are described in the text by Partington and in most physical chemistry laboratory manuals. The Dumas-bulb method is the easiest to use. Example calculations are given here, and experiments are found in the laboratory section.

The Dumas bulb has a neck drawn out to a fine tip. An excess of the pure liquid sample is put into the dry weighed bulb, which is then immersed almost to the tip in a bath with temperature well above the boiling point of the liquid. The sample vaporizes driving out the air and filling the bulb. It is quickly cooled and weighed. To find the weight of sample which had filled the bulb as a gas when hot, one must correct for the vapor pressure of the liquid, since that portion of air was not drawn back into the bulb upon cooling. For liquids of unknown vapor pressure, the bulb tip can be sealed with a flame before it is removed from the bath. Then the air-buoyancy correction can be made on the known total volume. The bulb volume is found by filling the bulb with water and weighing it.

---

* See J. R. Partington, *An Advanced Treatise on Physical Chemistry*, Vol. I. New York: John Wiley, 1949, pp. 745–776.

Example. A student makes a preliminary determination on CCl_4 to learn the techniques of the Dumas method. He wishes to calculate M by both the ideal and the van der Waals equations from this data: water bath $T = 99.1°C$, corrected bulb volume = 210.5 ml, P(corrected) = 730.6 torr, weight difference found = 0.993 g at 26°C.

Solution

a) First, make the weight corrections. The buoyancy factor for CCl_4 (d = 1.6 g/ml) is 1.0006 (see Chapter 1, Section 1.1). This makes the weight 0.994 g. A much larger effect is that of the vapor pressure of CCl_4 at 26°C, 125 torr. Thus $\frac{125}{730}$ of the original air is not in the bulb. Its weight is $(\frac{125}{730})$(210 ml)(1.14 mg/ml) = 41 mg.* If all the CCl_4 were condensed to liquid, the bulb would weigh 41 mg more or 1.035 g.

b) By the ideal gas calculation, $P = 730.6/760 = 0.9613$ atm,

$$n = \frac{PV}{RT} = \frac{(0.9613)(0.2105)}{(0.08205)(372.2)} = 0.006627 \text{ moles.}$$

Note that units are made to conform to those of R, liter-atm/mole-deg. Thus

$$M = 1.035 \text{ g}/0.006627 \text{ moles} = 156.2 \quad (\text{formula weight, } CCl_4 = 153.82).$$

c) By the van der Waals calculation in (15–7), with constants, $a = 20.39$ liter^2-atm/mole^2 and $b = 0.1383$ liter/mole, we get:

$$\left[0.9613 + n^2 \frac{20.39}{(0.2105)^2}\right][0.2105 - n(0.1383)] = n(0.08205)(372.2),$$

the van der Waals equation for n moles, which reduces to:

$$63.65n^3 - 96.87n^2 + 30.67n - 0.2024 = 0.$$

Cubic equations are not so bad if an approximate root is known as is the case from step (b). First let us go at it by brute force successive approximations. Rapid, rough, slide-rule work is sufficient until the final steps. First, we try the n from (b) as 0.00663.

This gives $\qquad -0.003 = 0.$

Next, we try $n = 0.00660$, which gives $\qquad -0.004 = 0.$

We have moved in the wrong direction so we try $n = 0.0067$.
This gives $\qquad -0.0003 = 0.$

Next we try $n = 0.0068$, which gives $\qquad +0.002 = 0.$

So the root we want is between the last two tries.
Next, we try $n = 0.00675$, which gives $\qquad +0.0002 = 0.$

Then we try $n = 0.00674$, which gives $\qquad -0.0001 = 0.$

Interpolating linearly to 0 = 0 suggests 0.006743 moles for n.

---

* The density of air at STP is 1.293 mg/ml, which is 1.14 mg/ml at these conditions.

A faster solution method suggests itself in the first approximation. One sees that the n^3 and n^2 terms contribute very little. So, we leave the n term unsubstituted in the first step, which gives

$$-0.0042 + 30.67\,n - 0.2024 = 0, \qquad n = 0.006736.$$

Repeating with this value for n gives

$$-0.0044 + 30.67\,n - 0.2024 = 0, \qquad n = 0.006743$$

as already obtained above. This n gives:

$$M = 1.035 \text{ g}/0.006743 \text{ moles} = 153.5$$

for the van der Waals formula weight. As expected, gases near the condensation temperature are nonideal, PV is below the ideal value (strong attractive forces), and M is high using the ideal-gas equation.

Limiting density method. For high-accuracy molecular-weight determination, it would be desirable to avoid any approximations in corrections for nonideality. As has been seen before in similar situations with K^0_{sp} and ε^0, an extrapolation method solves the problem. Here, the apparent M can be determined at several pressures and extrapolated to zero pressure. Historically, atomic weights of N and the inert gases have been found in this way.

Gaseous Equilibria

So far we have used molarity units for the concentration and activity terms in solution equilibria. For gas-phase reactions, both concentration and pressure units are in common use. The choice must be stated when constants are given. The equilibrium constant may have different numerical values for each means of expression: K_c and K_P mean K expressed in concentration and pressure units, respectively. The c is understood to mean moles/liter, but we must clarify whether P is given in atmospheres or torr (mm of Hg), etc.

Examples

1) Consider the simplest case A $\longrightarrow$ B, where both are gases. Assuming ideal gases, $c = n/V = P/RT$ may be substituted in K_c:

$$K_c = \frac{(\mathrm{B})}{(\mathrm{A})} = \frac{(P_b/RT)}{(P_a/RT)} = \frac{P_b}{P_a} = K_P.$$

2) However, for the case 2A $\longrightarrow$ B, this equality is not found:

$$K_c = \frac{(P_b/RT)}{(P_a/RT)^2} = \left(\frac{P_b}{P_a^2}\right) RT = K_P RT.$$

K can be expressed in other ways. The mole fraction, X, is sometimes a useful way of expressing K; however, K_X, for gases, is constant only at one temperature and pressure, while K_P and K_c do not vary with the total pressure, assuming ideal gases. For reactions having the same number of moles of gas reactants and products, $K_P = K_c = K_X$, since the conversion factors between the units all cancel. For other reactions, this is not the case as shown above, and attention must be paid to the units required.

The different K values imply different calculated free-energy values from $\Delta G^0 = -RT \ln K^0$. This is correct because the ΔG^0 is for different standard states in each case. Unit activity is taken as 1 atm in pressure units, ideal, or 1 M in concentration (Note that 1 M ideal gas at 0°C would be at 22.4 atm P), or $X = 1$, the pure gas at the pressure specified, for the mole fraction case.

Example. The student now wants to get the apparent molecular weight of acetic acid, and from it, the K_{eq} for the hydrogen-bonded dimer formation in the gas. He obtained the following data: $P = 711$ torr (0.935 atm), $T = 146$°C, V of new bulb $= 0.2300$ liter, weight corrected for buoyancy and vapor pressure $= 0.5065$ g.

Solution

a) By the ideal-gas calculation we have

$$n = PV/RT = 0.006258 \text{ moles of gas},$$
$$M = 0.5065 \text{ g}/0.006258 \text{ mole} = 80.79.$$

b) Performing the van der Waals calculation and profiting by the experience gained in the previous calculation, we substitute the n just obtained directly into the n^2 term of van der Waals' equation in the form (15–7) to get a new n, 0.006328, which does not change upon resubstitution. This gives

$$M = 80.04.$$

Since the formula weight of acetic acid is 60.05, a large fraction must have formed the dimer at this temperature. However, this means also that the van der Waals constants for pure acetic acid may give a poor approximation for the mixed gas. So, we keep in mind that the apparent molecular weight is only approximately 80.0. (A titration method for the acid is suggested in the laboratory section to avoid the uncertainties of the weight corrections.) The constants used were

$$a = 17.59 \text{ liter}^2\text{-atm/mole}^2 \quad \text{and} \quad b = 0.1068 \text{ liters}.$$

c) Then, obtain the dimerization equilibrium constant. The K_P is wanted in torr units (mm of Hg). A direct relation can be derived in this case for the experimental result, A, the apparent molecular weight, which must be the weighted average of the monomer and dimer weights, M and $2M$ ($M = 60.05$). Let x = mole fraction of monomer, P = total pressure, p_1 = monomer pressure, and $P - p_1$ = dimer pressure. Then

$$A = xM + (1 - x)2M = 2M - Mx \quad \text{and} \quad x = 2 - A/M = p_1/P.$$

Now, substitute in

$$K_P = P_{(\text{HA})_2}/(P_{\text{HA}})^2 = (P - p_1)/p_1^2 = (1 - x)/x^2P,$$
$$K_P = (A - M)M/(2M - A)^2P,$$

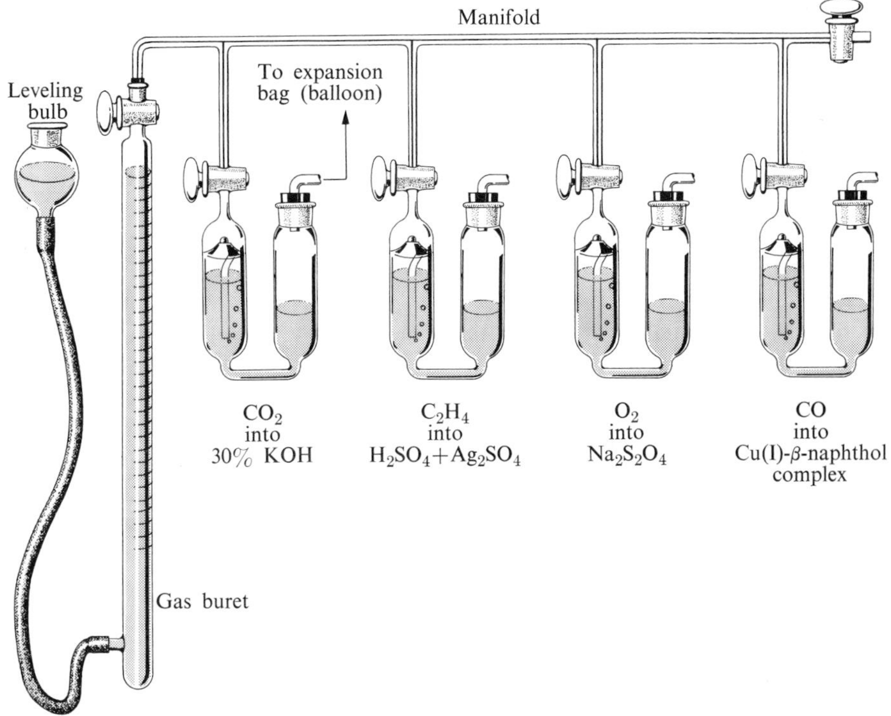

Fig. 15–5. Orsat volumetric gas-absorption apparatus. The gas sample is measured in the buret. The leveling bulb is raised to force the gas into one of the absorption pipets. The gas is then returned to the buret, and its decreased volume is read. The process is repeated to check for completion. (A simpler manifold with only one rubber tube connection can be used, changing the absorption pipet after each gas is removed.) The manifold volume is kept negligible by use of capillary tubing and short rubber tube connectors. Buret capacity is 100 ml. Gases must be removed in the order shown.

to get

$$K_P = \frac{(20.0)(60.05)}{(40.1)^2(711)} = 1.05 \times 10^{-3}\ \text{torr}^{-1}.$$

If P is in atmospheres, $K_P = 0.800\ \text{atm}^{-1}$.

Volumetric Gas-Absorption Methods

Measurement of the volumes of a gas mixture before and after removal of one component by absorption is a rapid method of determining the composition. We realize how widely the method can be applied if we consider the number of compounds that can be converted to gaseous products upon combustion, pyrolysis, etc. As described in the laboratory section, common gases, O_2, CO, CO_2, and unsaturates like C_2H_4 can be absorbed quantitatively in appropriate reagents in a closed system, and the volume measured. The volume loss divided by the original volume is the fraction of that component in the original mixture. An Orsat gas-absorption apparatus is shown in Fig. 15–5.

Common absorbents are:

Gas	Absorbent
O_2	Alkaline pyrogallol, Cr(II) or $Na_2S_2O_4$ solutions
CO_2	Strong bases as solid or in solutions
CO	Complexed Cu(I) solutions
C_2H_4 and other alkenes	H_2SO_4 with Ag_2SO_4 catalyst

Simple gas mixtures such as combustion and respiration products can be analyzed directly by absorbtion of the above gases. Mixtures containing H_2 and hydrocarbons can first be reacted with excess O_2 (in a strong bulb with a hot Pt wire catalyst). The contraction in volume represents H_2O formed as liquid and the Δn of the chemical equation. The original gas had been saturated with H_2O so that no vapor-pressure correction is needed. Constant temperature is required for all volume measurements. Next CO_2 is absorbed in base. The following examples show how much information can be derived from these figures.

It might seem that a composition obtained for the water-saturated gas would not be the same as that of the originally drier sample. It is the same however, because water vapor is removed with each component of the mixture absorbed. When added to a wet system, the gas sample increases a definite fraction, about 3%. For example, a 90 ml sample of 50% CO_2 would expand to 93 ml, but the KOH would remove the 45 ml of original CO_2 and 1.5 ml water vapor to give a volume change of 46.5 ml, 50% of the measured volume. The water must condense or the remaining gas would be supersaturated.

When mercury is used instead of water, the gas sample must be dry, since each absorbent removes an unknown amount of water. Water can be determined gravimetrically and is important in the carbon-hydrogen combustion methods discussed later.

Volumetric combustions. In addition to gravimetric C-H methods, volumetric combustions can be valuable for mixtures with sufficiently few components. What are the volume relations expected when compounds react with O_2?

a) For each ml of H_2 in the reaction, $2H_2 + O_2 \rightarrow 2H_2O$ (liquid), 0.5 ml of O_2 are required to produce less than 0.001 ml liquid water, effectively zero volume in the usual gas buret. If 10 ml H_2 were mixed with 50 ml O_2 and burned, 45 ml O_2 would be left: the volume contraction would be 15 ml, and 5 ml O_2 would be used.

b) Each ml of CH_4 in the reaction, $CH_4 + 2O_2 \rightarrow 2H_2O + CO_2$, requires 2 ml O_2 and produces 1 ml CO_2. If 10 ml CH_4 were burned with 50 ml O_2, there would be 10 ml CO_2 and 30 ml O_2 left, a contraction of 20 ml.

In this way, a table can be formed to show the volume relations and simplify identification and calculations of binary and some three-component mixtures (see Table 15–4). Some alkenes are shown although they can be absorbed before the combustion steps. Others could be derived as above.

Table 15–4. Combustion Contraction, O_2 Requirement and CO_2 Relations

Gas	$\Delta V/V_0$	V_{O_2}/V_0	V_{CO_2}/V_0
H_2	1.5	0.5	0
CO	0.5	0.5	1
CH_4	2	2	1
C_2H_4	2	3	2
C_2H_6	2.5	3.5	2
C_3H_8	3	5	3

Examples

1. Find the percent composition of 100 ml of a mixture known to contain only H_2, CO, CH_4, and N_2 if 20 ml is absorbed in Cu(I) complex solution, and the remaining 80 ml is burned with 100 ml O_2 to produce 105 ml of gas of which 30 ml is absorbed in KOH.

Let the volumes of the four gases be a, b, c, and d ml and let $b = 20$ ml from the first absorption. Volumes a and c can be found from the combustion data: From the table, we find that

$$\text{contraction} = 75 = 1.5a + 2c, \qquad \text{volume } CO_2 = 30 = c.$$

So $a = 10$ ml and, by difference, $d = 40$ ml. In this example, percent corresponds to number of milliliters.

2. The gas sample is 100 ml of the pyrolysis products in a study of dioxolane, $C_3H_6O_2$. It loses 22 ml in KOH, 15.4 ml in H_2SO_4 (assumed ethene), and 16 ml in CO absorbent. The remaining 46.6 ml is burned with 110 ml pure O_2. The resulting volume is 78 ml of which 22 is removed by KOH. Assume there was evidence that the gas burned was only H_2 and CH_4. What was the original percent composition and what conclusions can the researcher make?

The volume of CO_2, C_2H_4, and CO are given. The combustion gives

$$a = \text{ml } H_2, \qquad b = \text{ml } CH_4;$$

$$\text{contraction} = 78.6 = 1.5a + 2b,$$

$$\text{volume } CO_2 = 22 = b.$$

So $a = 23$. To summarize the composition we have CO, 16, CO_2, 22, C_2H_4, 15.4, H_2, 23, CH_4, 22. From this, the totals of the atoms of C, H, and O are:

$$C = 91 \text{ units}, \qquad H = 196 \text{ units}, \qquad O = 60 \text{ units}.$$

These are approximately in the required ratio 3:6:2, but there is a deficiency of C and O. The researcher might then look for other products to improve the mass balance. Overlooking formaldehyde might account for the missing C and O.

3. To illustrate the method of determining three components by combustion, consider 100 ml of a mixture containing only CO, CH_4, and C_2H_6 burned with 200 ml pure O_2. The resulting volume was 155 ml of which 140 is absorbed in KOH. Find the percent composition of the mixture. Let *a*, *b*, and *c* be the volumes.

   Four equations can be written:

$$\begin{aligned}\text{starting volume} &= 100\text{ ml} = a + b + c,\\ \text{contraction} &= 145\text{ ml} = 0.5a + 2b + 2.5c,\\ \text{volume } O_2 \text{ used} &= 185\text{ ml} = 0.5a + 2b + 3.5c,\\ \text{volume } CO_2 \text{ formed} &= 140\text{ ml} = a + b + 2c.\end{aligned}$$

From the first and last equations, by subtraction, we get $c = 40$. Then we double the third and subtract the fourth equation to get $b = 10$, and thus, $a = 50$. The percent composition is then CO = 50%, CH_4 = 10%, C_2H_6 = 40%.

Unfortunately, some mixtures of three gases produce combustion equations which are not independent. This case is presented in an exercise at the end of the chapter. Spectral measurements, gas chromatography, and mass spectroscopy are more commonly used for complex mixtures.

Gravimetric combustion analysis. One of the most valuable and widely used tools of chemical research is the carbon-hydrogen determination through combustion. A weighed sample of a pure compound is heated in a stream of O_2, and the CO_2 and H_2O formed are collected and weighed. The H_2O is collected in a weighed tube of a drying agent, and the CO_2 in a tube of basic material.*

An example of this important method follows:

Example. A 22.48 mg sample of a pure compound containing only C, H, and O was burned in a stream of O_2 and produced 16.39 mg H_2O and 66.76 mg CO_2. Find the empirical formula of the compound.

Water is 11.19% H, and CO_2 is 27.29% C, so that

$$16.39(0.1119) = 1.834 \text{ mg H}, \qquad 66.76(0.2729) = 18.22 \text{ mg C};$$

by difference,

$$22.48 - 20.05 = 2.43 \text{ mg O}.$$

Divide each by the atomic weight to give the relative numbers of gram-atoms,

$$1.819 \text{ H}, \qquad 1.517 \text{ C}, \qquad 0.1519 \text{ O}.$$

Divide by 1.517 to get 1.199, 1, 0.1001, which give the integral ratio: 12 H, to 10 C, to 1 O, so that the formula is $C_{10}H_{12}O$, corresponding to anethole suspected. Commonly, the percentage composition is reported and compared with that of the formula rather than showing the empirical formula calculated.

---

* Details of construction and use of apparatus are given, for example, in *The Examination of New Organic Compounds*, by W. T. Smith and R. L. Shriner, New York: John Wiley, 1956, pp. 19–25.

SUMMARY

Quantitative laws of ideal and real gas behavior are given and compared with observation. Methods for determining molecular weights of pure gases and the composition of mixtures are described. Examples are given on formula determination of organic compounds by means of combustion methods and on the study of reactions via gas analysis of products.

PROBLEMS

1. Finish the following table of ideal-gas values and plot them on the three types of graph discussed in the chapter (Fig. 15–1). Point out the difficulties met in trying to preserve significant figures on the different graphs. Check values of slopes and intercepts. This data is for 0°C. Assume four figures in the P data.

P, atm	V, liters	$1/V$	$\log P$	$\log V$
0.01000	2241	0.0004462	−2.0000	3.3505
0.02	1120		−1.6990	
0.1	224.1			
0.2	112.0			
1.0	22.41			
2.0				
10.				
20.				
100.				

2. At what temperature should H_2 have the same velocity that O_2 has at 100°C?
3. Graham's Law of Diffusion is derivable from the KMT equation. Determine the relative composition of the first gas diffusing from a pinhole in a container which holds an equimolar mixture of H_2 and O_2. Devise an apparatus for fractionating such mixtures.
4. Work through clearly, in your own words, the deduction of the KMT equations and the van der Waals equation.
5. Calculate the pressure of one mole of He and also of CO_2 at 0°C at molar volumes from 0.05 to 5 liters. Get enough points to plot the P-versus-V curves from both ideal and van der Waals' equations. Can you find an interpretation of the strange form of the CO_2 curve.
6. Differentiate Eq. (15–8) twice to get the derivatives in Eq. (15–14) and then continue to derive Eqs. (15–15 through 15–22).
7. Calculate van der Waals a and b from critical data for the five gases given in Table 15–2. Use P_c and V_c and Eqs. (15–15 through 15–18). Give a reason why you do not get the values in the table.

8. A 100 ml sample of a mixture of H_2, C_2H_2, and CH_2O was mixed with 160 ml pure O_2. After combustion, the volume was 130 ml of which 100 ml absorbed in KOH. Find the percent composition. What could be the empirical formula of a compound that produced these products?

9. Demonstrate that for *a*, *b*, and *c* volumes of H_2, CH_4, and C_2H_6 burned with a known volume of O_2 producing a known contraction and a known volume of CO_2, there is no unique solution to the equations for *a*, *b*, and *c*, while for H_2, CH_4, and C_2H_4 there is.

10. At 0°C and 100 atm pressure, the experimental volume of one mole of CO_2 is 0.0453 liter. What are the ideal and van der Waals values for V?

CHAPTER 16

PURE LIQUIDS

The closeness of neighboring molecules in liquids amplifies the effects which cause nonideal behavior in gases. It is not surprising that we have no general equations which tell the physical properties of pure liquids. Their freezing and boiling points, vapor pressures, and mutual solubilities must be determined experimentally. Here we look briefly at some of the quantitative knowledge of liquids which is available.

16.1 VAPOR PRESSURE

Experimental vapor-pressure data (Figs. 16–1 and 16–2), as well as a thermodynamic argument, show that for all liquids over at least short temperature ranges (50 or 100°)

$$\log P_v = k/T + c, \tag{16–1}$$

where P_v means vapor pressure and T is in °K. The constant k is different for each substance. From thermodynamics it can be related to the heat of vaporization, L, as $k = -L/2.303R$. If Eq. (16–1) is written for two P_v at two T and the equations subtracted, we get

$$\log (P_2/P_1) = -L/2.303R[1/T_2 - 1/T_1] = L/4.576[(T_2 - T_1)/T_1T_2], \tag{16–2}$$

where L is in calories. This is called the *Clausius-Clapeyron equation*, but is a special case of the van't Hoff equation for the variation of any equilibrium constant with temperature. (The vapor pressure is the equilibrium constant for the vaporization equilibrium.) The K_{eq} and heat term for any equilibrium can be substituted in Eq. (16–2) for P and L.

The heat of vaporization, L, actually changes slowly with T. The data plotted in Fig. 16–2 show only slight curvature for the 100° range. More detailed equations can be used to fit the experimental data quite closely.

Example 1. Given that L for H_2O = 542 cal/g and the vapor pressure measured at 90°C is 526 torr, calculate the vapor pressure at 100°C as check on the method.

In Eq. (16–2),

$$\log \frac{P_2}{526} = \frac{-542(18)}{4.576}\left(\frac{1}{373} - \frac{1}{363}\right),$$

$$P_2 = 7\bar{5}6.$$

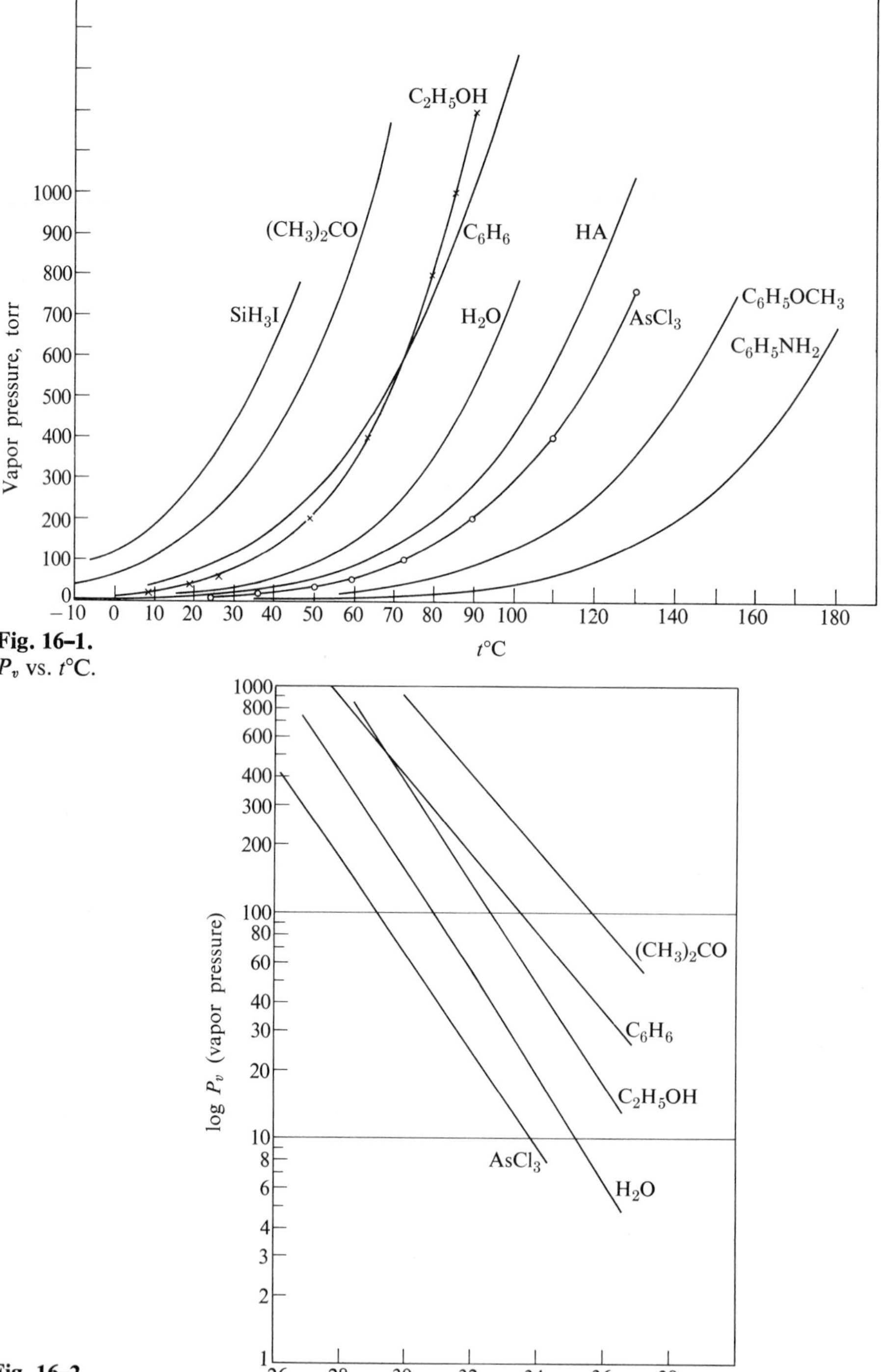

Fig. 16–1.
P_v vs. t°C.

Fig. 16–2.
$\log P_v$ vs. $1/T$.

This is actually 760 to the number of significant figures allowed. This can be seen in (16–2) in the $T_2 - T_1$ term which is 10°.

In distillation, one often has to compare a boiling point at some lower experimental P with the published value at 1 atm, T_b. Equation (16–2) allows this if one has the value of L for the liquid. This can be estimated from *Trouton's rule*, which states that

$$L/T_b = 21 \text{ cal/mole-deg.} \tag{16–3}$$

This can be put into (16–2) to derive a simplified equation for correcting boiling points, called *Craft's rule*. We can do this by using the approximation that $\ln x = 1 - 1/x$ for values of x near 1. Here we mean for x in (16–2), P_2/P_1 or $760/P_{\text{exp}}$. (Remember, $2.303 \log x = \ln x$.) So, we can write

$$\ln 760/P = 1 - P/760 = (760 - P)/760 = \Delta P/760.$$

Then, in (16–2),

$$\frac{\Delta P}{760} = -\frac{21T_b}{R}\left(\frac{1}{T_b} - \frac{1}{T}\right) = \frac{21}{R}\frac{\Delta T}{T}$$

by taking T_b as the same as the experimental temperature, T. Solve for ΔT to get

$$\Delta T = \frac{RT\,\Delta P}{760(21)} = 1.2 \times 10^{-4}\,T\,\Delta P, \tag{16–4}$$

which is Craft's rule for correcting boiling points obtained ΔP torr from 760.

Example 2. For an extreme case, one stormy day the corrected P reading was 701 torr in Sewanee, Tenn. (elevation, 2000 ft). Compare the published boiling point of water with that calculated by Craft's rule. In (16–4),

$$\Delta T = 1.2 \times 10^{-4}(373)(-59 \text{ torr}) = -2.6°.$$

Thus the boiling point is 97.4°C. This value is in fair agreement with the published value of 97.7°C considering the distance from 1 atm and also taking into consideration that water is a hydrogen-bonded liquid. This trouble is discussed below. (Equation (16–2), with L for water would give closer results.)

Trouton's rule (1884) suggests that the energy required to vaporize any liquid is proportional to the temperature at which a definite pressure is reached, say 1 atm. This is plausible considering that the greater are the forces between the molecules the higher should be the T_b as well as the L. How valid this rule is can be seen from Table 16–1. Liquids with H-bonding possibilities deviate as do very low boiling ones like H_2 and O_2.

Table 16–1. L/T_b for Various Liquids

Many hydrocarbons	20 to 21	HI	23
Esters	21	NH_3	23.6
CO_2, CS_2	21	H_2O and alcohols	26 (approximately)
Hg	21.5	O_2	18

Trouton's rule is therefore to be used as a rough approximation when L is not known. L can be found from (16–2) when vapor pressures have been measured at several temperatures.

The same forces that control T_b must also affect T_c, the critical temperature. One might expect T_b/T_c to be constant also. The ratio is found to be about $\frac{2}{3}$. This is called *Guldeberg's rule.* These rules allow estimation of vapor pressures if only the T_c is known, or, conversely, T_b and T_c can be estimated if one vapor pressure is known.

Example 3. Given the critical temperature, T_c of benzene as 562°K, estimate the vapor pressure of benzene at 25°C.

From

$$T_b/T_c = \tfrac{2}{3} \quad \text{and} \quad T_b = L/21, \qquad \tfrac{2}{3}T_c = L/21.$$

Putting these values in (16–2) gives

$$\frac{\log 760}{P} = \frac{21(\frac{2}{3})562}{4.576} \frac{(76°)}{298 \times (\frac{2}{3})562} = 1.17.$$

From which, $P = 51$ torr (experimental, 90).

Internal Pressure

Liquids are certainly held together in a definite volume which is able to resist change by external pressure. This force is called the internal pressure, P_i, and must be overcome to evaporate some of the molecules. It is closely related to volume, viscosity, surface tension, and heat of vaporization. Some insight as to its magnitude may be gained from van der Waals' equation. It can be identified with the a/V^2 term, the cohesive term. Since the molar volume of liquids is on the order of 0.1 liter, the internal pressure calculated as a/V^2 will be on the order of 10^3 atm. A comparison of experimental values with those calculated from a/V^2 is shown in Table 16–2.

Table 16–2

Liquid	P_i (experimental)	$P_i = a/V^2$
H_2O	20,000	16,800
$CHCl_3$	3,660	2,390
C_6H_6	3,640	2,270
CCl_4	3,310	2,190
$(C_2H_5)_2O$	2,370	1,610

Once again van der Waals' equation gives us a qualitatively valid picture with actual values about one-third low. The heats of vaporization calculated from a/V^2 have similar accuracy and order.

A similar concept is that of "solubility parameter" developed by J. H. Hildebrand. The solubility parameter, s, is the square root of the energy (in calories) of vaporization per milliliter:

$$s = \sqrt{E/V}.$$

It will be helpful in mutual liquid solubility correlations in the next section. It expresses the cohesive energy density. E is the energy of vaporization at a standard temperature (25°) at zero P. These may be approximated by $L - RT$, where L is a heat of vaporization at low P. The RT term removes the work done against atmospheric P, about 0.6 kcal.

SUMMARY

Vapor pressure-temperature relations of pure liquids are given. Uses of the Clausius-Clapeyron equation, Trouton's, Craft's, and Guldeberg's rules are presented.

PROBLEMS

1. Derive Craft's rule from the Clausius-Clapeyron equation and Trouton's rule. Calculate the normal boiling point of an ester found to distill at around 130°C at 716 torr.
2. Given only that the normal boiling point of CCl_4 is 76.8°C, use the equations of this chapter to estimate its vapor pressure at 0°, and at 20°C. Compare with published values.
3. The experimentally determined internal pressure of liquid CS_2 is 3670 atm. Calculate P_i from van der Waals' a, 11.62 atm-liter^2/mole^2. The density of the liquid is 1.26 g/ml.

CHAPTER 17

SOLUTIONS AND DISTILLATION

When two pure liquids are mixed, they may be completely soluble in all proportions (miscible) or only partly soluble in many degrees, almost to complete immiscibility. This property affects the ease of separation of liquids and their solvent uses.

In addition to the almost chemical reactions between acidic and basic liquids, solubility is favored by similarity of forces between the molecules of the pair to those between like molecules. Liquids with very different cohesive forces will have lower mutual solubility and/or large deviations from Raoult's Law (if other specific interactions do not operate). These forces are expressed in the solubility parameter, defined in the previous chapter, shown in Table 17–1. Correlations are found for "regular solutions" of nonpolar or low polarity liquids without specific chemical interactions. For example, C_6H_6 and $CHCl_3$ form nearly ideal solutions, while $CHCl_3$ is not miscible with nC_6F_{14}.

Table 17–1. Solubility Parameter, $s = \sqrt{E/V}$*

CS_2	10.0	cyclohexane	8.2
C_6H_6	9.2	$(C_2H_5)_2O$	7.4
$CHCl_3$	9.2	nC_6H_{14}	7.3
CCl_4	8.6	nC_6F_{14}	5.9

* From J. H. Hildebrand and R. L. Scott, *Regular Solutions*, Englewood Cliffs, N.J.: Prentice-Hall, 1962.

Another approach to the question of mutual solubilities is to include more polar liquids, arranging all in order of increasing dielectric constant. The dielectric constant is the ratio of the capacitance on the two plates of a capacitor with the liquid between them to that in a vacuum. It increases with the polarity and the polarizability of the substance. In such a list of solvents,* solvent pairs near each other are miscible while others are less soluble. Part of the list follows:

pentane
hexane
cyclohexane
benzene
toluene
carbon tetrachloride
chloroform
carbon disulfide
ethers
ketones
dioxane
amyl acetate
ethyl acetate
methyl acetate
cyclohexanol
ethanol
methanol
aniline
phenol
acetic acid
formamide
water

* See L. C. and D. Craig, "Extraction and Distribution" in *Technique of Organic Chemistry*, ed. by A. Weissberger, Vol. III. Part 1. New York: Interscience Publishers, 1956.

17.1 IMMISCIBLE PAIRS

In mixtures of almost immiscible pairs, each liquid exerts its own vapor pressure independently of the other. Steam distillation takes advantage of this. The mixture boils when the sum of the two vapor pressures equals atmospheric P. Derivation of the relative weights obtained shows the advantage gained by the low molecular weight of water:

$$P_{\text{atm}} = P_1^0 + P_2^0.$$

Assuming ideal gases, the concentration in the vapor will then be proportional to each partial pressure, and $n = \text{weight}/M$, so

$$\frac{P_1^0}{P_2^0} = \frac{n_1}{n_2} = \frac{\text{weight}_1}{\text{weight}_2}\frac{M_2}{M_1}.$$

Example. Methoxybenzene (anisole), boiling point 156°C, steam distills at 95°C at a total pressure of 744 torr. Compare the mole and weight ratio of anisole to water obtained.

At 95°, $P_{H_2O} = 634$ so $P_{\text{anisole}} = 110$

$$\text{mole ratio} = \tfrac{110}{634} = 0.174,$$
$$\text{weight ratio} = \tfrac{108}{18}\,\tfrac{110}{634} = 1.04.$$

Thus the method allows low-temperature distillation and gives over 50 weight percent anisole in the distillate in spite of its low vapor pressure.

17.2 IDEAL SOLUTIONS

In theory, an ideal solution of A and B may be thought of as one in which the forces between A and B molecules are identical with those between like molecules, A-A and B-B. Experimentally, a solution is ideal if it follows Raoult's Law, which means that the vapor pressure of each liquid component is reduced by the fraction of foreign molecules present. That is,

$$P_1 = X_1P_1^0 \qquad \text{(Raoult's Law).} \qquad (17\text{–}1)$$

The partial pressure of component *one*, over the solution, is equal to the mole fraction of that component in the solution times its pure vapor pressure. The same is true for a second component. From this a diagram of pressure versus mole fraction can be constructed at one temperature (Fig. 17–1). Raoult's Law gives straight-line variation of P with X:

$$P = P_1 + P_2 = X_1P_1^0 + X_2P_2^0. \qquad (17\text{–}2)$$

Since $X_1 + X_2 = 1$,

$$P = X_1(P_1^0 - P_2^0) + P_2^0.$$

Note well that the abscissa gives the X of each component *in* the solution but not in the vapor. The vapor will have a higher fraction of the more volatile com-

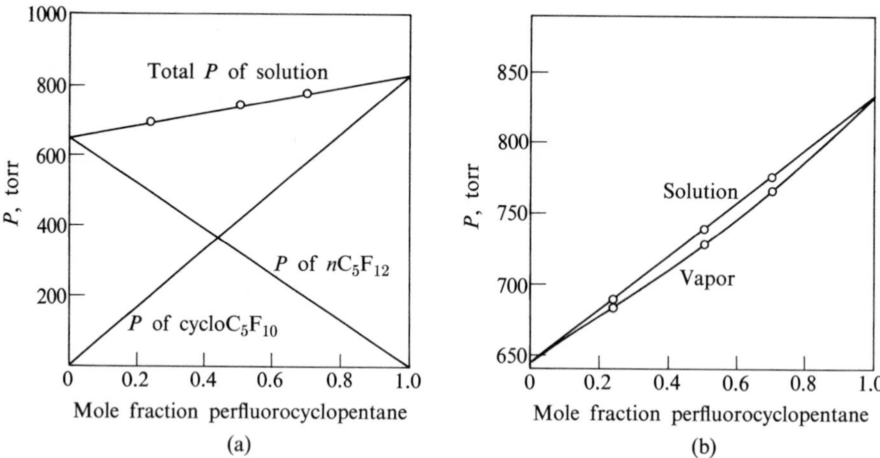

Fig. 17–1. Ideal pressure-vs.-mole fraction diagram of two fluorocarbons at 25°C.

ponent. The vapor line is also calculated from Raoult's Law,

$$X_{1\ \mathrm{vap}} = P_1/P,$$
$$X_{2\ \mathrm{vap}} = P_2/P.$$

From (17–2)

$$X_{1\ \mathrm{vap}} = P_1^0 X_1/(P_1^0 X_1 + P_2^0 X_2),$$

which is a curve as shown in Fig. 17–1(b).

Perfluorocyclopentane (A) and perfluoro *n*-pentane (B) were studied because each has a low solubility parameter, about 6, and hence very low intermolecular forces. Ideal solution behavior is to be expected.* At 25°, pure (A) has a vapor pressure of 833 torr, and (B), 646 torr. By Raoult's Law at 0.5 mole fraction of each, the total pressure should be 0.5 (833 + 646) = 740. Experimental points, circles, fall on the ideal line within the precision of the method used. On the second plot [Fig. 17–1(b)], the scale has been expanded and some experimental vapor composition points have been shown, which also agree with ideal behavior.

In distillation, the pressure is held constant while the boiling temperature changes with composition. We therefore need a temperature-versus-mole fraction diagram. One could be constructed for ideal solutions if vapor-pressure curves for each liquid are available. This should be done by choosing temperature values between the boiling points of the two liquids and then solving (17–2), with $P = 760$, for X_1 to find the composition of the solution which has that boiling point.

Example. Calculate the composition of a benzene-chloroform solution which will boil at 70° at 760 torr and the composition of the first vapor formed.

---

* See M. M. Newcome and G. H. Cady, *J. Am. Chem. Soc.* **78,** 5216 (1956).

From (17–2) $P = X_1(P_1^0 - P_2^0) + P_2^0$. At 70°, benzene, liquid 1, has $P_1^0 = 550$, and $CHCl_3$ has $P_2^0 = 1019$,

$$760 = X_1(550 - 1019) + 1019,$$

$$X_1 = 0.553, \qquad X_2 = 0.447 \quad \text{in the solution.}$$

In the vapor,

$$X_1' = 0.553\left(\tfrac{550}{760}\right) = 0.401, \qquad X_2' = 0.599.$$

The ideal curves in Fig. 17–2 were found in this manner.

17.3 REAL SOLUTIONS

The boiling-point diagram, Fig. 17–2, of benzene-chloroform shows moderate departure from ideal behavior. These are negative deviations from Raoult's Law. That is, strong attractions lower the vapor pressures and raise the boiling points. More extreme deviation is seen in the diagram for ethanol-ethyl acetate solutions (Fig. 17–3). Both the liquid and the vapor have the same composition at 0.540 mole fraction ester. This solution boils unchanged at 71.8°C at 1 atm P. Such behavior is quite common. The constant-boiling mixture is called an azeotrope. Its composition varies with pressure and it is not a definite compound.

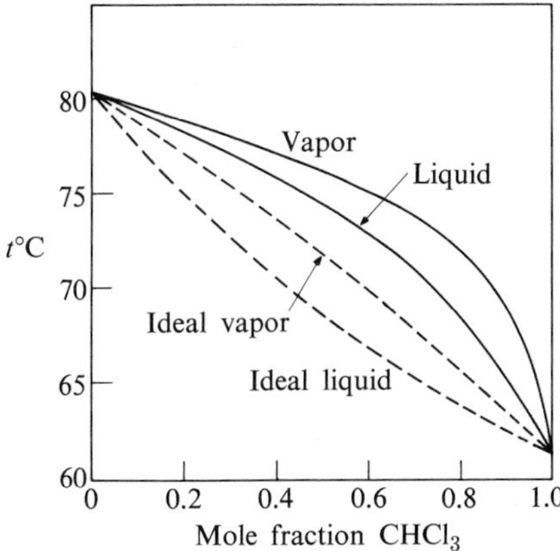

Fig. 17–2. Temperature-vs.-mole fraction diagram, real and ideal, for $CHCl_3$-C_6H_6, total P = 1 atm.

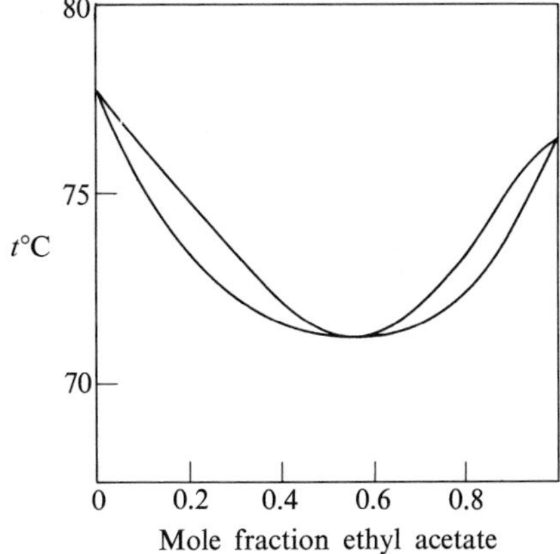

Fig. 17–3. Azeotropic diagram at 1 atm P for ethanol-ethyl acetate.

On the other hand, a few mixtures form maximum-boiling azeotropes. An example of importance is the HCl-H_2O system used to make constant-boiling HCl of composition known to 5 figure precision. (See the section on acid solutions and Project 1 in the laboratory section.)

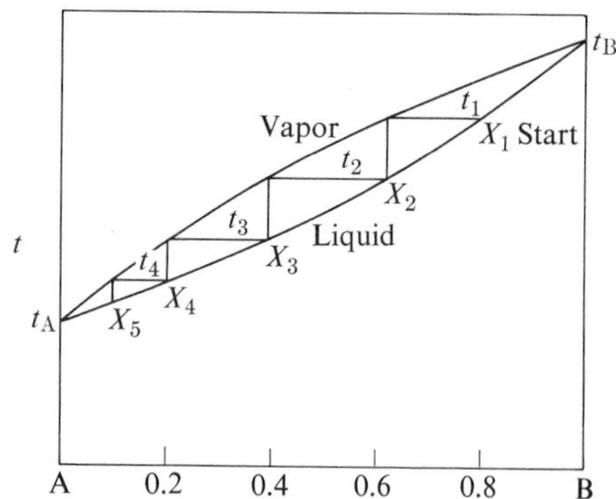

Fig. 17–4. Ideal fractional distillation; X_1 is put through four theoretical plates to reach X_5.

17.4 DISTILLATION

On a boiling-point diagram, a horizontal line from the liquid to the vapor curve ties together the solution and vapor which can be in equilibrium. These "tie lines" clarify the distillation process, as shown on the ideal diagram, Fig. 17–4. In simple distillation with no refluxing (one theoretical plate), the first material evaporated has the composition at the vapor end of the tie line. However, by evaporating, it has changed the composition of the pot toward a higher content of the less volatile liquid. In this way, the composition of the distillate and the pot move up the lines on the diagram until only the pure higher-boiling liquid remains. When there is a minimum-boiling azeotrope, simple distillation leads to a final pure component on the side nearest the starting mixture. For the maximum boiling cases, simple distillation leads to the azeotrope. In all cases, the boiling point rises during distillation.

The fractional-distillation diagram, Fig. 17–4, is almost self-evident. Ideally each vapor is condensed and the liquid again evaporated. Each step of the idealized process is called one theoretical plate. Figure 17–4 shows a starting mixture of 0.8 B going to a product at 0.1 B by a fractionation using four theoretical plates. Of course the ideal here is not attainable. Each evaporation changes the composition of the liquid left so that the steps cannot be sharp. The composition of the pot moves up toward B. The advantage of the fractionation is that component A is exhausted from the pot at an earlier stage than is the case with simple distillation. A larger amount of pure B can then be obtained. Conversely, for a higher-boiling impurity, (0.9 A-0.1 B) fractional distillation in a four-plate column would produce pure A for a considerable time before B starts. The student may convince himself of this by examining Fig. 17–4.

Where azeotropes can form, two different situations are found. For the common minimum-boiling case, fractionation leads down to the azeotrope so that the distillate has the azeotropic composition until the pot is exhausted of one of the components. Very little pure material can be obtained unless starting mixtures are far from the azeotropic composition. For a maximum-boiling case, the pure material in excess of the azeotropic amount will distill out of a very long fractionating column until the pot reaches the azeotropic values.

Fractional distillation is the classic case of a series of equilibrium stages used for separation. The concept used here will be valuable in understanding the methods to follow which are of broader application in quantitative chemical operations.

SUMMARY

The behavior of ideal and real solutions in distillation is described. Raoult's Law and the plate concept are discussed.

SUGGESTIONS FOR FURTHER READING

Methods of treating real distillations are similar to the total reflux cases presented here. In the following references, these methods are described and experimental methods are given for determination of HETP values, the height equivalent to a theoretical plate, for columns.

CAMPBELL, R. D., *J. Chem. Educ.* **39,** 348 (1962).

LAITINEN, H. A., *Chemical Analysis*, New York: McGraw-Hill, 1960, Chapter 25.

PROBLEMS

1. Interpret the distillation curves shown in Fig. 17–5 obtained by student titration of samples taken during preparation of constant-boiling HCl. Draw a general maximum-boiling T-vs.-X diagram to show why simple and fractional distillation give these results.

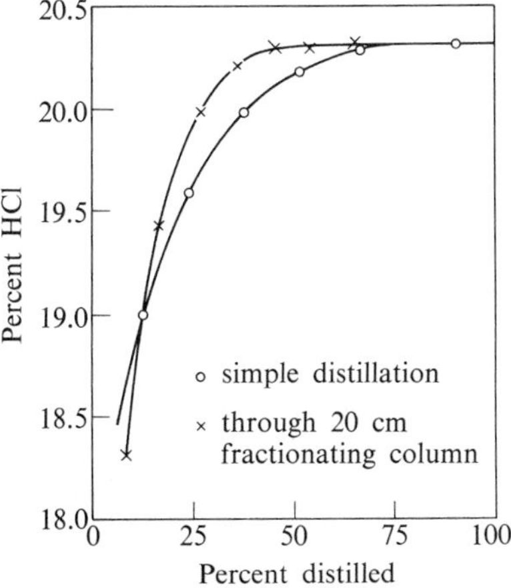

Fig. 17–5. Distillation of 6.0 M HCl at 715 torr P.

2. Benzene and toluene form practically ideal solutions. At 50°C, their vapor pressures are: benzene, 268.3 torr, toluene, 92.0 torr. Calculate and plot the *P*-*X* diagram for 50°C showing both liquid and vapor compositions.
3. At 75°C, the vapor pressures of benzene and chloroform are 650 and 1211 torr. Calculate the compositions of the liquid and the vapor at equilibrium at 75° and 1 atm.
4. Find data for a binary system which exhibits strongly nonideal behavior and plot *t*°C vs. *X* (or other composition term) for 1 atm pressure. Give liquid and vapor curves. [*Hint:* Look up H_2O-propanol in J. H. Perry, *Chemical Engineers' Handbook*, New York: McGraw-Hill, 1963.]
5. On your *t*-*X* diagram from Problem 4 or on the one given in the chapter for ethanol-ethyl acetate, indicate with lines and arrows and describe how the composition of the distillate and the pot change (a) during simple distillation, (b) during fractionation through a very long column. For each take these two separate starting mixtures: 95 mole percent A, and 5 mole percent A.

CHAPTER 18

EQUILIBRIA IN SOLVENT EXTRACTION SEPARATIONS

If a solute is soluble in both of two immiscible liquids, it will distribute itself between the two in a constant ratio of the activities in the two layers (assuming there are no side reactions like dimerization, ionization, etc.). This ratio is the partition coefficient, P, for

$$x_{\text{aq}} \rightleftharpoons x_{\text{org}},$$

$$P = \frac{(a_x)_{\text{org}}}{(a_x)_{\text{aq}}} \cong \frac{[x]_{\text{org}}}{[x]_{\text{aq}}} = \frac{(X - Y)/V_o}{Y/V_w}. \tag{18–1}$$

Since activity coefficients are generally unknown, the concentration ratio is taken as a constant under specific conditions. Here X is the number of moles of solute x originally taken in one layer of which there are V_w ml (it need not actually be water), Y is the number of moles of x remaining in that layer after extraction, and $(X - Y)$ moles are extracted into V_o ml of the other layer. These definitions simplify derivation of a useful expression for the fractions left after extractions. The fraction left in the original layer is simply Y/X. Rearranging (18–1), we get

$$f = Y/X = [1 + P(V_o/V_w)]^{-1}. \tag{18–2}$$

In repeated extraction with the same volumes, the same fraction of the first remainder will be left in V_w. Thus after n extractions, there remains

$$f_n = [1 + P(V_o/V_w)]^{-n}. \tag{18–3}$$

Figure 18–1 shows the calculated fractions left after 1 through 10 extractions with equal volumes of both liquids at various values of P. Note that quantitative extraction can be obtained, in theory, for any value of P if sufficient numbers of extractions are performed.

A large volume of combined extracts is not desirable. The great advantage of dividing the extractant into small portions can be shown by substituting into (18–3) for V_o the divided portions, V_o/n, for n extractions:

$$f_n = [1 + P(V_o/nV_w)]^{-n}.$$

To demonstrate the meaning of this equation, consider the example: 100 ml of each solvent with extractions made with various divisions of the organic solvent.

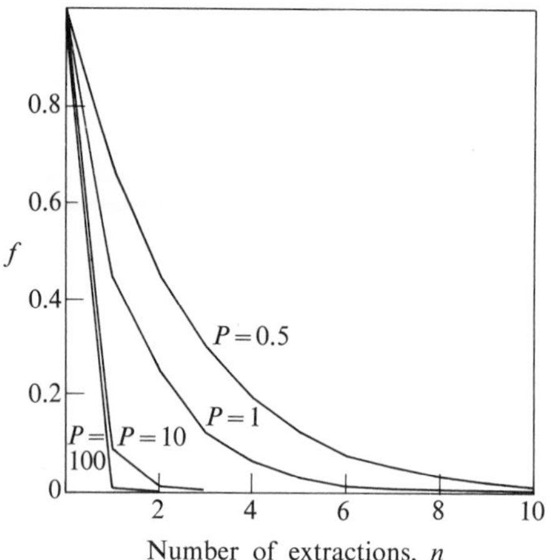

Fig. 18–1. Fractions left after n extractions at $P = 0.5, 1, 10, 100$.

Thus f_1 is for the whole 100 ml at once. Since $V_o = V_w$, the formula becomes

$$f_n = (1 + P/n)^{-n}.$$

When P is 0.1, $f_1 = 1/1.1$, $f_2 = (21/22)^2$, etc. See Table 18–1.

Table 18–1. Effect of Division of Extractant into Portions

P	f_1	f_2	f_3	f_4	f_∞
0.1	0.910	0.908	0.907	0.904	0.904
1	0.500	0.444	0.421	0.410	0.370
10	0.091	0.028	0.012	0.0067	4.6×10^{-5}
100	0.01	3.8×10^{-4}	2.5×10^{-5}	2.2×10^{-6}	10^{-43}

The last column in Table 18–1 gives the limiting value. This function, $(1 + P/n)^{-n}$, approaches e^{-P} (or $10^{-0.434P}$) as $n \to \infty$. So, the improvement by division levels toward this limit. In practice, quantitative extractions are used when P is in the range 10 to 10^4 or more. Here, extraction with 3 to 5 portions of about $\frac{1}{3}$ the aqueous volume achieves quantitative results. Division into smaller volumes of extractant is rarely much better for the same total volume of extractant. Washings of each layer can be kept small to reduce added liquid volumes.

18.1 COMPETING EQUILIBRIA INVOLVED

When the material undergoing extraction is involved in other equilibria in either phase, the observed distribution ratio, D, may vary with concentrations:

$$D = \frac{\text{total solute in phase 1}}{\text{total solute in phase 2}}. \tag{18–4}$$

If constants are known for all equilibria, the true constant for the extraction can be calculated in terms of the observed D. Conversely, D values under sufficiently varied conditions may allow determination of equilibrium constants. An example is explained in the laboratory section, Project 11, in which I_2 is distributed between CCl_4 and water with varied concentrations of KI. Assuming that the only competing reaction is the aqueous

$$I_2 + I^- \rightleftharpoons I_3^-,$$

one can evaluate the formation constant for I_3^- by finding D, if P for the distribution of I_2 between CCl_4 and pure water is known. One can easily obtain D through titration of the total I(0) in each phase of the various mixtures.

As the number of equilibria increase, the complexity of the extraction equilibrium does also. A few important cases are mentioned here; further examples are available in the literature cited at the end of this chapter.

If a solute has different forms (dimers, trimers, etc.) in each phase, one can write its equilibrium as

$$n[X_m]_w \rightleftharpoons m[X_n]_{org}, \qquad K_{eq} = \frac{[X_n]_{org}^m}{[X_m]_w^n}. \tag{18–5}$$

If n is not equal to m, the observed D (18–4), will vary with the total amount of X. For example, if HCl is distributed between water and benzene, it is found experimentally that D varies directly with the HCl concentration in the water layer at equilibrium. One can understand this in terms of the equilibrium

$$H_w^+ + Cl_w^- \rightleftharpoons HCl_{org}.$$

HCl is completely ionized in the very dilute water solutions and entirely associated in molecules in the benzene. The HCl concentration of the water, C_w, gives $[H^+] = [Cl^-]$. Thus

$$K_{eq} = \frac{[HCl]_{org}}{[H^+][Cl^-]} = \frac{[HCl]_{org}}{C_w^2},$$

$$D = \frac{[HCl]_{org}}{C_w} = K_{eq}C_w.$$

Thus D varies with C_w as observed.

The same is true for a weak acid, if we assume it to be so weak in water that a negligible amount is ionized and that it forms entirely a dimer, $(HA)_2$ in the organic layer, as do most carboxylic acids

$$2HA_w \rightleftharpoons [(HA)_2]_{org}.$$

Since the analytical concentration of HA in the organic layer is $2[(HA)_2]$, one can write just as above

$$K_{eq} = \frac{[(HA)_2]_{org}}{[HA]_w^2} = \frac{D}{2[HA]_w}.$$

So, again, D varies directly with the aqueous concentration.

If the acid is appreciably dissociated in water,

$$HA \rightleftharpoons H^+ + A^-, \qquad K_a = \frac{[H^+][A^-]}{[HA]},$$

one can use the α_1, fraction of the acid in the HA form (Chapter 8) to substitute for $[HA]_w$, $\alpha_1 C_w$ in the equilibrium expression for the extraction just derived

$$K_{eq} = \frac{[HA]_{org}}{2(\alpha_1 C_w)^2} = \frac{D}{2C_w}\left(1 + \frac{K_a}{[H^+]}\right)^2.$$

Here, D varies with C_w and also with $[H^+]$.

A common laboratory extraction is that of an uncharged metal ion complex, MX_n, where X^- is the ligand, usually a weak base in water. One may have to consider the equilibria:

1. complex formation,
2. HX reaction with water,
3. extractions of MX_n and HX into the organic layer,
4. reactions in the organic layer, especially dimerization.

The concentration and pH dependence of one common situation is not very difficult to derive, namely that for the case in which only MX_n and HX are extracted, as monomers. With D defined by (18–4), the true constants for the extractables are

$$P_M = \frac{[MX_n]_{org}}{[MX_n]_w}, \qquad P_{HX} = \frac{[HX]_{org}}{[HX]_w}. \tag{18–6}$$

From the formation constants of the metal complex, K_1 through K_n (Chapter 19), one can write (for the water layer)

$$\beta_n = K_1 K_2, \ldots, K_n = \frac{[MX_n]_w}{[M^{+n}][X^-]^n}. \tag{18–7}$$

If α_{0M} is the fraction of aqueous metal ion present in the form M^{+n},

$$[M^{+n}] = \alpha_{0M} C_M,$$

where C_M is the total metal ion concentration in all forms in water. This can be substituted into (18–7) to give

$$[MX_n]_w = \beta_n \alpha_{0M} C_M [X^-]^n.$$

But, from (18–6) and the K_a expression,

$$[X^-] = \frac{K_a[HX]_w}{[H^+]} = \frac{K_a[HX]_{org}}{P_{HX}[H^+]}.$$

Putting these into P_M (18–6) gives

$$P_M = \frac{[MX_n]_{org} P_{HX}^n [H^+]^n}{\beta_n \alpha_{0M} C_M K_a^n [HX]_{org}^n}. \tag{18–8}$$

The observed distribution ratio of metal is (18–4)

$$D_M = [MX_n]_{org}/C_M.$$

Collecting all constants into one K', in the P_M equation, we have

$$D_M = \left(\frac{P_M\beta_n K_a^n}{P_{HX}^n}\right)\alpha_{0M}\frac{[HX]_{org}^n}{[H^+]^n} = K'\alpha_{0M}\frac{[HX]_{org}^n}{[H^+]^n}. \qquad (18\text{–}9)$$

The dependence on $[HX]_{org}$ and $[H^+]$ predicted by (18–9) was tested by I. M. Kolthoff and E. B. Sandell* for a case where n is 2 and α_{0M} is effectively *one*; that is, at equilibrium very little complex is in the water layer, at the pH used. The case was the extraction of the zinc-dithizone complex into chloroform. Dithizone (diphenylthiocarbazone) is a monoprotic weak acid HDz, and the zinc ion forms an uncharged complex, $ZnDz_2$. In agreement with (18–9), the observed D_{Zn} was found to vary with the ratio $[HDz]_{org}^2/[H^+]_w^2$.

Detailed treatments of extractions of two major types, chelate and ion association, are considered in Chapter 6 of the book by Morrison and Freiser. Formulas derived for simple extraction in terms of P can be used with D under conditions for which D remains unchanged. They describe exactly only the ideal case, but give valuable qualitative description of the kinds of separations that may be expected in the complex cases. Naturally, for these, laboratory methods are developed empirically, usually with some D values as a guide. Students interested in biochemistry might look into journals on the subject. Extraction separations are very common and the methods of attacking specific problems may be illuminating. A few examples are cited toward the end of this chapter.

18.2 APPLICATIONS OF EXTRACTION SEPARATIONS

Table 18–2 lists a number of extraction methods for metallic elements. The methods for Fe(III) and U(VI) are macro methods, useful in the range from grams down to milligrams. Many of the other methods are micro methods. The references listed at the end of this chapter should be consulted for specific applications. Details of the Fe(III) extraction by methyl isobutyl ketone or di-isopropyl ether are given in the laboratory section. These solvents give rapid, clean separations of Fe(III) from most other elements which occur with iron.

The Fe(III) extraction from 7 to 8 *M* HCl by various solvents has some unusual features. There is a decrease in effective P at higher HCl concentrations due to increasing solubility of the solvent in the acid layer. (This is not the case for tributyl phosphate.) With di-isopropyl ether (iPE), two organic layers form at high iron concentrations. These have been found to be (1) a light yellow ether phase containing the iron as $HFeCl_4 \cdot 2(iPE) \cdot 5H_2O$ and (2) a denser, green ether layer containing the dietherate with fewer than five water molecules per iron. Both ether layers should be taken for Fe determinations.

---

* *J. Am. Chem. Soc.* **63,** 1906 (1941).

Table 18–2. Selected Solvent Extraction Separation Methods

Species	Dissolved in	Percent extracted and extractant	Separations and comments
Al(III)	pH 4.8–6.7 pH 8.2–11.5	100, 8-quinolinol 1% in CCl_4	Fe(III), Ni(II) if CN^- added. Be, Mg, Cr
Sb(V)	8 *M* HCl	99.5, diisopropyl ether	
Sb(III)	6.9 *M* HI	100, diethyl ether	
As(III)	11 *M* HCl	94, benzene	
Be(II)	pH 2	Acetylacetone	Al, U(VI) if EDTA added
Ce(IV)	1 *M* HNO_3	98, tributylphosphate	
Co(II) → (III)	pH 0.3–2	Acetylacetone in $CHCl_3$ with oxidation to Co(III)	Ni(II)
Co(II)	7 *M* SCN^-	75, diethyl ether	
Cr(III)	pH 0–2	Acetylacetone in $CHCl_3$	Slow reaction
Cu(II)	1.2 *N* HCl, cupferron	$CHCl_3$	Co, Ni, Zn
	pH 9	Dithizone in CCl_4 (13 ppm)	Co, Ni, Zn if EDTA added
Au(III)	1–3 *M* HBr	Diisopropyl ether	Fe(III) if PO_4^{3-} added
Fe(III)	8 *M* HCl	99.9, diisopropyl ether, *n*-butyl acetate,	Al, Cu, Co, Mn, Ni, Cr, Zn
	7 *M* HCl	methyl isobutyl ketone	
Pb(II)	CN^- citrate, pH 11+ diethyldithiocarbamate	CCl_4	All but Cd, Bi, Tl
Li(I)		Anhydrous LiCl soluble in 2 ethyl, 1-hexanol	Na, K
Hg(II)	pH 11 Diethyldithiocarbamate	CCl_4	If EDTA, all but Ag, Cu, Pd, Bi, Tl
	pH 1.5–2	Dithizone-CCl_4	Cu by EDTA
Ni(II)	pH 8 (approximate)	Dimethylglyoxime in CCl_4	Microgram colorimetric
Nb(V), Ta(V)	10 *M* HF, 6 *M* H_2SO_4 + 2 *M* NH_4F	Methylisobutyl ketone	All but As, Sn
Rare earths	12 *M* HNO_3	Tributylphosphate	Fractionations possible
Sn(II), (IV)	4.6 *M* HF	Ethyl ether	Ni, Cr, Co, Mn, etc. (not As or Sb)
U(VI)	Dilute HNO_3, $Al(NO_3)_3$	Ethyl acetate or tributyl phosphate or methyl isobutyl ketone	Fe(III), etc.
Zn(II)	pH 11	Diethyldithiocarbamate, CCl_4,	(Many interferences)
	pH 5.5	dithizone, CCl_4,	(Many interferences)
	2 *M* HCl	methyl dioctylamine, C_2HCl_3	Co, Ni, Mn

In dichromate titrimetric determinations of Fe or U, the two must be separated prior to reduction and titration. This could be done as above if the HCl is evaporated before continuing. A U(VI) extraction can be effected by several solvents (see Table 18–2) from an aqueous U(VI) solution which is about 2 M in HNO_3 and saturated in $Al(NO_3)_3$.

Quantitative separation of two solutes requires that their D values differ greatly and that one be near zero. When this is not the case, multiple extractions by the countercurrent method can be used.

Countercurrent Extraction

In 1944, L. C. Craig devised this method to separate several solutes of similar P values without using enormous solvent volumes. Countercurrent extraction refers to series extraction in which the extractant passes along the series over fresh volumes of the water (or lower layer liquid). This produces a remarkable distribution of the solutes among the successive liquid fractions. The technique has been widely used in organic and biochemical work.

To see how the distribution arises, let us take the common case of equal volumes of each solvent in Eq. (18–3). The solute is in the aqueous (or other) solvent in the first tube. All the other tubes have an equal volume of the solvent containing no solute. Into the first tube one puts an equal volume of the extracting solvent. The fraction $1/(P+1)$ remains in the lower layer, and $1 - 1/(P+1) = P/(P+1)$ is extracted. This is transferred to the second tube, and fresh solvent is also added to the first tube. The solute in each tube is now divided again between the layers in the same ratio so that we have

in tube 2	$1/(P+1)$ of $P/(P+1) = P/(P+1)^2$	remaining in lower layer,
	$P/(P+1)$ of $P/(P+1) = P^2/(P+1)^2$	in the upper layer;
in tube 1	$1/(P+1)$ of $1/(P+1) = 1/(P+1)^2$	remaining in lower layer,
	$P/(P+1)$ of $1/(P+1) = P/(P+1)^2$	extracted.

Next, a second set of transfers is made, the top layer of each tube is transferred to the next tube and fresh solvent added to tube 1. The sum of the contents of the upper part of tube 1 and the lower part of tube 2 is $2P/(P+1)^2$, now in tube 2. Tube 3 now contains the former upper layer of tube 2, $P^2/(P+1)^2$. In this manner, the process is continued and Table 18–3 is constructed.

Table 18–3. Distribution Fractions in Countercurrent Distribution

n transfers \ Tube, r =	1	2	3	4	5
0	1				
1	$1/(P+1)$	$P/(P+1)$			
2	$1/(P+1)^2$	$2P/(P+1)^2$	$P^2/(P+1)^2$		
3	$1/(P+1)^3$	$3P/(P+1)^3$	$3P^2/(P+1)^3$	$P^3/(P+1)^3$	
4	$1/(P+1)^4$	$4P/(P+1)^4$	$6P^2/(P+1)^4$	$4P^3/(P+1)^4$	$P^4/(P+1)^4$

Table 18–4

n \ $r =$	1	2	3	4	5	6	7	8	9	10	11
0	1										
1	$\frac{1}{2}$	$\frac{1}{2}$									
2	$\frac{1}{4}$	$\frac{2}{4}$	$\frac{1}{4}$								
3	$\frac{1}{8}$	$\frac{3}{8}$	$\frac{3}{8}$	$\frac{1}{8}$							
4	$\frac{1}{16}$	$\frac{4}{16}$	$\frac{6}{16}$	$\frac{4}{16}$	$\frac{1}{16}$						
6	$\frac{1}{64}$	$\frac{6}{64}$	$\frac{15}{64}$	$\frac{20}{64}$	$\frac{15}{64}$	$\frac{6}{64}$	$\frac{1}{64}$				
10	$\frac{1}{1024}$	$\frac{10}{1024}$	$\frac{45}{1024}$	$\frac{120}{1024}$	$\frac{210}{1024}$	$\frac{252}{1024}$	$\frac{210}{1024}$	$\frac{120}{1024}$	$\frac{45}{1024}$	$\frac{10}{1024}$	$\frac{1}{1024}$

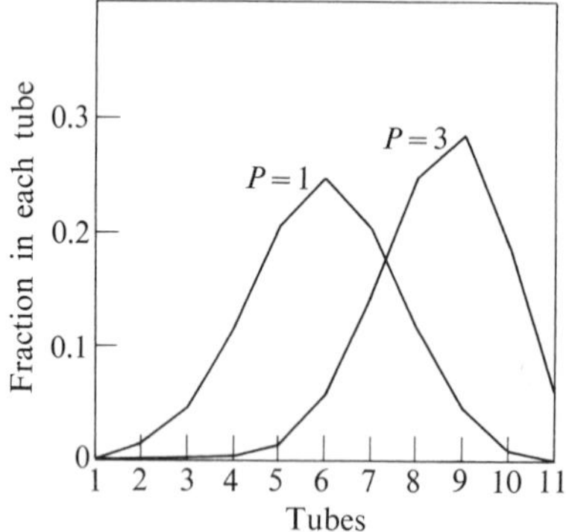

Fig. 18–2. Countercurrent distribution after 10 transfers (11 tubes).

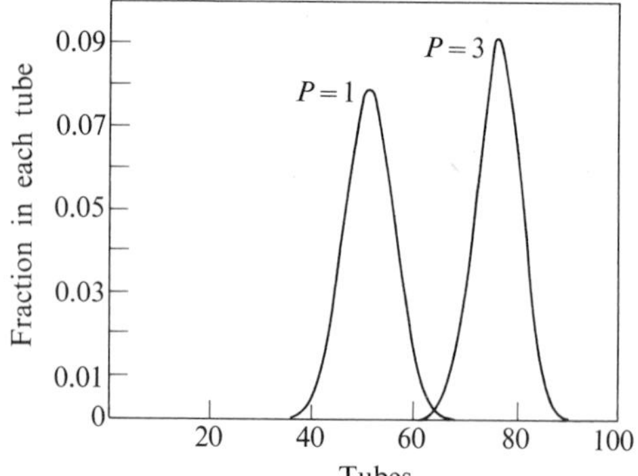

Fig. 18–3. Countercurrent distribution after 100 transfers (101 tubes).

The familiar pattern in Table 18–3 is the binomial expansion of $[1/(P + 1) + P/(P + 1)]^n$. A numerical example is useful to help clarify this procedure. The student can easily confirm that $P = 1$ gives a table of the form shown in Table 18–4.

Ten transfers require 11 tubes. The last row in Table 18–4 is plotted in Fig. 18–2 along with the fractions for a substance, B, of $P = 3$. This shows some separation. By increasing the number of tubes, the separation is increased. Apparatus has been built with hundreds of tubes interconnected so that transfers can be made by machine operation. The curves for several P values in 100 transfers are plotted in Fig. 18–3 to show the improved separation. Combining tubes 34 through 62 would give one over 99% pure A($P = 1$), while tubes 66 through 88 would hold most of the B($P = 3$) with less than 0.1% of the A as contaminant. Note that the maxima come at the middle tube for $P = 1$, and at tube $\frac{75}{100}$ for $P = 3$ ($\frac{3}{4}$ is extracted at each equilibration).*

* Calculations for 101 tubes were run on the IBM 1620 computer by Alan Darlington, The University of the South, 1966.

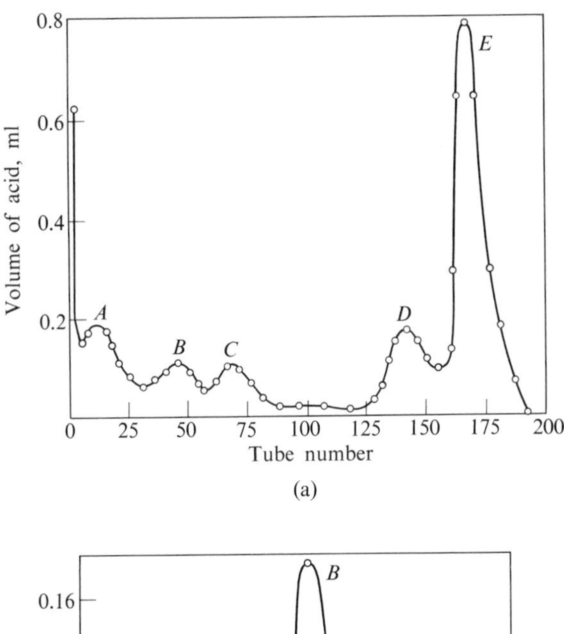

(a)

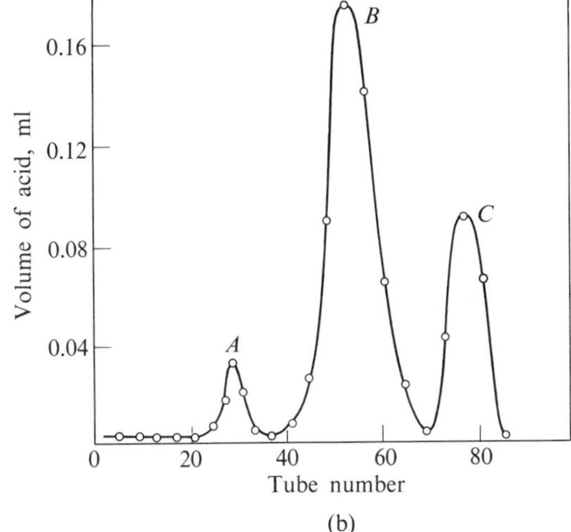

(b)

Fig. 18–4. Alkaloids of veratrine. (a) Countercurrent distribution of 5 g portion from a sample; 200 transfers between chloroform and pH 7.0, 0.5 *M* phosphate buffer: A = mixture (large part cevacine), B = unreported component, C = unknown X_1, D = sabatine, E = mixture (hydrophilic components). (b) Countercurrent distribution of 100 mg portion of peak E, hydrophilic components from distribution as shown in (a): A = sabatine, B = veracevine, C = sabine. The volume of acid in titration is a measure of the amount of alkaloid in each tube. [After G. R. Svoboda, *Anal. Chem.* **34,** 1559 (1962).]

Extensive biochemical applications of this separation method have been made to separate peptides, hormones, etc., which are difficult to separate by other methods.* An inorganic application in rare earth separations has been reported.

Rare earths were separated in large amounts using concentrated HNO_3 for one phase and tributyl phosphate diluted in an alkane mixture for the other. A continuous countercurrent method was devised in which the two phases flowed through a vertical mixing tube in opposite directions.†

A 200 tube Craig apparatus was used to separate some of the alkaloids of veratrine (Fig. 18–4). Aqueous buffer and $CHCl_3$ were the two phases.‡

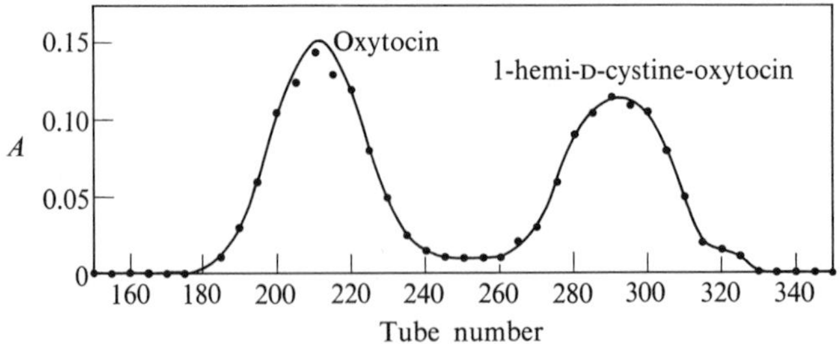

Fig. 18–5. Separations of diastereoisomers by countercurrent extraction by Nobel Prize winner Vincent du Vigneaud and coworkers, *J. Am. Chem. Soc.* **88,** 1310 (1966). (Absorbance, *A*, is proportional to concentration.) Countercurrent distribution of a mixture of purified 1-hemi-D-cystine-oxytocin (50 mg) and oxytocin (51 mg) after 550 transfers in 1-butanol-benzene-pyridine-0.1% acetic acid (6:2:1:9).

A truly complex mixture of oils from bituminous coal tar was separated by fractional distillation followed by extraction of the fractions in a 60 tube Craig apparatus with iso-octane and 90% ethanol for the two phases. Fifty-one materials including 19 identifiable specific compounds were separated.§

Example diagrams from actual cases are shown in Figs. 18–4 and 18–5.

SUMMARY

Equations are derived for simple and repetitive extraction and for countercurrent extraction. Example applications are given.

---

* The chapter by L. C. and D. Craig in Vol. III of *Technique of Organic Chemistry*, ed. by A. Weissberger, and the text by Laitinen give some examples.

† See B. Weaver, F. A. Kappelmann, and A. C. Topp, *J. Am. Chem. Soc.* **75,** 3943 (1953).

‡ See G. R. Svoboda, *Anal. Chem.* **34,** 1559 (1962).

§ See P. Estep, C. Karr, W. Warner, and E. Childers, *Anal. Chem.* **37,** 1715 (1965).

SUGGESTIONS FOR FURTHER READING

ARREGUIN, B., J. PADILLA, and J. HERRAN, *J. Chem. Educ.* **39,** 539 (1962). A clear demonstration of the Craig countercurrent method is possible with two indicators distributed between basic aqueous solution and *n*-butanol by six separatory funnel extractions.

CRAIG, L. C., and D. CRAIG, in *Technique of Organic Chemistry*, ed. by A. Weissberger, Vol. III. Part 1. New York: Interscience Publishers, 1956, pp. 149ff.

GUENTHER, W. B., *J. Chem. Educ.* **42,** 277 (1965) describes a demonstration of the three-phase behavior in the extraction system, $FeCl_3$-$HCl_{(aq)}$-diisopropyl ether.

LAITINEN, H. A., *Chemical Analysis*, New York: McGraw-Hill, 1960, Chapter 25, part 2 and Chapter 14, parts 6 and 7.

MORRISON, G. H., and H. FREISER, *Solvent Extraction in Analytical Chemistry*, New York: John Wiley, 1957.

WALTON, H. F., *Principles and Methods of Analytical Chemistry*, 2nd ed. Englewood Cliffs, N.J.: Prentice-Hall, 1964, Chapter 10.

PROBLEMS

1. Derive the formula for iterative solvent extraction (Eq. 18–3).
2. Make a table of fractions left unextracted when 100 ml of a solution are shaken with 100 ml of extracting liquid which is divided into 1, 2, 3, and 4 portions. Do this for cases of partition coefficients, $P = 1, 2, 10$, and 100. Calculate the limit f_∞ for each P.
3. Derive the binomial expression for countercurrent distribution. Show the expected distribution of a solute for which $P = 2$ among 11 tubes (10 transfers) with equal volumes of solvents. Plot as in Fig. 18–2.
4. Given that the effective partition coefficient is 100 in favor of the organic solvent for the removal of Fe(III) from 7 *M* HCl by methyl isobutyl ketone, calculate the percent extracted by 1, 2, and 3 extractions of 100 ml of the Fe(III)-HCl solution by 30 ml portions of MIBK.
5. Literature values for the solubility of I_2 in pure water and CCl_4 at 25°C are 0.00133 *M* and 0.114_4 *M*. Calculate *P*. Derive the proper equation for the following calculation and solve. How many 100 ml portions of fresh water are needed to wash 99% of the I_2 out of 10 ml CCl_4 saturated with I_2?

CHAPTER 19

ION-LIGAND EQUILIBRIA

Chemists have long recognized that charged species of more than one atom, such as NO_3^-, $SO_4^=$, UO_2^{++}, have great stability and can retain their identity through certain reactions. When large numbers of transition-metal complexes were discovered in the late 19th century, Werner, in 1892, formulated a new concept of coordination number to rationalize what seemed to be a new phenomenon, the combining of neutral "molecules" whose valency was already "satisfied" to form larger molecules. For example, consider the reaction

$$NiCl_2 + 6H_2O \rightarrow NiCl_2{\cdot}6H_2O,$$

where NH_3 and other bases could take the place of H_2O.

For the purposes of this text, we will consider complexing as taking place between Lewis acids and bases. For the above example, we may write

$$Ni^{++} + 6{:}OH_2 + 2Cl^- \rightarrow Ni({:}OH_2)_6^{++} + 2Cl^-.$$

Modern theory regards the Ni—O bond here as no different in kind from that in NiO. The older term, coordinate covalency, should not be understood to refer to some unique type of bonding. These bonds are similar to other covalent ones in that the negative electrons and the positive nuclei of two or more atoms achieve a more stable arrangement of charges together than apart. The term coordination chemistry generally connotes species like the transition-metal complexes, although it is difficult to make a fundamental distinction between them and species like $SO_4^=$ or NH_4^+.

The coordination number and geometry of most complexes we shall meet may be classified as outlined below.

VB hybrid term	*sp*	sp^3	dsp^2	d^2sp^3
Geometry	Linear	Tetrahedral	Square planar	Octahedral
Coordination number	2	4	4	6
Examples	$Ag(NH_3)_2^+$ UO_2^{++}	$FeCl_4^-$ $Co(SCN)_4^=$	$PtCl_4^=$ $Ni(DMG)_2$	$Co(NH_3)_6^{3+}$ $Cr(H_2O)_4Cl_2^+$

For quantitative uses, it is important to consider the number of ligands, the rate of formation, and the equilibrium constant of formation of the complexes in question.

19.1 INERT AND LABILE COMPLEXES

Most striking is the enormous range of rates of complex ion reactions. The ammonia complexes of Cu(II), Ni(II), and Zn(II) react with acids as fast as mixing occurs, while those of Co(III) and Cr(III) can remain in acid solutions for hours or days at room temperature. The first are *labile* and the second are *inert* complexes. It must be stressed that the speed of reaction has no direct relation to the thermodynamic stability expressed by the equilibrium constant or standard free energy of reaction. In all the above ammine examples, the equilibrium lies far to the side of NH_4^+ formation in acid solution. In the inert cases, it is the path (mechanism) which delays reaction: the activation energy is high. Slow reactions cannot be used for direct titration reactions.

There are some guides that can be followed in predicting and understanding inert behavior. Of the common metal ions, only Cr(III), Co(III), and sometimes Fe(II) and Fe(III) form inert complexes with simple anions and bases. Some structural correlations are outlined below. (For details consult the texts listed at the end of this chapter.)

Generally labile are complexes formed by:

1. ions having inert gas electron structures, e.g., Na^+, Mg^{++}, Al^{3+} or those with filled subshells, e.g., Zn^{++}, Ag^+, Cd^{++};
2. transition-metal ions with fewer than three d electrons or more than six d electrons, e.g., Sc(III) and the rare earths (d^0), Ti(III)(d^1), V(III)(d^2), Co(II)(d^7), Ni(II)(d^8), Cu(II)(d^9).

The picture for d^3 through d^6 ions is more complicated. Inert and labile behaviors for some of these ions are listed below, where the inert ions are arranged in their order in the periodic table.

Generally inert	d^3	d^5	d^6	d^6	d^6
	Cr(III)			Co(III)	
	Mo(III)		Ru(II)	Rh(III)	Pd(IV)
	W(III)	Re(II)	Os(II)	Ir(III)	Pt(IV)

Labile Mn(II), Fe(II), Fe(III) except with CN^- and a few other ligands.

Exceptions occur with pi-bonding (and some double-bonding) ligands like CN^-, CO, and many organic chelating agents. These all favor inert behavior though they do not produce it in all cases.

19.2 EQUILIBRIUM CONSTANTS

With the reservation about reaction time for inert cases, the equilibrium constant of formation tells whether quantitative use can be made of a complex. Relatively simple calculations with complexes were treated in Chapters 10 and 12, where they affected precipitations and electrode potentials.

In the Cu(II)-NH_3 system, we find a situation similar to that with citric acid discussed in Chapter 8. At some pH values, several citrate species exist together in appreciable amounts. All the following equilibria may be important simultaneously. These are presented as formations. (For traditional reasons, weak acids are still handled as "dissociations" with K_a's.)*

$$\begin{aligned}
Cu^{++} + NH_3 &\rightleftharpoons Cu(NH_3)^{++}, & \log K_1 &= 4.15,\\
Cu(NH_3)^{++} + NH_3 &\rightleftharpoons Cu(NH_3)_2{}^{++}, & \log K_2 &= 3.50,\\
Cu(NH_3)_2{}^{++} + NH_3 &\rightleftharpoons Cu(NH_3)_3{}^{++}, & \log K_3 &= 2.89,\\
Cu(NH_3)_3{}^{++} + NH_3 &\rightleftharpoons Cu(NH_3)_4{}^{++}, & \log K_4 &= 2.13.
\end{aligned} \tag{19–1}$$

(The K values are given for 30°C in 2 M NH_4NO_3. The $NH_4{}^+$ lowers $[OH^-]$ to prevent $Cu(OH)_2$ formation. The K^0 values would be hard to determine.) The rather slight change from K_1 to K_4 means that several species may exist together in some $[NH_3]$. Titration of Cu(II) by NH_3 is not feasible because of the overlap and because K_4 is too small to allow an abrupt change in $[NH_3]$ after four equivalents have been added.

An overall constant for $Cu(NH_3)_4{}^{++}$ can be derived by multiplying the expressions for K_1 through K_4. All the intermediate species cancel and leave

$$\beta_4 = K_{1\text{-}4} = K_1K_2K_3K_4 = \frac{[Cu(NH_3)_4{}^{++}]}{[Cu^{++}][NH_3]^4} = 10^{12.67}. \tag{19–2}$$

The reader must beware of such constants. True, if one could somehow know $[Cu^{++}]$ and $[NH_3]$ in a solution, it would be possible to calculate the concentration of the tetrammine. But, how can the first two be known? The originally added Cu^{++} and NH_3 are distributed among the complexes. At the extreme of large excess of NH_3, β_4 can serve. For example, if 0.010 M Cu^{++} is made 1 M in NH_3, approximate values for the tetrammine and other complexes can be found. Assume that most of the copper goes to the $Cu(NH_3)_4{}^{++}$ form. Then

$$\frac{(0.01)}{x(1 - 0.04)^4} = 10^{12.67}$$

and

$$x = [Cu^{++}] \cong 10^{-14.6}.$$

But

$$K_4 = 10^{2.13} = \frac{(0.01)}{y(1 - 0.04)}$$

and

$$y = [Cu(NH_3)_3{}^{++}] \cong 10^{-4}.$$

Here the triammine is about 1% of the Cu(II). The blue color in high $[NH_3]$

* Remember that the tetrammine is known to be $Cu(NH_3)_4(H_2O)_2{}^{++}$, and the reactions are replacements abbreviated as in (19–1). In complete form, the first is $Cu(H_2O)_6{}^{++} + NH_3 \rightleftharpoons Cu(H_2O)_5(NH_3)^{++} + H_2O$ (i.e., no water is shown).

is used as an approximate colorimetric method for $[Cu^{++}]$. At $[NH_3]$ below 1 *M*, the Cu(II) is more and more spread among the other complexes.

Clearly, it would be incorrect to use β_4 in many equilibrium calculations for such systems. The kind of situation often incorrectly presented is to use the overall β to find the $[NH_3]$ when solid $Cu(NH_3)_4SO_4$ is added to water. To say that x moles dissociate to x moles of Cu(II) and $4x$ moles of NH_3 is wrong, not even a good approximation to the real situation. Such a problem is difficult to treat exactly, but sometimes the same approximation made with polyprotic acids will work: that only the first step occurs to an appreciable extent. Treatment of all cases is shown in the following sections.

19.3 GRAPHICAL REPRESENTATIONS OF COMPLEX-ION EQUILIBRIA

The methods of calculating and diagramming the relative amounts of the species present were introduced in Chapter 8, where we used acetic and citric acid, with the proton considered as the ligand, as our examples. As in those cases, the calculation of the concentrations of all species from initial mixture data is difficult if we attempt it directly. Simpler algebra results if we first calculate the fraction of each species as a function of the concentration of free ligand.

Example 1. For the system Cu(II)-NH_3 calculate the values and plot the two diagrams: (a) for the fraction, α, of each species versus $\log [NH_3]$ and (b) for the distribution diagram.

Let A be NH_3 and C the total Cu(II) in all forms:

$$C = [Cu^{++}] + [CuA^{++}] + [CuA_2{}^{++}] + [CuA_3{}^{++}] + [CuA_4{}^{++}].$$

Substitute the stepwise K expressions to eliminate all complex ammine terms:

$$\begin{aligned} C = {} & [Cu^{++}] + K_1[Cu^{++}][A] + K_1K_2[Cu^{++}][A]^2 \\ & + K_1K_2K_3[Cu^{++}][A]^3 + K_1K_2K_3K_4[Cu^{++}][A]^4. \end{aligned}$$

Factor out the $[Cu^{++}]$ and use the C in the α expressions:

$$\begin{aligned} \alpha_0 &= [Cu^{++}]/C \\ &= (1 + K_1[A] + K_1K_2[A]^2 + K_1K_2K_3[A]^3 + K_1K_2K_3K_4[A]^4)^{-1}, \end{aligned} \quad (19\text{–}3)$$

The rest can be expressed in terms of α_0:

$$\begin{aligned} \alpha_1 &= [CuA^{++}]/C = K_1[Cu^{++}][A]/C = K_1[A]\alpha_0, \\ \alpha_2 &= [CuA_2{}^{++}]/C = K_1K_2[A]^2\alpha_0, \\ \alpha_3 &= [CuA_3{}^{++}]/C = K_1K_2K_3[A]^3\alpha_0, \\ \alpha_4 &= [CuA_4{}^{++}]/C = K_1K_2K_3K_4[A]^4\alpha_0. \end{aligned}$$

The fractions of each are seen to depend only on the free ligand concentration, and not on the amount of total Cu(II). Note that [A] is the free [A] after equilibrium is reached, not the amount added. We are now able to put in the K values given above to get α values at enough points to plot the curves. The student may verify these values given below for A = 0.1, 10^{-3}, 10^{-5} and others assigned in the problems.

[A]	α_0	α_1	α_2	α_3	α_4
0.1	2×10^{-9}	3×10^{-6}	9×10^{-4}	0.069	0.93
10^{-3}	0.010	0.141	0.451	0.351	0.047
10^{-5}	0.873	0.123	0.004	"0"	"0"

The notation "0" means negligible and not needed in calculation.

Note that the interpretation of the first line is: To obtain a free $[NH_3]$ value of 0.100 M, one must add enough NH_3 to convert 93% of the total Cu(II) to $Cu(NH_3)_4^{++}$ and 7% to $Cu(NH_3)_3^{++}$. Also, it is of interest that at $[A] = 10^{-3}$, all five species are present to 1% or more of the total Cu(II).

From α values at each power of ten and at the maxima, the curves in Figs. 19–1(a) and (b) were drawn. The maxima were found by differentiating $d\alpha_n/d[A]$ and setting it equal to zero. (Actually it is easier to find the minimum of $1/\alpha_n$.) In some cases these are quartic equations, but numerical approximation is not lengthy because an estimate of the maximum [A] coordinate can be made from the plot of the other points.

Approximate Sketch Method

From the K expressions, the log [A] values of crossings of the α lines can be determined readily. At crossings, two species have equal values of α, thus Cu^{++} and CuA^{++} cross at

$$K_1 = [CuA^{++}]/[Cu^{++}][A], \qquad [A] = 1/K_1 = 10^{-4.15}.$$

Similarly,

$$\begin{aligned} CuA^{++} &\text{ and } CuA_2^{++} \text{ cross at } [A] = 10^{-3.50}, \\ CuA_2^{++} &\text{ and } CuA_3^{++} \text{ cross at } [A] = 10^{-2.89}, \\ CuA_3^{++} &\text{ and } CuA_4^{++} \text{ cross at } [A] = 10^{-2.13}. \end{aligned}$$

Another crossing occurs at

$$K_1K_2 = [CuA_2^{++}]/[Cu^{++}][A]^2, \qquad [A] = (K_1K_2)^{-1/2} = 10^{-3.82},$$

the crossing of α_0 and α_2. All other pairs of species can be found like this down to α_0 and α_4, which cross at

$$[A] = \frac{1}{\sqrt[4]{K_1K_2K_3K_4}} = 10^{-3.17}.$$

For adjacent species with K values separated by at least two powers of ten, the crossings occur at α values of 0.5. This is not the case here, so we must calculate

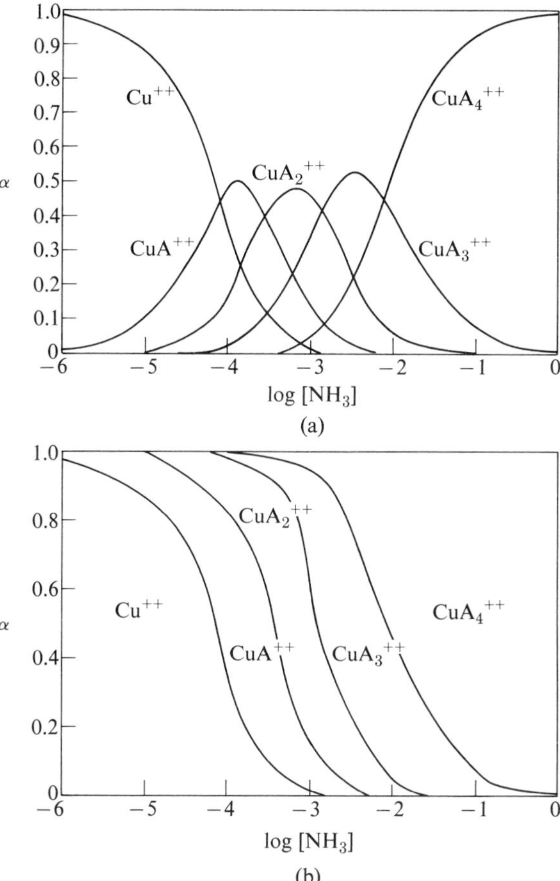

Fig. 19–1. (a) Abundances of species in the Cu(II)-NH_3 system (at 30°C in 2 M NH_4NO_3, where A is NH_3). (b) Distribution diagram of Cu(II)-NH_3 species.

the α values. Even so, the crossings serve to tell the [A] regions in which the several species have their largest fractions present. The student may check this on the Hg^{++}-Cl^- diagram, Fig. 19–4, and on his assigned problems.

The parallel between the crossings here and the buffered 1:1 cases for polyprotic acids should be apparent. These were pointed out in detail for citric acid in Chapter 8.

With the information obtained, one can now approach the problem of the original amounts of reactants.

Example 2. How many moles of NH_3 must be added to 1 liter of 0.020 M Cu(II) solution to make free $[NH_3] = 10^{-3}$? What are the concentrations of each species present?

From the diagrams or table, one calculates the part of the Cu(II) in each species as indicated in the following table.

α	$\times$ 0.020 = M	Moles NH_3 used	Total NH_3
0.010	2.0×10^{-4} Cu^{++}	0	45.7×10^{-3}
0.141	$2.8_2 \times 10^{-3}$ CuA^{++}	$2.8_2 \times 10^{-3}$	$+1 \times 10^{-3}$
0.451	$9.0_2 \times 10^{-3}$ CuA_2^{++}	$18.0_4 \times 10^{-3}$	46.7×10^{-3} or 0.047 moles
0.351	$7.0_2 \times 10^{-3}$ CuA_3^{++}	$21.0_6 \times 10^{-3}$	
0.047	9.4×10^{-4} CuA_4^{++}	$3.7_6 \times 10^{-3}$	
		Total: $45.6_8 \times 10^{-3}$	

Formation Curves

A useful concept is that of the ligand number, $\bar{n}$, the average number of ligands per metal ion (or acceptor),

$$\bar{n} = \frac{[\text{A total}] - [\text{A free}]}{C}$$

$$= \frac{[CuA^{++}] + 2[CuA_2^{++}] + 3[CuA_3^{++}] + 4[CuA_4^{++}]}{C}.$$

From the equations (19–3), this becomes

$$\bar{n} = \alpha_1 + 2\alpha_2 + 3\alpha_3 + 4\alpha_4. \tag{19–4}$$

From the calculations, or the diagrams above, the values of $\bar{n}$ are easily found and plotted versus the log $[NH_3]$, the formation curve in Fig. 19–2. Note that there is no abrupt change at any of the stepwise complex formations and that CuA_4^{++} is not formed quantitatively even at 1 M excess NH_3 concentration. Needless to say, this does not make a feasible titration method. Let us proceed to

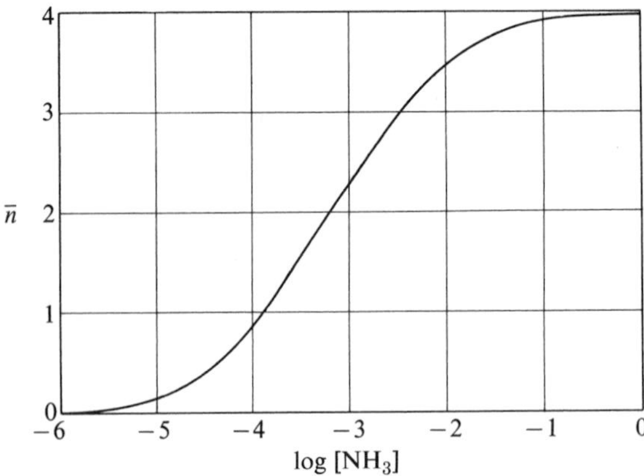

Fig. 19–2. Formation curve for the system Cu(II)-NH_3.

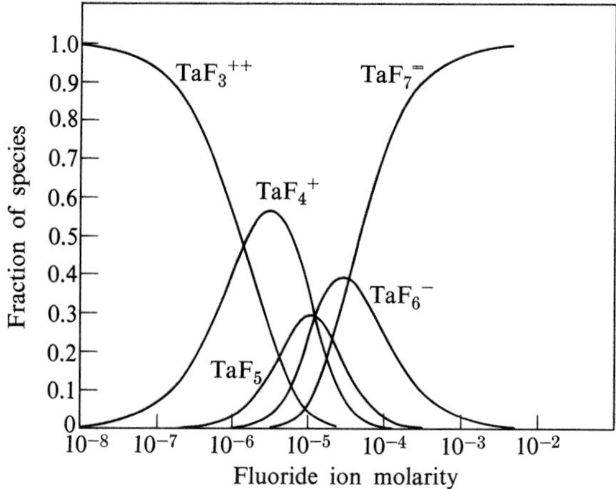

Fig. 19–3. Relative concentrations of tantalum fluoride complexes in 3 *M* perchlorate. Curves for the system Ta(V)-F^- were obtained from solvent extraction data and analyzed by computer techniques. [After L. P. Varga, *et al.*, *Anal. Chem.* **37,** 1003 (1965).]

a case of closely spaced K values but favorable enough to make a titration possible. The kind of diagram that results when K_n values are close together is shown in Fig. 19–3.

Hg(II)-Cl^- system. Of interest because of its value in Cl^- titration in colored and highly acid solutions are the equilibria in the system Hg(II)-Cl^-. The five species found are related by stepwise formation constants, determined in 0.5 *M* $NaClO_4$:

$$\begin{aligned} &HgCl^+ && \log K_1 = 6.74,\\ &HgCl_2 && \log K_2 = 6.48,\\ &HgCl_3^- && \log K_3 = 0.85,\\ &HgCl_4^= && \log K_4 = 1.00. \end{aligned}$$

The abrupt drop after $HgCl_2$ is attributed to the need for changing existing bond angles. Since $HgCl_2$ is linear, it must bend to make $HgCl_3^-$. Similar behavior is found with other Hg(II)-halide and SCN^-, CN^- systems, but not with the corresponding Zn(II) and Cd(II) systems.

The same equations used above apply here by replacing Cu by Hg and letting A be Cl^-. The relative abundance diagram and formation curve are shown in Figs. 19–4 and 19–5, respectively. Here, the formation of $HgCl_2$ is almost quantitative before any $HgCl_3^-$ forms. This point comes at much lower ligand concentration than for $Cu(NH_3)_4^{++}$. It would seem that titrations could be based on this behavior. Let us calculate the concentrations of important species present at the equivalence point, say 0.010 *M* $HgCl_2$ solution. Figure 19–4 shows that $HgCl_2$ can exist at about $[Cl^-] = 10^{-4}$ as almost the only species of Hg(II). It

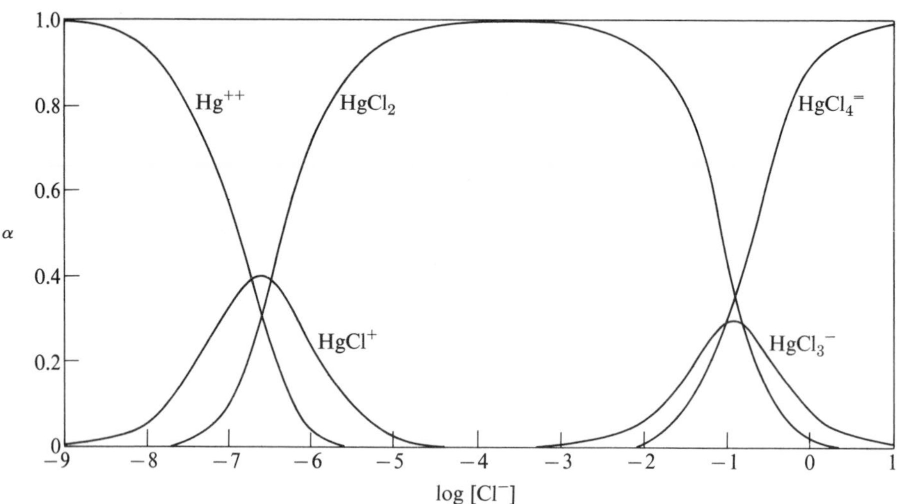

Fig. 19–4. Relative abundances of species in the system Hg(II)-Cl^-. Calculated from log K_n values: 6.74, 6.48, 0.85, and 1.00.

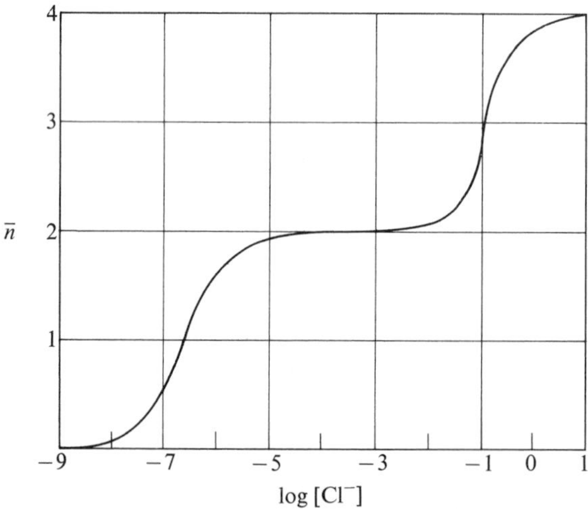

Fig. 19–5. Formation curve for Hg(II)-Cl^-.

is reasonable to try approximations based on this assumption:

$$\begin{matrix} x & & x & & 0.01 - x \\ HgCl^+ & + & Cl^- & \rightleftharpoons & HgCl_2\ , \end{matrix} \qquad K_2 = 10^{6.48} \cong 0.01/x^2,$$

$$x = 10^{-4.24}.$$

These values for $HgCl^+$ and Cl^- are compatible with the diagram, which shows at $[Cl^-] = 10^{-4.2}$, $[HgCl^+] = \alpha_1 C \cong (0.01)(0.01) = 10^{-4}$. Putting these values

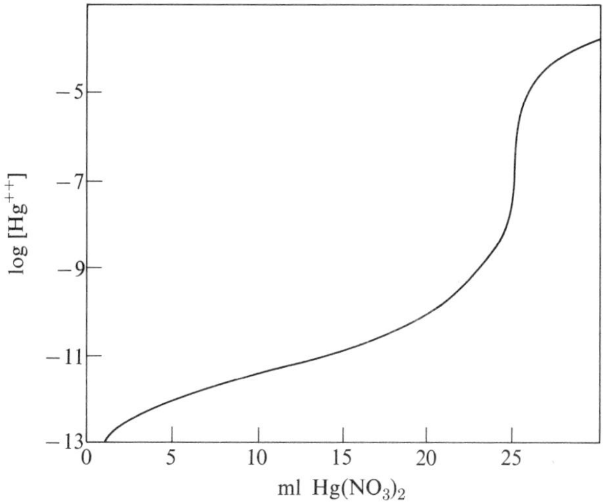

Fig. 19–6. Titration curve for 50 ml 0.0100 M Cl^- by 0.0100 M Hg^{++}.

into K_1 gives:

$$K_1 = 10^{-6.74} = 10^{-4.24}/[Hg^{++}](10^{-4.24}),$$
$$[Hg^{++}] \cong 10^{-6.7}.$$

An indicator for this $[Hg^{++}]$ is the $FeNO(CN)_5^{=}$ ion which is used in about 10^{-3} M concentrations. The K_{sp} of $HgFeNO(CN)_5$ is 3×10^{-9}. Thus the Hg^{++} is about the right concentration for us to expect another drop to cause precipitation. This precipitate of the "nitroprusside" is a highly visible milkiness which can be seen even in deeply colored solutions. The endpoint error may be rather large and is determined empirically for precise work. The error can be calculated by the methods used for precipitation titration, described in Chapter 10. Other Hg^{++} indicators are diphenyl carbazone and diphenyl carbazide which form colored complexes. The K_3 value is low enough to keep down interference from $HgCl_3^-$ formation at the equivalence point. The above values in K_3 show $(HgCl_3^-) \cong 10^{-5}$. It is rather the release of Hg^{++} and an early endpoint which is the problem, at very low concentrations. At higher concentrations, the reaction

$$HgCl_2 + Hg^{++} \rightleftharpoons 2HgCl^+, \qquad K = K_1/K_2 = 1.8,$$

removes some of the Hg^{++} needed to react with the indicator, and the endpoint comes late. Standardized conditions can control these errors.

The contrast in the diagrams for the systems Cu(II)-NH_3 and Hg(II)-Cl^- is clear. A titration curve, Fig. 19–6, for Cl^- by Hg^{++}, both 0.0100 M, can be calculated by assuming Hg^{++} goes to $HgCl_2$ when Cl^- is in excess so that one uses $K_1K_2 = [HgCl_2]/[Hg^{++}][Cl^-]^2$ to approximate $[Hg^{++}]$. At the endpoint, the $[Hg^{++}]$ in the 3.3×10^{-3} M $HgCl_2$ solution is found as in the example above. After the equivalence point, K_2 and K_1 are used in succession to get the $[Hg^{++}]$.

At the start, log $[Hg^{++}]$ is $-\infty$. An indicator is needed that signals $[Hg^{++}]$ between 10^{-7} and 10^{-6}.

Examination of K values shows that few complexes with monodentate ligands are suitable for titrations. Besides several mercury complexes, only the cyanides of silver and a few others exhibit the behavior we see in the Hg(II) cases. Best known is the Liebig titration for CN^-,

$$Ag^+ + 2CN^- \rightarrow Ag(CN)_2^- \qquad \log K_1K_2 = 20,$$
$$(\log K_3 = 0.70, \qquad \log K_4 = -1.13).$$

As with $HgCl_2$, the third and fourth complexes do not interfere. CN^- can be titrated with standard $AgNO_3$ to an endpoint indicated by precipitation of white AgCN. That is, after the equivalence point, more Ag^+ gives

$$Ag^+ + Ag(CN)_2^- \rightarrow \underline{2AgCN}, \qquad K_{sp} = 2 \times 10^{-16}.$$

Nickel, cobalt, copper, and zinc can be determined by addition of known excess CN^- and back titration with $AgNO_3$. The expected complexes are formed with nickel, copper, and zinc. Cobalt(II) forms $Co(CN)_5OH^{3-}$ with air oxidation or $Co(CN)_6{}^{3-}$ with H_2O_2 present. Methods have been developed using precipitation of AgI as the indicator. In view of the advantages of EDTA methods, cyanide titrations of metal ions are rarely needed.

As soon as one moves from mono- to polydentate ligands, the K values increase so that many possibilities for titrations appear. These are discussed in Chapter 21.

19.4 CALCULATION OF SPECIES PRESENT IN COMPLEXING MIXTURES

Thus far, the mathematically simpler problems have been used: finding species distribution when the unbound ligand concentration is known and when simplifying approximations are obvious—in the Cu(II)-NH_3 and Hg(II)-Cl^- examples given. More commonly, only the equilibrium constants and the materials used to make the solution are given. Then the procedure for calculation of the concentrations of all possible species may not be obvious. Successive approximations from the equilibrium-constant expressions may be a time-consuming approach. The following suggestions and examples should help in rapid solution, especially if the α and $\bar{n}$ diagrams are already available for the system.

Step 1. For a first approximation, add the total available ligand and cation and combine them until one is exhausted (just as was done for polyprotic acid cases in Chapter 5, case V, Examples i, ii, and iii). Use these results in the appropriate K_n expression as a two-species approximation. Solve for the unbound ligand concentration.

Step 2. See if the α and $\bar{n}$ diagrams agree with the approximation found in Step 1 at the ligand concentration found.

Step 3. If there is disagreement in Step 2, use material-balance conditions and the α and $\bar{n}$ diagrams to make more accurate calculations. Examples follow to show cases requiring this step.

A useful relation for applying Step 3 is found from the ligand material balance. Let M be the cation, A the ligand, and C_A the total ligand. Then

$$C_A = [A] + [MA] + 2[MA_2] + 3[MA_3] + \cdots$$

Divide by the total cation in all forms, C_M, to get

$$\frac{C_A}{C_M} = \frac{[A]}{C_M} + \frac{[MA] + 2[MA_2] + 3[MA_3] + \cdots}{C_M}.$$

The last term is simply $\bar{n}$ (Eq. 19–4) so

$$C_A/C_M = [A]/C_M + \bar{n}. \qquad (19\text{–}5)$$

This equation shows what values of unbound ligand, [A], are possible to give values of $\bar{n}$ in specific mixtures of total cation and ligand. Only one such pair of [A] and $\bar{n}$ will be allowed by the set of K_n values for the system. Thus the simultaneous solution of Eq. (19–4) and (19–5) to eliminate $\bar{n}$ and solve for [A] should solve any problem. However, the combination usually gives cubic or higher-degree equations in [A]. A graphical solution is simple to apply as shown in the following examples.

Example 1. Find the concentrations of NH_3 and all Cu(II) species when equal volumes of 0.050 M $Cu(NO_3)_2$ and 0.15 M NH_3 are mixed. Both solutions are also 2 M in NH_4NO_3. The temperature is 30°C.

Step 1. Since $C_M = 0.0250\ M$ and $C_A = 0.0750\ M$, $C_A/C_M = 3.00$. The situation is identical to starting with 0.025 M $Cu(NH_3)_3^{++}$ and allowing it to reach equilibrium. Since some NH_3 must be released to establish any equilibrium, assume only dissociation to give equal amounts of $Cu(NH_3)_2^{++}$ and NH_3, x. Then,

$$K_3 = 10^{2.98} = \frac{[MA_3]}{[MA_2][A]} = \frac{(0.025 - x)}{x^2},$$

$$x = 0.0046 = 10^{-2.34} = [A].$$

Step 2. The α and $\bar{n}$ diagrams, Figs. 19–1 and 19–2, show that this $[NH_3]$ is not compatible with the presence of only MA_2 and MA_3. A large proportion of MA_4 must form.

Step 3. Find the intersection of Eq. (19–5) with the formation curve, Fig. 19–2. By rapid trial and error, one can get quite close to the simultaneous solution, putting various [A] values into (19–5). Rearrange (19–5) to

$$\bar{n} = 3 - [A]/0.025.$$

Then the points are:

[A]	10^{-2}	$10^{-2.5}$	$10^{-2.6}$	10^{-3}
$\bar{n}$	2.60	2.87	2.90	2.96

The intersection of this function with Fig. 19–2 is seen to occur at log [A] = --2.55 and $\bar{n}$ = 2.89. The α values can now be read from the abundance diagram or the distribution diagram, Figs. 19–1(a) or (b), $\alpha_0 = 0.00$, $\alpha_1 = 0.03$, $\alpha_2 = 0.25$, $\alpha_3 = 0.52$, $\alpha_4 = 0.20$. Each is multiplied by C_M, 0.025 M, to get the species concentrations:

$$CuNH_3{}^{++} = 7.5 \times 10^{-4}\,M, \qquad Cu(NH_3)_2{}^{++} = 0.0062\,M,$$
$$Cu(NH_3)_3{}^{++} = 0.013\,M, \qquad Cu(NH_3)_4{}^{++} = 0.0050\,M.$$

Since α_0 cannot be read from the curve, K_1 gives the value of $[Cu^{++}]$:

$$K_1 = 10^{4.15} = \frac{7.5 \times 10^{-4}}{[Cu^{++}](10^{-2.55})}, \qquad [Cu^{++}] = 1.9 \times 10^{-5}\,M.$$

Example 2. Calculate the major species concentrations in a solution made 0.0500 M in $HgCl_2$ and 0.0800 M in HCl.

For Step 1. Since C_M is 0.0500 and C_A is 0.180 M, $C_A/C_M = 3.60$. Examination of Fig. 19–5 and then Fig. 19–4 for $\bar{n}$ about 3.6 suggests that this puts the system in the log $[Cl^-]$ region, -1 to -2, where a two-species approximation will clearly not be valid. Thus, go directly to Step 3. Equation (19–5) is

$$\bar{n} = 3.60 - [A]/0.0500.$$

Appropriate points are:

$[Cl^-]$	10^{-1}	10^{-2}	$10^{-1.3}$	$10^{-1.26}$
$\bar{n}$	1.60	3.40	2.60	2.50

Then, the intersection with the formation curve (19–5) is seen at log $[Cl^-] = -1.25$. The abundance diagram here, Fig. 19–4, gives, approximately, $\alpha_2 = 0.64$, $\alpha_3 = 0.22$, $\alpha_4 = 0.14$ and thus, major-species concentrations of:

$$HgCl_2 = 0.032\,M, \qquad HgCl_3{}^- = 0.011\,M \qquad \text{and} \qquad HgCl_4{}^= = 0.007\,M.$$

Other, minor, species can be calculated from appropriate K_n expressions. For example, if one needs $[Hg^{++}]$,

$$K_1K_2 = 10^{13.22} = \frac{[HgCl_2]}{[Hg^{++}][Cl^-]^2} = \frac{0.032}{[Hg^{++}](10^{-1.25})^2},$$

$$[Hg^{++}] = 6.1 \times 10^{-13}.$$

These examples point out the usefulness of α and $\bar{n}$ diagrams in solving all problems on complexing mixtures when two-species approximations cannot be made.

Fe(III)-SCN^-

We have not abandoned the concept of activity coefficients. We have been using K, not K^0, values in this work because they usually are determined at a high constant ionic strength, I. The requirements of pH and the high charges on the ions make extrapolation or calculation of K^0 difficult. It must be emphasized that the K_n values are valid only at the conditions of their determination. As an example of the effects the medium can have, let us examine the diagram for the system Fe(III)-SCN^- (Fig. 19–7) for which many investigations have produced K values at various ionic strengths. There is wide variation in the values reported for K_2, K_3, and K_4 so, rounded approximations are used here:

	$\log K_1$	$\log K_2$	$\log K_3$	$\log K_4$
$I = 0$	3.0	1.6	0	0
$I = 1$ to $2\,M$	2.0	1.2	0	0

(The value 0 means a K reported about $= 1$.) Note that the largest effect is on the K involving the most highly charged species. Calculation of α values is done as above for Cu^{++}-NH_3 etc., and produces the diagrams shown in Fig. 19–7(a) and (b) for $I = 0$ and the high I case. One can see that assignment of $FeSCN^{++}$ as the red ion is correct at the endpoint of the Volhard titration where Fe^{3+} is in excess, but not in titration of Fe^{3+} by Hg(I) in the presence of 1 M SCN^-.

A well-known general chemistry experiment involves visual color comparison to find a value of K_1 for $FeSCN^{++}$. If that were done with SCN^- in excess of Fe(III), erratic results would be predicted from the diagrams. However, with Fe(III) in excess of SCN^-, K_1 tells that the free $[SCN^-]$ remains below 10^{-3} ($I = 0$) or 10^{-2} (high I), and good results are obtained with the assumption of 1:1 complex formation.

It is convenient to consider SCN^- as the central group and look at a diagram of α versus $\log [Fe^{3+}]$, uncomplexed. With the condition that Fe(III) must be always greater than SCN^-, only K_1 is needed and a simple diagram for 1:1 complexing is shown in Fig. 19–7(c), like that for HA. Only the zero I case is shown in Fig. 19–7(c). It dictates sensible experimental conditions. A color reference solution having most (say 90%) of the SCN^- complexed must have 10^{-2} M free Fe^{3+}. To do this with 10^{-3} M SCN^- requires $(10^{-2} + 10^{-3})\,M =$ 0.011 moles/liter of Fe(III) which is feasible. In K_1,

$$K_1 = 1000 = \frac{10^{-3}}{10^{-2}[SCN^-]}, \qquad [SCN^-] = 10^{-4}\,M.$$

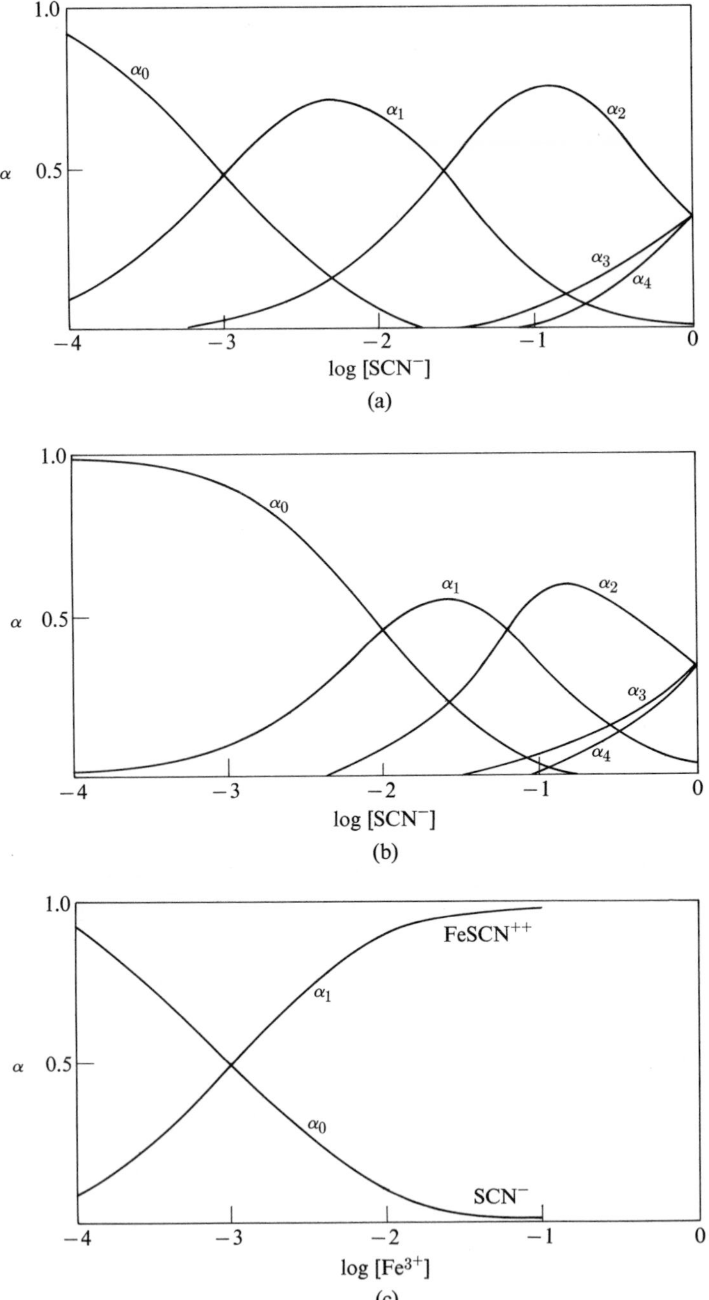

Fig. 19–7. The system Fe(III)-SCN^- (a) with $I = 0$ (b) with $I = 1$ to $2\ M$. (c) The system Fe(III)-SCN^- with Fe(III) always in excess of SCN^-.

This agrees with the first diagram at $\log[SCN^-] = -4$ where the ratio $[FeSCN^{++}]/[Fe^{3+}]$ is also about $\frac{1}{10}$. Remember that Fig. 19–7(c) is only correct in the low $[Fe^{3+}]$ sector when Fe(III) is in excess of the SCN^-. If the higher complexes form, the complete diagram applies.

In cases of polynuclear complex formation, extensions of methods shown here apply. Examples may be found in the text by Butler.

SUMMARY

Mathematical and graphical uses of stepwise formation constants are presented. Distribution, abundance, formation, and titration curves are plotted and described.

SUGGESTIONS FOR FURTHER READING

BJERRUM, J., *Metal-Ammine Formation in Aqueous Solution*, 2nd ed., translated. Copenhagen: Haase and Son, 1957. Experimental details and results are given starting on p. 123.

BUTLER, J. N., *Ionic Equilibrium*, Reading, Mass.: Addison-Wesley, 1964. In Chapters 8 through 10 details of complex equilibrium calculation methods are presented with many examples worked and illustrated.

HARVEY, K. B., and G. B. PORTER, *Introduction to Physical Inorganic Chemistry*, Reading, Mass.: Addison-Wesley, 1963.

JONES, M. M., *Elementary Coordination Chemistry*, Englewood Cliffs, N.J.: Prentice-Hall, 1964. Chapter 8 surveys methods of determination of equilibrium constants.

RINGBOM, A., *Complexation in Analytical Chemistry*, New York: Interscience, 1963. Ringbom suggests the use of identical equations for metal complexing and acid-base equilibria by considering H^+ the ligand and A^{-n} the central group analogous to the metal ion. This unified treatment allows him to make a single diagram for titration errors for all types of titrations (pp. 77ff and 160ff). The reader may well note the formal mathematical parallel between our α equations for polyprotic acids in Chapter 8 and for polyligand metal complexes in Chapter 19.

Stability Constants of Metal-Ion Complexes, ed. by L. G. Sillen and A. E. Martell, Special Publication 17, The Chemical Society, London, 1964. An invaluable compilation of data and references through 1963.

PROBLEMS

Assume in all these problems the same ionic strength for which K's are given.

1. Check the α_0 to α_4 calculations in the example on the system Cu(II)-NH_3 at $[A] = 0.1\ M$. Also find α values at $[A] = 10^{-2}$ and 10^{-4} and check your agreement with the diagrams.
2. How many moles of NH_3 should be added to 1 liter of $0.030\ M\ Cu^{++}$ to make the free $[NH_3] = 10^{-2}$. Use results from Problem 1.

3. The system Ag(I)-NH_3 forms only two ammines, log K_1 = 3.20 and log K_2 = 3.83. Calculate enough α values to sketch an abundance diagram and a distribution diagram. Calculate (show method) the [A] value for the maximum of $AgNH_3^+$ (α_1).
4. Show calculations to two significant figures of the concentration of Hg(II) species present in 0.050 *M* $HgCl_2$ (a) alone, (b) with 0.10 *M* HCl (added), (c) with 0.10 *M* $Hg(NO_3)_2$ (added).
5. Show that the maximum of α_1, $HgCl^+$, occurs at [A] = $(K_1K_2)^{-1/2}$. Calculate the [A] value and check it with Fig. 19–4.
6. Refer to the similar example in the chapter and calculate α_0 to α_4 for a solution originally 0.010 *M* in Fe(III) and 1.00 *M* in Cl^-, where log K_1 = 0.62, log K_2 = 0.11, log K_3 = −1.40, log K_4 = −1.92.
7. a) Use the values from Problem 6 and calculate enough other α values (say at $[Cl^-]$ = 0.1 and 10 *M*) to sketch α versus log $[Cl^-]$ for the system Fe(III)-Cl^-. From this, what can you say about the conditions for $FeCl_3$ extractions?
   b) Show calculations of the maxima for α_1, α_2, and α_3 in this system.
8. Calculate the concentrations of all species in a solution containing 0.025 *M* total Cu(II) and 0.025 *M* total NH_3 in 2 *M* NH_4NO_3 at 30°C.
9. Calculate crossing [A] values, α_1 maxima, and sketch α_0, α_1, and α_2 curves for the systems M-A having log K_1 and log K_2 values: (a) 4, 2, (b) 2, 4, and (c) both 2. The height of the α_0-α_2 crossing must be calculated to show the interesting contrasts of these cases.
10. Estimate log K_n values for TaF_4^+ through $TaF_7^=$ from Fig. 19–3. Explain your assumptions. In general, describe the major features of α curves for various possible relative K_n values. (See Problem 9.)
11. Sketch an approximate α diagram for a complexing system, M-A, in which complexes MA through MA_4 are formed with stepwise formation constants all equal to 10^2. [The Zn(II)-NH_3 system approaches such behavior.]

CHAPTER 20

DETERMINATION OF FORMULAS AND EQUILIBRIUM CONSTANTS OF COMPLEX IONS

So far, we have examined the behavior of complexing mixtures without concern for the determination and reliability of the stepwise formation constants of complexes. Among the equilibria we have studied, they are the most difficult to investigate and are known with the least precision for reasons that will become apparent.

20.1 METHODS OF FORMULA DETERMINATION

Consider the difficulty in determining the species involved in the K_n steps of the systems discussed in Chapter 19. Most chemical methods would upset the equilibrium, but physical methods usually give only a single-species concentration, while three are required to find K. The similar magnitudes of the K values, which means that a number of complex species are present at once, preclude the kind of approximation to two major species possible with H_3PO_4. Methods have been developed employing the $\bar{n}$ equation with enough measurements under different conditions so that one has sufficient simultaneous equations to solve for all the K_n values. A spectral or potentiometric property of one or more species is usually measured. Unfortunately, the equations of the set often differ so slightly that little precision remains after solving them.

First, let us consider the relatively simple situation in which only one complex forms:

$$mX + nY \rightleftharpoons X_mY_n.$$

The formula, values of m and n, or the ratio m/n can be determined if some property proportional to the complex concentration can be measured under conditions of high fraction of X complexed. Job's method, or the method of continuous variation, holds the sum of [X] and [Y] constant. A maximum in the property measured then occurs at the ratio X/Y of the complex. This is shown in Table 20–1. (Arbitrary concentration units are used and $[X] + [Y] = 1$.)

Even if complexing is not quantitative near the middle of the variation, the end portions may be extrapolated to find the intersection if the data are good. Example plots are shown (Fig. 20–2). Only the ratio m/n is found: for example, $Ag_2(en)_2^{++}$ would appear as 1:1.

Another graphical method holds one concentration constant while adding increments of the other. Any unique property of the concentration of complex

Table 20–1. Job's Method for Complex Formula Determination

Concentration		Maximum possible concentration of X_mY_n at m/n ratios			
X	Y	1:1	1:2	2:1	2:3
1.0	0	0	0	0	0
0.9	0.1	0.1	0.05	0.1	0.033
0.8	0.2	0.2	0.1	0.2	0.067
0.7	0.3	0.3	0.15	0.3 maximum	0.1
0.6	0.4	0.4	0.2	0.3 maximum	0.133
0.5	0.5	0.5 maximum	0.25	0.25	0.167
0.4	0.6	0.4	0.3 maximum	0.2	0.2 maximum
0.3	0.7	0.3	0.3 maximum	0.15	0.15
0.2	0.8	0.2	0.2	0.1	0.1
0.1	0.9	0.1	0.1	0.05	0.05

will increase until the stoichiometric ratio is reached after which it remains constant. The values of m and n are actually found here. For Y constant and added X, C_x, in small increments, the maximum possible complex formed, C, is equal to C_x/m. Differentiating $C = C_x/m$ gives

$$dC/dC_x = 1/m.$$

If the property measured is the light absorbance of C, A, and the molar absorbance, a, is known, then for unit thickness path length,

$$A = aC, \qquad \text{and} \qquad dA/dC_x = a/m.$$

A plot of the measured A versus C_x should be a straight line of slope a/m. Similarly, holding X constant and adding Y, we find n.

These methods are practical to use largely for 1:1 complex formation and a few others for which K_n values are of widely different magnitude so that one complex predominates in the concentration region used.

Another approach is to plot log terms if K is not large. Since

$$K_f = [C]/[X]^m[Y]^n,$$

we get

$$\log K = \log [C] - m \log [X] - n \log [Y].$$

For absorbance measurements on C, substitute for C from $A = aC$,

$$\log A = \log a + \log K + m \log [X] + n \log [Y].$$

If [Y] is held constant while [X] is varied (a and K are constant), then

$$\lim_{[X]\to 0} \left[\frac{d \log A}{d \log [X]}\right]_{[Y]} = m,$$

the plot of $\log A$ versus $\log [X]$ is a straight line of slope m, assuming that [X]

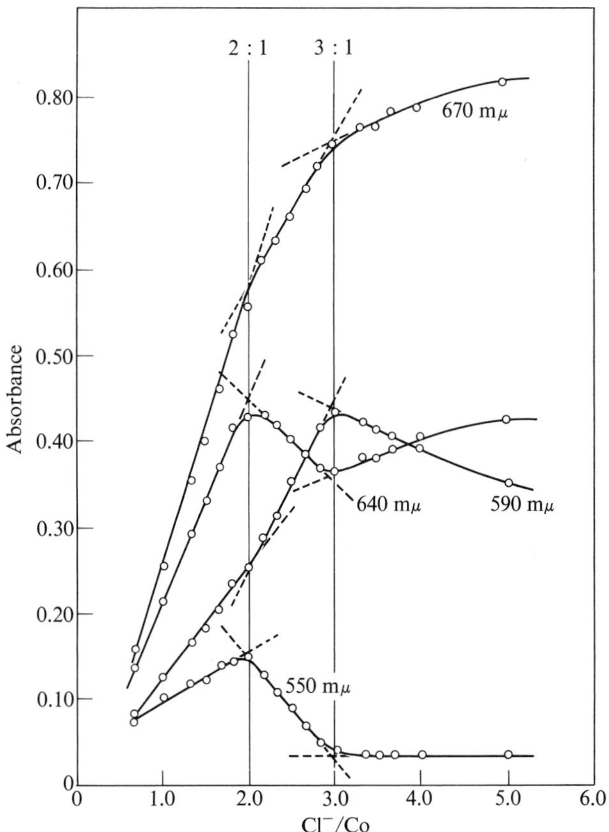

Fig. 20–1. Examples of mole-ratio plots for solutions of $Co(ClO_4)_2$ + LiCl in acetone. (See p. 220.)

can be taken as proportional to the X added. While the last condition is true in the limit, the method is restricted to K values that are not too large to allow appreciable dissociation at measurable concentrations. In a famous paper H. E. Bent and C. L. French* applied this method to the system Fe(III)-SCN^- to find that m and n are 1 at low concentrations of the red complex solutions. Before this work it had been believed that the red ion was $Fe(SCN)_6^{3-}$. The method works here because the K_1 [for $Fe(SCN)^{++}$] is about 200.

In a few cases, a simple extension of the above methods can give some information on multiple complex formation. The mole-ratio method, holding [X] or [Y] constant while the other is varied, is useful if K values are sufficiently different. Any property of C will change until its stoichiometric ratio of X/Y is reached. If K values are large, the lines will be straight with changes in slope at ratios

---

* *J. Am. Chem. Soc.* **63,** 568 (1941).

corresponding to the complexes formed. An example of the use of this method is the paper of D. Fine* on the system of blue Co(II)-Cl^- complexes in acetone. The diagram, shown in Fig. 20–1, indicates pronounced changes in slope at ratios 2:1 and 3:1, indicating that $CoCl_2$ and $CoCl_3^-$ are stable complexes. However, the K_4 is evidently too small to produce much complexing to $CoCl_4^=$ at the 4:1 ratio. Its value, found by other means, was about 10^2. The K_2 of 10^9 and the K_3 of 10^5 produce an observable slope change with this method.

20.2 CALCULATION OF K_f VALUES FROM EXPERIMENTAL DATA

With only one complex forming, the K_f can be found easily from a Job plot if the conditions produce significantly less than quantitative complexing. This is the case if K_f is not large or if sufficiently dilute solutions can be used. Remember that dilution increases dissociation of all weak electrolytes, as with HA,

$$K_f = R/[\mathrm{Y}], \qquad \text{where } R = [\mathrm{XY}]/[\mathrm{X}]$$

so that, as [Y] is decreased by dilution, XY must dissociate to keep K_f constant.

Two examples of student results are shown in diagrams of Job plots of two Fe(III) complexing systems with basic ions in acid solutions, Fig. 20–2. The extrapolations of the extreme slopes should intersect at the A values of 100% complex formation in the equal-volume mixtures. Published values of the acidity constants of the ligands will be used. (An acid-base titration at the pH meter would serve to evaluate an unknown K_a.)

The Fe(III)-azide data were taken by mixing solutions each 0.0020 M in Fe(III) or NaN_3 each 0.0010 M in $HClO_4$. (Assume pH 3.0.) Since the observed A was 0.203 and the extrapolated A was 0.35, then 0.203/0.35 = 0.58 is the fraction of the Fe(III) complexed in the equal-volumes solution. This gives $[FeN_3^{++}] = 5.8 \times 10^{-4}\ M$, and $[Fe^{3+}] = 4.2 \times 10^{-4}$. From the K_a of hydrazoic acid, $10^{-4.72}$,

$$[N_3^-] = K_a[HN_3]/[H^+] = 10^{-4.72}(4.2 \times 10^{-4})/(10^{-3})$$

by assuming most of the N_3^- is present at pH 3 as HN_3: $[N_3^-] = 8 \times 10^{-6}$. We now have the terms for calculating the first approximation of K_f for the FeN_3^{++} ion:

$$K_f = \frac{5.8 \times 10^{-4}}{(4.2 \times 10^{-4})(8 \times 10^{-6})} = 1.7 \times 10^5 = 10^{5.23}.$$

Now, it is important to check the assumption that complexing was essentially complete at the extremes of the plot. Take the 1:9 ratio solution: It has total Fe(III) = 0.00020 M and N_3^- = 0.0018 M

$$[N_3^-] = K_a(0.0016)/10^{-3} = 3.0 \times 10^{-5} \quad \text{(assuming 100\% complexing).}$$

* *J. Am. Chem. Soc.* **84,** 1139 (1962).

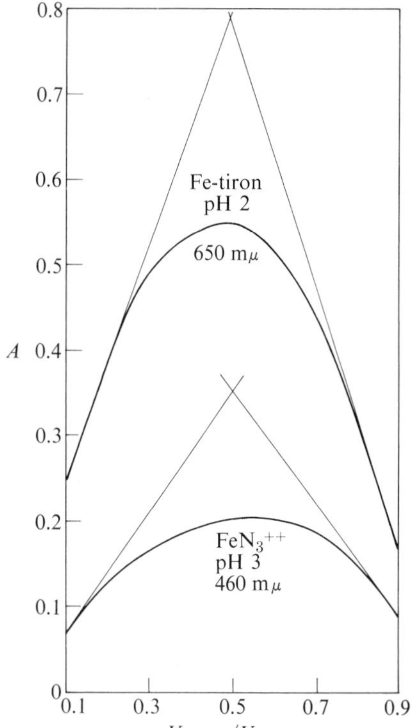

Fig. 20–2. Continuous-variation plots for two Fe(III) complexes. Equimolar solutions of Fe(III) and ligand are mixed with the total volume constant. The extrapolations show 1:1 complexing and the approximate α_1 values (student data).

$$\text{In } K_f = 1.7 \times 10^5 = 0.00020/[Fe^{3+}](3 \times 10^{-5}),$$

$$[Fe^{3+}] = 4 \times 10^{-5}\ M.$$

This is about 20% of the Fe(III) present. A second approximation to K_f can be made by replotting A values corrected to complete complexing with the first K_f. (There was really not enough $HClO_4$ used to justify pH 3. Even so, the K_f agrees with the order of magnitude of published values.)

In the Fe(III)-tiron case, Fig. 20–2, each solution was 6.0×10^{-3} M and had 0.010 M $HClO_4$ with pH 2.0. The ligand is 4,5-dihydroxybenzene-1,3-disulfonic acid. The sulfonic acid groups are strong while the OH groups are weak acids. Let the dissolved material be written $H_2L^=$. The remaining two proton K_a values are $K_{a3} = 10^{-8.31}$, $K_{a4} = 10^{-13.07}$. At pH 2 and in the equal-volumes solution where total Fe(III) and tiron are both 3.0×10^{-3} M,

$$K_3K_4 = [L^{4-}][H^+]/[H_2L^=] = 10^{-21.38},$$
$$[L^{4-}] = 10^{-21.38}(3 \times 10^{-3})/(10^{-2})^2 = 10^{-19.9} = 1.2 \times 10^{-20}.$$

From the extrapolation lines, as before, the complex is

$$[FeL^-] = (0.55/0.78)(3.0 \times 10^{-3}) = 2.1 \times 10^{-3}\ M$$

and the iron left is $[Fe^{3+}] = 9 \times 10^{-4}$, so we can get

$$K_f = 2.1 \times 10^{-3}/(9 \times 10^{-4})(1.2 \times 10^{-20}) = 2 \times 10^{20}.$$

The first approximation may be checked as before. This one is also in reasonable agreement with published values. In both cases, proton competition (K_a's known) with Fe(III) (K_f unknown) for the ligand is used to give measurable dissociation.

Bjerrum's Method

As an illustration of the complexities met in multiple complex systems, consult the spectrophotometric and potentiometric (pH meter) experiments on metal ion complexes described in the laboratory section. Some details are explained here.

As examples of K determinations in systems with several complexes present at once, the important metal-ion–ammonia systems are considered. Easily studied labile ammonia complexes are formed by the following ions under conditions which inhibit OH^- complexing and precipitation: Mg(II), Co(II), Ni(II), Cu(I), Cu(II), Zn(II), Ag(I), Cd(II), Hg(II). The inert ammines of Cr(III), Co(III), and the platinum metals have also been intensively studied.

Jannik Bjerrum developed methods of calculating stepwise K_n values from obtainable data.* The key to the problem lies in the $\bar{n}$ function, the ligand number, and its plot against log [A], the formation function curve. Equations derived in Chapter 19 show that $\bar{n}$ depends only on [A] and K_n values. Bjerrum's method consists in determining the [A] and $\bar{n}$ experimentally and solving for K_n values.

In metal-ammine systems, with a large quantity of NH_4NO_3 present, the pH gives a direct measure of the free $[NH_3]$, since, from K_a for NH_4^+,

$$K_a = [H^+][NH_3]/[NH_4^+].$$

If the $[NH_4^+]$ and ionic strength are held constant (often 2 M) in all solutions, a measure of pH before and after addition of M^{++} gives:

$$\begin{aligned} [H^+]_1[NH_3]_1 &= [H^+]_2[NH_3]_2, \\ \log [H^+]_1 - \log [H^+]_2 &= \log [NH_3]_2 - \log [NH_3]_1, \\ \Delta pH &= \Delta \log [NH_3]. \end{aligned}$$

So, when the initial $[NH_3]$ is known, the pH gives the final $[NH_3]$ free in the complexing solution. The total M^{++} added is also known, so

$$\bar{n} = [NH_3] \text{ complexed}/[M^{++}] \text{ added}.$$

The $\bar{n}$ values are then plotted against log $[NH_3]$ to obtain the formation curve.

Equations in Chapter 19 show that if $\bar{n} = 0.5$ occurs at $[M^{++}] = [MA^{++}]$, then $K_1 = [A]^{-1}$ (at $\bar{n} = 0.5$). Similarly, K_2, K_3, etc., are estimated from the

* See J. Bjerrum, *Metal Ammine Formation in Aqueous Solution*, Copenhagen: Haase and Son, 1957.

curve at $\bar{n} = 1.5$, 2.5, etc. Bjerrum has derived general equations for further approximations. We shall look at a second approximation which gives good results if the successive K values decrease and are not too close together.

The first approximation assumes that $\bar{n} = 0.5$ when α_0 crosses α_1. This is quantitatively true only if the species MA_2 is negligible. Referring to the $\bar{n}$ curve for $Cu(NH_3)_n{}^{++}$ complexes in Fig. 19–2, one can use the 0.5 and 1.5 values as estimates of K_1 and K_2 and see that the ratio of $Cu(NH_3)_2{}^{++}/Cu(NH_3)^{++}$ is about 1:7 at $\bar{n} = 0.5$. A better approximation may be made from the crossings of alternate n curves as described in Chapter 19. When $K_1K_2 = 1/[A]^2$ at $\bar{n} = 1$, $\alpha_0 = \alpha_2$. This is because $[MA_2] = [M]$ and the major species is probably MA, thus, $\bar{n}$ must be one. We shall check the $[MA_3]$ later for validity.

For this second approximation we shall include the MA_2 formed at $\bar{n} = 0.5$, but assume the MA_3 is negligible. At this low ligand ratio we assume that we may use the $\bar{n}$ equation with only terms for M, MA, and MA_2. From Chapter 19, this is

$$\bar{n} = \alpha_1 + 2\alpha_2 = K_1[A]\alpha_0 + 2K_1K_2[A]^2\alpha_0$$

and

$$\alpha_0 = (1 + K_1[A] + K_1K_2[A]^2)^{-1}.$$

These combine to yield

$$\bar{n} = \frac{1 + 2K_2[A]}{(K_1[A])^{-1} + 1 + K_2[A]}. \tag{20–1}$$

We now substitute the first approximate $K_2 = [A]^{-1}_{1.5}$ at $\bar{n} = 0.5$, where $[A] = 10^{-4.40}$ to obtain an improved value of K_1. (This takes into account the MA_2 present.) The approximate K_1 read from the $\bar{n}$ diagram at 0.5 is $10^{4.4}$. This improvement gives $10^{4.25}$.

Next, reading K_1K_2 at $\bar{n} = 1.0$ gives about $10^{7.75}$. The improved K_1 above gives $K_2 = 10^{3.50}$. Returning this value to the K_1 calculation above does not change it.

We now check the validity of assuming that MA_3 is negligible at $\bar{n} = 0.5$ in the previous calculation,

$$K_3 = 10^{2.9} = \frac{[MA_3]}{[MA_2](10^{-4.4})}.$$

So, only about $\frac{1}{30}$ of the MA_2 forms MA_3, and the approximation is valid to two significant figures. The K_3 and K_4 are found in the same manner.

Now, at $\bar{n} = 1.0$ one should check the assumption that only M, MA, and MA_2 are present in appreciable amounts. In K_3,

$$K_3 = 10^{2.9} = \frac{[MA_3]}{[MA_2](10^{-3.9})}.$$

This shows that MA_3 is about 10% of the MA_2 at $\bar{n} = 1.0$. Thus further approximations will be required if more than one significant figure is needed in K_2.

One further approximation of the many that can be tried will be shown. If the maximum of MA_2 occurs at $\bar{n} = 2.00$, it follows that

$$[M] + [MA] = [MA_3] + [MA_4].$$

By the usual substitutions of K expressions and the approximation $[MA] = [MA_3]$ at $\bar{n} = 2$, it can be seen that

$$K_1K_4 = [A]^{-2} \qquad (\text{at } \bar{n} = 2).$$

Using the $[A] = 10^{-3.20}$ and the $K_1 = 10^{-4.26}$ gives $K_4 = 10^{2.14}$.

When the adjacent K values are more closely spaced than in the copper-ammine system, or if higher complexes are more stable than lower, $K_1 < K_2$, etc. [as with $Ag(NH_3)_2{}^+$], the half-integral $\bar{n}$ method alone may not suffice for high precision. The Ag(I)-NH_3 system is an example of some of the problems met.

The two ligand case: MA_2. Consider the Ag(I)-NH_3 system under conditions of constant ionic strength (say, 2 M NH_4NO_3) and with sufficiently low $[OH^-]$ so that the Ag(I) can be assumed to be present in only three forms: $Ag^+(aq)$, $Ag(NH_3)^+(aq)$, and $Ag(NH_3)_2{}^+$, hereafter called M, MA, and MA_2.

The experimental formation curve for the system, Fig. 20–3, is shown plotted from Bjerrum's data at 22°C in 2 M NH_4NO_3. Note that a calculated curve with $K_1 = 0$ (that is, no MA is present) and $K_{f2} = 10^{7.30}$ comes close to the experimental curve. In such situations, the formation curve is not very sensitive to K values but does reveal the product K_1K_2 as shown below. One needs a different means of examining the data. Fortunately, for the case with no higher complexes than MA_2, it is not difficult.

The definition of $\bar{n}$, the average number of ligands per metal ion, shows that at the point $\bar{n} = 1$, $[M] = [MA_2]$. This must be the case whether or not any MA forms in the system:

$$\bar{n} = 1 = \frac{[MA] + 2[MA_2]}{[M] + [MA] + [MA_2]} \qquad \text{or} \qquad [M] = [MA_2]. \tag{20–2}$$

From this, in general, the product K_1K_2 must then be

$$K_1K_2 = \frac{[MA_2]}{[M][A]^2} = \frac{1}{[A]^2} \qquad (\text{at } \bar{n} = 1).$$

The experimental curve gives about $10^{-3.65}$ for [A] at $\bar{n} = 1$. Thus K_1K_2 is $10^{7.30}$. (This is the value K_{f2} must have if no MA forms.) The $\bar{n}$ values at 0.5 and 1.5 are $[A] = 10^{-3.95}$ and $10^{-3.35}$. Applying the method used on the Cu(II)-NH_3 system to these values suggests first approximations for K_1 and K_2 of $10^{3.95}$ and $10^{3.35}$. But this leads directly to a contradiction of the data. At $\bar{n} = 0.5$ this method assumes that $[M] = [MA]$ and $[MA_2]$ is negligible. But substituting the [A] at $\bar{n} = 0.5$ into the K_2 expression shows

$$K_2 = 10^{3.35} = \frac{[MA_2]}{[MA](10^{-3.95})} \qquad \text{or} \qquad \frac{[MA_2]}{[MA]} = 0.25.$$

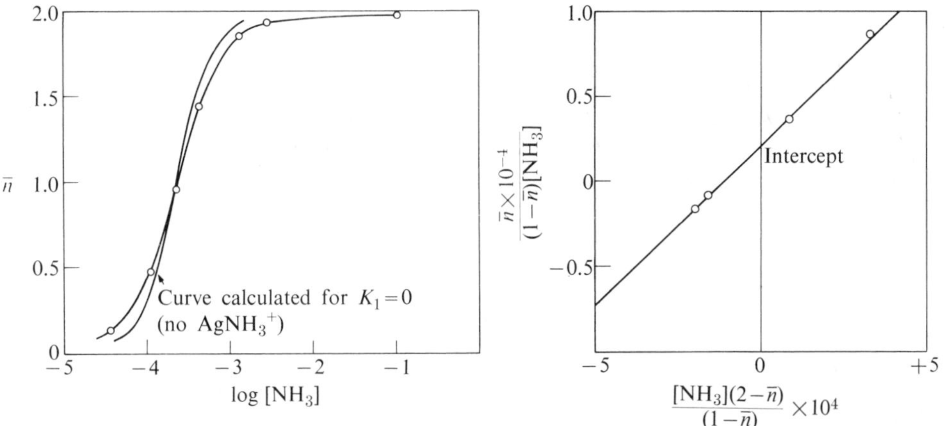

Fig. 20–3. Experimental formation curve for the system Ag(I)-NH_3 at 22°C in 2 *M* NH_4NO_3 (Bjerrum's data, points shown).

Fig. 20-4. Plot of Eq. (20–4) for Ag(I)-NH_3.

With so large a fraction of MA_2 present at this point, [M] would have to be much greater than [MA] to yield an $\bar{n}$ value of 0.5. Similarly, with K_1, one can show that M is not negligible at $\bar{n} = 1.5$. So we have an accurate product K_1K_2, but need a way to find one value of K accurately.

Values for K_1 and K_2 can be determined graphically or by direct substitution with the $\bar{n}$ equation (as in Eq. 20–1), which is derived by combining the definitions of Eqs. (19–3) and (19–4):

$$\bar{n} = \frac{K_1[A] + 2K_1K_2[A]^2}{1 + K_1[A] + K_1K_2[A]^2}. \tag{20–3}$$

Clearly, with data for $\bar{n}$ and [A] and a product K_1K_2 known, one can solve for K_1. This can be rearranged to give a form suitable for a linear plot of $\bar{n}$-[A] data. Write β_2 for K_1K_2, multiply through by the denominator, and collect terms in [A] to get

$$\bar{n} = K_1[A](1 - \bar{n}) + \beta_2[A]^2(2 - \bar{n}).$$

Divide by $(1 - \bar{n})[A]$ to get

$$\left[\frac{\bar{n}}{(1 - \bar{n})[A]}\right] = K_1 + \beta_2\left[[A]\frac{(2 - \bar{n})}{(1 - \bar{n})}\right]. \tag{20–4}$$

The composite variables in brackets are plotted in Fig. 20–4. Equation (20–4) predicts a slope of β_2 and an intercept of K_1. Figure 20–4 shows an intercept about 0.21×10^4 or $10^{3.32}$ (K_1) and a slope of $10^{7.27}$ for $K_2 = 10^{3.95}$. Direct substitution of Bjerrum's data into (20–3) or (20–4) with $K_1K_2 = 10^{7.30}$ gives K values which agree closely. (These values do not agree exactly with Bjerrum's values, since the ones here were read from this small plot to illustrate the method.)

Table 20–2. Experimental Data for the System Ag(I)-NH_3 at 22°C in 2 *M* NH_4NO_3 (From Bjerrum)

$-\log [NH_3]$	4.416	3.961	3.666	3.377	2.875	2.564	1.001
$\bar{n}$	0.123	0.492	0.981	1.463	1.872	1.942	1.986

Some of Bjerrum's data are listed in Table 20–2. (Note that $\bar{n}$ data nearer *zero* and *two* give usable points in Fig. 20–4.)

SUMMARY

Use of experimental data to find stepwise formation constants is explained. Job's method for 1:1 cases and Bjerrum's potentiometric method for metal-ammines are explained in detail.

SUGGESTIONS FOR FURTHER READING

See the references at the end of Chapter 19, especially Chapter 8 of the book by M. M. Jones, and the texts by Butler and by Bjerrum.

ALBERT, A., and E. P. SERJEANT, *Ionization Constants of Acids and Bases*, New York: John Wiley, 1962. This text gives details of experimental methods of determining equilibrium constants and a brief chapter on stepwise formation constants of coordination compounds.

CHABEREK, S., and A. E. MARTELL, *Organic Sequestering Agents*, New York: John Wiley, 1959. Chapters 3 and 4 point out methods used to investigate specific systems.

ROSSOTTI, F., and H. ROSSOTTI, *The Determination of Stability Constants*, New York: McGraw-Hill, 1961 is a detailed treatise.

PROBLEMS

1. From the formation curve for Cu(II)-NH_3 complexes in Chapter 19, estimate the K_1 through K_4 values. Explain how you do this and compare the results with the K values used to plot the curves.
2. Repeat Problem 1 for the Hg(II)-Cl^- system.
3. For the system Hg(II)-I^-, calculate log $[I^-]$ at which the α curves cross for: Hg^{++} and HgI^+, Hg^{++} and HgI_2, HgI^+ and HgI_2, HgI_2 and HgI_3^-, HgI_3^- and $HgI_4^=$. Roughly sketch a plausible diagram of α versus log $[I^-]$. (For this system, $\log K_1 = 12.9$, $\log K_2 = 11.0$, $\log K_3 = 3.8$, $\log K_4 = 2.2$.)
4. Moser and Voigt [*J. Inorg. and Nuclear Chem.* **4,** 354 (1957)] measured the extraction of HgI_2 from pure water and KI solutions into benzene. Calculate K_3 and K_4 from

the data given assuming that:

i) In pure water only HgI_2 exists to any important extent.
ii) In the KI solutions, some HgI_3^- and $HgI_4^=$ form.
iii) Only HgI_2 extracts into benzene.
iv) HgI_2 water solubility is very low, a tracer method was used, therefore, $[I^-]$ is unchanged by complex formation.

All aqueous solutions were at constant ionic strength, 0.03 *M*.
In pure water $P = [HgI_2]_{org}/[HgI_2]_{aq} = 47.2$.
In 0.0100 *M* KI, $D = [HgI_2]_{org}/[Hg_{total}]_{aq} = 0.380$.
In 0.0200 *M* KI, $D = [HgI_2]_{org}/[Hg_{total}]_{aq} = 0.120$.
Compare the assumptions and answers with those in Problem 3.

5. a) From Bjerrum's data for the system Ag(I)-NH_3 at 22°C, evaluate K_1 from Eq. (20–4) at one low and one high value of $\bar{n}$. Take $K_1K_2 = 10^{7.30}$ from Fig. 20–3.
b) Calculate

$$\frac{\bar{n}}{(1 - \bar{n})[A]} \quad \text{and} \quad \frac{[A](2 - \bar{n})}{(1 - \bar{n})}$$

and plot them to determine K_1 and K_2. Can you now explain why the points and size coordinates of Fig. 20–4 were chosen?

6. Bjerrum's data for the system Hg(II)-NH_3 at 21 to 22°C in 2 *M* NH_4NO_3 for $\bar{n} = 1.6$ to 4 (but variable, 0.1 to 1 *M* for $\bar{n} = 0.4$ to 1.3 for experimental reasons) are given below. Neglect the variable ionic strengths and plot the formation curve.
a) Estimate K_1 through K_4 by the half-integral method.
b) Check these by considering the system as two separable MA_2 systems (Eq. 20–4). (Bjerrum gives log *K* values of 8.8, 8.7, 1.00, 0.78.)

$-\log [NH_3]$	$\bar{n}$	$-\log [NH_3]$	$\bar{n}$
9.23	0.441	2.604	2.017
8.96	0.655	1.522	2.238
8.63	0.969	1.120	2.638
8.535	1.290	0.807	3.132
8.34	1.62	0.477	3.502
8.09	1.92	0.195	3.656
7.06	1.98		

7. In a Job plot like Fig. 20–2, for the system Fe(III)-Cl^-, the line segments for the ratio of complex to free Fe^{3+} are 1:4 at the total Fe(III) to Cl^- ratio of 1:1 in a mixture where both are 0.075 *M* (total).
a) Find K_1 assuming only $FeCl^{++}$ forms.
b) What is $\bar{n}$ in this mixture?

CHAPTER 21

COMPLEX FORMATION TITRATIONS

21.1 CHELATION

The use of two or more donor atoms per ligand results in more stable complexes than corresponding monodentate complexing does. This stability can be illustrated by examining the log β values for one of the many examples studied, Cu^{++} with several nitrogen donor ligands:

Tetracomplexed Cu(II)	$Cu(NH_3)_4^{++}$	$Cu(en)_2^{++}$	$Cu(trien)^{++}$
log β (overall)	12.7	20.2	20.5
Rings formed	0	2	3

(en is $\underline{N}H_2CH_2CH_2\underline{N}H_2$ and trien, $\underline{N}H_2CH_2CH_2\underline{N}HCH_2CH_2\underline{N}HCH_2CH_2\underline{N}H_2$.) The log β values may also be interpreted as pCu^{++}, or $-\log\,[Cu^{++}]$, values for a hypothetical solution containing 1 *M* each of the complex and free ligand. The increased stability of chelated complexes is general, and five-membered rings are favored over those with four or six atoms.

The chelate effect is plausible if one considers the probability (entropy) argument that four ligand molecules must find the metal ion for $Cu(NH_3)_4^{++}$, two for $Cu(en)_2^{++}$, and one for $Cu(trien)^{++}$. The last should be easiest. Another way of stating this is: other factors (bond energies) being equal, the entropy increase favoring these reactions should increase in the order of the change in the number of particles, Δn, in the reaction (increasing disorder):

Reaction	Δn
$Cu(H_2O)_6^{++} + 4NH_3 \rightarrow Cu(NH_3)_4(H_2O)_2^{++} + 4H_2O$	0
$Cu(H_2O)_6^{++} + 2en \rightarrow Cu(en)_2(H_2O)_2^{++} + 4H_2O$	2
$Cu(H_2O)_6^{++} + trien \rightarrow Cu(trien)(H_2O)_2^{++} + 4H_2O$	3

It is clear from the β values that other factors do play a role in determining stability. Differing basicity and steric effects are two of them.

As shown in Chapter 19, titrations based on the Cu(II)-NH_3 system are not feasible. However, the β values for the chelates above do suggest that quantitative complexing of Cu(II) is possible. Strong complexing is known with many polydentate ligands used for selective complexing (masking) in analytical procedures. Oxalate, citrate, tartrate, triethanolamine, and dimethylglyoxime are examples.

21.2 EDTA

Under the name Trilon B, Farbenindustrie of Germany introduced ethylenediaminetetraacetic acid (EDTA) about 1935. After World War II, G. Schwarzenbach at the University of Zurich made extensive studies of its complexes with metal ions. After discovering several indicators for metal ions, he developed titration methods which have become widely used.

The molecule is a tetraprotic acid, H_4Y, with two basic nitrogen atoms in addition. It thus has six possible ligand sites when all four protons are removed.

```
HOOC—CH2                    CH2—COOH
        \                  /
         N—CH2—CH2—N
        /                  \
HOOC—CH2                    CH2—COOH
```

A solid scale model shows how neatly the bond angles and distances allow all six basic positions to come together around an M^{+n} acceptor ion.

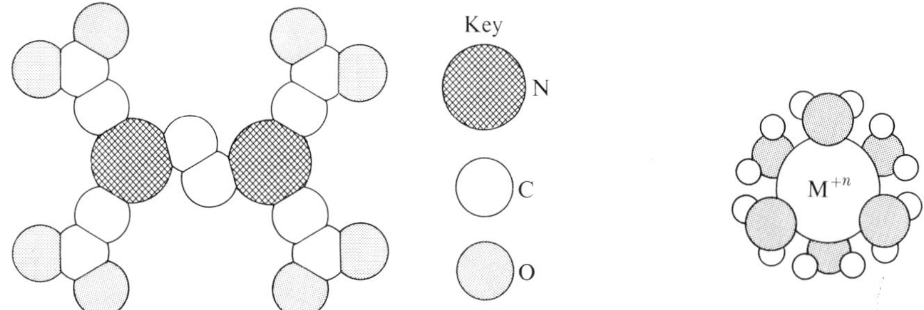

Fig. 21–1. The EDTA-4 ion in spread open form. (H atoms are not shown.)

Figure 21–2

By rotation around the bonds, the four carboxyl groups and the two amino nitrogens (Fig. 21–1) can surround a metal ion, just touching the six octahedral positions shown in the hexaquo ion in Fig. 21–2. The reader can see this clearly with scale models. There are too many atoms to permit this to be shown clearly on paper.

Contrary to the zwitterion structure one might expect, D. Chapman* reports that infrared bands show that protons are not on the N positions in the acid, H_4Y, nor in the disodium salt, Na_2H_2Y. The latter, the commonly used form of EDTA, is stabilized by H-bonding between the carboxyl anions. Chapman suggests that the proton in the HY^{3-} ion does move to the N, which accounts for a high pK_4.

The acid constants for the parent acid at 20°C and 0.1 M ionic strength are $\log K_1 = -2.07$, $\log K_2 = -2.75$, $\log K_3 = -6.24$, and $\log K_4 = -10.34$. By

* *J. Chem. Soc.*, 1766 (1955).

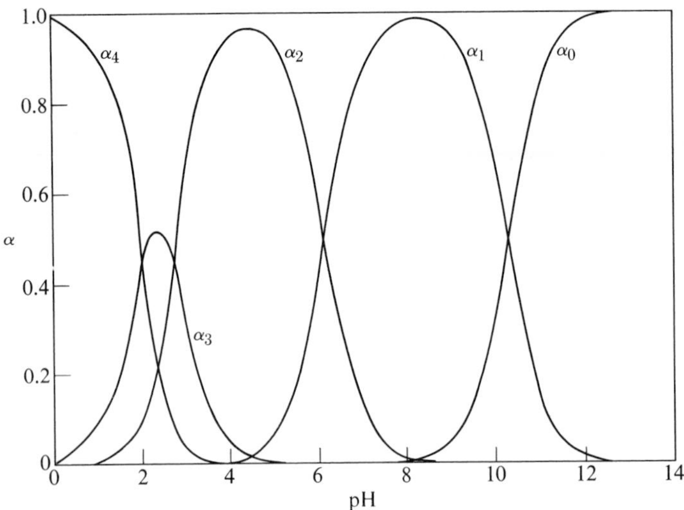

Fig. 21-3. Fraction of EDTA present in various ionic forms: α_4, as H_4Y; α_3, as H_3Y^-; α_2, as H_2Y^-; α_1, as HY^{3-}; α_0, as Y^{4-}.

the methods used in Chapter 8 for citric acid, the α diagram, Fig. 21–3, is derived. To use the values given in Table 21–1 for the formation constants of EDTA complexes, the pH and α_0 values (for Y^{4-}) of EDTA are needed. At low pH the α_0 values cannot be read from the α diagram. A plot of log α_0 versus pH is given in Fig. 21–4 to facilitate calculations. Only 1:1 complexing between metals and EDTA is important:

$$K_f = [MY]/[M][Y^{4-}]. \tag{21–1}$$

The appropriate charges in each case apply to M and MY.

Table 21–1. Formation Constants of EDTA Complexes at 20°C, Ionic Strength 0.1.

Metal ion	log K	Metal ion	log K
Fe^{3+}	25.1	Al^{3+}	16.13
Th^{4+}	23.2	La^{3+}	15.50
Hg^{++}	21.80	Fe^{++}	14.33
Cu^{++}	18.80	Mn^{++}	13.79
Ni^{++}	18.62	Ca^{++}	10.70
Pb^{++}	18.04	Mg^{++}	8.69
Zn^{++}	16.50	Sr^{++}	8.63
Cd^{++}	16.46	Ba^{++}	7.76
Co^{++}	16.31	Ag^+	7.3

From G. Schwarzenbach, *Complexometric Titrations*, translated by H. Irving, New York: Interscience, 1957.

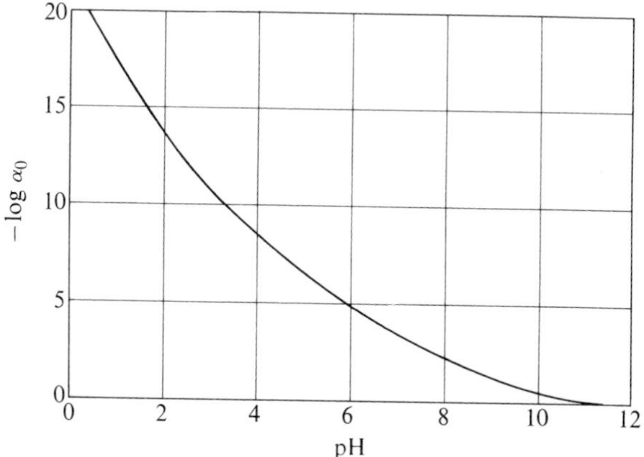

Fig. 21.4. α_0 values for EDTA. The fraction in the Y^{4-} ion form at pH 0 to 12. (The values of H_4Y from pK_1 through pK_4 are 2.07, 2.75, 6.24, 10.34.)

Detailed and exact calculations of all species present in a solution of EDTA, NH_3, and Zn(II) could be done by the methods outlined above. However, approximate calculation first serves to establish feasibility and pH requirements of titrations.

Example 1. Find the minimum pH required for titration of Mg(II), Zn(II), and Fe(III). Take quantitative to mean that one part in 10^4 remains uncomplexed by EDTA when one drop (0.05 ml) excess 0.02 *M* EDTA is added after equivalence. Let total metal ion be 10^{-2} *M* at a final volume of 100 ml.

For all three cases,

$$K_f = [MY]/[M][Y^{4-}] = 10^{-2}/10^{-6}[Y^{4-}],$$
$$[Y^{4-}] = 10^4/K_f,$$

is the condition for quantitative titration. From EDTA,

$$[Y^{4-}] = \alpha_0[\text{EDTA excess}] = \alpha_0 \frac{(0.05 \text{ ml})(0.02\ M)}{100 \text{ ml}} = 10^{-5}\alpha_0.$$

Combining the two Y^{4-} equations gives

$$\alpha_0 = 10^9/K_f.$$

For Mg(II), $\alpha_0 = 10^9/10^{8.7} = 10^{0.3} = 2,$

which means that one drop excess EDTA cannot complex enough of the Mg(II) to meet the condition. Two drops will do so if $\alpha_0 = 1$, at pH about 12. See Fig. 21–4.

For Zn(II), $\alpha_0 = 10^9/10^{16.5} = 10^{-7.5}$. α_0 has this value at pH 4.5.

For Fe(III), $\alpha_0 = 10^9/10^{25} = 10^{-16}$.

Thus Fe(III) complexing is quantitative to well below pH 2. These results agree with the pH values indicated for these titrations by experiment. (See the laboratory section.)

More complete calculation. The example just given assumed no complexing of the metal ion except by the EDTA. In the basic solutions required for some indicators or for sufficiently high Y^{4-} concentration, metal hydroxides precipitate unless complexed by NH_3, ethanolamine, etc. This lowers the metal aquo ion concentration and raises the pH required for quantitative titration. Let us reconsider the example for NH_3 complexing (omit possible OH^- effects). Compare the effect on the titrations of Zn(II) and Cu(II) in an ammonia buffer. Now one needs alpha expressions for both the metal and the EDTA:

$$[M^{+n}] = \alpha_{0M} C_M$$

and

$$[Y^{4-}] = \alpha_{0Y} C_Y, \tag{21–2}$$

where α_{0M} is the fraction of the total metal ion C_M (C_M is the metal *not* in the MY complex) which is left in aquo form, M^{+n}.

In the EDTA K_f expression, these give

$$K_f = \frac{[MY]}{\alpha_{0M} C_M \alpha_{0Y} C_Y}.$$

For repeated calculations, as in finding a titration curve, some convenience is gained by rearranging this to get a conditional K_f'

$$K_f' = K_f \alpha_{0M} \alpha_{0Y} = \frac{[MY]}{C_M C_Y}. \tag{21–3}$$

As before, C_Y is the excess EDTA not in MY, and we take it to be 10^{-5} *M* at this endpoint condition (0.05 ml of 0.02 *M* in 100 ml). K_f' is constant for a given condition of pH and NH_3 concentration.

When $[NH_3]$ is greatly in excess of C_M, as explained in Chapter 19, the α_{0M} term reduces to the β_4 expression alone (This is a good approximation for Zn^{++} and Cu^{++} with 0.1 *M* NH_3, but is less good for Cd^{++} and Ni^{++}, for example, where one may use the extended α_0 terms.):

$$\alpha_{0M} = \frac{1}{\beta_4 [NH_3]^4}. \tag{21–4}$$

With the endpoint C_M as before, 10^{-6} *M*, Eqs. (21–2) and (21–4) give

$$[Zn^{++}] = \frac{10^{-6}}{10^{9.46}(0.1)^4} = 10^{-11.5},$$

$$[Cu^{++}] = \frac{10^{-6}}{10^{12.67}(0.1)^4} = 10^{-14.7}.$$

Putting these into the K_f expressions we get

for Zn, $$K_f = 10^{16.5} = \frac{0.01}{10^{-11.5}\alpha_{0Y}10^{-5}},$$

$\alpha_{0Y} = 10^{-2}$ which occurs about pH 8.3 on the α_{0Y} curve.

For Cu, $$K_f = 10^{18.8} = \frac{0.01}{10^{-14.7}\alpha_{0Y}10^{-5}},$$

$\alpha_{0Y} = 10^{-1.1}$, about pH 9.2 on the α_{0Y} curve.

Thus one finds that the greater K_f for $CuY^{=}$ is more than balanced by the greater NH_3 complexing so that a higher pH is required for quantitative EDTA titration. In practice, one keeps the NH_3 concentration low to minimize metal complexing and adjusts the pH with NH_4^+ for a safe pH, about 10, which gives a ratio about $\frac{3}{1}$ for NH_3/NH_4^+.

Example 2. Calculate points on a titration curve of 25.00 ml of 0.02000 *M* Zn^{++} by 0.02000 *M* EDTA at pH 10.0 and 0.10 *M* free NH_3.

Since Zn^{++} is related to the total Zn(II) outside the $ZnY^{=}$ complex by a constant, Eq. (21–2), we can plot $-\log$ [Zn(II)] rather than $-\log [Zn^{++}]$ more simply, and the resulting curve will be just as valid. If K_f' is large enough, we can calculate the total Zn(II) before the equivalence point simply as that left after assuming 100% reaction with the EDTA added. At, and just after, the equivalence point, the conditional constant is used. The reader may confirm these values:

milliliters EDTA added	0	12.5	20.0	24.0	24.5	25.00	25.5	26.0	30.0
−log [Zn(II)]	1.7	2.2	2.6	3.4	3.7	6.25	8.8	9.1	9.8

For example, at 20.0 ml one has 0.1 mmole Zn(II) left in 45 ml at 0.0022 *M*. Then, $-\log(0.0022) = 2.65$.

At the equivalence point, from Eq. (21–3), we have

$$K_f' = K_f\alpha_{0M}\alpha_{0Y} = 10^{16.5}10^{-5.5}10^{-0.5} = 10^{10.5},$$

where α_{0M} was obtained from Eq. (21–4), and α_{0Y} from Fig. 21–4 at pH 10. From Eq. (21–3) at the equivalence point,

$$C_M = C_Y = \sqrt{[MY]/K_f'} \quad \text{and} \quad [\text{Zn(II)}] = \sqrt{0.01/10^{10.5}} = 10^{-6.25}.$$

At 30.0 ml, there is still only 0.500 mmole of $ZnY^{=}$ and 0.10 mmole excess EDTA in 55 ml. Putting these into the K_f' equation gives

$$[\text{Zn(II)}] = \frac{0.5}{0.1(10^{10.5})} = 10^{-9.8}.$$

Figure 21–5 shows this curve. The indicator range is obtained similarly.

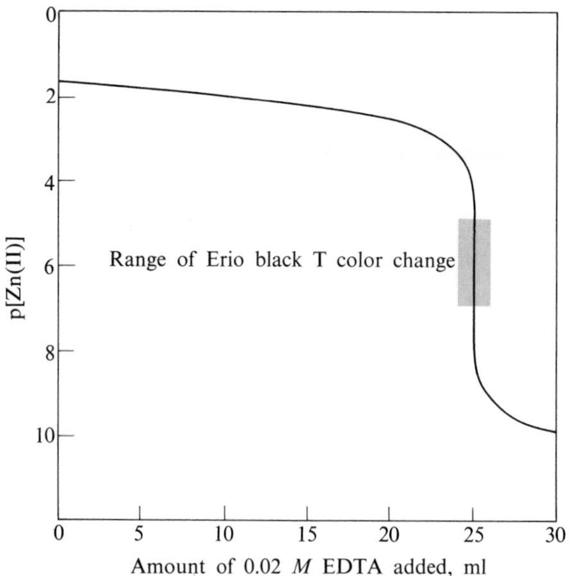

Fig. 21–5. Calculated titration curve of 25 ml 0.02 *M* Zn(II) by 0.02 *M* EDTA at pH 10 and 0.1 *M* $[NH_3]$.

A suitable indicator for the titration must release Zn^{++} at these endpoint conditions, pH 10.0 and $[Zn(II)] = 10^{-6.25}$. Erio black T forms a 1:1 complex, ZnIn, with an apparent indicator constant $10^{11.4}$ at pH 10. Just as with $ZnY^{=}$, one can write

$$K_{In} = 10^{11.4} = \frac{[ZnIn]}{C_M \alpha_{0M} C_{In}}, \tag{21–5}$$

where C_{In} is the total indicator concentration outside ZnIn (here, $H_2In^- + HIn^= + In^{3-}$). This indicator is blue between pH 7 and 11; ZnIn is red.

As with acid-base indicators (see p. 77), one can calculate the range of $-\log C_M$ over which the ratio red/blue $= [ZnIn]/C_{In}$ changes from $\frac{10}{1}$ to $\frac{1}{10}$ to give a visual color change. From Eq. (21–5),

$$R = \frac{[ZnIn]}{C_{In}} = 10^{11.4} \alpha_{0M} C_M.$$

Therefore for Zn(II),

$$R = \tfrac{10}{1} \quad \text{when} \quad [Zn(II)] = \tfrac{10}{1} 10^{-11.4} 10^{5.5} = 10^{-4.9},$$

$$R = \tfrac{1}{10} \quad \text{when} \quad [Zn(II)] = \tfrac{1}{10} 10^{-11.4} 10^{5.5} = 10^{-6.9}.$$

Thus the equivalence point calculated above, $[Zn(II)] = 10^{-6.25}$, is included within the indicator range.

The error if one takes the midpoint,

$$R = 1 \qquad \text{when} \qquad \text{Zn(II)} = 10^{-5.9},$$

of the range as the endpoint can be found using Eq. (21–3):

$$C_{\text{Y}} = \frac{\text{MY}}{K_f' C_{\text{M}}} = \frac{(0.01)}{10^{10.5}10^{-5.9}} = 10^{-6.6}.$$

Now, in going from $C_{\text{Y}} = 10^{-6.6}$ to the equivalence point, $10^{-6.25}$, one must add an amount of EDTA corresponding to that increase plus the amount newly complexed with Zn(II), in a total volume of 50 ml,

$$\frac{(\text{ml EDTA})(0.02\ M)}{50\ \text{ml}} = (10^{-6.25} - 10^{-6.6}) + (10^{-5.9} - 10^{-6.25}),$$

from which

$$\text{ml EDTA} = 0.0025\ \text{ml},$$

$$\text{percent error} = -\frac{0.0025}{25}(100) = -0.01\%.$$

That is, the slope of the titration curve is sufficiently steep to ensure negligible indicator error in this case. The indicator range is indicated on the curve, Fig. 21–5. Tables of constants for indicators are given in the texts by Laitinen and by Ringbom.

It can be seen from Eqs. (21–3) and (21–4) that titration curves must become considerably flatter if $[NH_3]$ is increased—note the fourth-power dependence on $[NH_3]$ in $\alpha_{0\text{M}}$. If the conditional K_f' falls below 10^8, the endpoint drop in $-\log C_{\text{M}}$, becomes too small to use with visual indicators. Potentiometric endpoint determination can sometimes be used in such cases. See the example Fe(III)-EDTA titration given in Chapter 24, p. 269.

Throughout this section we used the n in the expression α_n to refer either to the number of ligands attached to a metal ion or to the number of protons on an anion, as we did in Chapter 8. Some texts use a different system for each, using n to refer only to the number of charges on the anion.

Buffering for Acidic EDTA Titration

Now let us consider buffering at pH 5 to 6 for EDTA titrations with xylenol orange indicator. One must control pH without adding high concentrations of good ligands for the ions being titrated. Phosphate or citrate would be poor choices. A 6:1 buffer of acetate:acetic acid sets a pH of about 5.4 and serves some cases. However, Pb(II), Cu(II), and Fe(III) may be extensively complexed if the acetate concentration rises above 0.1 M. At lower acetate concentrations, Zn(II), and most other ions commonly titrated at this pH, can be titrated without interference. A more generally used buffer involves the base hexamine [synonyms:

urotropin, hexamethylenetetramine, $(CH_2)_6N_4$] shown below.

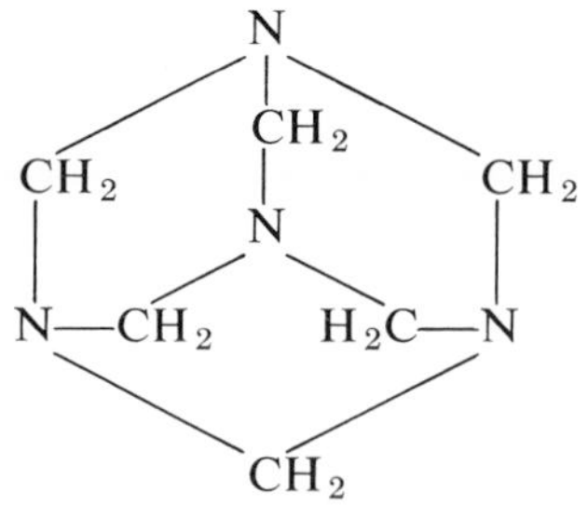

N
CH_2
CH_2 CH_2
N
N—CH_2 H_2C—N
CH_2

Hexamine is the compound formed upon mixing formaldehyde and ammonia. It is quite soluble, 670 g/liter of water and is a very weak base, with pK_b near 9. It accepts only one proton so that, when an excess is added to dilute acid, the buffer hex-$Hhex^+$ is formed. Since pK_a for $Hhex^+$ is 5.1, ratios of hex/$Hhex^+$ between 1:1 and 4:1 give buffers between pH 5.1 and 5.7. The base seems to be a weak ligand for metal ions, although little quantitative data is available. Large excess should not be added. It is generally used in the solid form. One gram excess in 100 ml is 0.07 *M* (formula weight, 140).

Many other anions can interfere with EDTA titrations. Chloride in more than trace amounts seems to interfere with Bi(III) titration at pH 1. In general, one should keep concentrations low and use NaOH, $HClO_4$ and HNO_3 for required neutralizations.

Indicators

Indicators for EDTA titrations must show a color change upon complexing the metal ion, but the stability of the EDTA complex of the ion must be greater than that of the indicator. If not, the metal ion "blocks" the indicator, and will not release it to give a color change at the equivalence point. This has been a serious problem in EDTA work. Fortunately, now, many indicators are available so that a suitable one can usually be found for the need at hand.

Erio Black T, one of the first and most frequently used indicators, is an azo-naphthol dye. It can be used with Zn, Ca, and Mg ions at pH 7 to 11 where it is blue and its metal complexes are red.

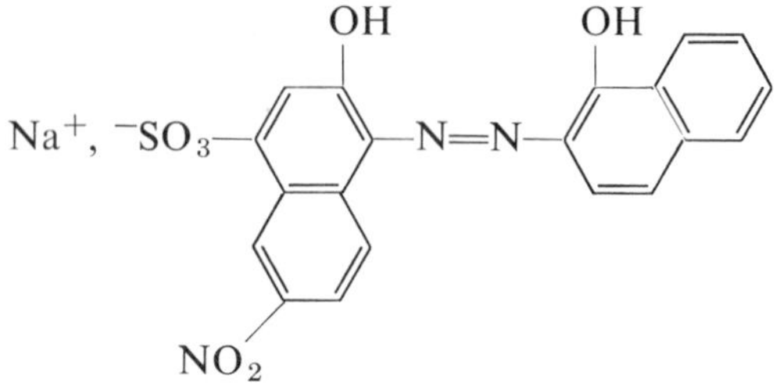

OH OH
Na^+, $^-SO_3$— —N=N—
NO_2

Erio black T

However, it gives very stable red complexes with Cu, Ni, Co, Fe(III), and Al ions which block the indicator. Routine addition of CN^- or $S^=$ is practiced in EDTA titration of hard water, etc., to remove the interference of these ions. Ca and Mg can then be titrated with EDTA in basic solution with this indicator. *Murexide* (purpuric acid ion), *calcon* and *calmagite* (azonaphthols) are substitutes for erio black T which have advantages for some applications.

At the high pH used with these indicators, NH_3 or other complexing agents are required to prevent hydroxide precipitation of most metal ions. This can lower the sharpness of the endpoint since less metal ion is available for EDTA complexing. It is advantageous to use acidic solution titration when K_f values permit as is the case for most metal ions except alkaline earths. However, erio T is protonated below pH 7 and is useless. Xylenol orange is used in the pH range 1 to 6. It is a triphenyl methyl-type dye derived from cresol red (*o*-cresolsulfonephthalein) by condensation with formaldehyde and iminodiacetic acid.

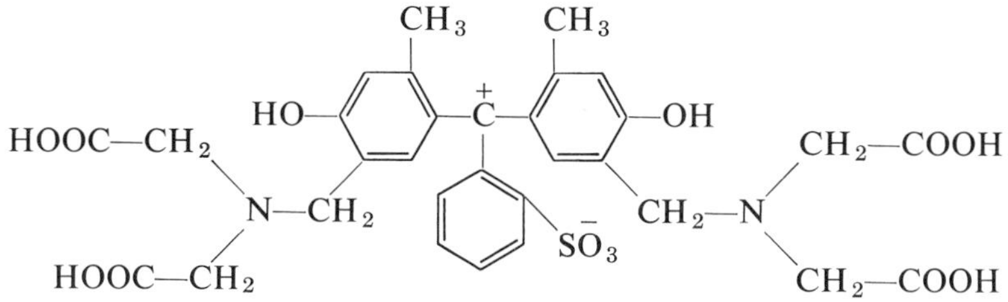

Xylenol orange

Direct titrations of many +2 and +3 ions are feasible with this indicator. It is blocked only by Fe(III) and Al(III). These can be determined by back-titration methods where EDTA is added to complex the metal ion before the indicator is added. It is recommended for its trouble-free uses of broad applicability. (See the laboratory section.) Pyrocatechol violet, bromopyrogallol red, and thymolphthalexone are dyes of similar structure useful in certain titrations. Copper PAN is another azo dye useful for Cu^{++}. Many other indicators have been tested including such specific ones as SCN^- for Fe(III).

21.3 EXAMPLES OF EDTA METHODS AND SELECTIVITY

Because EDTA is such a good complexing agent, titration of metal ion mixtures usually requires either prior separation or masking by selective complexing agents.

It would seem that some selectivity through pH control in titration could be obtained. At pH 5, Zn(II) might be titrated without interference from Mg(II) provided an indicator sensitive only to Zn(II) is used.

Standard methods of separation like precipitation, solvent extraction, and ion exchange can be combined with EDTA methods to reduce the time for mixture analysis. Another means is to use an agent forming a more stable complex than does EDTA with an ion to be masked. A few examples illustrate some methods devised for specific problems.

1) *Extraction:* The sample of Zn(II) and Cu(II) [or Ni(II)] is made 3 *M* in SCN^- and extracted with portions of methyl isobutyl ketone to remove the Zn(II). Each component can be titrated with EDTA.*

2) *Masking:* To the same ions, at pH 10, KCN is added to complex the ions [Cu^{++} forms $Cu(CN)_2^-$]. The $Zn(CN)_4^=$ can be unmasked by CH_2O which reacts with CN^- to form $CH_2(CN)OH$. The CH_2O reaction with the other CN^- complexes is slow enough to allow titration of Zn(II) by EDTA. Another sample without CN^- is used to get the total of both ions.

For a mixture of Sn and Pb (e.g., solder), the total of both ions can be found by a back-titration EDTA method at pH 5.5. Then excess NaF is added which frees the EDTA from Sn(IV) giving $SnF_6^=$. The back-titration is continued to find Sn.

3) *Ion exchange:* A Zn(II), Cu(II), and Ni(II) sample in 4 *M* HCl is passed through a strongly basic anion resin in the Cl^- form. $ZnCl_4^=$ and $CuCl_4^=$ (if present) are retained. $NiCl^+$ passes through, if present. The Cu(II) is eluted with 0.5 *M* HCl and Zn(II) with 3 *M* HNO_3. Each can then be titrated with EDTA.†

4) *Kinetic and pH effects:* A rapid estimation of Fe, Ni, and Cr in a stainless steel can be performed on one sample using pH and kinetic effects. (This is not a high-precision method.) EDTA slightly in excess of the Fe(III) is added to the sample which has had Cl^- boiled out. The pH is set at 1.1 with HNO_3, and a back titration with standard Bi(III) to the xylenol orange endpoint is made. Ni(II) is not complexed at this pH. Next the solution is buffered at pH 5.5, and excess EDTA is added for the Ni(II) and back titrated with standard Zn(II). EDTA in excess of the Cr(III) is added, and the solution is heated near 100°C for 15 min to complete the complexing of Cr(III). A final back titration gives the Cr(III). The intense color of the Cr-EDTA complex dictates a sample containing only about 10 mg of Cr. (A fluorescence indicator, calcein, under ultraviolet light is useful in such a case.) A number of other examples are given in detail in the laboratory section.

The pH effect depends on the stabilities of both the EDTA and the indicator complexes of ions. For example, excess EDTA will complex some Zn(II) or Ni(II) even at pH 2. However, xylenol orange does not, thus giving its color change at the proper point in titrations of Bi(III) and EDTA at pH 1 to 2.

For effective masking, the added ligand must prevent the reaction of the metal ion with EDTA. This may be effected through tighter complexing (favorable K_{eq}) or through the kinetic effect of a slow reacting (inert) complex. A summary of masking agents is presented in Table 21–2. Details of their use with mixtures can be found in the texts listed in the references.

---

* *Treatise*, Part II, Vol. 3, p. 158.

† See *Treatise*, Part I, Vol. 3, p. 1565.

Table 21–2

Ligand	To mask	Conditions, etc.
CN^-	Cu, Co, Ni, Zn, Fe, Hg, Cd	pH > 7. Only Zn and Cd are freed by CH_2O or $CCl_3CH(OH)_2$.
OH^-	Al, Mg	
F^-	Sn(IV), Ti(IV), Ca, Mg, Al	
I^-	Hg(II)	Specific
2,3-dimercaptopropanol (BAL*)	Hg, Cd, Zn, Pb, As, Sb, Sn, Co, Cu	Ni titrated in presence of others
Thiourea	Cu	Allows Fe titration in presence of Cu
Thioglycolic acid	Ions which precipitate $S^=$ in acid	Allows titration of Co, Ni with Cu masked

* British anti-Lewisite

In solutions with no other acid or base present, the pH effect of EDTA complexing can be used quantitatively

$$M^{++} + H_2Y^= \rightarrow MY^= + 2H^+.$$

Excess EDTA (as Na_2H_2Y) is added, and standard base is used to titrate the hydronium formed in the complexing. A direct titration can be done with K_4Y or Na_4Y standard solution, $M^{++} + Y^{4-} \rightarrow MY^=$. The excess Y^{4-} after the equivalence point produces a jump in pH.

Many other chelating molecules have been synthesized and investigated. Some are superior to EDTA for certain applications. One will be mentioned. EGTA, ethyleneglycol-bis(β-aminoethylether)tetraacetic acid, has the same K_f as EDTA toward Ca^{++}, but a K_f which is 10^3 smaller for Mg^{++}, so that Ca^{++} can be titrated in the presence of Mg^{++}. This is better than the EDTA method for these two ions which required precipitation of $Mg(OH)_2$ which occludes some of the Ca^{++}. A distinction between Zn and Cd can be made with EGTA though not with EDTA.

EDTA can itself be used as a masking agent. In determining K^+ by precipitation with tetraphenylborate ion, most +2 and +3 ions can be masked with EDTA to prevent any interference.

SUMMARY

Applications and completeness calculations for EDTA titrations are given. Selectivity effected by pH and masking is described.

SUGGESTIONS FOR FURTHER READING

DIEHL, H., "Development of Metallochromic Indicators," *Anal. Chem.* **39,** 30A (1967). This is a fascinating personal account of some trials and errors in the very rapid growth of EDTA methods. Highly recommended.

FLASCHKA, H. A., *EDTA Titrations*, New York: Pergamon Press, 1959.

LAITINEN, H. A., *Chemical Analysis*, New York: McGraw-Hill, 1960, Chapter 13 (Complex Formation Titrations).

REILLEY, C. N., *et al.*, *J. Chem. Educ.* **36,** 555 and 619 (1959) discuss EDTA methods.

RINGBOM, A., *Complexation in Analytical Chemistry*, New York: Interscience, 1963. Tables of data and details of calculations concerning indicators and titrations are given.

Treatise on Analytical Chemistry, ed. by I. M. Kolthoff and P. J. Elving, Part I, Vol. 3 and Part II, Vol. 3. New York: Interscience, 1961. EDTA and other methods are given throughout these volumes under the appropriate elements.

VOGEL, A. I., *Quantitative Inorganic Analysis*, 3rd ed. New York: John Wiley, 1961. Chapter IV gives many EDTA methods.

WALTON, H. F., *Principles and Methods of Chemical Analysis*, 2nd ed. Englewood Cliffs, N.J.: Prentice-Hall, 1964, Chapter 21 (Complex-Forming Titrations).

PROBLEMS

1. Calculate log $[Hg^{++}]$ for a titration of 100 ml of 0.0100 M Cl^- by 0.0500 M $Hg(NO_3)_2$ at three points:
   i) half-way to equivalence,
   ii) at equivalence,
   iii) one ml after the equivalence point.
2. Calculate the lowest pH for 99.9% formation of $ZnEDTA^=$ in 0.010 M analytical concentration of Zn(II) and EDTA. Repeat for Hg(II) and Fe(III).
3. Find the ratio of $[ZnY^=]/[Zn^{++}]$ at pH 2, 4, and 6 at the equivalence point. Assume effectively 0.01 M pure $ZnY^=$. Use the α_0 values for EDTA (H_4Y) given in the chapter, and log K_f = 16.5. What do the results suggest about the pH for quantitative titration?
4. Suggest EDTA titration methods for determination of each ion in the following pairs in the presence of the other one.
   a) Ca^{++}, Fe(III)
   b) Pb(II), Zn(II)
   c) Cu(II), Zn(II)
   d) Sn(IV), Pb(II)
5. The effective indicator complex formation constant for Zn(II) erio T is 10^{12}. Given that the erio T is about 10^{-5} M, find the amount of $[Zn^{++}]$ required to complex half the indicator. At pH 10 and $ZnY^=$ = 0.01 M, determine how many milliliters from the equivalence point this occurs for 0.02 M EDTA in 100 ml volume.

6. Calculate the log of total concentration of Cu(II) uncomplexed by EDTA during titrations of 20.00 ml 0.02000 *M* $Cu(NO_3)_2$ by 0.02000 *M* EDTA at pH 5.0 and at pH 10.0. Assume no interference at pH 5.0 and assume free $[NH_3]$, 0.1 *M* at pH 10.0. Plot the two titration curves on the same graph. Get points at 0, 10, 50, 90, 99, and 100% of equivalence and also 0.1 and 1.0 ml after equivalence.

7. Find the concentration of free Cu^{++} aquo ion at the start and at the equivalence points of the titrations in Problem 6.

8. A sample containing only Fe and Ni (Ferro-nickel, Invar, Durimet-A, etc.) is to be used in EDTA determination of both metals. If the alloy is 30% Ni, and 0.02 *M* standard EDTA is convenient to use, what size samples should be taken to achieve ±2 ppth precision (±0.05 ml) in the titrations? Fe(III) is to be determined at pH 1, and Ni at pH 5.5.

CHAPTER 22

CHROMATOGRAPHIC METHODS

The term *chromatography* has come to refer to a variety of techniques having in common selective sorption and desorption from a flowing phase onto a stationary sorbent in successive stages each approaching equilibrium. The process is carried out in columns or tubes of sorbent, on paper strips, and on thin layers of sorbent on glass plates. The flowing phase can be liquid or gas solutions.

Early scientific applications of selective sorption were made by D. T. Day at the U.S. Geological Survey in the 1890's. The varied colors of petroleums led him to study their behavior when they were passed through limestone and soils which effected fractionations. Mikhail Tswett, who was educated in Switzerland and worked in Russia, developed column chromatography around 1900 in his extensive work on the plant pigments, chlorophyll, carotene, xanthophyll, etc. Not until the 1940's did others begin to use this powerful method of separating and identifying materials in organic and biochemical research. Extension to paper and gas chromatographic methods has made these among the most widely used techniques of modern investigations. Ion-exchange properties of certain clays (aluminosilicates) (zeolites) have been known for a century and had been used to soften hard water. Synthesis of polymers with much greater ion-exchange capacity and selectivity began in the 1930's, and they have become a major addition to tools of the chemist.

22.1 CHROMATOGRAPHIC PROCESSES

Separations are performed by three main techniques: elution, displacement, and frontal analysis.

Elution

Elution methods are most common. The sample is sorbed at a small starting zone of the column or strip. A suitable solvent is passed (down a column, up or down paper strips). This elution can separate substances according to their relative affinities for the sorbent and the solvent. Several solvents may be added in succession. The component of highest mobility (the one which combines low sorbability and/or higher solubility) will move to fresh sites along the path of flow and eventually may appear in the effluent. In some cases, elution is performed only until separate bands of colors are seen on the column or paper. These can be identified, and sometimes their quantities can be estimated.

In paper chromatography, the relative distance moved is a characteristic useful for identification or location. The R_f value is defined as the ratio of the distance moved by a substance to the distance moved by the solvent. Published values are tabulated for many compounds with specific solvents. These are merely a guide as variations of paper, temperature, etc., make desirable the running of knowns to find the R_f under particular experimental conditions. Extensive use of paper methods has been made for amino acids. Inorganic qualitative analysis separations are easily made on paper. For example, Fe(III), Co(II), and Ni(II) as chlorides are spotted on a paper strip and developed with 0.5 *M* HCl in 87% acetone. The three separate with R_f values Fe(III) = 1, Co(II) = 0.3, and Ni(II) = 0. Color reagents at those distances serve to identify the ions. Details of many applications are given in the references cited at the end of the chapter.

With 1-butanol containing 20% 12 *M* HCl as solvent, many metal ions can be separated on paper strips. Reeves and Crumpler* sprayed the paper with 8-hydroxyquinoline to form colored products with the ions. In cases of close R_f values, very different colors are seen in fluorescence under ultraviolet light. The method works in ascending paper-strip chromatography as well as in the descending method reported.

Ion	Al(III)	Ni(II)	Co(II)	Cu(II)	Bi(III)	Zn(II)	Cd(II)	Hg(II)	Fe(III)
$R_f \times 100$	3	4	19	40	51	78	83	84	93
Color under ultraviolet	yellow	red	red	red	red	yellow	yellow	red	purple

The color under ultraviolet refers to that of the 8-hydroxyquinolate complex. These are all yellow in white light except for the Fe(III) complex which is black.

Lists of R_f values appear in many reference books on chromatography. A recent compilation of values for over 400 compounds of biochemical interest in 10 solvents is given by K. Fink, R. Cline, and R. Fink.†

Derivation of an equation for the position of the maximum concentration of a species (a peak) as a function of volume of eluent and the partition coefficient follows closely the derivation of the equation for countercurrent distribution. The discrete steps of the latter led to a binomial distribution (Chapter 18), whereas the continuous change in column flow leads to a Poisson distribution. Both approach the Gaussian (error curve) as the number of stages increases. This application of the theoretical plate concept was made by A. J. P. Martin and R. L. M. Synge in 1941. Details may be found in *Chemical Analysis* by H. A. Laitinen (New York: McGraw-Hill, 1960), in which Chapter 25 is a unified view of the theory of multistage equilibrium separations.

* W. Reeves and T. Crumpler, *Anal. Chem.* **23,** 1576 (1951).

† *Anal Chem.* **35,** 389 (1963).

The concept of the height equivalent to a theoretical plate, HETP, is frequently useful in discussing multistage processes. As in distillation (Chapter 17) it refers to the length of a given column in which one stage of equilibrium occurs (length/number of plates). For chromatographic columns, this is on the order of 0.02 mm so that very large numbers of plates are involved in most chromatographic operations. The HETP increases with the square of the sorbent particle diameter and is proportional to the rate of liquid flow. Therefore finely divided packing particles and slow flow rates are often used to achieve efficient separations.

Displacement

Again, the sample is placed at a small starting zone. However, the next liquid passed over it contains a solute which sorbs more strongly than the sample. The sample is displaced from the sorbent sites and pushed ahead of the displacement front. The components of the sample will assort themselves in bands with the least sorbable pushed ahead of the next least sorbable, etc., until the final band of displacer is reached. In contrast to elution, each band is in contact with its neighbors so that complete separations cannot be made. However, very pure fractions of the components can be obtained if the adjoining band portions are discarded. A preparative example is given in Chapter 23.

Frontal Analysis

In this method, the sample is distributed in a large volume of solvent which is passed through the column of sorbent. Each component is sorbed until the sites are saturated in each layer of the sorbent it meets. Any additional component must pass on to a fresh layer or displace a less sorbable component. In this way, bands develop: the leading front being a band of the least sorbable component (A). Behind this, a band follows containing the second least sorbable component (B) but also containing A from the fresh solvent flowing in. Next comes a band of C containing A and B. The method is used to separate pure A and to tell the number of components in the mixture.

Numerous combinations and variations of these methods are practiced. Details are given in the texts cited in the references.

22.2 GAS CHROMATOGRAPHY

Gas chromatography, which was introduced about 1952, has found wide application. A stream of carrier gas, usually helium, flows slowly through the tube of sorbent. The sample is introduced in a puff from a hypodermic syringe. Because gases have low viscosity, the flow is more rapid than it is in methods using liquids, and long columns can be used. Column lengths from a few centimeters up to several meters are common. A gas thermal-conductivity cell is often used to detect the amount of heavy gas in the He stream. The wide usefulness becomes apparent when one sees that the apparatus is enclosed and heated so that compounds, or their derivatives, having vapor pressures of about 10 torr at 100°C, or higher, can be sampled. Homologous series like the esters, alcohols, amino acids, etc., can be separated, identified, and estimated if calibrating mixtures are first determined with the apparatus. Samples on the order of 1 ml of gas, or 1 microliter of liquid (about 1 mg of matter) are usable. Feats which previously had been forbiddingly difficult are now possible, such as the determination of the components (18^+) of coffee aroma, diagnosis of some illness from the patient's breath, and rapid identification of bacteria from their metabolic products.

Amino acids, to cite one example of substances of low volatility, or which decompose on heating, are converted to methyl, or other, esters which have sufficient vapor pressure to permit gas chromatography at moderate temperatures. While more complete and precise analysis of protein amino acids is possible by ion-exchange resin chromatography, the gas method takes one-tenth the time and needs only one-hundredth the sample weight.

The column effluent can be fed to infrared, or mass, spectrometers to obtain further information on the structures of unknowns. In a very short time, gas chromatography has become an important research tool.

In the next chapter we consider details of ion-exchange separations. Practical instructions for their use and for use of paper chromatography of amino acids and metal ions are presented in the laboratory section. Valuable review chapters on recent developments in basic analytical methods are published in the journal, *Analytical Chemistry*, in April of even-numbered years, 1968, 1966, etc. There are sections on chromatography, ion exchange, and gas chromatography, among many others. These provide a good start in searching for newer applications.

SUMMARY

Elution, displacement, and frontal analysis processes are described for column, paper, and gas chromatography.

SUGGESTIONS FOR FURTHER READING

Chromatographic and Electrophoretic Techniques, 2nd ed., ed. by I. Smith, Vol. I. New York: Interscience, 1960. Discusses apparatus, techniques, and R_f values for many types of compounds.

Chromatography, ed. by E. Heftmann. New York: Reinhold, 1961.

LAITINEN, H. A., *Chemical Analysis*, New York: McGraw-Hill, 1960. Chapter 25 is a broad view of multistage equilibrium processes.

LEDERER, E., and M. LEDERER, *Chromatography*, 2nd ed. New York: Elsevier, 1957. Contains tables of R_f values for many organic compounds.

Treatise on Analytical Chemistry, ed. by I. M. Kolthoff and P. J. Elving, Part I, Vol. 3. New York: Interscience, 1961. Contains detailed chapters on various types and applications of chromatography.

PROBLEMS

1. From recent issues of journals, find examples of the use of ion exchange, paper chromatography, and countercurrent distribution. State the reference, solvents, sample size, and other conditions. Is the method given clearly enough so that you could follow it with the proper equipment?
2. Compare conditions, times, and especially amounts of amino acids that can be separated by paper chromatography and by ion exchange. Consult reference works for this. List your references.
3. Consult some reference to find out what thin-layer chromatography is. How is it like, and unlike, paper chromatography? What are its special advantages over other methods?

CHAPTER 23

ION-EXCHANGE METHODS

In 1850, two British soil chemists discovered that soil can remove K^+ in solutions passed through it, replacing K^+ by an equivalent amount of Ca^{++}. In 1913 the method of water softening by natural and synthetic inorganic exchangers of cations was introduced. Synthesis of much more efficient organic resin exchangers began in 1935. These have become an invaluable part of the chemist's tools in the laboratory and in industry. Only a few examples of resins and applications are given here to illustrate the scope of the field.

Styrene and divinylbenzene are copolymerized into a product in small bead form which is then treated to introduce the functional groups desired.

Cation-exchange (acidic) resins can be made by sulfonation of the polymer. A typical formula is:

$$\text{—CH—CH}_2\text{—CH—CH}_2\text{—CH—CH}_2\text{—CH—CH}_2\text{—etc.}$$

$$\begin{array}{cccc} | & | & | & | \\ C_6H_4 & C_6H_4 & C_6H_4 & C_6H_4 \\ | & | & | & | \\ SO_3^- & \text{CH—CH}_2 & SO_3^- & SO_3^- \\ H^+ & \vdots \quad | & H^+ & H^+ \end{array}$$

The divinylbenzene units (second ring) form links with other chains. The degree of this cross-linking is expressed by the manufacturers as the percentage of divinylbenzene in the polymerizing mixture. It affects the hardness, speed, and selectivity of the resin. Most common is the 8% resin, while 2, 4, 12, and 16% resins are available for certain uses.

Anion-exchange (basic) resins can be formed by chloromethylation followed by reaction with a tertiary amine to produce a "strongly basic" quarternary ammonium ion site. (By that term is meant that the quaternary ammonium hydroxide is a strong base.) A typical structure would be formed by replacing the $-SO_3^-$, H^+ in the cation resin with $-CH_2\text{—}NR_3^+$, OH^-. Because the OH^- form is less stable above 50°, the resin is sold in the Cl^- form which is easily converted to OH^- by washing with dilute NaOH solution.

23.1 SELECTIVITY

The selectivity of ion-exchange processes is a major factor in their utility. In general:

1. More highly charged ions are held more strongly than ions with lower charges, at the same concentrations.
2. Among ions of the same charge, the larger (less hydrated) are held more strongly at the same concentrations. (Remember that the effective sizes of hydrated ions may change in the opposite direction. See the Kielland table 9–2.)
3. Selectivities widen with increase in cross-linkage of the resin.

Some quantitative means of expressing the affinity of ions for the resin sites is desirable. Several are in use. For the equilibrium on a cation resin, where R^- is one resin site, one can write

$$A^+R^- + B^+ \rightleftharpoons B^+R^- + A^+, \qquad K^0 = \frac{(BR)(A^+)}{(AR)(B^+)}.$$

Here B^+ is the new cation put onto the resin which was in the A^+ form. The parentheses are used to represent activities. Since activities in the resin are difficult to determine, an effective K, in concentration units, under specific conditions is often reported. If one imagines the resin covered with a given concentration of A^+, its sites are all AR. Then one adds only a trace of B^+ so that the quotient $(A^+)/(AR)$ is effectively unchanged. The quotient $(BR)/(B^+)$ is then a measure of the distribution of B^+ between resin sites and the solution under these conditions. It is called a distribution quotient. If, instead of units of concentration in the resin phase, we use mmoles per plate volume of the column taking resin and solution together, the result is a convenient distribution ratio, often written D, or K_d.

Consistent, relative D values can be obtained in batch experiments by equilibrating a known weight of resin with a known volume of a standard ion solution. The ion concentration remaining in solution at equilibrium is then determined by a suitable titration. The distribution coefficient can be expressed by

$$D = \frac{\text{mmole ion in 1 g of resin}}{\text{mmole ion in 1 ml solution}} \qquad \text{(at equilibrium).}$$

This is usually what is meant by D in the literature. A major problem with this is the variable weight of the resin which strongly holds water. Reproducible drying is an uncertain operation. A superior distribution expression which is independent of moisture content is based on milliequivalents of resin rather than weight.* The capacity of the resin is simply determined by a titration. (In Laboratory Project 12, an anion resin in the Cl^- form is weighed, and its Cl^- is exchanged by NO_3^- and titrated with standard $AgNO_3$.) One can then divide the numerator of

* J. S. Fritz and H. Waki, *Anal. Chem.* **35,** 1079 (1963).

the previous D expression by the capacity in meq/g to get

$$D_e = \frac{\text{mmole ion per meq resin}}{\text{mmole ion per ml solution}}.$$

This coefficient based on milliequivalents of resin is designated D_e. For a resin having 3.0 meq/g, D_e is $\frac{1}{3}$ of D. The example curves of log (D) versus concentration in Figs. 23–3 and 23–4 have similar shapes for either D. (The resin samples for batch D and for capacity determinations are weighed at the same time so that the water content will cancel.)

By application of successive plate theory (binomial distribution) to ion-exchange column elution, S. Mayer and E. Tompkins (*J. Am. Chem. Soc.* **69,** 2866, 1947) deduced the remarkably simple relation,

$$V_{\text{max}} = D_c,$$

where V_{max} is the number of column volumes, after the first, required to elute the peak of the substance of column distribution ratio D_c. A column volume is the solution volume filling the empty spaces between the resin particles. This helps to design columns and procedures when D values have been determined.

23.2 APPLICATIONS

The simplest application is conversion of one ion in solution completely to that of the exchanger.

Examples

1. A known weight of pure NaCl passed through a large excess of cation resin in the H^+ form emerges as an equivalent solution of HCl useful for standardizing a base solution.
2. Materials like LiCl or $Cu(NO_3)_2$ which are hygroscopic and wet can be treated as in Example 1 and their purity found.
3. All interfering ions of one charge can be replaced. For example, many cations interfere by coprecipitation in the gravimetric $SO_4^=$ determination by $BaSO_4$. A sample of alum, $KAl(SO_4)_2 \cdot 12H_2O$, passed through a cation exchanger as in Example 1 emerges as a dilute solution of H_2SO_4 ready for precipitation of pure $BaSO_4$.
4. Complete removal of ions is effected by passage through a cation resin in the H^+ form followed by an anion OH^- resin to produce pure water (deionization).
5. To collect ions from very dilute solution, large volumes are passed through a resin leaving ions on the resin which can then be collected in a smaller volume by elution.

Separations of several ionic components in solution is a major success of ion-exchange methods. Elution bands are ideally like those in countercurrent extrac-

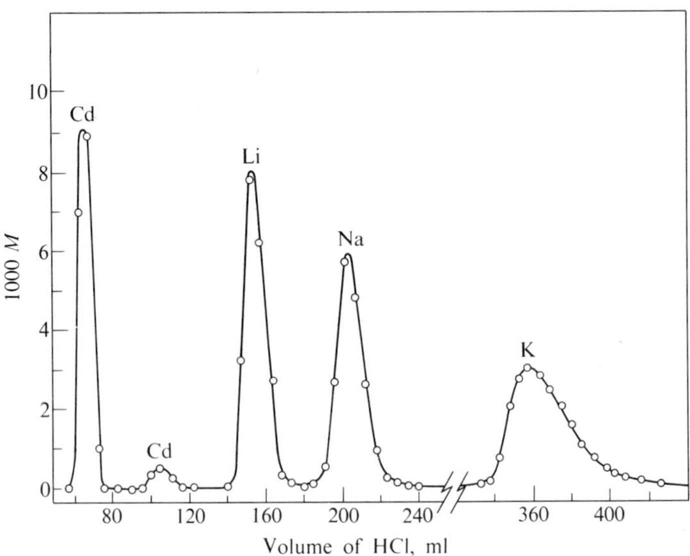

Fig. 23–1. Separation of Cd, Li, Na, and K with about 0.2 mmole of each present. (37 cm × 2.4 cm² colloidal Dowex 50; 0.70 *M* HCl, flow rate = 0.55 cm/min; Mg starts at 650 ml.) [From W. Rieman, *Record Chem. Progr.* **15,** 85 (1954).]

tion (Chapter 18). A typical example, Fig. 23–1, shows the cation resin separation of Li^+, Na^+, K^+ [with some Cd(II) present] by elution with 0.7 *M* HCl. To plot such a curve, small samples are taken successively during the elution and the ions determined, in this case by evaporation and weighing of the alkali metal chloride. A clean separation of these elements is difficult by any other means. Here, 0.7 *M* HCl was found to give the right degree of competition of H^+ and metal ions for the resin sites. But, is Cd(II) violating the rule that +2 ions are more strongly sorbed than +1 ions? No, Cd(II) in 0.7 *M* HCl is $CdCl^+$, $CdCl_2$, etc., so that it is reasonable that it can be removed first and might exhibit two peaks. (The two peaks are not expected for labile complexes.)

The effect of complexing can be used in both directions: to reduce the sorbability of a component as was just seen with Cd(II), or to convert it to a more sorbable species. Chloro complexing together with *anion* exchange has proved a powerful separation technique as developed at Oak Ridge by K. A. Kraus and coworkers. A large number of metal ions form anionic chloro complexes which exchange with quarternary ammonium resins in the Cl^- form. One has much control over the process since the equilibria depend on the [HCl] of the eluting solvent. Figure 23–2 shows a sharp separation of six metals with successively decreasing [HCl] eluants. Ni(II), which forms only the cations Ni^{++} and $NiCl^+$ in aqueous chloride solutions, is not sorbed and comes out in the first column volume of HCl. The other ions form large, or small, equilibrium concentrations of such anionic species as $MnCl_4^=$, $CoCl_3^-$, $CuCl_4^=$, $FeCl_4^-$, $ZnCl_4^=$,

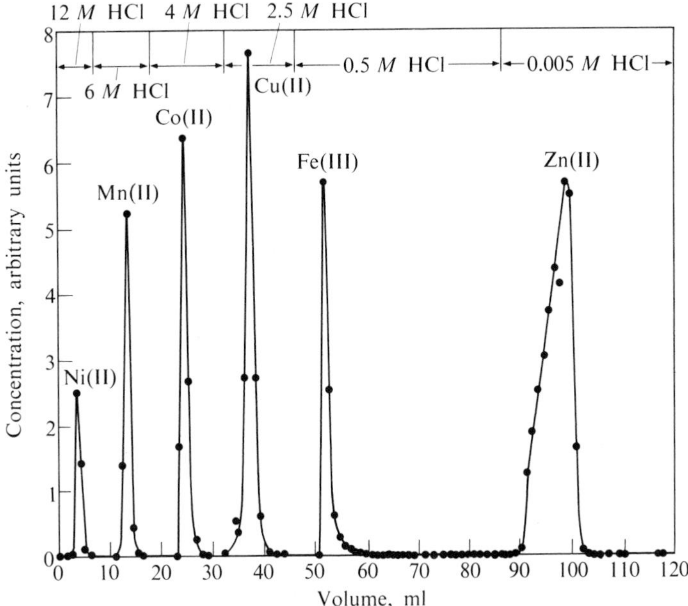

Fig. 23–2. Separation of the transition elements Mn to Zn (Dowex 1 column; 26 cm × 0.29 cm; flow rate = 0.5 cm/min). [From K. A. Kraus and G. E. Moore, *J. Am. Chem. Soc.* **75,** 1460 (1953).]

and others. The order of elution is clearly not that of the formation constants of the complex ions alone, but also depends on the affinities for the resin sites. The stepwise formation constants for the Cl^- complexes of Mn(II), Co(II), and Zn(II) are all on the order of one or less, yet Zn(II) is far more strongly held than the others, so much so that 3 *M* HNO_3 is now often used to elute it rather than the

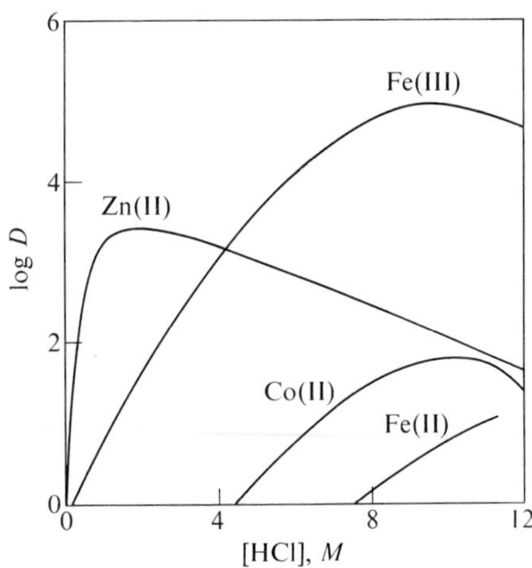

Fig. 23–3. Variation of log *D* with HCl concentration for a strongly basic anion exchange resin, quarternary ammonium ion type. *D* rises with HCl because of increased anionic complex formation and falls because of increased competition for sites by the Cl^- ion. [From K. A. Kraus and F. Nelson, *Proc. 1st U. N. Conf. Peaceful Uses At. Energy* **7,** 113 (1955).]

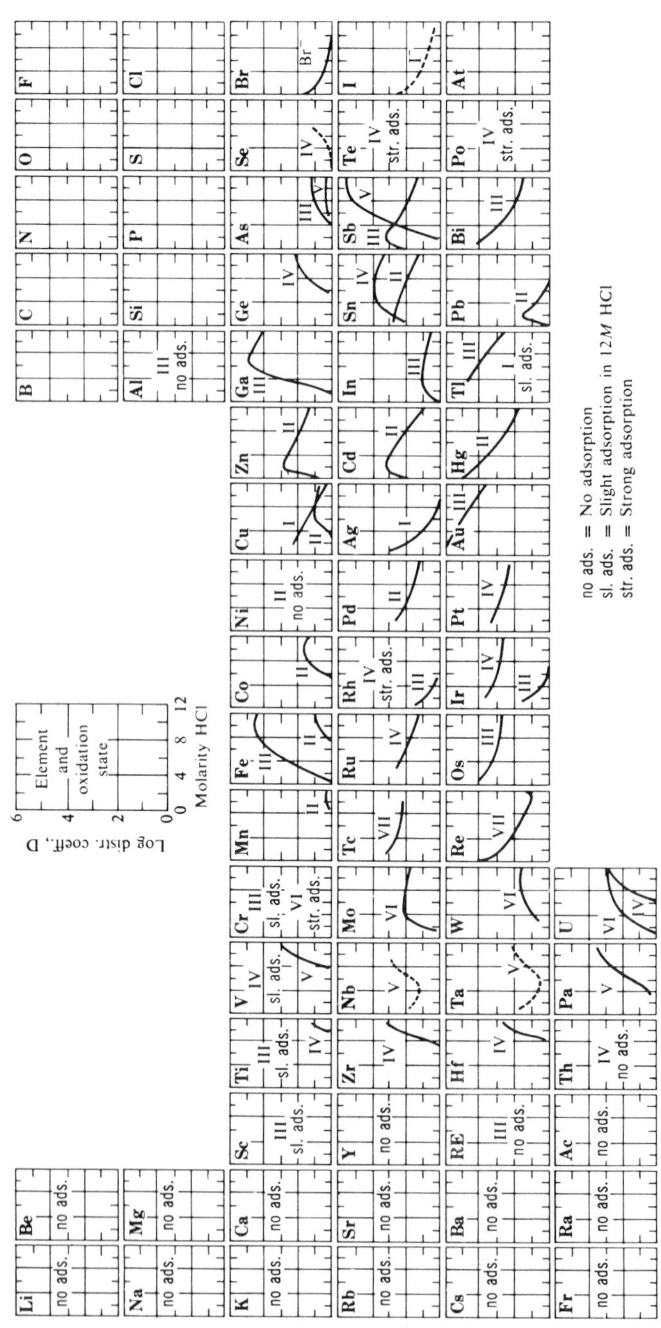

Fig. 23–4. Absorption of the elements by Dowex 1-X10 from HCl solution. (From Kraus and Nelson, *loc. cit.* and J. S. Fritz and G. H. Schenk, *Quantitative Analytical Chemistry*, Boston: Allyn and Bacon, 1965.)

very dilute HCl in Fig. 23–2. Moreover, D varies with [HCl] in different ways for each ion as shown in Figs. 23–3 and 23–4. This permits even more flexibility in separations. Note that Co(II), Zn(II), and Fe(III) all have high D values in 9 M HCl. When 4 to 5 M HCl is passed through, the D value for Co(II) falls to about one, and it elutes easily while for Zn(II) and Fe(III) the D value remains high. At 1 M HCl, the D value for Fe(III) falls to one while that for Zn(II) remains high.

To suggest the possible uses of this method, a few of many known D values determined by Kraus are listed in Table 23–1: the maximum D is listed for the concentration of HCl at which it occurs.

Table 23–1

Ion	[HCl] maximum	log D_{max}	Ion	[HCl] maximum	log D_{max}
Au(III)	1	7	Fe(III)	10	4.5
Bi(III)	1	4.5	Mn(II)	11	0.3
Cd(II)	2	3.5	Pb(II)	1	1.5
Co(II)	9	1.7	Sb(III)	2	3
Cu(II)	4	2	Zn(II)	2	3.2

The alkali and alkaline earth metal ions, Al(III), Ni(II), and Cr(III) are the only common metal ions not sorbed on anion resins from HCl solutions. This, and the variations in D, make numerous valuable separations possible. The D given is on a volume basis for 1 ml resin and 1 ml interstitial solution.

Anion exchange of 52 elements in sulfuric acid solutions has been studied by Strelow and Bothma [*Anal. Chem.* **39**, 595 (1967)]. As expected, +3 and higher oxidation states were found to have high D values. The +2 ions have little ability to form anionic sulfato complexes in aqueous solutions.

We noted in Chapter 20 that complexing of Co(II) by halides, etc., was increased by removing water and adding acetone. Similar solvent effects can be used in ion exchange. The acetone effect has been used to increase the selectivity of cation exchange of metal ions.* As expected, elution by increasing concentrations of acetone, with HCl constant at 0.5 M, occurs in the reverse order of that in the anion-exchange HCl method.

Nitrate complexing of metal ions is generally weak in water solutions. By adding up to 90% tetrahydrofuran in a solvent of 0.6 M HNO_3, nitrato complexing of Pb(II) and UO_2^{++} are favored allowing separations by either cation or anion methods.†

Complex formation by F^-, Br^-, citrate, EDTA, and many other ligands has been used to effect separations in specific cases. Separation of the rare earths, an

* See J. Fritz and T. Rettig, *Anal. Chem.* **34,** 1562 (1962).
† J. Korkisch and S. Ahluwalia, *Anal. Chem.* **38,** 497 (1966) and **36,** 1793 (1964).

insoluble problem in classical analytical chemistry, was an early success of the ion-exchange method. It was developed in connection with the study of fission products in the 1940's.* Citrate complexing was useful here. A student experiment on the separation of rare earths is described by W. L. Jolly† using oxalate precipitations to determine an elution curve. It should be adaptable to EDTA titrations to shorten the time required. The interested student might try this instead of the project on Fe, Co, Ni separation in the laboratory section.

Elution in a synthetic application appears in the separation of a +1 and a +3 ion on a cation resin.‡ To obtain pure $Cr(H_2O)_5SO_4^+$ ion, the mixture in which it was formed together with $Cr(H_2O)_6^{3+}$ was sorbed on cation resin and eluted with 2 *M* HCl. The violet Cr^{3+} aquo ion band remained near the top while the green sulfato complex was eluted from the column.

Use of the displacement method is illustrated by the separation of pure monochlorochromium ion, $Cr(H_2O)_5Cl^{++}$ from a mixture in which it is always formed.§ The mixed chloro ions were sorbed on cation resin and washed with 0.001 *M* $HClO_4$. Three bands formed: (1) at the top, violet aquo ion, Cr^{3+}, (2) dark green $CrCl^{++}$, (3) a small amount of green $CrCl_2^+$. Displacement was effected with Ce(III) in 0.1 *M* $HClO_4$. The $CrCl_2^+$ came out first and was discarded. The Ce(III) sorbs and pushes the violet Cr^{3+} band ahead of it. The Cr^{3+} pushes the $CrCl^{++}$ which, in turn, pushes the $CrCl_2^+$ out first. Both these chromium ion projects were a part of undergraduate research at Carleton College.

SUMMARY

Applications and equilibria of ion-exchange resins are given. Determination of distribution coefficients and elution curves is described.

SUGGESTIONS FOR FURTHER READING

Physical Methods of Chemical Analysis, Vol. IV, ed. by W. G. Berl. New York: Academic Press, 1961. Contains a chapter on ion exchange by W. Rieman and R. Sargent.

Samuelson, O., *Ion Exchange Separations in Analytical Chemistry*, New York: John Wiley, 1963.

Walton, H. F., *Principles and Methods of Chemical Analysis*, 2nd ed. Englewood Cliffs, N.J.: Prentice-Hall, 1964. Chapter 8 discusses ion exchange.

---

* See B. Ketelle and G. Boyd, *J. Am. Chem. Soc.* **69,** 2800, 1947.

† *Synthetic Inorganic Chemistry*, Englewood Cliffs, N.J.: Prentice-Hall, 1960, p. 162.

‡ J. Finholt, *et al.*, *Inorg. Chem.* **4,** 43, 1965.

§ See J. Finholt *et al. Inorg. Chem.* **3,** 1801, 1964.

PROBLEMS

1. Given that 0.0500 mmole $CoCl_2$ in 15.0 ml 8 *M* HCl was shaken with 1.0 g (dry) anion-exchange resin, and 10.0 ml of the supernatant liquid then required 0.77 ml of 0.0100 *M* EDTA for titration of the remaining Co(II), find the apparent distribution coefficient for Co(II) under these conditions (on the basis of 1 dry gram/1 ml).
2. From Kraus' *D* values for chloro-anion exchange, outline methods that might separate (a) Cu(II) and Mn(II) and (b) Co(II) and Zn(II).

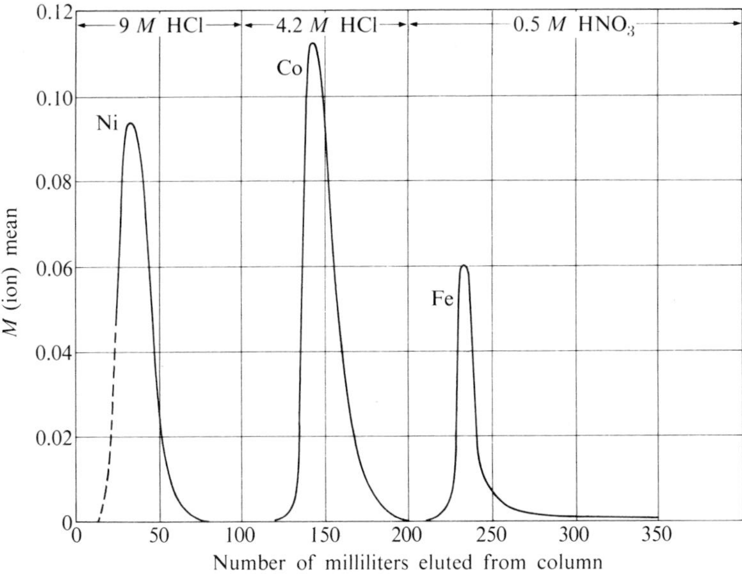

Fig. 23–5. Typical separation of Fe(III), Co(II), and Ni(II) on strongly basic resin Dowex 21K, 100 to 200 mesh; column volume is about 60 ml.

3. A 327 mg sample of a Konel type alloy was dissolved in HCl, oxidized to Fe(III), and separated as shown in the diagram of the results of titrations of successive samples in Fig. 23–5. Estimate the percent of Ni, Co, and Fe in the alloy from the diagram. Once you have determined the proper conditions by obtaining the diagram how should you more easily get the composition of a new sample?
4. Outline a method for analysis of a Nichrome type steel using ion-exchange separations and EDTA titrations. (See a listing of alloys if you do not know what Nichrome is.)
5. Describe the behavior, in volumes of 6 *M* HCl used, during elution of Co(II) and Cu(II) from an anion resin if their column *D* values are 5 and 10, and the column volume is 20 ml. Explain your reasoning.

CHAPTER 24

SOME IMPORTANT LABORATORY INSTRUMENTAL METHODS

The application of modern optical, electronic, and other types of instrumentation to chemical detection and measurement are enormous both in number and significance. This is mainly because of the ease and speed of operation once the instruments are adjusted to the problem at hand and calibrated. Three of the methods most frequently used by chemists are described here:

1. measurement of light absorption,
2. potentiometric methods with emphasis on the pH meter,
3. electrolytic methods.

We should emphasize that, in general, instruments must be calibrated and retested with known quantities. The understanding and care used by the person doing this determines the reliability of the results. Instruments do not make chemical determinations by themselves.

24.1 MEASUREMENT OF LIGHT ABSORPTION

Light absorption by a solute in a solvent that does not absorb the specific wavelength of light being used depends only on the solute concentration and the length of the light path. Thus spectrophotometric measurements provide a rapid nondestructive determination method for colored species.

The Bouguer-Lambert Law is a statement of the experimentally verifiable dependence of absorption on path length. (Monochromatic light is assumed in the following discussion.) The radiant power, P, of an absorbable wavelength decreases by the same fraction for each successive length, b, of the solution. The mathematical expression of the law is

$$dP/P = -k_1 db.$$

Integration between P_0 and P, $b = 0$ and b gives

$$\ln (P/P_0) = -k_1 b$$

(P_0 is the incident light power).

Beer's Law states that the fraction decrease in P for a fixed b is the same for each successive increment of concentration c:

$$dP/P = -k_2\,dc.$$

Integration from P_0 to P and $c = 0$ to c gives

$$\ln (P/P_0) = -k_2 c.$$

The two laws thus state the linear dependence of $\ln (P/P_0)$ on b and c, each of which may be varied independently. This means they can be combined:

$$\log (P/P_0) = -\epsilon bc = \log T,$$

where ϵ is the combined constant including the conversion to $\log_{10}$ and the *transmittance*, T, is P/P_0. The *absorbance*, A, defined as $-\log T$ gives

$$A = \epsilon bc,^* \tag{24–1}$$

where A is thus a positive number directly proportional to concentration and path length.† Since spectrophotometers measure P with and without the sample of absorbing matter in the path in arbitrary units, only the ratio is needed for T and A. Their scales are usually calibrated in T and A units so that either may be read directly.

The significance of the constant ϵ can be seen by considering unit path length and unit concentration, usually taken as 1 cm and 1 M. Thus ϵ is the absorbance

---

* The combination of the two laws can be made rigorously. (Conversion from ln to log is absorbed in the last constant.) From $A = k_1 b$ (at constant c),

$$\left(\frac{\partial A}{\partial b}\right)_c = k_1 = \frac{A}{b}.$$

And from $A = k_2 c$ (at constant b),

$$\left(\frac{\partial A}{\partial c}\right)_b = k_2 = \frac{A}{c}.$$

Now A, in general, is a function of only b and c. The complete differential must be

$$dA = \left(\frac{\partial A}{\partial b}\right)_c db + \left(\frac{\partial A}{\partial c}\right)_b dc.$$

Combining these gives

$$dA = \frac{A}{b}\,db + \frac{A}{c}\,dc \qquad \text{or} \qquad d\ln A = d\ln b + d\ln c.$$

Integrating and lumping all constants into one, $\ln \epsilon$, gives

$$A = \epsilon bc.$$

† Radiant power, P, is energy per unit area per unit time, for example, photons/cm^2-sec. *Intensity* is not correctly a synonym for P; it is expressed per unit solid angle.

of a 1 molar solution 1 cm thick. It is called the molar *absorptivity*. It may be convenient to use c in g/liter (in cases of unknown formulas). Then the constant is written as a, the specific absorptivity, the absorbance of a solution having 1 g/liter, 1 cm thick. Common older terms often used in the literature are: ϵ, molar extinction coefficient, and A, optical density. Here, we follow the system of nomenclature suggested by spectroscopists and other groups, which is outlined in the accompanying chart.

Spectrometry Nomenclature*

Absorbance, A. (Not optical density, absorbancy, or extinction.) Logarithm to the base 10 of the reciprocal of the transmittance $A = \log_{10}(1/T)$.

Absorptivity, a. (Not k.) (Not absorbancy index, specific extinction, or extinction coefficient.) Absorbance divided by the product of the concentration of the substance (in g/liter) and the sample path length (in cm), $a = A/bc$.

Absorptivity, Molar, ϵ. (Not molar absorbancy index, molar extinction coefficient, or molar absorption coefficient.) Product of the absorptivity, a, and the molecular weight of the substance.

Frequency. Number of cycles per unit time.

Infrared. The region of the electromagnetic spectrum extending from approximately 0.78 to 300 microns.

Micron, μ. Unit of length equal to 10^{-6} m.

Millimicron, mμ. Unit of length equal to one thousandth of a micron. Almost but not exactly equal to 10 Å.

Sample Path Length, b. (Not l or d.) Internal cell or sample length, usually given in centimeters.

Spectrograph. Instrument with an entrance slit and dispersing device that uses photography to obtain a record of spectral range. The radiant power passing through the optical system is integrated over time, and the quantity recorded is a function of radiant energy.

Spectrometer, Optical. Instrument with an entrance slit, a dispersing device, and with one or more exit slits, with which measurements are made at selected wavelengths within the spectral range, or by scanning over the range. The quantity detected is a function of radiant power.

Spectrophotometer. Spectrometer with associated equipment, so that it furnishes the ratio, or a function of the ratio, of the radiant power of two beams as a function of spectral wavelength. These two beams may be separated in time, space, or both.

Transmittance, T. (Not transmittancy or transmission.) The ratio of the radiant power transmitted by a sample to the radiant power incident on the sample.

Ultraviolet. The region of the electromagnetic spectrum from approximately 10 to 380 mμ. The term without further qualification usually refers to the region from 200 to 380 mμ.

Visible. Pertaining to radiant energy in the electromagnetic spectral range visible to the human eye (approximately 380 to 780 mμ).

Wavelength. (One word.) The distance, measured along the line of propagation, between two points that are in phase on adjacent waves—units Å, mμ, and μ.

Wavenumber. (One word.) Number of waves per unit length. The usual unit of wavenumber is the reciprocal centimeter, cm^{-1}. In terms of this unit, the wavenumber is the reciprocal of the wavelength when the latter is in centimeters in vacuo.

* Adapted from *Anal. Chem.* **39,** 1943 (1967). Sources used in this compilation were: ASTM Committee E-13 on Absorption Spectroscopy (1959 revision of tentative definitions); H. K. Hughes *et al.* [*Anal. Chem.* **24,** 1349 (1952)]; and *Chemical Abstracts.*

Many solutions at 1 M are so dark that neither the human eye nor the phototube can detect light at absorption peaks. So, ϵ must usually be calculated from measurements on dilute solutions.

Example 1

a) A fresh solution of 1.00 g $[CrCl_2(H_2O)_4]Cl \cdot 2H_2O$ (formula weight, 266.5) in 100 ml transmits 14.9% of 450 mμ light. Calculate A, a, and ϵ, if the cell is 1.00 cm thick.

We have

$$A = -\log 0.149 = 0.826,$$
$$a = A/bc = 0.826/(1)(10 \text{ g/liter}) = 0.0826,$$
$$\epsilon = 0.826/(1)(0.0376\ M) = 22.0.$$

b) Find the concentration of $CrCl_2{}^+$ in a solution of $A = 0.608$ in the 1 cm cell at 450 mμ.

The concentration is

$$c = A/\epsilon b = 0.608/22(1) = 0.0276\ M.$$

The speed and ease of A measurement with the recent development of reliable and precise instruments of moderate cost and simple operation has made its use probably the most common type of determination in chemical laboratory work. However, there are serious limitations to its use for mixtures. The absorption of other species present must be zero or else must be known and corrected for at the wavelength used. Simultaneous determination of several species under some favorable conditions may be possible. The method will be given later.

Photometric Error

The effect of *photometric error* can be calculated. It is plausible that neither very dark nor nearly transparent solutions will be amenable to precise determination. The basic equation can be solved for c, differentiated with respect to T, and divided through by c to give:

$$c = \frac{-\log T}{ab}, \qquad dc = \frac{-\log(e)}{ab}\frac{dT}{T}, \qquad \frac{dc}{c} = -\frac{0.4343}{abc}\frac{dT}{T}.$$

The relative error is the fraction change in c, (dc/c) per unit change in T, (dT). Calling the relative error f (and using $abc = -\log T$) we have

$$f = \frac{dc/c}{dT} = \frac{0.4343}{T(\log T)}. \tag{24–2}$$

The relative error, f, can now be calculated at various values of T. It goes through a minimum which can be found by differentiating and setting equal to zero as usual,

$$\frac{df}{dT} = 0.4343\left[\frac{-0.4343}{T^2 (\log T)^2} - \frac{1}{T^2 \log T}\right] = 0,$$

$$\log T = -0.4343,$$

$$A = 0.4343,$$

$$T = 0.368.$$

This tells us that the minimum uncertainty in c resulting from error in measured T occurs at a transmittance of 36.8%, or $A = 0.4343$. Fortunately, the minimum occurs on a broad curve so that the relative error remains small between about 10 and 80% T (1.0 to 0.1 A). The error, f, calculated at several values of T is:

T	0.95	0.90	0.60	0.368	0.30	0.10	0.01
f	20.5	10.6	3.26	2.72	2.77	4.34	21.7

A photometric error (in T) of 1% at $T = 0.368$ produces an error of 2.72% in c, while at $T = 0.90$ the error would be about four times as great. When highest precision is wanted, concentration should be adjusted to give T in the range 30 to 50%.

Determination of Several Absorbing Substances

Mixtures of n absorbing species can, in theory, be determined by getting an A reading at a peak wavelength for each one. This gives n equations in n unknowns. The ϵ for each species must be known at each wavelength used. Thus for two species, the A measured is the sum of A for each species, x and y. At wavelengths 1 and 2,

$$A_1 = \epsilon_{x_1} bc_x + \epsilon_{y_1} bc_y, \qquad A_2 = \epsilon_{x_2} bc_x + \epsilon_{y_2} bc_y.$$

When A_1 and A_2 are measured, c_x and c_y are the only unknowns. In practice, the concentrations and absorbances of the species must be within certain limits if valid solutions to the equations are to be found.

Example 2. Find the concentrations of x and y in a solution in a 1 cm cell if at the first wavelength, $A_1 = 0.640$ where $\epsilon_{x_1} = 600$ and $\epsilon_{y_1} = 400$, and at the second wavelength, $A_2 = 0.450$ where $\epsilon_{x_2} = 400$ and $\epsilon_{y_2} = 500$.

To obtain the answer, we first write for A_1 and A_2

$$0.640 = 600x + 400y, \qquad 0.450 = 400x + 500y.$$

Multiply the first by $\frac{2}{3}$ and subtract from the second equation to get:

$$0.023 = 233y, \qquad y = 1.0 \times 10^{-4}, \qquad x = 1.0 \times 10^{-3}.$$

Note that the likely minimum error of 0.002 in each A measurement would lead to about 16% error in x and y. If x and y were more nearly the same concentration, for these ϵ values, the error would be much less.

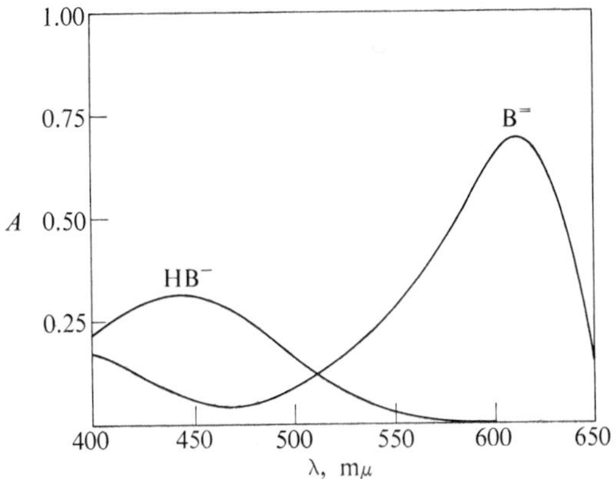

Fig. 24–1. Absorbance of 1.5×10^{-5} *M* bromcresol green in 1 cm cell at pH = 8 ($B^{=}$) and pH = 2.3 (HB^{-}). Ionic strength = 0.005 *M*.

An example of a much more favorable case of mixtures is the peak of the base form of bromcresol green, BCG, which occurs at a wavelength where the acid form is transparent. The curves shown in Fig. 24–1 are for the same concentration but at different pH where effectively 100% is in one form or the other. (It is a diprotic acid, H_2B, in which the first H^+ is strong. See the details of this experiment in the laboratory section.)

At 610 mμ, at pH 8 we assume all the BCG is in the blue basic form, $B^{=}$. The molar absorptivity can be calculated as

$$\epsilon = A/bc = 0.695/(1)(1.5 \times 10^{-5}) = 4.6_4 \times 10^4.$$

This is an intense color: compare the $CrCl_2^+$ above at $\epsilon = 22$. The uncertainty here arises from the unknown purity of the indicator. It turns out that an accurate concentration is not required: only the ratio of base to acid form is needed to determine K_a for BCG.

In a buffer calculated to have $[H^+] = 2.0 \times 10^{-5}$, the A was measured as 0.282 at 610 mμ. Find K_a. Since only the blue $B^{=}$ absorbs,

$$[B^{=}]/[HB^{-}] = 0.282/(0.695 - 0.282) = 0.682$$

and

$$K_a = [H^+][B^{=}]/[HB^{-}] = 2.0 \times 10^{-5}(0.682) = 1.3_6 \times 10^{-5},$$

which agrees well with published values for this indicator.

In more general terms, for the case of constant total concentration of two absorbing substances where both may be absorbing at the wavelength used, one can say

$$[B^{=}]/[HB^{-}] = x/(1 - x),$$

where x is the fraction in the $B^{=}$ form. Knowing the A for pure $B^{=}$, A_1, and for pure HB^{-}, A_2, at this same concentration, then we see that when they are mixed, the observed A must be

$$A = xA_1 + (1 - x)A_2.$$

This can be solved for x to give

$$x = \frac{A_2 - A}{A_2 - A_1} \quad \text{and} \quad 1 - x = \frac{A - A_1}{A_2 - A_1}.$$

So the ratio can be found from the experimental absorbances as

$$[B^=]/[HB^-] = x/(1 - x) = (A_2 - A)/(A - A_1).$$

This simple formula is used in the following examples.

To check where both forms absorb, look at 460 mμ where $B^=$ absorbs least: $A = 0.197$, $A_1 = 0.044$, and $A_2 = 0.300$. Thus

$$\frac{x}{1 - x} = \frac{0.300 - 0.197}{0.197 - 0.044} = 0.674,$$

which is in satisfactory agreement with the previous value which is more reliable because of the more favorable A range used and the larger difference between the two forms at 610 mμ.

Besides indicator applications, this method of calculation would be useful for such problems as finding the proportions of iron in Fe(II) and Fe(III) forms, and of Cr distributed between Cr(III) and $Cr_2O_7^=$, and similar problems where the total is likely to be known.

Instruments

The simplest use of light absorption is for visual comparison. An unknown in a test tube can be compared with a series of tubes containing standards at evenly spaced concentration intervals. Once the standards are prepared, this method permits rapid determinations to 1 or 2 significant figures in a range where that may be sufficient. For example, Mn in lake water (oxidized to MnO_4^-) can be determined as 1, 2, 3, etc., ppm. Appropriately colored glasses can be used in place of solution standards. *Comparators* of this kind are manufactured for use in water analysis, etc., for Cl_2, and pH, with indicators.

Instead of varying concentration for matching colors, one can vary the light path length, since absorbance is linear in both. If the length, b, is adjusted, either in the known or unknown, until both appear to have the same depth of color, then

$$A_1 = A_2 = \epsilon b_1 c_1 = \epsilon b_2 c_2, \qquad c_2 = (b_1/b_2)c_1.$$

That is, one must look through twice as much of a solution which is half as concentrated as the standard to see the same amount of the colored species. The advantage of this method is that only one standard needs to be prepared. A mechanical device for performing the path-length variation is the Duboscq colorimeter.

Beer's law is strictly valid only at single wavelengths. Colorimetry is thus an approximate method, which is good for broad absorption bands, but poorer for sharp and narrow bands. Improved accuracy and precision are obtained by filtering the light, or better still, by sorting out a narrow band of wavelengths with a monochrometer, usually a prism or grating. These techniques are combined with photocell detectors, replacing the eye, to make filter photometers and spectrophotometers. Photometers with glass filters are useful for routine measurements to 2 to 3 significant figures. With spectrophotometers, 3 to 4 significant figures can be obtained under the best conditions.

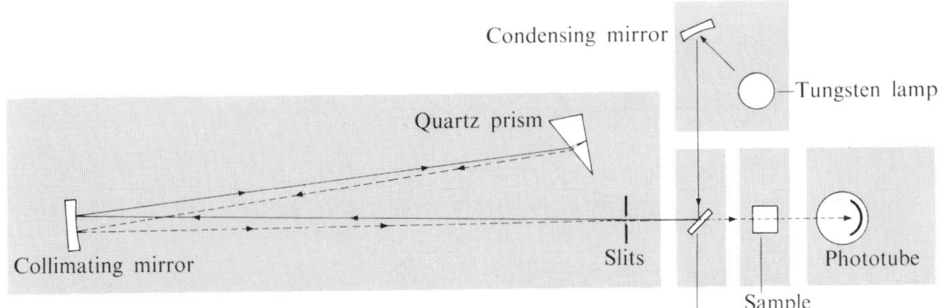

Fig. 24–2. Top view of DU. Light from the tungsten lamp is focused by the condensing mirror and directed in a beam to the diagonal-slit entrance mirror. The entrance mirror deflects the light through the entrance slit and into the monochromator to the collimating mirror. Light falling on the collimating mirror is rendered parallel and reflected to the quartz prism where it undergoes refraction. The back surface of the prism is aluminized so that light refracted at the first surface is reflected back through the prism, undergoing further refraction as it emerges from the prism. The desired wavelength of light is selected by rotating the wavelength selector which adjusts the position of the prism. The spectrum is directed back to the collimating mirror which centers the chosen wavelength on the exit slit and sample. Light passing through the sample strikes the phototube, causing a current gain. The current gain is amplified and registered on the null meter. (Courtesy of Beckman Instrument Co.)

The optical system of a typical spectrophotometer, the Beckman DU (Fig. 24–2), shows the arrangement of the light source, monochrometer, sample cell, and the photocell detector. The entrance and exit slits are one above the other. With this type of instrument, the blank (solvent) is measured first and set at 100% $T(A = 0)$. Then the sample is inserted in the path and measured. Both steps must be repeated at each wavelength. This single-beam method is capable of 4-figure precision. Faster work is possible with double-beam instruments which pass the light alternately through sample and solvent tubes (or which use two beams) and automatically compare the two to give a reading of A or T.

24.2 pH METERS AND POTENTIOMETRY

Without doubt, finding acid-base levels of aqueous solutions as expressed in pH units is the most frequently performed chemical measurement. Whether the method used is simple indicator dyes, color comparators, or electronic pH meters, some means of pH determination is available in almost every laboratory which uses any wet materials. Measurement and control of pH are so vital to pure and applied biology and chemistry that accurate and reliable pH meters were among the first laboratory instruments developed and mass-produced.

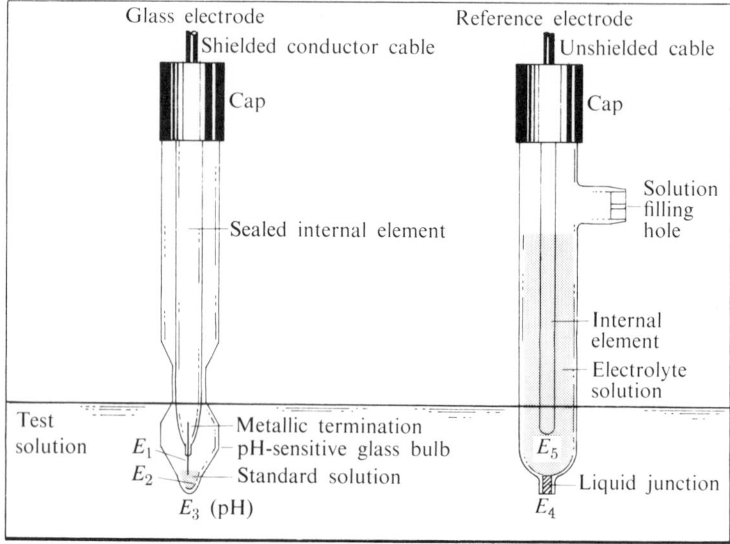

Fig. 24–3. The electrode system of the pH meter. (Courtesy of Beckman Instrument Co.)

Sørensen presented a potentiometric method (H_2-Pt electrode) and defined the pH concept in 1909. Glass-electrode devices were developed in the 1920's. The early electrode of MacInnes and Dole (1930) consisted of a glass tube with a thin membrane of a special pH-sensitive glass sealed on one end and containing dilute HCl with an Ag-AgCl electrode dipping into it. Since the electrode responds to the pH of an external solution, when it is combined with a standard reference cell, the voltage measured is found to be a linear function of pH, within certain limitations. This cell can be represented (Fig. 24–3)

1) Ag; AgCl, $HCl_{(a)}$ ‖ glass ‖ H^+ test solution | $KCl_{(sat)}$, $Hg_2Cl_{2(s)}$, $Hg_{(l)}$ (the SCE),

where the conventions used are as follows:

; is a metal electrode boundary surface,

, separates materials which are present together in one solution,

| is a liquid junction (a boundary allowing ionic contact but hindering free mixing of bulk solution),

|| is a special glass surface of high electrical resistance.

By comparison, a cell for pH measurement with the hydrogen electrode is written

2) Pt; $H_{2(g)}$, H^+ test solution | SCE.

This reads, hydrogen gas (1 atm unless other stated) in contact with Pt and the test solution which is in restricted ionic contact (salt bridge) with a saturated calomel electrode [SCE as given in (1)]. Since the left half is zero for unit activity H^+ and the right is a known constant, the measured voltage gives the pH:

$$\mathcal{E} = \mathcal{E}_{SCE} - \mathcal{E}_{H^+},$$

where $\mathcal{E}_{H^+} = -0.0592 \log [H^+]f_+ = 0.0592\,\text{pH}$, if pH is allowed to stand for $-\log (a_{H^+})$. pH standards reproducible to 0.001 unit tested and recommended by the NBS are listed in Chapter 7. The problem of a rigorous meaning for pH was mentioned there. Ambiguity is introduced by uncertainty in liquid junction potential and in the interpretation of activity of one ion (negative ions must also be present in the solution). It has been suggested that pH be defined as what the pH meter measures. For much laboratory work this is what it is taken to be. Calculation of $[H^+]$ from pH measurements to more than two figures is of dubious significance. This does not alter its value for comparing acidities and finding the changes at the endpoints of titrations.

Measuring the voltage of an electrolytic cell like (2) is easily performed with a common slide-wire potentiometer in which a resistance is adjusted so that an opposed known potential is just equal to the unknown cell. A galvanometer indicates no deflection when balance is achieved. Since no current flows, true equilibrium potentials are measured. Readings can be taken during titration to plot curves and find endpoints. (See the examples in Chapter 4.) The Pt electrode serves as conductor. For example, in the Fe(II)-dichromate titration a Pt wire and the SCE would give the cell

Pt; Fe(II), Fe(III) | SCE.

As explained in Chapter 12, this is equivalent to the cell

Pt; Cr(III), $Cr_2O_7^{=}$ | SCE,

since the Fe and the Cr half-cells are at equilibrium in the same solution.

In the cell with the glass electrode, however, one must reckon with the solid glass boundary, symbolized by ||, which is not a good conductor. While the resistance of electrolytic cells may be a few thousand ohms at most, glass-electrode resistance ranges from 10 to 500 megohms at 25°C and rises sharply as the temperature falls. Since galvanometers cannot detect the small currents available through the glass-electrode cell (1), other instrumentation had to be devised. The modern pH meter uses an electronic voltmeter with ac vacuum-tube amplification.

Research models reading to 0.001 pH unit became available in the 1960's. The usual laboratory meter can be read to 0.01 unit, but its absolute pH value is probably reliable to about ± 0.1 unit. Highest possible accuracy is obtained if the unknown pH is near that of the buffer used to standardize the instrument.

The Glass Electrode

How does the glass electrode work? To answer this question, let us consider the composition and behavior of the glass membrane. For example, Pyrex®, a borosilicate hard glass, does not give any usable pH response. The glasses which do are composed of: SiO_2, 60 to 75 mole percent, R_2O (where R is Li, Na, K, Cs), 17 to 32%, and MO or M_2O_3 (where M is Ca, Mg, Be, La, etc.), 3 to 16%. These are soft glasses which exhibit extensive ion-exchange properties at their surfaces. After soaking, many of the R^+ sites on the glass surface are replaced by H^+. The glass now functions as a "protode," and should be kept wet. An external potential can cause more H^+ to enter the surface layer on one side and R^+ to migrate through the glass and enter the solution on the other side. Conversely, with no potential, a difference in $[H^+]$ at the two surfaces produces the potential difference which is a measure of pH. Since this depends on proton transfer, not electron exchange, it is remarkably free of the disturbing effects which redox agents have on other pH electrodes. High concentrations of H^+, OH^-, and Na^+ do disturb the glass surface, and recovery time in pure water may be required. The common glass electrodes are useful between pH 0 and 10 with little correction. Special glass electrodes are available for use from pH 0 to 14. Lists of corrections for Na^+ and for pH above 10 are available. (See the references cited at the end of the chapter.) Usually the pH reading is too low above 10 and too high below 1.

Some acidity indication can be obtained with glass-electrode pH meters in the following solvents in addition to water for which they are designed: methanol, ethanol below 90%, H_2O_2, acetic acid, formic acid, acetonitrile, and dimethylformamide. Most other solvents cannot be used.

Other Ion Electrodes

Electrodes composed of glass compositions sensitive to ions other than H^+ are now commercially available. They also respond to H^+ so that the acidity of sample solutions must be low. Selective glass electrodes are made for Li^+, Na^+, K^+, NH_4^+, Ag^+, Cs^+, and Rb^+. Two other types of ion-selective electrodes have recently been introduced for use with pH meters. (a) The liquid-liquid membrane using an ion-exchange liquid enclosed by a porous membrane is used for Ca^{++}, Mg^{++}, Cu^{++}, Cl^-, ClO_4^-, and NO_3^-. (b) Precipitate-impregnated and solid-state membrane electrodes are used for the anions F^-, Cl^-, Br^-, I^-, and $S^=$.

® Pyrex is a registered trademark of Corning Glass Co.

The ion-selective electrodes respond to concentrations down to about 10^{-5} M. They should become especially useful for such analytically difficult ions as Na^+, K^+, Ca^{++}, Mg^{++}, and F^-.*

Potentiometric Titration

While the simple slide-wire potentiometer cannot be used with the glass electrode, the pH meter can serve for a potentiometer for most electrolytic cells as well as for pH determination. The Pt, Ag, etc., indicating electrode can be used opposite the SCE or even opposite the glass electrode if the pH will remain approximately constant during the titration. Actual experimental curves made in this way for the Fe(II)-dichromate titration are shown in Chapter 13.

The pH meter (or other potentiometer) can be used to indicate the endpoint in any titration if the redox potential changes sufficiently at the equivalence point. Usually this will be about 0.06 V (60 mV) with 2 drops of reagent to obtain 1 ppth precision in a 50 ml titration. In the Nernst equation for a one-electron oxidation this means

$$\mathcal{E} = 0.06 = -0.0592 \log (R_2/R_1) \qquad \text{or} \qquad R_2/R_1 = 0.1,$$

that is, a tenfold change in the ratio of oxidized to reduced forms. Whether this can occur depends on the K_{eq} under the conditions used. Improving the endpoint jump by complexing Fe(III) with H_3PO_4 is demonstrated in the calculated and the experimental curves for the Fe(II)-$Cr_2O_7^=$ titration in Chapter 13.

The applications of potentiometric endpoint detection are many. A broad sampling of methods is given in the text by Vogel. This method is especially required for colored and opaque solutions and those for which no good indicator is available. Even some titrations which would not seem to involve redox can be performed in this way. For example, the direct titration of Fe(III) with EDTA at pH 3 will signal its end at a Pt electrode. This is because, as discussed in Chapter 13, some Fe(II) must exist in the Fe(III) solution since a zero value for Fe(II) gives an infinite potential in the Nernst equation

$$\mathcal{E} = \mathcal{E}^0 - 0.0592 \log ([\text{Fe(III)}]/[\text{Fe(II)}]).$$

With only a trace of Fe(II) present, the ratio [Fe(III)]/[Fe(II)] will change rapidly near the equivalence point, since the K_f values for the EDTA complexes are 10^{25} for Fe(III) and 10^{14} for Fe(II). Thus Fe(II) forms negligible EDTA complex at pH 3 (see Chapter 21). The oxidation potential falls rapidly as the Fe(III) is removed by excess EDTA. In addition to the experimental titration curve shown in Fig. 24–4 (a), the first and second derivative curves approximated from the data are shown in Fig. 24–4(b). The first derivative, the slope, goes through a maximum at the end(inflection) point. The second derivative goes through zero

* See the review by G. A. Rechnitz, *Chemical and Engineering News*, June 12, 1967, p. 146.

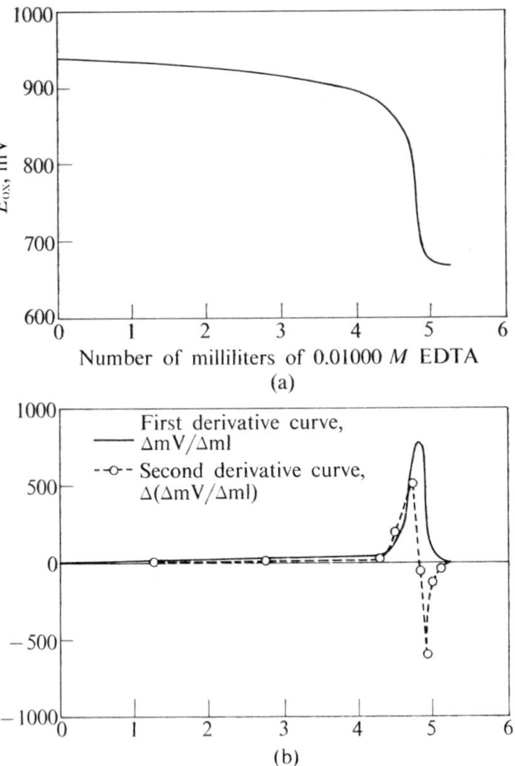

Fig. 24–4. (a) Titration curve for 100 ml of approximately 0.0005 *M* Fe(III) by 0.01 *M* EDTA at pH 3. At pH meter: glass electrode vs. Pt. (Arbitrary mV scale.) (b) First and second derivative curve.

at this point. The latter seems to be the easiest to determine with precision on the graph. It is used for much potentiometric titration work. Instruments for automatic titration have been developed to read first or second derivative, or to record them. Table 24–1 shows how to calculate and plot the data.

The endpoints of titrations of silver ion and halides are indicated by a silver metal electrode. The half-cell potential of

$$Ag + Cl^- \rightarrow \underline{AgCl} + e^-$$

depends on the log of $[Cl^-]$ (or $[Ag^+]$) and undergoes a jump or drop around the equivalence point. It is valuable in colored and more dilute (0.001 *M*) solutions where visual indicators are poor. For example, rapid titration by $AgNO_3$ of ice-cold acidic ($HClO_4$) chromium chloride solution serves to determine the nature of the complexes present and to check their purity. $[Cr(H_2O)_4Cl_2]Cl$ gives one equivalent of Cl^-, and $[Cr(H_2O)_5Cl]Cl_2$ gives two under these conditions, since the chromium complexes are sufficiently inert to be titrated in this way.

Table 24–1. Titration Data and Calculation of First and Second Derivative Values for the Titration of Fe(III) by EDTA with a Pt Electrode at pH 3

ml	mV	−ΔmV/Δml	Plot at, ml	Δ(ΔmV/Δml)	Plot at, ml
0	936				
		6	0.5		
1.02	930			0	1.25
		6	2.0		
2.99	917			18	2.75
		24	3.5		
4.00	893			19	3.81
		43	4.12		
4.23	883			25	4.24
		68	4.37		
4.51	864			198	4.50
		266	4.63		
4.75	800			534	4.70
		800	4.77		
4.80	760			−60	4.81
		740	4.85		
4.90	686			−593	4.89_5
		147	4.94		
4.97_5	675			−114	4.98
		33	5.02		
5.07	672			−33	5.09
		0	5.20		
5.33	672				

Note that the average rates of change are being used for the derivatives; therefore one takes the mean volume of the interval for plotting. This might be simplified by taking equal volume intervals during the titration, but that is difficult, time consuming, and frequently introduces errors.

Automated titration devices have been developed which cut off the flow of titrant when the proper potential value is reached. Titration curves can be automatically plotted by a recording potentiometer whose paper moves at constant speed while a pen indicates potential, if the buret is arranged to deliver solution at a constant rate with efficient stirring. These devices are valuable in routine analysis.

24.3 ELECTROLYTIC METHODS

Electrolytic conduction of direct current, in contrast to metallic conduction, produces chemical change: oxidation takes place at the anode and reduction at the cathode. Under certain favorable conditions this change may be adaptable to quantitative measurements. The simplest is the plating out and weighing of a metal. As commonly used for copper determinations, the method is capable of high precision and accuracy in the absence of interfering metal ions.

The concentrations and oxidation potentials of the species in a solution determine the electrode reactions. For example, in 0.1 M $CuSO_4$ with 1 M HNO_3 present, Cu^{++} is the more easily reduced cation, and H_2O is more easily oxidized than $SO_4^{=}$ or NO_3^{-}. (The OH^-, about 10^{-14} M, is assumed to be too dilute to carry much of the current.) The cathode and anode reactions upon electrolysis are then

$$Cu^{++} + 2e \rightarrow \underline{Cu},$$
$$2H_2O \rightarrow \overline{O_2} + 4H^+ + 4e.$$

Thus an excess of negative ions will exist in the vicinity of the cathode, and an excess of positive ions will form near the anode. This *polarization* opposes the direction of electrolysis. Furthermore, the backvoltage of the spontaneous cell reaction given by the Nernst equation must also be considered. The observed *decomposition voltage* required to give continuous electrolysis is determined by the combination of these effects and the diffusion and kinetic (activation energy) properties of the species reacting. The net excess above the reversible voltage calculated from the Nernst equation is called the *overvoltage*. This may be small, for most metal deposition, or high, for many gas evolutions. At a mercury cathode, for example, the overvoltage for reduction of H^+ to H_2 is high enough to allow Zn^{++}, Ni^{++}, etc., to accept electrons in acid solution when the $\mathcal{E}^0$ value alone would suggest that only H_2 is evolved.

Once the applied voltage on an electrolytic cell is raised to the decomposition value, current flows and Ohm's Law is followed, the current increasing linearly with applied voltage, until the rate of ion diffusion limits the current flow or the decomposition voltage of other species is passed.

For the $CuSO_4$ solution mentioned above, the half-cell $\mathcal{E}^0$ values are +0.337 V for Cu, and −1.229 V for O_2, as written. The $\mathcal{E}$ value for the whole cell is

$$\mathcal{E} = \mathcal{E}^0 - 0.0592 \log Q = -0.892 - \frac{0.0592}{4} \log \frac{(0.2 \text{ atm})(1)^4}{(0.1)^2} = -0.911,$$

where it is assumed that the O_2 pressure is 0.2 atm (20% of air) and that the activity coefficients approximately cancel. Other data give an O_2 overvoltage on Pt of about 0.4 V and that of Cu is negligible. The observed electrolysis voltage, the decomposition potential, is thus 1.31 V. To carry the electrolysis to 99.99% completion for Cu, the Nernst equation shows a change in $\mathcal{E}$ of

$$\Delta\mathcal{E} = 0.0592 \log (10^{-5}/10^{-1}) = -0.12 \text{ V}.$$

Thus a voltage of 1.31 + 0.12 = 1.43 V is required to do this. In practice, 2 V can be used, to allow for uncertainty in the measured voltage. The best conditions of voltage, acidity, and current have been determined by trial. (See the laboratory section on brass alloy analysis.)

Methods and Examples

Platinum gauze electrodes are used with dc applied from storage batteries or a rectifier capable of giving up to 6 V and 5 amp. A high wattage variable resistor allows regulation of the current and voltage (not independently) which are read on a voltmeter and an ammeter in the circuit.

In copper deposition, it is found that HNO_3 must be present to reduce H_2 formation which can make the Cu flake off the cathode. The reaction is

$$NO_3^- + 10H^+ + 8e \rightarrow NH_4^+ + 3H_2O.$$

The nitrate ion is a depolarizer which relieves the excess negative charge build-up at the cathode by this reaction. A sufficiently low current to reduce only the Cu would require a very long time for completion of the reduction. Such a slow (overnight) process is sometimes used. Some of the NO_3^- may be reduced only to NO_2^- which inhibits Cu deposition. The NO_2^- is removed by addition of urea during electrolysis,

$$2NO_2^- + CO(NH_2)_2 + 2H^+ \rightarrow 2N_2 + CO_2 + 3H_2O.$$

Lead can also be determined by electrolysis. In about 1 to 2 *M* HNO_3 solution, it cannot deposit on the cathode with copper, but forms its dioxide at the anode,

$$Pb^{++} + 2H_2O \rightarrow \underline{PbO_2} + 4H^+ + 2e.$$

Under a rather narrow range of conditions, these two elements can be determined in one operation for analysis of alloys which contain both. With an initial HNO_3 concentration of 1.8 *M*, all the lead and part of the copper deposit on the two electrodes. The reactions of HNO_3 and urea above, together with addition of water, lower the nitric acid concentration so that Cu deposition becomes complete. Addition of a few drops of H_2SO_4 and one, and only one, drop of 0.1 *M* HCl gives more adherent deposits. More than a trace of chloride will dissolve some platinum and reduce PbO_2. A larger amount of sulfate will not precipitate $PbSO_4$ in this HNO_3 solution, but it is not desirable if an anion-exchange separation is to follow in a brass analysis.

Similar constant-current electrodeposition methods have been developed for Zn, Cd, Co, Ni, Ag, Bi, etc. (See the text by Vogel.) These still have some application in routine industrial determinations.

Complex formation is used to improve separations and adherence of deposits. From acid $AgNO_3$ solutions, Ag forms loose crystals, while from basic cyanide solution such as $Ag(CN)_2^-$, it gives an adherent layer. Metals above hydrogen can rarely be reduced (without amalgam formation) in acid solutions. Ni^{++} and Co^{++} will deposit well from their NH_3 complex solutions. Zinc can be deposited from NaOH solutions, $Zn(OH)_4^=$, which serves as a separation from Al(III).

Separations may also be effected by controlling the applied voltage at a value between the decomposition potentials of the two metals to be separated. This can be done manually with a variable resistor, but automatic equipment is also available for the purpose.

Coulometry. If we can measure the time and amount of current accurately, instead of the weight of deposit, we can use these measurements to find the amount of electrolytic reaction by Faraday's Laws. We need currents small enough to give 100% current efficiency and also an endpoint indicator. We may think of this method as a titration by a stream of electrons. When current is multiplied by time, the product is in coulombs, and division by the Faraday (96,493.5 coul/eq) tells the number of equivalents reacted. An auxiliary potentiometer cirçuit is often used to signal the sudden change in $\mathcal{E}$ at the endpoint and to shut off the current and timer together. This recently introduced method has the advantages of micro applications and use of unstable species; Cr^{++}, Br_2, and Cl_2 can be produced electrolytically in the solution where they are to react. Quantitative brominations can be achieved, for example, by this method.

A current of 10.0 milliamperes, mA, flowing for 50.0 sec to oxidize the Fe^{++} in a sample indicates the Fe content to be

$$\frac{(0.1 \text{ amp})(50 \text{ sec})}{96{,}500}(55.8) = 0.29 \text{ mg}.$$

(Volumetrically, this would require only 0.5 ml of some 0.01 N reagent.) Coulometric titrations can be performed with currents as low as 0.1 mA for even smaller amounts.

Linear Titration Methods: Conductivity and Polarography

Measurement of a property which is directly proportional to the concentration of a reactant or product of a titration reaction can give a plot consisting of two straight lines intersecting at the equivalence point. (Most titrations previously treated involve log-concentration diagrams.) The linear methods may employ electrical conductivity, current flow, or light absorbance, for example. They are somewhat more difficult to use and have more limited (yet valuable) applications than indicator and potentiometric methods. Some illustrations of the uses and special advantages follow.

Conductivity of electrolyte solutions. A standard Wheatstone bridge circuit can be arranged to measure the resistance of solutions. A resistance reading, R, is obtained in ohms and is usually converted to the specific resistance, r ohm-cm, the resistance between two platinum squares 1 cm on a side and 1 cm apart. The units arise since R varies directly with the distance, d, between the electrodes and inversely with their area, A,

$$R = r(d/A), \qquad r = R(A/d).$$

More convenient for chemistry is the specific conductance, L, which varies directly with concentration:

$$L = 1/r = d/RA \text{ ohm}^{-1} \text{ cm}^{-1}. \tag{24–3}$$

To express concentration-dependence, the equivalent conductance, Λ, is used:

$$\Lambda = VL = \frac{1000\,L}{N} \text{ cm}^2 \text{ equiv}^{-1} \text{ ohm}^{-1}. \tag{24–4}$$

This may be understood as the conductance of a volume V of solution containing one gram equivalent of the electrolyte placed between electrodes of sufficient area to accommodate the solution in a thickness of 1 cm. The volume V must be expressed in cubic centimeters. Thus a 0.1 N solution contains one equivalent in 10,000 cc (ml). The normality refers only to the ionic charges, i.e., 0.1 N $KMnO_4$ is also 0.1 M and 0.1 M $CaCl_2$ is 0.2 N.

The equivalent conductance of weak electrolytes is small at high concentrations and increases with dilution. Remember that the fraction of acetic acid ionized is only about 1% at 0.1 M, but approaches 100% at infinite dilution. Strong electrolytes have high equivalent conductance which increases only slightly with dilution. Extrapolation to infinite dilution is possible for strong electrolytes to get the limiting conductance at infinite dilution, Λ^0. These extrapolated limiting values can be combined with transference numbers to derive limiting ionic conductances, λ^0. Kohlrausch in 1875 postulated that ions behave independently of each other at infinite dilution. Thus the conductances of individual ions in Table 24–2 help us to understand titrations and equilibrium-constant determinations based on conductivity measurements.

Table 24–2. Limiting Equivalent Conductances of Ions at 25°C

Ion	λ^0	Ion	λ^0
H^+	349.8	OH^-	198.0
Na^+	50.1	BrO_3^-	55.8
K^+	73.5	IO_3^-	40.5
Ag^+	61.9	CH_3COO^-	40.9

Conductance titrations. Figures 24–5 and 24–6 show conductance plotted against fraction titrated for the cases of strong acid or weak acid titrated by strong base. The conductance is corrected for dilution, multiplied by $(V + V^0)/V^0$, the volume increase factor when V ml of base is added to V^0 starting volume.

In the titration of HCl by NaOH solution, before the equivalence point, the much lower-conducting Na^+ ion is replacing the H^+ ion, and the corrected conductance decreases linearly. After equivalence, the added NaOH serves only to increase the conductance. Note that one does not have to stop on the equivalence point in this method. Several points before and after equivalence establish the two lines whose intersection gives the equivalence point.

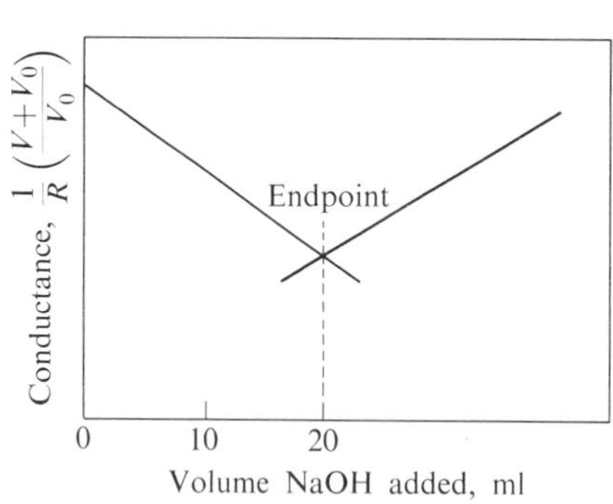

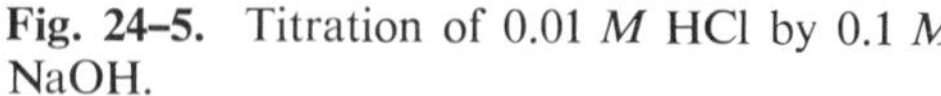

Fig. 24–5. Titration of 0.01 *M* HCl by 0.1 *M* NaOH.

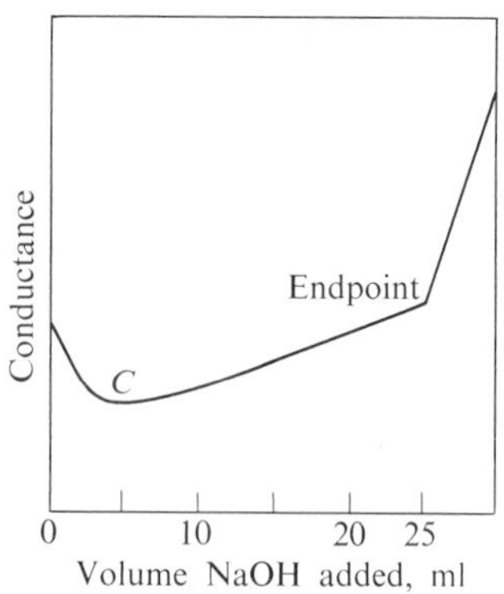

Fig. 24–6. Titration of 0.01 *M* $HC_2H_3O_2$ by 0.1 *M* NaOH.

For the acetic acid titration (Fig. 24–6), a minimum occurs before the equivalence region is attained. Early in the titration, the acetate ion formed suppresses the acid ionization by the common-ion effect. As more base is added, conductance increases after the effect of adding Na^+ and $C_2H_3O_2^-$ overcomes the common-ion effect of the $C_2H_3O_2^-$. After equivalence, a sharper rise due to the presence of NaOH occurs as in the previous case. The obtuse angle of intersection makes determination of the equivalence point less precise than in the strong acid case (Fig. 24–5). Mixtures of acids can sometimes be titrated, and small amounts of other electrolytes do not interfere. Precipitation titrations can be carried out if ionic conductance differences are favorable. Some advantages of conductometric titrations are:

1. Acids or bases which are too weak to give sufficient change in pH to make other methods feasible can be determined by this method. Measurements are made away from the equivalence point where common ions force more complete association than obtains at equivalence.
2. Very dilute solutions can be determined, since the *change* in conductance may still be quite large.
3. Color or opacity does not interfere.

Determination of equilibrium constants by conductance. The conductance of solutions of weak electrolytes or of saturated solutions of slightly soluble ionic compounds gives a method of calculating the ionic concentrations and thence the equilibrium constant. Some examples follow.

The ion product of water. After strenuous purification of water, Kohlrausch in 1894 found its specific conductance to be 6.2×10^{-8} ohm^{-1}cm^{-1} at 25° C. The concentrations of H^+ and OH^- can be obtained from Eq. (24–4) using the sum of their ionic conductances, $349.8 + 198.0 = 547.8$ for the equivalent conductance.

The solution is so dilute that infinite dilution and activity coefficients equal to *one* can be assumed:

$$[H^+] = [OH^-] = \frac{1000(6.2 \times 10^{-8})}{547.8} = 1.1_3 \times 10^{-7} \text{ equiv/liter.}$$

Its square is K_w. This is somewhat high, but shows fair agreement with potentiometric measurements. The modern value is 1.004×10^{-7}.

Acetic acid. In a classic paper in 1932, McInnes and Shedlovsky* determined K_a^0 for acetic acid through conductivity measurements on a series of dilute acetic acid solutions. Equation (24–4) can again be used to find the ionic concentrations. However, infinite dilution approximations in the use of limiting ionic conductances are less valid. In the dilute solutions, ionic strength was so low that activity effects were much smaller. For example, 1.0283×10^{-3} M acetic acid had equivalent conductance 48.133 ohm^{-1}. At 100% ionization, $H^+ + C_2H_3O_2^-$ would have $349.8 + 40.9 = 390.7$ ohm^{-1} equivalent conductance. If there were no interionic effects, the fraction ionized should be

$$\alpha_0 = 48.133/390.7 = 0.12320.$$

This fraction is simply related to K_a by Eq. (8–2)

$$K_a' = \alpha_0^2(C_{HA})/(1 - \alpha_0) = 1.780 \times 10^{-5}.$$

They determined actual conductances of H^+ and $C_2H_3O_2^-$, at the ionic concentrations used, to correct for the differences from infinite dilution. For example, the equivalent conductance found for this solution was 388.9 instead of the value of 390.7 used above, a change of about 0.5%. They then plotted log K_a' versus $\sqrt{I}$ to obtain $K_a^0 = 1.753 \times 10^{-5}$, which is in excellent agreement with 1.749×10^{-5} found by potentiometric means. The K_a^0 values of many weak electrolytes have been accurately determined by this method.

Solubility. Measurement of the specific resistance of a saturated solution of a slightly soluble electrolyte permits one to calculate the solubility from Eq. (24–4). For example, the specific resistance of water shaken with pure silver iodate was 42,000 ohms. The limiting ionic conductances give: Ag^+, $61.9 + IO_3^-$, $40.5 = 102.4$ for one equivalent of $AgIO_3$. From (24–4),

$$N = 1000/(42{,}000)(102.4) = 2.3_5 \times 10^{-4} \text{ equiv/liter,}$$
$$K_{sp} = N^2 = 5.5 \times 10^{-8}.$$

The solution is so dilute that the infinite dilution approximations should be valid within the precision of the measurement. Of course, the simple conductance method does not cope with associated $AgIO_3$ molecules or complexes formed. (A radioactive tracer study shows that $AgIO_3$ exists in these solutions only to the extent of 10^{-7} M, under 1 ppth of the dissolved $AgIO_3$.) Reactions of either ion with

---

* *J. Am. Chem. Soc.* **54,** 1429.

water would introduce further complications. For this reason, potentiometric means are more often used for solubility study, since added electrolytes to control pH and ionic strength can be used.

Electrolytic Current-Voltage Methods

In contrast with potentiometry where a changing cell voltage is measured as titration proceeds, *amperometric* methods involve an impressed voltage and measurement of the resulting current flow. The minute quantity of matter electrolyzed is negligible.

The simplest of these methods is the "*dead stop*" or biamperometric method. Two platinum electrodes are placed in the solution under a potential of 0.01 to 0.1 V, well below the decomposition potential of the materials present. A microammeter in the circuit is read as the titration proceeds. When both the oxidized and reduced forms of a readily reversible couple are present in appreciable concentrations, a current can flow. If this situation changes abruptly at the endpoint, the current can fall nearly to zero or start up from zero for the reverse condition. A common use is in the detection of endpoints in I_2 titrations (Fig. 24–7) like the Karl Fischer water determination, where starch is not useful. Before the equivalence point, I_2 concentration is negligible and the applied voltage is insufficient to oxidize I^- at the anode or to reduce H_2O at the cathode. As soon as excess I_2 has been added,

$$I_2 + 2e^- \rightleftharpoons 2I^-,$$

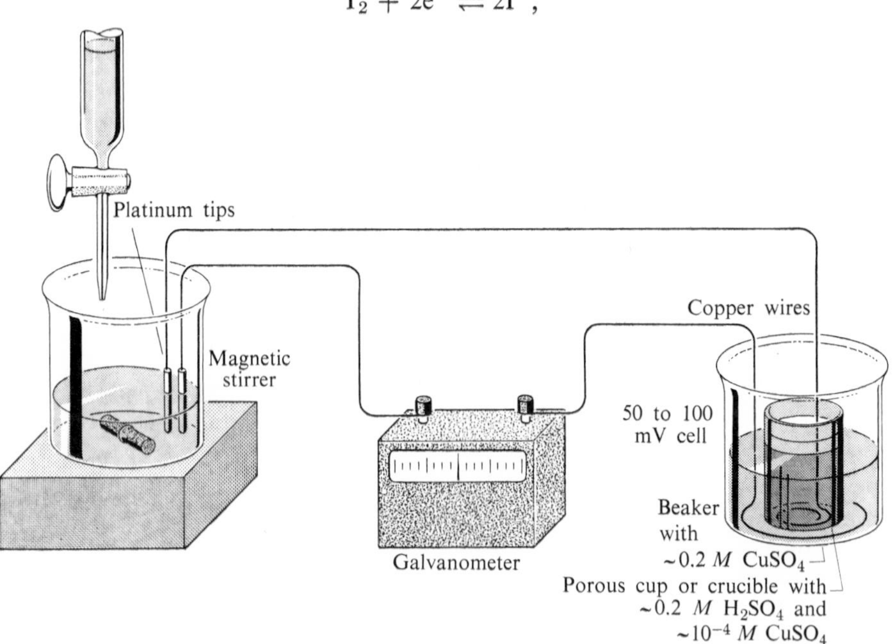

Fig. 24–7. Simple "dead stop" arrangement for I_2 endpoints, using a Cu(II) concentration cell source of potential.

oxidation of I^- at the anode and reduction of I_2 at the cathode can occur ($\mathcal{E}_{cell} = 0$) to give a current observable on the microammeter. Similarly, in iron titrations,

$$Fe(III) + e^- \rightleftharpoons Fe(II),$$

both forms are present in large quantity during the titration, and there is a large current flow. At equivalence, one species concentration becomes very low, and the current falls nearly to zero. After equivalence, the current may rise sharply, if the oxidizing (or reducing) agent used for titration produces a reversible couple. In such a case, a V-shaped intersection of two lines fixes the endpoint.

Dropping mercury polarography. This method, invented by Jaroslov Heyrovsky in the 1920's in Prague, utilizes a steadily dropping, polarizable mercury electrode. The current, measured as voltage is increased, leads to both qualitative identifications and quantitative estimations in the concentration range 10^{-2} to 10^{-5} *M* for a wide variety of ions and molecules in solution. The decomposition voltage is characteristic of the substance, and the limiting current attained depends directly on concentration as expressed in the Ilkovic equation:

$$i_d = 607nD^{1/2}m^{2/3}t^{1/6}C,$$

where i_d is the average current during the life of a drop, in microamperes, n is the number of electrons in the redox step of the species, D is the diffusion coefficient of the species in $cm^2\ sec^{-1}$, m is the mass of mercury flowing per second, t is the drop time in seconds, and C is the concentration of the species in millimoles/liter.

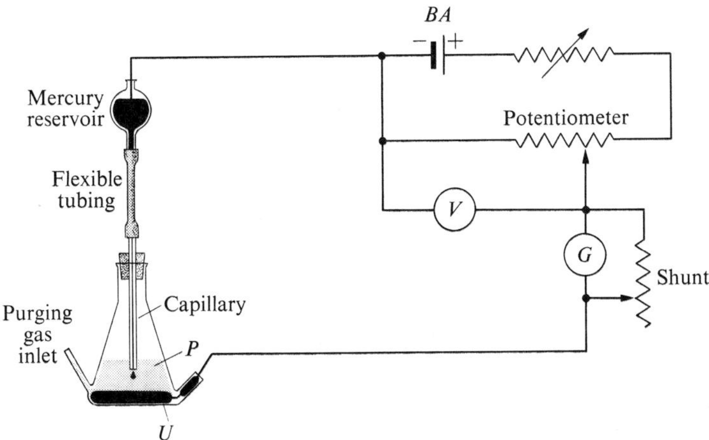

Fig. 24–8. Schematic diagram of the basic polarographic apparatus: *P*, polarizable dropping mercury electrode; *U*, unpolarizable mercury pool electrode. As shown, the dropping mercury electrode is commonly the cathode. (After H. A. Strobel, *Chemical Instrumentation*, Reading, Mass.: Addison-Wesley, 1960.)

Figure 24–8 shows a schematic diagram of the arrangement of the apparatus. The dropping mercury electrode is usually the cathode and the mercury pool, the anode. The tube is of diameter 0.02 to 0.05 mm, and the reservoir is raised to give a drop rate of 3 to 5 sec. The sample in the presence of a supporting electrolyte is placed in the cell and the voltage is gradually increased. Figure 24–9 shows a typical curve for an ion like Cu^{++}. Only a small current flows before the decomposition voltage, *D*, is reached. Further voltage increase gives more current flow as Cu^{++} reduction occurs. (Note that a current measured in microamperes produces a negligible quantity of Cu deposition in the few minutes used.) A limiting current is reached when the rate of diffusion of Cu^{++} ions to the drop becomes the limiting factor. This depends on its concentration. The distance from the base line to the limiting current line, i_d, must be determined for each substance with a solution of known concentration. The concentrations of unknowns can then be found by direct proportion.

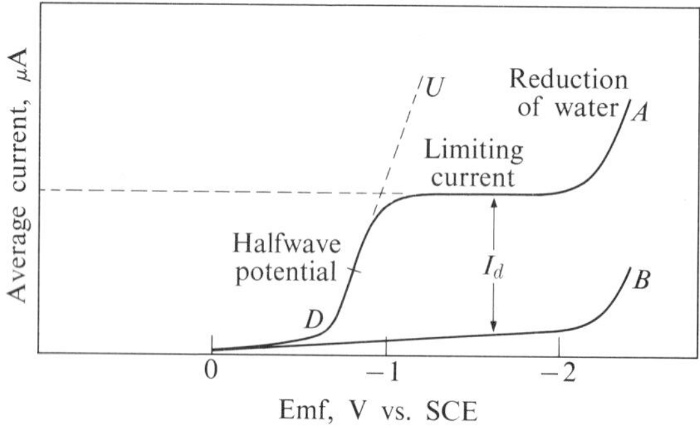

Fig. 24–9. Smoothed current-voltage curves for a dropping mercury electrode: *A*, electrolysis of solution of electroactive species and supporting electrolyte; *B*, electrolysis of solution of supporting electrolyte. (After H. A. Strobel, *Chemical Instrumentation*, Reading, Mass.: Addison-Wesley, 1960.)

The halfwave potential is characteristic of Cu^{++}. Several ions can be determined in the same solution if their halfwave potentials are sufficiently separated, for example, Cu^{++}, −0.01 V, Pb^{++}, −0.45 V, Ni^{++}, −1.0 V, Mn^{++}, −1.5 V, all versus the saturated calomel electrode (SCE) can be determined in dilute KCl solution.

Many organic molecules can be determined by this method. Formaldehyde, −1.5 V, and acetaldehyde, −1.9 V in LiOH-LiCl solution can be determined in one solution in the concentration range 10^{-2} to 10^{-4} *M*.

The special advantages of the method are:

1. The dropping mercury presents an ever-fresh surface of very small area to give reproducible polarization.

2. Small samples and low concentrations can be used.
3. It is rapid and nondestructive.

The instrumentation is simple. Care is required to prepare a clean capillary tube and clean mercury. An assembly for manual polarograms is easily made from common laboratory items.*

The method has many research uses. Solubility and complex formation studies often use polarography. The metal-EDTA formation constants were determined by Schwarzenbach by this means (Chapter 21).

SUMMARY

Light absorption. Absorbance is proportional to concentration (Beer's law) at constant path length and wavelength. The photometric error function shows that minimum error occurs at 37% transmittance, and error remains small in the region, 30 to 50% transmittance. Simultaneous equations allow determination of mixture compositions from absorbances at two or more wavelengths.

Potentiometric methods. Cell measurements, with emphasis on the glass electrode pH meter, are described. A description of the use of first and second derivative titration curves is given.

Electrolysis methods. Electrodeposition, coulometry, and amperometry are discussed.

SUGGESTIONS FOR FURTHER READING

BATES, R. G., *Determination of pH*, New York: John Wiley, 1964.

DETAR, D. F., *Anal. Chem.* **38,** 1794 (1966). Computer techniques for making Beer's law calculations of concentration from spectral data are given. Methods for extending the simple two-component calculation shown in this chapter to multiple-component mixtures are also discussed.

FRASER, R. D. B., and E. SUZUKI, *Anal. Chem.* **38,** 1770 (1966) describes the resolution of overlapping absorption bands by least-squares procedures.

STROBEL, H. A., *Chemical Instrumentation*, Reading, Mass.: Addison-Wesley, 1960, Chapters 6, 7, 15, and 17.

VOGEL, A. I., *Quantitative Inorganic Analysis*, 3rd ed. New York: John Wiley, 1961, Chapters 6, 8, and 16.

---

* Such an assembly is described by O. H. Müller in *The Polarographic Method of Analysis*, Easton, Pa.: Chemical Education Publishing Co., 1951, p. 34.

PROBLEMS

1. Describe clearly the meaning of the Bouguer-Lambert and Beer Laws, then combine them and define absorbance, transmittance, and specific and molar absorptivity.
2. A given solution transmits 20.0% of the light at a certain wavelength. What dilution will cut the absorbance in half? What will double the transmittance? Construct two conversion tables: (a) A in 0.1 intervals to T, and (b) T in 0.1 intervals to A.
3. Derive the error function in c for an error in T. Calculate the relative error for $T = 0.01, 0.1, 0.35, 0.45, 0.9, 0.99$.
4. a) A solution containing 40.0 mg/liter of K_2CrO_4 (formula weight, 194.2) in 0.05 M KOH shows a peak at 375 mμ with $T = 0.102$ in a 1.00 cm cell. Find A, ϵ, and a.
   b) If the solution is diluted with an equal volume of 0.05 M KOH, what should be the measured T and A?
   c) Given that for 40.0 mg/liter of a mixture of K_2CrO_4 and K_2SO_4 (transparent) under the same conditions, $T = 0.204$. Find A and the percent K_2CrO_4 in the mixture.
5. The molar absorptivities of two Cr species at two wavelengths are:

	370 mμ	430 mμ
$CrO_4^{=}$	4800	410
$CrCl_2^{+}$	3.0	20.2

   A fresh solution of an unknown mixture of the two gave A values of 0.600 at 370 and 0.849 at 430 mμ. Find the molarity of each. Could the determination have been made if the concentrations of the two species were reversed? Prove that dilution is an unsatisfactory solution to the problem.
6. In 50% acetone and 0.8 M SCN^-, the deep blue $Co(SCN)_4^{=}$ of $\epsilon = 1830$ at its maximum at 622 mμ is quantitatively useful. Calculate the percent of its total expected water that has been lost from a sample of $Co(NO_3)_2 \cdot 6H_2O$ (formula weight, 291) if 70.0 mg/liter in a 1.00 cm cell read $A = 0.477$ under the above conditions.
7. An oxidation titration of Fe(II) to Fe(III) can be performed in the presence of excess EDTA, at a pH where both are highly complexed.
   a) Find the change in reduction potential expected at the half-titration point ($\mathcal{E}_r^0 = 0.771$ V) when excess EDTA is added. Note that you only need the ratios of Fe(III)/Fe(II). Compare the $\mathcal{E}_r$ change between 1 ppth before and after the equivalence points in titrations of Fe(II) with Ce(IV) ($\mathcal{E}_r^0 = 1.6$ V) and with I_2($\mathcal{E}_r^0 = 0.54$ V).
   b) Find the change in reduction potential with, and (c) without, excess EDTA added.
8. a) Find the minimum time required to plate out 508 mg Cu as done in the laboratory at 2 amps and 2 V.
   b) Given that the current efficiency in Part (a) decreases linearly with time from 100% to 1.0% during the process, determine how long it would take.
9. In coulometric procedure for Fe(1e change), at 1 mA, how many micrograms of Fe correspond to each second? Given that time can be read to ±0.2 sec overall, determine the smallest Fe sample that can be determined to within 1%.

10. Four experimental values of the equivalent conductance of low-concentration solutions of acetic acid in pure water are given. Finish the table (as shown in the text for the last point), and plot log K'_a versus $\sqrt{I}$ to find log K^0_a. The ionic strength is $\alpha_0 C_{HA}$.

C_{HA} mole/liter, $\times 10^5$	Λ experimental	α_0	α_0^2	$1 - \alpha_0$	K'_a	I	$\sqrt{I}$	log K'_a
2.801	210.3	0.5383						
15.32	112.0							
21.84	96.47							
102.83	48.13							

CHAPTER 25

NONAQUEOUS SOLVENTS, SOME QUANTITATIVE ORGANIC METHODS

From examples discussed in previous chapters and as a result of your laboratory work you will have noted that important changes in dissolved species may occur as the solvent is altered or changed entirely. For example, cobalt(II) chloride dissolves in water mainly as pink $Co(H_2O)_6^{++}$, $2Cl^-$, but it dissolves in acetone as a blue mixture of chloro complexes up to $CoCl_4^{=}$. Changing the organic solvent shifts the equilibrium-quotient value in the esterification and the keto-enol equilibrium studies.

Most soluble electrolytes are poorer conductors in other solvents than they are in water solutions. This results in some cases from the lower dielectric constant and proton donor-acceptor ability of the other solvent. Electrolytes form such stable hydrates in water that plus and minus ions, well shielded by highly polar H_2O molecules, can move independently and migrate with electric current when potential is applied. In most other solvents where solvation energies are low, ion pairs, or often large clusters of ions, remain together giving the same effect as weak electrolytes.

25.1 ACID-BASE REACTIONS

Acids such as $HClO_4$, HCl, and HNO_3 react effectively to completion with water to give hydronium ions in dilute solution. In solvents with less proton-accepting ability, less basic solvents, these three acids reveal quite different strengths. Conversely, acid strength is accentuated by basic solvents like ethylenediamine in which phenols can be titrated as acids by strong base. Phenols are too weakly acidic for feasible titrations in water. Such a weak base as an amino acid can be titrated by $HClO_4$ in an acidic solvent like glacial acetic acid.

It should be clear that molecules do not really become stronger in acidic or basic character in different solvents, but they may react more extensively with some than others. For feasible titration, the main requisite of the solvent is not strongly acidic or basic character, but much weaker acidic or basic character than the substances being reacted in it. For example, phenol in water ($pK_a = 10$) does not donate protons to an added base much better than does H_2O. In ethylenediamine, the solvent readily accepts protons from phenol. In a ketone or in acetonitrile, the solvent neither accepts nor donates protons easily so that any indicator of acidity level will change sharply around the endpoint of a titration of phenol by a strong base. Methyl isobutyl ketone MIBK has been found to combine the abilities of acetone and acetonitrile in differentiating both strong and weak acids and bases. It is called a wide-range solvent by Bruss and Wyld whose titration curves (Fig. 25–1) show this dramatically for several strong and weak acids titrated by the strong base tetrabutylammonium hydroxide, all in MIBK.

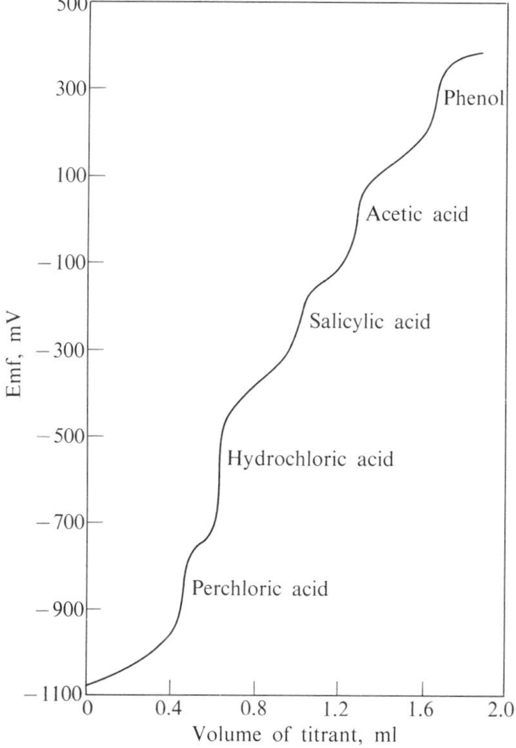

Fig. 25–1. Resolution of strong-weak-very weak acid mixture in methyl isobutyl ketone; 0.2 *N* tetrabutylammonium hydroxide titrant, glass-platinum (in titrant) electrodes. The potential range shown is approximately 1.45 V, which corresponds to a 24 pH unit change over the entire titration range. The titration of 0.1 *M* strong acid with strong base in water would produce only a 12 pH unit change if a 100% excess of base were added. [After D. B. Bruss and G. E. A. Wyld, *Anal. Chem.* **29**, 232 (1957).]

After this introduction it is useful to classify solvents as follows:

1. Those which have pronounced acid-base properties, symbol $\mathcal{S}$H.
   a) Amphiprotic (water and alcohols which can gain or lose protons). For example, with added acid,

$$HA + \mathcal{S}H \rightleftharpoons \mathcal{S}H_2^+ + A^-,$$

and with added base,

$$B + SH \rightleftharpoons S^- + HB^+.$$

Strong acids and bases, if any exist, are leveled to SH^+ and S^- by reaction with these solvents.

b) Amphiprotic but with acid or base character dominant (for example, H_2SO_4, $HC_2H_3O_2$, ethylenediamine, liquid NH_3). $HClO_4$ is a weak acid in glacial acetic acid:

$$HClO_4 + HC_2H_3O_2 \rightleftharpoons H_2C_2H_3O_2^+ + ClO_4^-, \qquad pK_a = 4.87,$$

and phenol is a weak acid in ethylenediamine:

$$C_6H_5OH + C_2H_4(NH_2)_2 \rightleftharpoons C_6H_5O^- + C_2H_4NH_2NH_3^+.$$

2. Very weak bases with negligible acidity (ketones, acetonitrile, ethers).
3. Those for which both acidity and basicity is negligibly weak (the "inert" solvents, benzene, chloroform, hexane, etc.).

In type 1 solvents, neutralization can be represented by the solvent acid and base ions:

Examples

	$SH^+ + S^- \rightarrow 2SH,$
water,	$H_3O^+ + OH^- \rightarrow 2H_2O,$
$HC_2H_3O_2(HA)$,	$H_2A^+ + A^- \rightarrow 2HA,$
NH_3 (liquid),	$NH_4^+ + NH_2^- \rightarrow 2NH_3,$
CH_3OH,	$CH_3OH_2^+ + CH_3O^- \rightarrow 2CH_3OH.$

However, as many substances are weak in solvents other than water, molecular equations might as well be written as they definitely should be for the type 2 and 3 solvents. For example, sodium acetate and perchloric acid react in glacial acetic acid as

$$NaA + HClO_4 \rightarrow HA + NaClO_4,$$

and in a ketone, a neutralization is

$$HA + (C_4H_9)_4NOH \rightarrow HOH + (C_4H_9)_4NA,$$

where all materials shown act as weak electrolytes.

Applications

Titration of acids. To titrate acids which are too weak for, or insoluble in, water (carboxylic acids, phenols, enols, sulfonamides, sulfa drugs, and imides). For stock base, Na is dissolved in CH_3OH,

$$2Na + 2CH_3OH \rightarrow 2Na^+,CH_3O^- + H_2,$$

where the sodium methoxide is shown as an ion pair. For standardization, a weighed sample of pure benzoic acid dissolved in methanol is titrated using thymol blue as indicator. Then, unknown acids can be titrated in methanol, or for progressively weaker acids, the solvent may be acetone, dimethylformamide, or ethylenediamine with azo violet indicator(*p*-nitrobenzeneazoresorcinol). Tetra-alkyl ammonium hydroxides which give more soluble products in some cases are often used as the base titrant.

Titrations of bases (amines, amino acids). A stock of $HClO_4$, 0.1 to 0.001 M in glacial acetic acid is used. Acetic anhydride can be added to remove the water added with the 70% $HClO_4$. A base solution for back titration is sodium acetate in $HC_2H_3O_2$. (Acetate ion is the strongest base in this solvent system.) The $HClO_4$ is standardized against pure potassium acid phthalate. (Note that it is a base here forming phthalic acid as product. It is used as a standard acid in water.)

An amino acid sample is dissolved in a measured excess of the $HClO_4$ stock and back titrated to a methyl violet endpoint with the sodium acetate. In case of fuzzy endpoints or colored samples, potentiometric titration with glass and calomel electrodes can be employed.

Differentiation of amines. Aliphatic, and the much less basic aromatic amines can be distinguished in mixtures by $HClO_4$ titration in type 2 or 3 solvents like acetonitrile or chloroform. (Both are leveled to A^- in glacial acetic acid solvent.)

Acetic acid is used as the solvent in the method for determination of primary, secondary, and tertiary aliphatic amines. The total of all amines is first found by $HClO_4$ titration. A second aliquot of the sample is then allowed to react with excess acetic anhydride which acetylates only primary and secondary amines effectively removing them as bases. An $HClO_4$ titration then tells the amount of tertiary amine present. Excess salicylaldehyde added to a third portion forms Schiff bases with primary amines leaving the secondary and tertiary for titration.

The Mercury(II) Acetate Method

The very strong bonding between Hg(II) and halide type ions is the basis of a clever method for determining any compound yielding these ions. $Hg(C_2H_3O_2)_2$ is added to the sample in glacial acetic acid where it forms HgX_2 and acetate ions, the strong base ions, which can be titrated with standard $HClO_4$. This method is especially useful in pharmaceutical laboratories for amine hydrochlorides; alkaloids and their hydrochlorides both titrate. Ionic Cl^-, Br^-, I^-, and SCN^- compounds can be determined by this method. The reaction with an amine hydrochloride is

$$HgA_2 + 2NR_3H^+, Cl^- \rightarrow HgCl_2 + 2A^- + 2NR_3H^+.$$

(Note the analogy to the use of HgO as a base standard in water: $\underline{HgO} + 4I^- + H_2O \rightarrow HgI_4^{=} + 2OH^-$.) The excess HgA_2 is so slightly dissociated that it does not interfere in the titration of free A^- as a base.

Other methods. Indirect acid-base methods for organic compounds are based on acetylation of OH groups, saponification of esters, oximation of carbonyl groups, and bisulfite addition to aldehydes. The ester method is described since it can be applied to the determination of the purity of the starting material in esterification studies, and it is an interesting use of ion exchange.

The ester sample, 0.2 g, is weighed and refluxed for one hour with a few milliliters 2 *M* KOH in a larger volume of 2-propanol. The exact quantity of KOH need not be known. The mixture is washed through a column of a cation resin in the H^+ form with 50% aqueous methanol. All excess KOH forms water, and the organic acid ion, A^-, from the ester forms HA which is then titrated with aqueous standard 0.05 *M* NaOH to the phenolphthalein endpoint.

25.2 ACID-BASE EQUILIBRIA IN NONAQUEOUS SOLVENTS

The dielectric constant (see Chapter 17) and autoprotolysis (autoionization) constants, where known, of several solvents are:

	Dielectric constant	p*K*(auto)
Methanol	32.6	16.7
Ethanol	24.3	19.1
Water	78.5	14.00
Acetic acid	6.13	14.45
Formic acid	58.5	6.2
NH_3 (−33°C)	22.0	
Ethylenediamine	12.9	
Dimethylformamide	36.7	
Acetone	20.7	
Acetonitrile	36	
Methyl isobutyl ketone	13.1	
Benzene	2.3	

In liquids of higher dielectric constant such as water, alcohols, formic acid, etc., soluble salt-like compounds dissociate so that equilibrium calculations are similar to those in water. Some acid constants are:

	pK_a in water	pK_a in CH_3OH	pK_a in C_2H_5OH
Benzoic acid	4.18	10.4	9.4
Salicylic acid	2.97	8.7	7.9
Bromcresol green	4.9	9.8	10.6

In glacial acetic acid, no electrolytes are highly ionized. Therefore equilibrium constants must be used for all materials involved in acid-base reactions in this solvent. For added acid HX,

$$HX + HA \rightleftharpoons H_2A^+,X^- \rightleftharpoons H_2A^+ + X^-,$$

where ionization and dissociation are shown as separate steps. For a base, B, added to the solvent, the steps are

$$B + HA \rightleftharpoons BH^+,A^- \rightleftharpoons BH^+ + A^-.$$

For the neutralization product, "salt," we must also write

$$BHX \rightleftharpoons BH^+,X^- \rightleftharpoons BH^+ + X^-.$$

In each case, the two equilibria can be combined so that we write HX for the sum of HX and H_2A^+,X^-, B for the sum of B and BH^+,A^-, and BHX for the sum of BHX and BH^+,X^-. Thus

$$K_a = \frac{[H_2A^+][X^-]}{[HX]}, \qquad K_b = \frac{[BH^+][A^-]}{[B]}, \qquad K_{salt} = \frac{[BH^+][X^-]}{[BHX]}.$$

These are overall constants. Some known values in acetic acid, HA, are:

Acid	pK_a	Base	pK_b	"Salt"	pK_{salt}
$HClO_4$	4.87	NaA	6.68	$NaClO_4$	5.48
H_2SO_4(1 H)	7.24	KA	6.15	KCl	6.88
HCl	8.55	Urea	10.24	LiCl	7.08
		H_2O	12.53		

The strongest acid available, $HClO_4$, is about as strong in acetic acid as acetic acid is in water.

We use the conventions of aqueous solutions in writing only the major species in reactions, molecules for weak electrolytes. Thus the neutralization of, say, an amine B by $HClO_4$ in acetic acid should be shown as

$$B + HClO_4 \rightarrow BH^+,ClO_4^- \qquad \text{(or } BHClO_4\text{)}.$$

The student can show, using charge- and material-balance principles and the K expressions above, that a buffer of $HClO_4$ and $NaClO_4$ in glacial acetic acid has acidity as given by

$$[H^+] = \left[\frac{K_aC_a + K_s}{1 + K_{salt}C_b/K_aC_a}\right]^{1/2},$$

where C_a and C_b refer to the total of the nondissociated acid and base present and K_s is the autoionization constant of the solvent. It was used as we did with K_w since, here, $(H^+) = K_s/(A^-)$. (See Chapter 5.)

A solution of $NaClO_4$ alone in acetic acid will be analogous to a compound like NH_4CHO_2 (Eq. 5–5) in water where both ions react with solvent. The student can show that with the approximation that $[HClO_4] = [NaA]$,

$$[H^+] = [K_a K_s/K_b]^{1/2}.$$

D. Pietrzyk and J. Belisle,* found that 2,4-dinitrobenzene sulfonic acid is almost as strong as $HClO_4$ in acetic acid solvent and in MIBK where it is useful for titration of bases. It is a convenient solid compound.

Extensive detail of titration and equilibrium calculations in these solvents is given in the *Treatise on Analytical Chemistry.*

25.3 SOME REDOX METHODS FOR ORGANIC COMPOUNDS

Bromination is used in the keto-enol equilibrium study in the laboratory section. The enol form of β-diketones reacts rapidly with bromine. The excess Br_2 is removed by adding β-naphthol. In general, the reaction of $3Br_2$ with phenols and aromatic amines having unsubstituted *ortho* and *para* positions is applicable to quantitative use. A measured excess of Br^--BrO_3^- solution is added to the sample with some strong acid to produce Br_2 *in situ*,

$$5Br^- + BrO_3^- + 6H^+ \rightarrow 3Br_2 + 3H_2O.$$

Then KI is added to make I_2 from the excess Br_2, so that thiosulfate titration can be used to complete the determination. Br_2 has also been used to determine unsaturation.

Iodine oxidation, mainly the iodoform reaction, has been applied to assay of aldehydes, methyl ketones, and some sugars:

$$RCOCH_3 + 3I_2 + 4OH^- \rightarrow RCOO^- + CHI_3 + 3I^- + 3H_2O.$$

Excess I_2 in basic solution gives this reaction. After acidification, the remaining I_2 can be titrated as usual.

Nitrous acid oxidations have been applied to amine determinations. With primary aliphatic amines, the Van Slyke reaction occurs:

$$RNH_2 + HNO_2 \rightarrow N_2 + ROH + H_2O.$$

The reaction is complicated in mechanism but useful for small samples where the volume of N_2 measured amplifies well (1 mg $N_2 \cong$ 1 ml gas).

Primary aromatic amines are diazotized in acid solution,

$$ArNH_3^+,Cl^- + HNO_2 \rightarrow ArN_2^+ + Cl^- + 2H_2O.$$

---

* *Anal. Chem.* **38,** 969 (1966).

Excess HNO_2 can be measured, or a spectrophotometric determination can be made of a colored coupling product of the diazonium ion with phenol, etc.

25.4 THE KARL FISCHER TITRATION

Determination of water in nonaqueous solvents can be valuable in the study of reactions involving water and also in assessing the water impurity in other liquids. An iodine method was developed by Karl Fischer in 1935. It is a direct titration of water by a mixture of iodine, sulfur dioxide, and pyridine in methanol. The 1:1 I_2/H_2O stoichiometry results from an overall reaction,

$$I_2 + H_2O + SO_2 + 3C_5H_5N + CH_3OH \rightarrow 2C_5H_5NH^+ \cdot I^- + C_5H_5NH^+ \cdot CH_3OSO_3^-.$$

At the endpoint, the first excess of I_2 is detected visually or electrically. Mixtures of I_2 and SO_2 are not stable. In the two-solution method the solution of pyridine and SO_2 in methanol is first added and then titrated with standard I_2 in methanol. A stabilized reagent is made by substituting methyl cellosolve for methanol. A known concentration solution of water in methanol is used to standardize the reagent. Agents which reduce iodine interfere. The method is quite specific for water and has found wide application.

Besides direct determination of water in liquids, functional groups which undergo reactions that produce or consume water quantitatively can be determined by the Karl Fischer method. A few of the many applications follow.

Alcohols. By esterification with excess acetic acid and BF_3 catalyst, a mole of water forms from each OH group:

$$ROH + HA \rightarrow RA + H_2O.$$

Amines. Primary and secondary amines are acetylated with excess acetic anhydride in pyridine. The remaining anhydride is found by adding excess water. The water not used up in hydrolysis is titrated.

Aldehydes and ketones. Aldehydes and ketones can be oximated with hydroxylamine hydrochloride in pyridine to produce water:

$$R_2CO + NH_2OH \rightarrow R_2C{=}NOH + H_2O.$$

SUMMARY

Nonaqueous titrations are used for substances not soluble in water and in cases where the acid-base nature of water is unsuitable. Equilibrium calculations in pure acetic acid are explained. Widely useful determinations of organic substances through bromine and iodine reactions are described.

SUGGESTIONS FOR FURTHER READING

FRITZ, J. S., and G. S. HAMMOND, *Quantitative Organic Analysis*, New York: John Wiley, 1957.

KOLTHOFF, I. M., and S. BRUCKENSTEIN, "Acid-Base Equilibria in Nonaqueous Solutions" in *Treatise on Analytical Chemistry*, ed. by I. M. Kolthoff and P. J. Elving. Part I, Vol. 1. New York: Interscience, 1959. (Chapters 10 through 13 have been reprinted in paperback form under the title *Acid-Bases in Analytical Chemistry*.)

SIGGIA, S., *Quantitative Organic Analysis via Functional Groups*, 3rd ed. New York: John Wiley, 1963.

VOGEL, A. I., *Elementary Practical Organic Chemistry*, New York: Longmans, Green and Co., 1958. Part III gives directions for laboratory performance of quantitative organic determinations.

PROBLEMS

1. Write the self-ionization equilibrium reactions and name compounds which would give relatively strongly acidic or basic solutions in these solvents. Write the reaction of the compound with the solvent in each case.
   a) pure acetic acid b) ethanol c) dimethylformamide d) dihydrogen sulfate
2. Name the important reactive species present when the first of each of the following pairs is dissolved in the second.
   a) HCl in methanol b) NaOH in acetic acid c) NH_4Cl in liquid NH_3
   d) $NaNH_2$ in liquid NH_3 e) Phenol in liquid NH_3 f) Na in methanol
3. Calculate the pH of glacial acetic acid. Calculate the pH of 0.1 *M* $HClO_4$ in acetic acid.

CHAPTER 26

THERMODYNAMICS OF CHEMICAL EQUILIBRIUM

Classical thermodynamics was developed largely in the nineteenth century through attempts to find relations among heat, motion, and temperature. Rumford (1798) showed that mechanical work can be converted to heat. This led to the First Law of Thermodynamics, conservation of energy. Carnot (1824) discovered the important limitations on conversion of heat to work. This is basic to the Second Law. Applications to chemical and phase equilibrium were made by J. W. Gibbs about 1875. The Third Law (Nernst, 1908) was helpful in extending the possibilities of calculations and caused many chemists to gather precise data on heat capacities and cell voltages.

The main use of thermodynamics in chemistry involves free energy and heat data for calculation of equilibrium constants and their changes with temperature. Because of the number of variables to be considered in chemical reactions, their mathematical relationships must be approached in a logical and systematic way. There are many advanced texts on thermodynamics and physical chemistry that present carefully written accounts of the subject. Nevertheless, beginning students can grasp and use several valuable relations without being able to derive them, just as they make extensive use of the concept of atomic energy levels without going through quantum mechanics.

General chemistry students are often introduced to the use of energy, entropy, and free energy data of pure substances. Since the use of these data involve elusive, abstract concepts, it is understandable if the student is unsure of the meanings of these relations. Frequent exposure to numerical examples involving familiar reactions will help give some feeling for the concepts and will facilitate the assimilation of later rigorous approaches. This chapter points out applications of thermodynamics to equilibria treated in this text. No attempt is made to give a detailed introduction to the Laws of Thermodynamics and the relations derivable from them.

26.1 THERMODYNAMIC RELATIONS

The state, or condition, of a substance can be specified by state variables. For gases we saw that the state is described by the amount of matter, n, pressure, volume, and temperature. Thermodynamics adds two more state variables, the energy, E, from the First Law, and the entropy, S, from the Second Law. Three others, which are combinations of the ones given, have special uses in chemistry: H, enthalpy, G, the Gibbs free energy, and A, the Helmholtz free energy.

The First Law states that no process occurs that does not balance in energy gained and lost when all forms are considered, commonly heat and work. In most chemical processes this can be reduced to

$$\Delta E = Q - W \qquad \text{or} \qquad dE = đq - đw. \tag{26–1}$$

That is, the energy change in a system equals the heat gained, Q, minus the work done by the system, W. ($đ$ signifies an inexact differential; various combinations of Q and W values can give the same ΔE.) The total energy change of the system and its surroundings is always

$$\Delta E - Q + W = 0. \tag{26–2}$$

"The energy of the universe is constant," is a statement of the First Law.*

In many chemical processes, work is only that done in expansion or contraction of the system against constant, atmospheric pressure so that $đw = p\,dv$ and $W = P\,\Delta V$.

The Second Law summarizes experience that all spontaneous processes result in an increase of the entropy of the universe. Entropy, S, expresses the spreading out of energy, in a statistical interpretation, the disorder. It is measured in units of energy per mole per degree, and it is defined by the relations,

$$\Delta S = Q_{\text{rev}}/T \qquad \text{or} \qquad dS = dq_{\text{rev}}/T, \tag{26–3}$$

where Q_{rev} is the reversible heat change: the heat exchanged when the process is carried out in a reversible manner. This means that the process can be reversed to produce the initial state with no more energy expended than was involved in the forward process.

The First Law can now be written, substituting Eq. (26–3) in (26–1),

$$dE = T\,dS - P\,dV. \tag{26–4}$$

The other useful functions are *defined* as

$$H = E + PV, \qquad G = H - TS, \qquad A = E - TS. \tag{26–5}$$

From these,

$$dH = dE + P\,dV + V\,dP \tag{26–6}$$

$$dG = dH - T\,dS - S\,dT$$

$$dG = dE + P\,dV + V\,dP - T\,dS - S\,dT \tag{26–7}$$

Substituting (26–4) for dE gives

$$dG = V\,dP - S\,dT. \tag{26–8}$$

* "Universe" is a thermodynamic term for "the system plus all of the surroundings which can be affected by any changes in it."

Equations (26–4) and (26–8) have far-reaching consequences in chemistry. Before deriving some of them, let us look at some details on the meanings of *S*, *G*, and *T*.

Entropy

The Third Law of Thermodynamics states that $S = 0$ at 0°K for all pure crystalline substances. Therefore from (26–3) absolute entropy values can be calculated if heat-absorption data, heat capacities, are available. Integrating (26–3), where $dq = c_p\, dT$, gives

$$S = \int_0^T c_p\, dT/T.$$

Heat capacities can be expressed in two ways: c_p, calories per mole per degree at constant pressure where expansion work, *PV*, is done and c_v, at constant volume where no work is done. Entropies found by taking the area under the experimental plot of c_p/T versus *T* or c_p versus ln (*T*) are called Third Law entropies.

Following the advice in Bent's text, "The best way to become acquainted with birds is to look at some birds. A good way to become acquainted with entropy is to look at some entropies," we look at some entropies in Table 26–1.

Table 26–1. Third Law Entropies at 25°C (Except for Ice) in cal/mole-deg

C (diamond)	0.58	Na_c	14.4
C (graphite)	1.36	K_c	15.2
B_c	1.56	Rb_c	16.6
Fe_c	6.49	Hg liquid	18.5
Cu_c	7.96	Hg gas	41.8
Ag_c	10.21	H_2O_c (0°C)	9.9
Au_c	11.4	H_2O liquid	16.7
Cl_2 gas	53.3	H_2O gas	45.1
$AgCl_c$	23.0	CO_2 gas	51.1

c stands for crystalline

One sees that entropy is associated with the condition of the substance. There is an inverse correlation between hardness (tightness of bonding) and an increase with molar volume upon going from solid to liquid to gas. For formation of one mole of solid AgCl from the elements, $\Delta S = -13.9$ entropy units (cal/deg). This can be attributed to the great increase in order, or tightness of bonding, for Cl in changing from the gas to the AgCl crystal. A similar argument is used in relation to complex formation in Chapter 19.

Another way to look at entropy may be derived from (26–4). When there is no expansion work (heating a solid), $P\, dV = 0$ and

$$dE = T\, dS \quad \text{and} \quad T = \left(\frac{\partial E}{\partial S}\right)_v. \tag{26–9}$$

That is, the absolute temperature of a substance is a measure of the calories that must be added to it to increase the entropy by one unit. A cold body undergoes a large entropy increase when one calorie is added, T is small. A hot substance has relatively little entropy change when a calorie is added, T is larger. Since T is related to the ease of accepting or donating heat, it is reasonable that it should be related to entropy change.

Since entropy increase is a spontaneous process, heat added to a system will flow into the body with lowest ratio $\partial E/\partial S$ in (26–9), that is, the lowest T, where it will cause the greatest increase in entropy. This is the basis of what has been called the zeroth Law of Thermodynamics: two objects in contact with each other come to the same temperature.

Free Energy

In mixtures having a possibility of chemical reaction, equilibrium means the ΔG is zero for the reaction under the prevailing conditions. That this must be so follows from the spontaneity of entropy increase, the Second Law. An example may clarify this.

From the definition of G in (26–5), the equilibrium condition is

$$\Delta G = \Delta H - T\,\Delta S = 0 \qquad \text{and} \qquad \Delta H = T\,\Delta S. \tag{26–10}$$

That is, the energetic effect of the reaction on the surroundings, ΔH, just balances that in the system, $T\,\Delta S$. For example, 1440 cal melt 1 mole of ice at 0°C. This is a reversible process, so from (26–3) the entropy change is

$$\Delta S = \Delta H/T = 1440/273.15 = 5.27 \text{ cal/deg.}$$

The loss of energy and entropy of the surroundings (unfavorable) is balanced at zero degrees by the gains of the system (favorable). Neither melting, nor freezing is favored: they are in equilibrium. However, if it could be arranged to have ice melt to water at +10°C, (26–5),

$$\Delta G = 1440 - 283(5.27) = 1440 - 1490 = -50 \text{ cal.}$$

Or at −10°C,

$$\Delta G = 1440 - 263(5.27) = 1440 - 1390 = +50 \text{ cal.}$$

Free energy decreases in spontaneous changes and increases in nonspontaneous changes. Table 26–2 summarizes how the factors change.* This agrees with experience and the Second Law. The net, or total, entropy change is positive, and the free-energy change is negative, for the spontaneous process, and vice versa.

* Actually in this example, ΔH and ΔS do change with temperature. However, these changes almost cancel upon subtraction to get ΔG. Therefore T is the really important term in fixing the entropy balance. A more correct ΔG at +10°C is 56 cal, but this only changes the net ΔS to +0.20.

Table 26–2. Thermodynamics of Melting Ice at Three Temperatures (Approximate)

1 mole ice → water, °C	ΔH_{syst}, cal	ΔG_{syst}, cal	ΔS_{syst}	ΔS_{surr}	ΔS_{total}, cal/deg
+10	+1440	−50	+5.27	−5.09	+0.18
0	+1440	0	+5.27	−5.27	0
−10	+1440	+50	+5.27	−5.48	−0.21

Note that the total ΔS is made up of two terms, for the system and for the surroundings,

$$\Delta S_{syst} = 5.27 = S_{water} - S_{ice},$$

$$\Delta S_{surr} = -\Delta H_{syst}/T \qquad \text{(heat of melting is taken from the surroundings).}$$

Thus the total entropy change is

$$\Delta S_{total} = -\Delta H_{syst}/T + \Delta S_{syst}$$

or

$$(T\,\Delta S)_{total} = (-\Delta H + T\,\Delta S)_{syst} = -\Delta G_{syst}.$$

Thus ΔG expresses the total entropy effect of the change and is also an indicator of spontaneity changing in the opposite direction from the entropy change. Both are zero for a process under equilibrium conditions. The usefulness of free energy is that it can be expressed in terms of system properties alone and is more easily obtainable than total entropy change. So, by finding enthalpy and entropy values for reacting materials, one can tell whether spontaneous reaction is possible. Further, one can calculate the equilibrium constant.

Equilibrium and Free-Energy Relations

The standard free-energy change for a chemical reaction is the difference in G^0 of the products and reactants in the balanced chemical equation. The G^0 refers to the molar free energy of each substance in its standard state: one atmosphere for gases, unit activity for solutes, pure liquids, and solids, all at 25°C. In practice, the G_f^0, free energy of formation from the elements, is tabulated and used since G^0 cannot be evaluated, and the G^0 of the elements cancels when subtractions are made in any balanced chemical equation. The standard G^0 for each element is taken as zero for this reason.

We can make plausible the relation of ΔG^0 to the K_{eq}^0 as follows. At one temperature ($dT = 0$), from (26–8),

$$dG = V\,dP = RT\,d\ln P$$

for one mole of an ideal gas, ($V = RT/P$). Integrate to find ΔG, the change upon going from a standard state ($G = G^{0\prime}$ and $P = 1$) to another pressure, P:

$$\Delta G = G - G^{0\prime} = RT\ln P,$$

$$G = G^{0\prime} + RT\ln P. \tag{26–11}$$

Remembering that the molar free energy of one substance is the same in each phase at equilibrium, we see that this pressure can be the partial pressure of the gas over an ideal solution, by Raoult's Law,

$$P = XP^0.$$

Inserting this in (26–11) gives

$$G = G^{0\prime} + RT \ln X + RT \ln P^0.$$

We are still at constant temperature so that P^0, the normal vapor pressure, is a constant. By analogy then, one may accept that a general expression for the molar free energy of substances in solution is

$$G = G^0 + RT \ln a, \tag{26–12}$$

where the activity, a, has been introduced to take into account any deviations from ideality of gas and solution. G^0 now includes all conversions so that it is G when $a = 1$ as required by the equation. Now, in the general chemical equation,

$$a\mathrm{A} + b\mathrm{B} + \cdots \rightleftharpoons c\mathrm{C} + d\mathrm{D} + \cdots$$

Subtract the G expressions (26–12) for each side of this equation to get

$$\Delta G = \Delta G^0 + RT \ln \frac{(a_\mathrm{A})^a (a_\mathrm{B})^b \ldots}{(a_\mathrm{C})^c (a_\mathrm{D})^d \ldots}.$$

At equilibrium, $\Delta G = 0$, and the ln expression is the equilibrium constant, K^0_{eq}, so that

$$\Delta G^0 = -RT \ln K^0_{\mathrm{eq}}.$$

The following simple relations are very useful:

$$\Delta G^0 = -RT \ln K^0_{\mathrm{eq}} = -n\mathfrak{F}\mathcal{E}^0. \tag{26–13}$$

Knowledge of only one of ΔG^0, K^0, or $\mathcal{E}^0$ allows calculation of the others. ($\mathcal{E}^0$ is the standard cell potential for a redox reaction.) Many equilibrium-constant values that we have used are difficult or impossible to measure directly so that they must be obtained from thermal or cell measurements. Examples from cell data in Chapter 12 were shown for the K^0_{sp} determinations of AgCl and AgBr. Also, [from Eq. (26–5) above] if ΔH^0 and ΔS^0 can be found, ΔG^0, K^0, and $\mathcal{E}^0$ can be calculated.

From Eqs. (26–13) and (26–5), it can be shown that the temperature variation of these properties is

$$\frac{d(\Delta G^0/T)}{dT} = -\frac{\Delta H^0}{T^2} = -R\frac{d(\ln K^0)}{dT} = \frac{n\mathfrak{F}}{T}\left(\frac{d\mathcal{E}^0}{dT}\right) - \frac{n\mathfrak{F}\mathcal{E}^0}{T^2}. \tag{26–14}$$

This allows calculation of K, $\mathcal{E}$, or ΔG at other temperatures when one K value and ΔH are available. One important example, shown in Chapter 16, is the variation of vapor pressure of pure liquids with temperature. Vapor pressure is the equilibrium constant for the process

$$\text{liquid} \rightleftharpoons \text{gas},$$

the pressure being constant at equilibrium at one temperature. The activity of the pure liquid is unity. ΔH is the heat of vaporization. Substituting P for K and L for ΔH in (26–14) and integrating gives the Clausius-Clapeyron equation (Chapter 16). Similarly, cell measurements of $\mathcal{E}$ at several temperatures permit calculation of ΔH^0, ΔG^0, and then ΔS^0.

Examples of the use of these equations follow.

1) The low solubility of HgS makes direct measurement of its K_{sp} impossible. The heat of reaction, ΔH^0, has been found to be 64,490 cal/mole for:

$$\underline{HgS} \rightarrow Hg^{++} + S^{=}.$$

Third Law entropies give an estimated ΔS^0 of -31.7 cal/mole-deg. Then,

$$\Delta G^0 = \Delta H^0 - T\,\Delta S^0 = 64{,}490 - 298(-31.7) = 73{,}940 \text{ cal/mole}.$$

From (26–13), the K^0_{sp} can be found:

$$\log K^0_{sp} = -73{,}940/2.303RT = -73{,}940/1364 = -54.2.$$

The K^0_{sp} of about 10^{-54} makes it clear why direct measurement is out. It should take about 10^4 liters to dissolve one pair of ions.

2) Thermal data point up some interesting facets of neutralization. It is experimentally easy to mix solutions of acids and bases of known concentration in an insulated container and read the temperature rise on a thermometer reading to 0.01°C. Specific heats in calories per gram per degree are known for the product solutions so that one can calculate ΔH for one mole of reaction. Experiments with various strong acids and bases lead to the determination of a value of -13.36 kcal/mole for the ΔH^0 of

$$H^+ + OH^- \rightarrow H_2O.$$

The weak acids HCO_3^- ($pK^0_a = 10.33$) and NH_4^+ ($pK^0_a = 9.24$) having similar strength give sharply different heats of neutralization with NaOH solution. A student experiment gave:

$$HCO_3^- + OH^- \rightarrow CO_3^= + H_2O, \qquad \Delta H^0 = -9.66 \text{ kcal/mole}, \qquad (a)$$

$$NH_4^+ + OH^- \rightarrow NH_3 + H_2O, \qquad \Delta H^0 = -1.11 \text{ kcal/mole}. \qquad (b)$$

Subtracting the heat for strong acid-base reaction from each gives the heats of the ionization reaction of each acid:

$$HCO_3^- \rightarrow H^+ + CO_3^=, \qquad \Delta H^0 = 13.36 - 9.66 = 3.70, \qquad (a)$$

$$NH_4^+ \rightarrow H^+ + NH_3, \qquad \Delta H^0 = 13.36 - 1.11 = 12.25. \qquad (b)$$

From (26–13) and the known K_a^0 values we get

$$\Delta G^0 = -1.364 \log 10^{-10.33} = 14.1 \text{ kcal/mole}, \tag{a}$$

$$\Delta G^0 = -1.364 \log 10^{-9.24} = 12.6 \text{ kcal/mole}. \tag{b}$$

Now the entropy change can be calculated,

$$\Delta S^0 = \frac{\Delta H^0 - \Delta G^0}{T} = \frac{3.70 - 14.1}{298} = -35 \text{ eu}, \tag{a}$$

$$\Delta S^0 = \frac{\Delta H^0 - \Delta G^0}{T} = \frac{12.25 - 12.6}{298} = -1.2 \text{ eu}. \tag{b}$$

The large entropy decrease in (a) can be understood if we take into consideration the much stronger association of the water dipoles with the doubly charged product $CO_3^=$ than with neutral NH_3 molecules. This correlates with other properties: the specific volume of a 1 *M* solution of Na_2CO_3 is 0.91 ml/g while that of NH_3 is 1.01 ml/g. That is, a mole of carbonate ions pulls H_2O in closely enough to make the volume 10% less than 1 *M* NH_3. Acid strength, equilibrium, is determined by the balance of the heat term and the structure (entropy) effect.

One can ponder the figures for acid dissociations in Table 26–3 to help relate chemical knowledge of acid strength, size, and charge (n) of ions to thermodynamic quantities. The process considered is

$$HA^n \text{ (aq)} \rightarrow H^+ \text{ (aq)} + A^{n-1} \text{ (aq)}.$$

This suggests that the acid proton, which is hydrogen bonded to the acid and some water around it, severed the bond to the acid and moved away with the H_2O. This is often written

$$HA^n + H_2O \rightarrow H_3O^+ + A^{n-1},$$

which suggests a bimolecular mechanism of doubtful validity. (Furthermore, the major proton species in acid solutions is $H_9O_4^+$, not H_3O^+.)

The spontaneous direction term, ΔG^0, is determined by the heat exchange with the surroundings, ΔH^0, and the internal reorganization of energy term, $T\Delta S^0$:

$$\Delta G^0 = \Delta H^0 - T\Delta S^0.$$

For oxy-acids (acid H on —O—H), the charge and size effects strikingly demonstrate how increasing negative charge makes the dissociation unfavorable. The more negative, and smaller, ions hold water dipoles more tightly (ΔS^0 is negative) and the heat of hydration of H^+ and A^{n-1} may overcome the bond dissociation energy for the O—H of the acid to make ΔH^0 exothermic (H_3PO_4, $H_2C_2O_4$, etc.). When the charge density of the product A^{n-1} has less effect on the water (non-oxy-acids like NH_4^+), ΔS^0 is not so negative and ΔH^0 is endothermic.

Of course, the difference in hydration of the reactants and products must be considered in interpreting such effects on the energy terms of the reaction. $\Delta H \cong \Delta H^0$ has been assumed for experimental results in dilute solutions in this chapter.

Table 26–3. Thermodynamics of Acid Dissociations (ΔG^0 in kcal/mole, ΔH^0 in kcal/mole, ΔS^0 in cal/mole-deg.) Given for Each Acid of Charge n

$n = 0$	ΔG^0	ΔH^0	ΔS^0	$n = -1$	ΔG^0	ΔH^0	ΔS^0
OXY-ACIDS							
H_2SO_3	2.6	−4.6	−25	HSO_4^-	2.6	−5.2	−26.2
H_3PO_4	2.9	−3.1	−20.8	$HC_2O_4^-$	5.8	−1.3	−24.5
HCOOH	5.1	0	−17.2	HSO_3^-	7.2	+0.9	−21.2
$HC_2H_3O_2$	6.5	−0.1	−20	$H_2PO_4^-$	9.8	0.9	−29.9
H_2CO_3	8.1	+1.8	−23	HCO_3^-	14.1	3.55	−35.4
H_2O	19.1	13.4	−19.2				
OTHER ACIDS							
H_2Se	5.2	6.5	+1.4	HSe^-	13.6	7.0	−22.3
H_2S	9.5	5.2	−14.6	HS^-	17	14.2	−10
HCN	12.8	10.9	−1.6				
$n = 1$				$n = -2$			
NH_4^+	12.6	12.4	−0.7	$HPO_4^{=}$	16.4	3.5	−44

3) More difficult to interpret is the thermal data for esterification. The experimental K (not K^0) is 2 to 5, depending on solvent,*

$$C_2H_5OH + HC_2H_3O_2 \rightleftharpoons CH_3COOC_2H_5 + H_2O.$$

The published standard free energies of formations of the pure liquids from their elements are:

$$-41.77 \quad - \quad 93.8 \rightleftharpoons -7\bar{6}.5 \quad - \quad 56.69 \text{ kcal/mole}.$$

Subtracting reactants from products gives ΔG^0 for the reaction as $+\bar{2}.4$ kcal/mole and K^0, 0.018 for the reaction as written. Note that uncertainty in G values, especially for the ester, amount to about 1 kcal. This makes an uncertainty of nearly fivefold in K^0. This is often the sad result when one must subtract numbers of similar magnitude. So, we can only conclude that K^0 would seem to be on the order of 0.003 to 0.1. How can this be compared with the experimental results above? One would need to know the free energy of dilution of each pure liquid to the concentration in the equilibrium mixture. Only if this were the same for each of the four, as might happen at high dilution in an "inert" solvent, might one expect to get the low, thermodynamic, value for the measured equilibrium quotient. (See project 4 in the laboratory section.)

* A. Darlington and W. B. Guenther, *J. Chem. and Eng. Data.* **12,** 605 (1967).

SUMMARY

Uses of compiled thermodynamic data to calculate equilibrium constants and cell voltages are given. Some of the meanings of entropy and free-energy changes are discussed.

SUGGESTIONS FOR FURTHER READING

BENT, H. A., *The Second Law*, New York: Oxford University Press, 1965. This text is a lucid introduction to the use of thermodynamic properties in chemical calculations.

MAHAN, B. H., *University Chemistry*, Reading, Mass.: Addison-Wesley, 1965. Chapter 8 surveys chemical thermodynamics and gives worked examples.

Selected Values of Chemical Thermodynamic Properties, National Bureau of Standards Circular 500. Compiled by F. D. Rossini *et al.* U.S. Gov't. Printing Office, Washington, D.C. Contains extensive critical tables of data for elements, ions, and compounds. A more convenient list for students is given in Bent's book for several hundred species.

PROBLEMS

1. Would you expect formic acid vapor to decompose on passing through a heated glass tube? Calculate the K_{eq}^0 at room temperature for the reaction given the G_f^0 values under each substance for the gas phase.

$$\begin{array}{ccccc} HCOOH & \rightarrow & CO & + & H_2O \\ -80.2 & & -32.8 & & -54.6 \text{ kcal/mole} \end{array}$$

2. The standard H_f^0 values for HCOOH, CO, and H_2O gases are -86.7, -26.4, and -57.8 kcal/mole (see Problem 1). How does K_{eq} change with temperature? Calculate K at 100° C, assuming ΔH^0 for the reaction is constant.

3. Find K_{sp}^0 for CdS given the G_f^0 values under each species.

$$\begin{array}{ccccc} \underline{CdS} & \rightarrow & Cd^{++} & + & S^{=} \\ -33.6 & & -18.6 & & +20.0 \text{ kcal/mole} \end{array}$$

LABORATORY SECTION

LABORATORY DIRECTIONS

In this section we attempt to give sufficient directions for students to be able to perform the laboratory manipulations, calculations, and evaluation of results. Inclusion of the complete details of every step of every process would make tedious reading and would be unnecessary for most people. Often, a brief demonstration by the instructor can replace hundreds of written words. Students will be wise to return to descriptions of basic operations and reread them after they have had some experience in the laboratory. The descriptions will be even more meaningful then and may prevent sliding into bad habits. Of course, they cannot be repeated whenever the operation recurs, although reminders may be inserted at opportune spots. For the novice, acquisition of proper laboratory technique requires some personal instruction. You can be sure that the author has overlooked inclusion of details that seem obvious to him but which may puzzle you. Ask your instructor when uncertainty threatens the progress of your work. A few general points follow:

1) An unmodified compound name or formula calls for use of the pure solid, liquid, or the most commonly available solution form, as for HCl (37%). However, this will usually be made explicit unless it is clear from the context by having been mentioned just before. (See the common concentrated reagent list inside the back cover.)

2) For the work described in this section, use a dropper which delivers about 20 drops to the milliliter. Fine-tipped droppers may produce drops as small as 50 to 100 to the milliliter. Count drops into a small graduated cylinder to find out what the $\frac{1}{20}$ ml drop looks like.

3) Keep your notebook open, but away from liquid work at all times. Enter all data and any unforseen occurrences. Do not trust to memory.

4) Buret and other meniscus levels can be made sharply visible by holding behind them a white card with a dark patch on it so that the dark area is just below the meniscus. A black rubber tube looped around the glass under the meniscus also works well in proper lighting. Learn to find the *lowest* possible position of the meniscus. This gives self-consistent readings upon subtraction. A very important precaution is to cross-check the first few buret readings with other people to find obvious misreadings and one common mistake: reading fractions *up* from the unit milliliter number.

5) It is good practice to label your reagents with your name, date, concentration, amount of added acid, etc., so that they will be ready for use without the necessity of consulting your notebook for details. Labeling with the date permits ready reference to the notebook, which, of course, is also dated. On extended projects it is helpful to include the grams per liter, etc., so that the solution can be remade quickly from information on the label.

6) Plastic, polyolefin bottles are resistant to basic solutions, which attack glass. Bases should not be stored in ground glass bottles or flasks. Transfer them to plastic after mixing. These plastics are resistant to most dilute solutions and alcohols, but not to solutions of iodine, I_2, silver, and mercury ions. These should be stored in glass and in the dark.

7) Drying solids in the oven is good, but more drying may not be better. Look up the proper temperatures and times. Do not dry overnight. Temperatures below 110°C are mandatory for certain organic compounds, a temperature of 120° is good for many ionic solids, but it is not hot enough for good drying of Na_2CO_3 and AgCl in one hour.

8) Extensive detail and alternatives to procedures are available in treatises on analytical chemistry. Learn where these are in your library and consult them when you want more information and a greater understanding of procedures.

WEIGHING AND CALIBRATION

The instructor will demonstrate the use of the balance assigned to you. Both the classical equal-arm balance and the single-pan semiautomatic balance are delicate instruments capable of giving highly precise and accurate results to the nearest 0.1 mg. Treat them with care and follow instructions to get the best possible weighings and to protect them. (An equal-arm balance with weights costs about $200, and a single-pan balance, over $500.) Report spills and other accidents to the instructor so that proper measures may be taken immediately. The balance and its surroundings should be clean at all times. Do not take any liquids or fuming solids uncovered to the balance. When you are in doubt, ask a question rather than risk damage.

To calibrate, check the balance against laboratory standard weights, if available for this purpose. Check the optical scale, if any, according to the manufacturer's instructions. Since most pipets are already correct to better than 1 ppth (or in any case that reproducible), the following calibration duplicates serve as a test of your weighing methods.

Flasks stated to be within NBS tolerances (Corning A, and other trade name designations), are usually reliable to well under 1 ppth unless they have been directly heated or otherwise abused. Pipets are similarly reliable. However, burets are sometimes found with large error, and whenever a new one is put into use, it should be checked.

Calibration of Pipets and Burets

Calibrate the 25 and 50 ml pipets using the following proper drainage methods.

Use of pipets. Choose pipets without chipped tips. Clean well using an aspirator or rubber bulb to draw cleaning solution into the pipet until it is about $\frac{1}{4}$ full. (For cleaning instructions, see Chapter 3.) Rinse with much tap water, then three times with small portions of the liquid to be measured in it. (For calibration, rinsing once with distilled water is enough.)

Take the temperature of a small beaker of distilled water and make it within 2 degrees of room temperature by warming or cooling as needed. Weigh a small conical glass-stoppered flask, which is dry on the outside. Record the temperature and immediately suck water into the pipet until the level is above the mark. Remove the suction device and slip the index finger over the end at the same moment. Holding the pipet vertically with its tip against wet glass, rotate the pipet against the finger to lower the level to the mark, using the bottom of its meniscus to determine the level. Lift the pipet and wipe off any drops on the outside of the tip. Drain it into the receiver, touching the tip to the side when the drainage is nearly complete. Decide on a definite time (say 20 sec) that you will always use in waiting for the drainage after the level has reached the tip. Do not move the pipet during this time. Then lift it gently away from the receiver so that no more liquid falls out. In this way, high precision and reproducibility can be attained. Immediately cover and weigh the bottle. Weighing to the nearest milligram is enough. Calculate the volume from Table 1–2.

The bottle can be emptied well and the neck and stopper dried with tissue before reweighing to repeat a calibration. (Constant impurities like the moisture have no effect on calibration here. Indeed, it might be well to add some dry NaCl to the bottle to hold the moisture and also lower the vapor pressure of the water added.) Make duplicate determinations on each pipet.

Burets. The burets may be calibrated by weighing water delivered from them as described above. They may be quickly checked with the pipets. Fill and drain the buret no faster than one-half milliliter per second to the 50.00 ml mark. Pipet into it 25 ml water (lower the pipet tip to 25 ml) and check readings for 5 min. Repeat for the upper half. From the pipet calibration determine the error in the buret. If the error is large, tell your instructor. (This method is open to criticism because of uncertainty in the drainage rate. See the following discussion.)

Buret drainage is quite a different problem from drainage of a pipet which always has the same volume and flow time in use. Experiment will show that rapid flow from a buret leads to significant error unless inordinately long times elapse before the final reading is taken. For example, in three experiments, 50 ml were run out of a buret in 18, 60, and 120 sec, respectively. The added volume drained down after 2, 5, 10, and 60 min was:

Drainage time, min	I(18 sec), ml	II(60 sec), ml	III(120 sec), ml
2	0.08	0	0
5	0.18	0.02	0
10	0.24	0.05	0.006
60	0.31	0.11	0.06

These readings continue to increase up to at least four hours. A definite rate as well as waiting time must be observed for reliable work. Note that the rapid 18 sec titration followed by a 5 min wait and a 120 sec titration followed by a 3 to 5 min wait would give readings differing by 0.18 ml and actual volumes differing by about 0.25 ml, an error on the rapid titration of 5 ppth.

The rate of flow is important. The National Bureau of Standards specifies minimum delivery times for burets for precise work, about 100 sec for your 50 ml burets. (The specifications are given by length.) If yours runs faster than this, slow it to no faster than one-half milliliter per second when you open the stopcock. Check final readings immediately upon finishing the titration and again after several minutes. If the second level is more than 0.01 ml above the first, the buret was drained too fast. If this should happen, a reading after 10 min may give fairly accurate results. In experiments requiring rapid titration, a speed no faster than this maximum of one-half milliliter per second is intended.

As an illustration of the magnitude of the likely error from buret holdup from fast delivery, the following experiment was done. A 50 ml buret, with 53 cm graduated, was found to deliver full volume in 60 sec with the stopcock wide open. Two weight calibrations were made: one with the stopcock wide open and 60 sec delivery, the other with delivery slowed to 130 sec. Buret readings were taken up to 24 min after delivery in each case. The slower delivery sample weight agreed with the volume read from the buret any time up to 10 min after delivery, while the faster one did not reach the proper value until 14 min had elapsed. If the volume was read in the first 5 min, as is customary, the error in the fast-delivery volume would be 0.05 ml or 1 ppth. A plot of the amount of drainage appears in Fig. L–1.

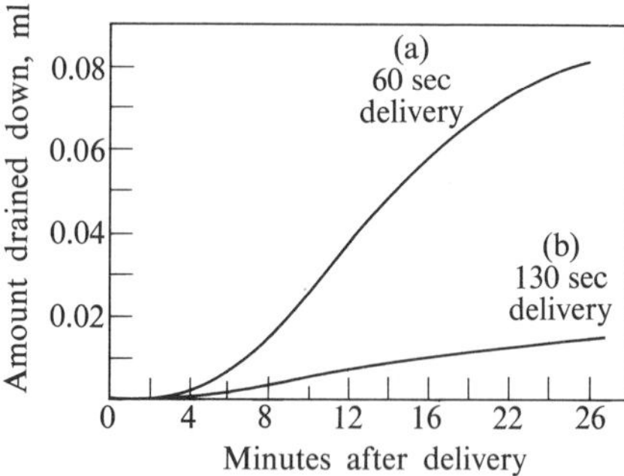

Fig. L–1. Drainage after delivery of 50 ml from buret: (a) fast, (b) slow.

Volumetric flasks. These are almost always calibrated to contain a stated volume. They may be weighed empty and dry, then filled to the mark and reweighed, and the volume calculated as before. However, they may be checked more quickly with Morse-Blalock calibration bulbs. These are large pipets used to deliver the desired volume to the dry flask. If calibrated Morse-Blalock bulbs are not available, use the weight method after choosing a balance of sufficient capacity. Obviously, 0.1 mg weights are not needed for 1000 g of water for which 0.1 g provides one part in ten thousand.

ACID-BASE STUDIES

PREPARATION OF SOLUTIONS

Acid-Base Indicator Solutions

Phenolphthalein, 0.5%. Dissolve 500 mg in 50 ml ethanol and add 50 ml water.

Thymolphthalein, 0.05%. Dissolve 50 mg in 60 ml ethanol. Add 40 ml water.

Bromcresol green, 0.1%. Dissolve 100 mg of the sodium salt in 100 ml water. (For the acid form, mix 100 mg with 14.4 ml 0.01 *M* NaOH in a mortar. Dilute to 100 ml with water.)

Mixed indicator for pH 8.1. Mix 30 mg cresol red and 90 mg thymol blue with 27.5 ml 0.01 *M* NaOH in a mortar. Dilute to 100 ml with water. (Use sodium salts without NaOH if they are available.)

NaOH

(Try to make the base a little more concentrated than the acid.) Make a stock of NaOH (2 liters if projects are to be done) (or get some of the common lab stock if so instructed). Fill a plastic stock bottle with the proper volume of freshly distilled or boiled water. Rapidly, with a graduated cylinder, measure and add the 50% NaOH and restopper both bases. For 0.1 *M* NaOH take 6 ml/liter; for 0.2 *M* take 11 ml/liter of the concentrated NaOH. Cool and shake it well. For use, fill a clean 250 ml plastic bottle so that the main stock will be opened as little as possible. But, be sure it is well mixed first.

Suspect NaOH solutions may be tested for $CO_3^{=}$ content by titration (as described below in the section on comparison) with HCl to the phenolphthalein pH 8, endpoint, then adding bromcresol green, and finishing the titration, pH 4. The number of milliequivalents of HCl required from pH 8 to pH 4 equals the number of millimoles of $CO_3^{=}$ present. This will be greater than the amount in the stock, as some CO_2 is absorbed during titration. Fresh air is about 0.03% CO_2 by moles or volume; human breath about 3% CO_2. Don't breathe on the bases!

HCl

Approximate. Prepare one or two liters, as instructed, by adding 9 ml/liter (for 0.1 *M*) or 17 ml (for 0.2 *M*) of concentrated reagent grade HCl to distilled water in a glass or plastic stock bottle. Stopper and shake well to mix.

Exact. Weigh a small glass-stoppered erlenmeyer or conical weighing bottle to 1 mg. It need not be dry inside. Away from the balance, add CB HCl (16 ml per liter, for 0.1 *M*, 32 for 0.2 *M*) being careful not to wet the lip. (If wet, dry with filter paper and stopper.) Reweigh the bottle. Transfer it quantitatively via funnel into the volumetric flask which is half-full of water, rinsing the bottle well with a stream from the wash bottle. Swirl and make up to the mark with water. Mix well and transfer to a clean storage bottle. Calculate N_a. Table L-1 gives absolute percent by weight but, more useful, it also gives the apparent weight which contains one mole of HCl. Here you do not make buoyancy corrections on your weight of CB HCl. This means, for example, that 18.019 g CB HCl, weighed in air the usual way, contains 0.10000 moles HCl if the acid had been distilled at 760 mm pressure.

Table L–1. Constant Boiling (CB) HCl (Density, 1.096 g/ml, 25°C)

Distillation pressure, mm	Percent HCl	CB HCl, g air weight/mole	Distillation pressure, mm	Percent HCl	CB HCl, g air weight/mole
700	20.360	178.93	740	20.269	179.77
715	20.329	179.24	750	20.245	179.98
730	20.293	179.56	760	20.221	180.19

CB HCl preparation. Add water to 505 ml of concentrated HCl (37.2%) to make one liter, cooled. Read atmospheric pressure and distill the acid rapidly (3 to 8 ml/min) preferably in all-glass apparatus. Put aside the first 600 ml, which may be used for lab stock dilute HCl. The remainder will have the composition in Table L–1. Check the pressure again at the end of distillation. It keeps well when tightly stoppered. Groups of students may make smaller fractions of this amount for their use.

(A fractionating column with about 20 cm of clean, dry glass beads, or the like, enables one to obtain a higher yield of CB HCl, but it requires longer time. Adjust the boiling rate to reflux the acid and allow one drop to come over every 2 to 3 sec. After collecting about 10 ml at this rate, increase the rate gradually to 2 to 3 drops/sec. Good CB HCl comes after the first 40% by this method, while it comes after about 60% in simple distillation. It seems that the remaining HCl in the pot after the azeotrope is reached can be cooled and used without distillation. But, further testing should be made before this is accepted. Students may do this as part of their project on this standard acid.)

Comparison of Acid and Base Stock Solutions

Shake up the stock solutions again. Pipet 50.00 ml of acid into a 300 ml erlenmeyer flask, first rinsing the pipet with three *small* portions of the acid. Rinse and fill the buret with the base stock, rapidly to keep down air contact. Make a neat table in your notebook to record up to six duplicate titrations. (See Chapter 3.) Read the buret to 0.01 ml, add 2 drops phenolphthalein solution to the flask of acid and titrate it with the base until the first pale pink remains after swirling.

Try to add half-drops toward the end. (If it takes more than one buret, add water to the approximate acid so that about 48 ml of base will be used. Mix well. For exact CB HCl, use the 25 ml pipet.) Repeat to get three successive titrations agreeing within about one part per thousand (ppth.)*

If you have trouble, call on the instructor rather than continuing to make titrations and wasting stocks. Failure to mix the stocks usually accounts for gross error here. Haste and carelessness in using pipet and buret usually give much smaller, but significant error.

If CB HCl is used, calculate the N_b from the known N_a of the HCl stock. Otherwise, standardize one of them as follows:

Standardizations of acid. (Amounts are given for 0.2 *N* acid and base stocks.)

a) Na_2CO_3. Put about 2.0 g primary standard or reagent grade anhydrous Na_2CO_3 in a weighing bottle and dry for at least one hour at 120° or higher (not over 300°C).† Meanwhile, rinse and fill a buret with the acid to be standardized. Clean a 50 ml pipet, a 250 ml volumetric flask, a powder funnel, and three 300 ml titrating flasks. None needs to be dry.

Cool the dry Na_2CO_3, covered, in a desiccator. Have the volumetric flask about $\frac{1}{3}$ full of water. Weigh the bottle of Na_2CO_3 and empty it carefully into the flask through a funnel. Swirl and wash down any powder on the funnel. Immediately recap and weigh the empty weighing bottle. The tenths of a milligram need only be approximated for so large a sample.

Swirl to dissolve all the solid and fill the volumetric flask to the neck with water. Adjust to the mark with a fine-tipped wash bottle or dropper. Stopper the flask and invert many times to mix, but handle it by the fingers only to avoid warming it.

Carbonate titration method. Pipet 50.00 ml aliquots of the Na_2CO_3, as you become ready to titrate each, into erlenmeyer flasks. Add 3 drops of bromcresol green indicator (0.1%) and titrate with acid to the first permanent yellow-green color. (If it is blue-green, add a drop more of acid.) Bring it to a boil over a flame and swirl well. Cool by running tap water over the side while swirling the flask. This takes only 1 to 2 min. The color will usually return to blue. Carefully complete the titration by half-drops to a green-yellow color. (Back titration by base is possible if you over-run the endpoint.)

Other possible indicators are methyl orange (plain or modified), methyl purple (not methyl violet), or methyl red. With acids above 0.2 *M*, results almost as accurate can be obtained without boiling if vigorous swirling is practiced as the endpoint is approached.

---

* The CO_2 of the air gradually fades the endpoints. This can be demonstrated by blowing into the flask and swirling.

† The first unknown solid may also be dried at this time and stored in the desiccator.

Average the titrations and calculate N_a and N_b from the purity and rational equivalent weight of Na_2CO_3 (52.99).

b) Tris(hydroxymethyl) aminomethane (THAM). Dry about 4.5 g of primary standard THAM as in (a), but at 100°C. Weigh, take aliquots, and titrate as in (a) but do not boil. Average the titration volumes and calculate N_a and N_b from the purity and rational equivalent weight of THAM (121.04).

c) HgO. Take, without drying, about 4 g of yellow HgO. (It may be dried in a desiccator.) Proceed to weighing as in (b) but also put 80 g KBr in the volumetric flask and swirl to dissolve HgO before filling. Average the titrations and get N_a and N_b. (The rational equivalent weight of HgO = 108.30.)

Standardization of base. (Amounts are given for 0.2 N base.)

KHP (Potassium hydrogen phthalate). Dry about 8 g primary standard or reagent grade KHP and proceed as in (b) above titrating $\frac{1}{5}$ aliquots with NaOH to a phenolphthalein endpoint. Alternatively, 1.5 g samples may be weighed into flasks for each titration. Average the titrations (if done by aliquots) and calculate N_a and N_b from the purity and rational equivalent weight of KHP (204.14).

Titrations of Carbonate-Hydroxide Mixtures

In Chapter 7 we discussed the theory of indicators and titration curves for mixtures of bases with widely different strengths. Here, we compare two methods of performing such titrations.

1) A two-indicator titration scheme: Titration with HCl to pH about 4 gives the total hydroxide and carbonate present (A). Titration of a fresh aliquot to pH 8.1 gives the hydroxide plus half the carbonate (B). Thus carbonate content can be calculated from $2(A - B)$, and the hydroxide from $A - 2(A - B) = 2B - A$.

2) $BaCO_3$ precipitation: Excess $BaCl_2$ is added to an aliquot to remove all the carbonate as $BaCO_3$. Titration with HCl to pH 9 measures the remaining hydroxide. (Below pH 9 some $BaCO_3$ dissolves forming HCO_3^- and giving high results.) Thymolphthalein is superior to phenolphthalein for this purpose. The precipitate occludes some $Ba(OH)_2$ giving low results for hydroxide. For this reason, most of the hydroxide titration is made before adding $BaCl_2$. Some workers recommend a hot titration for the same reason. You may wish to compare results each way.

Solutions. For unknowns (per student for 0.2 M HCl titrations) use 30 to 45 meq each of NaOH and Na_2CO_3 dispensed as a solution.

Supply 50 ml of 0.5 M $BaCl_2$ per student (104 g/liter). See the previous section on indicators.

As the color standard use 0.5 g $NaHCO_3$ and 0.4 g NaCl in 80 ml water. Add 5 drops of the mixed indicator (thymol blue-cresol red). Cover to keep out fresh CO_2 which changes the pH and color. Make fresh each hour.

Procedure. Obtain the unknown (hand in your labeled 500 ml volumetric flask if requested) and dilute to 500.0 ml immediately with freshly distilled water (or boiled and cooled.) Mix well.

Step A. Titrate not more than three 50 ml aliquots (pipet) as described previously for carbonates. Calculate the total number of milliequivalents of base.

Step B. Pipet one 50 ml aliquot at a time to keep down CO_2 absorption. Add 5 drops of the mixed (thymol blue-cresol red, $\frac{3}{1}$) indicator and titrate with HCl to a color matching the bicarbonate standard. It is important to have the same amount of indicator in each titration and in the standard. Constant swirling is critical. Local excess acid will cause CO_2 evolution and high results.

Step C. Take one 50 ml aliquot at a time. Add 5 drops of thymolphthalein indicator and titrate with HCl until 1 ml less than the expected volume is added ($2B - A$). Add 12 ml of 0.5 M $BaCl_2$ and continue titration until the blue just fades out. Swirl constantly. On repetitions, add up to 0.5 ml less than the required HCl before the $BaCl_2$ addition. (Note that you can get only nine 50 ml aliquots of unknown.)

Results. Report the totals for your entire sample: milliequivalents of base, milliequivalents of $CO_3^{=}$, milliequivalents of OH^-, the last two by each of the two methods. Often the agreement is not close. Discuss the reasons for this.* From your observations while making the titrations, what is your estimate of the reliability limits within which the various endpoints can be fixed? What reliability limits does each place on the calculated number of millimoles of each species?

Unknown Solid Acid or Base (Heat-Stable Compounds)

Dry and weigh samples of the size indicated with the unknown. Proceed as for the standardization given above for Na_2CO_3 or KHP. Calculate the percentage purity or the equivalent weight as directed. Give the individual results and the average of at least four samples (titrations, if aliquots are assigned). Report the standard deviation and the estimated experimental reliability limits.

PROJECT 1. *Investigation of the composition of the distillate during preparation of constant boiling HCl (CB HCl)*

Groups may distill HCl, some using about 10 ml more, some 10 ml less of the 12 M HCl than the amount directed above, to find which approaches CB composition more easily and how much should be discarded in the distillation.

Each group should distill 100 ml of the starting stock acid. First, find the pressure. Then rinse two 25 ml graduated cylinders with 6 M HCl, and then with the first 5 ml of distillate collected in one. Collect six successive 13 ml portions,

* See I. M. Kolthoff *et al.*, *Volumetric Analysis*, Vol. II. New York: Interscience, 1947, pp. 56, 59, 108–109, 133.

alternating the graduates and transferring each portion to a weighed stoppered bottle. Also, take 13 ml of the remaining pot acid. Workers may weigh one or more of the seven samples and transfer quantitatively to a 500 ml volumetric flask as outlined above. Dilute each to the mark, mix well, and titrate 50.00 ml aliquots with 0.2 N NaOH (25 ml aliquots for 0.1 N_b). Use phenolphthalein. (Alternatively, the 13 ml portions may be collected after each 100 ml of a distillation of 1000 ml of acid.)

Calculate the percent by weight of HCl (correct for buoyancy) in each portion and plot against the number of milliliters distilled as abscissa. Note that the first 13 ml portion is an average of the composition of milliliters 6 through 18 and so must be plotted at 12.5 ml.* If desired, the composition might be determined by gravimetric chloride.

PROJECT 2. *Comparison of acid-base standards*

In his preparations of solutions, each student may use a different solid to standardize his acid or base, the acid also being known from the weight of CB HCl taken. Then each can report:

1. the percent purity of the standard, assuming his HCl is correct;
2. the difference (in ppth) between the N_a calculated from CB HCl and from his standard;
3. the N_b both ways and the standard deviation of the class set of results for N_b, provided that common base stock is used by all.

Other standards are listed on p. 41, 42 and in analytical treatises where directions for use and discussion of reliability may be found.

PROJECT 3. *A pH titration and interionic effects on K_a values*

Weigh out the solid polyprotic acid (or take a proper volume of a liquid sample) so that you will have 9 meq total acid (that is, 3 mmole citric or phosphoric acid, for example). Add a definite volume of water and keep track of the water added, using a wash bottle as little as possible. (If you made H_3PO_4 up to 90 ml, you would have 0.1 N acid to start.) Titrate as demonstrated at the pH meter† with 0.2 M standard NaOH. Take pH readings every 3 ml except around inflections: then, every 1 to 3 drops as is necessary to follow changes. Use an indicator as well, if desired, and record ml base, pH, and color, after each addition. Different groups of experimenters may add known weights of NaCl to give different ionic strengths.

Plot pH versus milliliters of base (abscissa); also plot $\Delta pH/\Delta V_b$ versus milliliters of base (V_b). Estimate the delta quotient, slope, to only two significant figures from the first graph or data as convenient. Estimate K_a values for the acid. (Explain how this is done. See Chapters 7 and 8.) With class data, plot

* See Titus and Smith, *J. Am. Chem. Soc.*, **63**, 3266 (1941).
† See p. 362.

log K_a versus $\sqrt{I}$ to get K_a^0 values for each K of the acid. Explain or derive this equation. Take pH read to mean $-\log (a_{H^+})$.

Alternative plans. Follow the mixed base or Na_2CO_3 standardization titrations on the pH meter. Titrate Na_3PO_4 or other base with standard HCl solution at the pH meter. Titrate a weak acid with a weak base at the pH meter, trying also to use a proper indicator.

Titrate several amines with HCl and determine pK values from the titration curves. Correlate with structure.*

PROJECT 4. *The ethanol-acetic acid equilibrium*

One of the most important reactions in the history of chemical theory is the esterification,

$$C_2H_5OH + HC_2H_3O_2 \rightleftharpoons H_2O + C_2H_5OOC_2H_3,$$

which we shall abbreviate hereafter as EtOH + HA $\rightleftharpoons$ H_2O + EtA. Its rates and equilibrium, studied a century ago by Berthelot, St. Gilles, Guldeberg, Waage, and van't Hoff, led to an understanding of the dependence of rate and equilibrium constant on concentrations in chemical reactions. As often happened, rough experiments gave a correct view of broad general laws of nature, while later, refined measurements revealed less simple behavior. In this reaction, which is very slow without a strong acid catalyst, the equilibrium quotient, Q, expressed in moles is found to vary with the catalyst used and with the amount of catalyst and each of the components present at equilibrium. In so complex a mixture, activity coefficients are not available to permit calculation of the true thermodynamic constant K_{eq}^0.

For half a century, physical chemistry students have determined the equilibrium "constant" of this reaction, approaching it from both sides with high concentrations of HCl catalyst present. Under such conditions, Q ranges from about 5 to 12. One wonders how many careful students were mystified about where their technique was at fault. At least, the temperature effect is small (Q changes less than 0.5% per degree) so that close temperature control is not required.

If each component is measured at the start, a titration of HA at equilibrium serves to tell how much of each component has reacted or formed, and Q can be calculated. One might expect to find a constant Q by dilution in an inert solvent like acetone. Also the effects of the large amount of ionic catalyst might be nullified by use of a cation-exchange resin in the H^+ form. This experiment is an investigation of the effects of several variables on Q. For the reaction above,

$$Q = \frac{(\text{EtA})(\text{H}_2\text{O})}{(\text{EtOH})(\text{HA})}\cdot$$

Here, moles, mole fraction, and molarity give the same Q. Weight does not.

* See R. E. Griswold, *J. Chem. Educ.* **42,** 483 (1965).

Materials. Distilled water, reagent grade acetic acid, ethyl acetate and absolute ethanol are required. The ester and alcohol can probably be used as received if stored over $CaSO_4$, Drierite. The HA purity can be quickly found from its freezing point on a calibrated thermometer: percent purity = 100 − 0.53 (16.6 − t_f°). For example, a freezing point of 16.0° indicates 99.7% HA.

The remaining materials are:

standardized 0.2 or 0.1 *M* NaOH, carbonate free (Na_2CO_3 below 0.2% of the NaOH),
phenolphthalein indicator,
reagent grade acetone,
Dowex 50-X8, 50 to 100 or 100 to 200 mesh strongly acidic cation-exchange resin, or the like,
50, 100, and 200 ml bottles equipped with polyethylene-lined screw caps have been found to be gas tight for this experiment.

Procedure. Each student makes (if they are not provided) two accurate stock mixtures, one of the following two sets, each of which is designed to give one high and one low *Q* value based on published research.

Set A	1)	10 ml HA 100 ml EtOH	2)	10 ml EtA 100 ml H_2O
Set B	1)	10 ml EtOH 100 ml EtA 10 ml H_2O	2)	50 ml HA 50 ml EtA 10 ml H_2O

(If the effect of soluble acid catalyst is to be tested, some students will add 10.00 ml, or more, of 6 *M* HCl (or $HClO_4$). The catalyst stock must be standardized and its amount subtracted to find HA from the titrations.) Weigh a dry glass-stoppered or plastic-capped bottle to 1 mg. Add each liquid from a rinsed graduate or pipet and weigh the bottle after each. Mix well by swirling.

For resin-catalyst study, wash strongly acidic cation-exchange resin, 50 to 100 (or 100 to 200) mesh by decantation with several portions of 3 *M* HCl, H_2O, and finally, ethanol. Use the ethanol to transfer to a filter and allow it to drain well. Put approximately 10 ml of the resin (or each student use a definite weight) into a dry filter and wash with three 10 ml portions of the stock allowing each to drain. Slurry it with more stock and transfer to a small dry storage bottle. Fill the bottle nearly full with stock and stopper well. Weigh to 1 mg. Make a duplicate pair with each stock and store in the desk or in a 25° constant-temperature bath. (They may stand in 5 cm water in a large beaker or insulated container to reduce temperature fluctuations.) Hold the temperature at 25° ± 1° for the day before titration. Swirl at least once a day allowing at least five days for equilibration. One to two weeks will be safer. The student may check this by doing titrations every few days until a constant value is attained. Weigh the bottle before titration to check for evaporation which should be well under 1 ppth.

To sample, weigh a stoppered weighing bottle half-full of water (to reduce vapor pressure) and add 1 to 5 g by pipet from the bottle of stock equilibrated on resin. The sample size depends on the amount of HA expected and the molarity of your NaOH. Weigh the stoppered weighing bottle and transfer its contents quantitatively with water to a titration flask. Titrate with constant swirling to the phenolphthalein endpoint with 0.1 or 0.2 *M* NaOH. (Slow titration, poor mixing, and 0.5 *M* NaOH have been shown to give high results due to ester reaction with NaOH.) Repeat until the number of milliliters NaOH/g sample agrees to 2 ppth. (If soluble acid catalyst was used instead of resin, dilute 25.00 ml of the 6 *M* acid to 500.0 ml and titrate 25.00 ml aliquots with 0.2 *M* standard NaOH. Dilute to 1000.0 ml for 0.1 *M* NaOH.)

Dilution study. Some students may dilute 10 ml of stock mixture with 50, 100, 150, etc., (for different students) acetone. Do this by weight to 1 mg. Add resin and proceed as above, using larger bottles and samples for titration. These samples can be weighed in the titration flask on a top-loading balance to 0.01 g. Dilution slows the reaction so that two weeks should be allowed for equilibration.

Results. Calculate the number of moles of each material at the start, applying buoyancy and purity corrections where known. Do not forget the water in the acid catalyst (6 *M*) if used. From the titration, calculate the number of moles of HA in the *total* mixture at equilibrium. From the stoichiometry, calculate the moles of each material at equilibrium. Get *Q*. Try to correlate class and published results with composition and catalyst. High EtOH and EtA are reported to give *Q* as low as 1.9, while high HA and H_2O mixtures may give *Q* as high as 4.5 for the resin catalyst. What is expected for acetone dilution? With soluble acid catalysts much higher *Q* may be found. Discuss likely errors and the uncertainty in *Q* produced by them.

REFERENCES

DARLINGTON, A., and W. B. GUENTHER, *J. Chem. and Eng. Data* **12,** 605 (1967), gives results with resin catalysts.

Encyclopedia of Chemical Technology, ed. by R. E. Kirk and D. F. Othmer, Vol. 5. New York: Interscience, 1950, pp. 782, 788. General review.

JONES, W. J. and A. LAPWORTH, *J. Chem. Soc.* **99,** 1427 (1911) gives results with HCl.

TRIMBLE, H. M., and E. L. RICHARDSON, *J. Am. Chem. Soc.* **62,** 1018 (1940) gives results with $HClO_4$.

Titration can be used to follow the rate of basic hydrolysis of esters. A project on the relation of rate to structure (Hammett sigma-rho relation) is given by J. A. Leisten, *J. Chem. Educ.* **38,** 302 (1961).

PROJECT 5. *Determination of K_a^0 for an indicator: interionic effects*

Spectrophotometric examination of acid and base forms of an indicator can lead to determinations of the relative proportions in each form at proper pH values and thus to K_a. The K_a values at several ionic strengths can be extrapolated to zero I to give K_a^0.

Light absorbance, A, is proportional to concentration of the absorbing species (see Chapter 24) at constant light path length. If each solution has the same total indicator concentration, A serves to measure the concentrations of acid and base forms if their colors are sufficiently different. This experiment is taken from R. W. Ramette, *J. Chem. Educ.* **40,** 252 (1963).

Bromcresol green (BCG) is a diprotic acid, H_2B. One proton is strong, on a sulfonic acid group, the other, a phenolic OH, is weak. Thus the equilibrium may be abbreviated:

$$\underset{\text{yellow}}{HB^-} \rightleftharpoons H^+ + \underset{\text{blue}}{B^=},$$

$$K_a^0 = \frac{[H^+][B^=]}{[HB^-]}\frac{f_+f_=}{f_-} \cong K_af_=.$$

Assume that f_+ is equal to f_-, which is increasingly accurate as $I \to 0$. Using the Debye-Hückel extended equation for $f_=$ (since that is better for doubly-charged ions) with ion diameter 7 Å (see the Kielland table, Table 9–2, p. 94) gives

$$\log f_= = \frac{-2.04\sqrt{I}}{1 + 2.3\sqrt{I}}.$$

Taking logs of the K^0 equation and substituting gives

$$\log K_a^0 = \log K_a - \frac{2.04\sqrt{I}}{1 + 2.3\sqrt{I}}.$$

Letting $x = \log K_a$ and $y = \sqrt{I}/(1 + 2.3\sqrt{I})$ gives

$$x = 2.04y + \log K_a^0.$$

So, we shall plot x versus y to get a straight line of slope 2.04 and intercept $\log K_a^0$. The x and y will be known from the experiment.

Solutions. Each student should obtain the following solutions: $3 \times 10^{-4}\,M$ bromcresol green (25 ml),

> (For stock use 210 mg of the acid indicator in 10 ml ethanol + 3.0 ml 0.1 M NaOH (or 216 mg of the sodium salt of the indicator) diluted to one liter. The exact molarity is not needed. Variations in purity may require experimentation to find a concentration giving absorbance about 0.6 in the pH 8 solution diluted as described.)

0.200 *M* sodium acetate (25 ml), 27.2 g $NaC_2H_3O_2 \cdot 3H_2O$ per liter,
0.100 *M* acetic acid (50 ml), 5.75 ml glacial acetic acid per liter,

(Standardize against known NaOH if the pH meter is not to be used to determine the pH of mixtures.)

1.5×10^{-5} *M* bromcresol green at pH 2 and 8 (5 ml of each),

(For stocks use 25.0 ml of 3×10^{-4} *M* BCG (for pH 2), 1 ml 6 *M* HCl, and (for pH 8) 25 ml 0.2 *M* $NaC_2H_3O_2$, diluted to 500 ml.)

0.10 *M* KCl 7.46 g/liter (for 10 to 20 students).

The concentrations of indicator are given for 1 cm cells. If a pH meter is used to get the pH of the mixtures, calculate H^+ molarity using the appropriate activity coefficient, since the meter reads $-\log$ (activity H^+). If the solutions are correct, the pH meter and the pH calculated with the proper K_a values will agree within 0.02 pH units. (This assumes that the pH meter has been set properly: freshly made 0.05 *M* (10.12 g/liter) potassium acid phthalate is 4.01 at 25°.)

For use of the pH meter, see p. 362.

Procedure. Into four 100 ml volumetric flasks, pipet 5.00 ml of 3.0×10^{-4} *M* BCG and 5.00 ml of 0.200 *M* sodium acetate. Add successively 5.00, 10.00, 15.00, and 20.00 ml of 0.100 *M* acetic acid to form four buffers between pH 4 and 5. Then, as assigned, add 0, 10, 20, *or* 30 ml of 0.100 *M* KCl to all four according to your ionic strength: 0.01, 0.02, 0.03, or 0.04 (or higher if desired to show deviations from the Debye-Hückel equations). All four solutions are to be made the same ionic strength and the K_a values averaged. Other K_a values at different ionic strengths will be obtained from the other workers.

Dilute each flask to the mark with water and mix well. Determine the absorbance, *A*, as instructed at 610 mμ, the peak of the blue base form. Also measure the *A* of the stocks available at pH 8 (NaA only) and pH 2 (0.01 *M* HCl). If possible, record or plot curves of *A* versus wavelength for the last two, and one of your solutions.

Results. First, find the proper K_a value of acetic acid to use at your ionic strength and calculate the $[H^+]$ in each solution. Then combine it with your experimental ratio of $[B^=]/[HB^-]$ to get K_a values for BCG. (See an example calculation of this in Chapters 8 and 24.) Plot your mean value with those of other workers at different *I* to get K_a^0 for BCG. Discuss the errors, precision, and agreement with published values. Write the structural formula of the indicator.

A similar experiment with methyl red is given by A. I. Vogel in *Quantitative Inorganic Analysis* (3rd ed. New York: John Wiley, 1961), p. 814.

PRECIPITATION STUDIES

SILVER AND CHLORIDE TITRATION METHODS

The Volhard thiocyanate method for silver determination can be reversed and used to determine chloride. This Swift modification of the Volhard method is preferred if the following determinations of $AgBrO_3$ solubility are to be performed. Otherwise, the direct Mohr titration may as well be used. Swift and coworkers* report results within 1 ppth by their revised method given here. These methods are discussed in Chapter 10.

Solutions. As primary standard use 0.1 *M* $AgNO_3$. $AgNO_3$, melting point, 212°, decomposes at 444°, is an excellent standard if it is heated just to melting to release traces of water. It must not touch paper, metals, or organic matter: do *not* store in plastic containers. Clean a 100 ml beaker and dry over a flame. Cool and weigh to 1 mg. Use a porcelain spoon to weigh into the beaker about 8 g pure $AgNO_3$. Melt it carefully over a small flame. Cool slightly and remelt. Do not overheat to decompose it. Cool and weigh to 1 mg. Add about 50 ml water and warm to dissolve. Transfer quantitatively to a 500 ml volumetric flask using a funnel and washing the beaker frequently with a stream of water from a wash bottle. If proper cleanliness is maintained, the solution will be clear. Fill to the mark and mix well. Calculate the molarity from the rational formula weight of $AgNO_3$, 169.87.

Make up a 0.1 *M* solution of thiocyanate by putting 8 g NH_4SCN or 10 g KSCN into a clean liter bottle, glass or plastic, and filling with water. Mix well. If desired, either solid may be dried at 110° and weighed into a volumetric flask to test its value as a primary standard.

To make 2 *M* Fe(III) indicator (0.5 liter per 10 students) use 404 g $Fe(NO_3)_3 \cdot 9H_2O$ and 35 ml of 16 *M* HNO_3 in 500 ml.

For Mohr indicator use 0.25 *M* K_2CrO_4: 4.9 g/100 ml (called "5%").

Titration of silver. Pipet 25 ml standard $AgNO_3$, or the unknown, into a 300 ml flask. Add 30 ml water, 5 ml 16 *M* HNO_3 (colorless), and 1.0 ml of 2 *M* Fe(III) indicator. Titrate with the SCN^- solution to the first permanent red-brown tinge in the white suspension of AgSCN. Three trials agreeing to 1 to 3 ppth will do. Try to conserve $AgNO_3$ so you will have enough. You could do a further check on the $AgNO_3$ solution against standard HCl solution by the Volhard or Mohr

---

* *Anal. Chem.* **22,** 306 (1950).

methods. To use the Mohr method neutralize the solution with $NaHCO_3$. Salvage all silver remains if instructed.

Titration of chloride: revised Volhard method. In a 300 ml flask, place an aliquot or sample containing 2 to 4 mmole Cl^- in about 30 ml total solution. Add

7 ml concentrated HNO_3 (colorless),
10 ml 2 *M* Fe(III) indicator,
1.0 ml (pipet) 0.01 SCN^- made by diluting your 0.1 *M* stock $\frac{1}{10}$.

Wash down the sides with a little water and titrate, with swirling, with standard $AgNO_3$ solution until the red $FeSCN^{++}$ just disappears. (Save the first one to compare with later titrations, since the end color is not pure white, but the change is sharp.) Much water should not be added or the indicator concentration will not be correct. For calculation, subtract the number of mmoles of SCN^- from the total Ag^+ used for the $SCN^- + Cl^-$, all in mmoles.

Mohr titration of chloride. To a neutral sample of about 50 ml, add 1 ml 0.25 *M* K_2CrO_4. Titrate with standard silver solution until a faint red-brown tinge can be seen after swirling. Yellow light helps. (The endpoint may be quite difficult to see under some fluorescent lights.) An acid solution may be neutralized with solid $NaHCO_3$ until the end of effervescence before titration. The pH must be between 6.5 and 10.5 (see Chapter 10), and the solution should be cool. If the total volume at the endpoint runs above 100 ml, another milliliter of K_2CrO_4 indicator should be added.

GRAVIMETRIC CHLORIDE

Clean and draw water through four glass or porcelain filter crucibles. The mat is soft; do not scrape it or poke it with any hard objects. To remove previous silver residues, gentle brushing followed by NH_3 and dilute EDTA solution will remove small bits. Large amounts may be loosened by adding some granular zinc and covering with 1 *M* HCl.

After thorough washing, dry at least $\frac{1}{2}$ hour at 120° or higher with the crucibles raised by glass rods so that air may circulate around the bottom of the crucibles. Cool in the desiccator and weigh. Repeat until the change is less than 0.3 mg.

Place the samples containing about 3 mmoles chloride (solid unknown, CB HCl samples, etc., as directed) into 400 ml beakers. Take the volume up to 200 ml with water. Add 1 ml dilute HNO_3. (Test for acidity if there is any doubt.) (Add no acid for HCl samples.) In subdued light (the blue of daylight and fluorescent light is especially harmful), add 30 ml 0.1 *M* $AgNO_3$, a little at a time with constant stirring. Leave a stirring rod in the beaker all the time. Cover and heat to boiling but do not boil. Add more $AgNO_3$ 1 ml at a time until no further precipitation occurs. Do not add a large excess and do not boil the mixture. Let it stand in the dark for several hours (or overnight). Filter each sample through a crucible using a stirring rod and wash bottle, as demonstrated by the instructor. The wash bottle should be filled with 250 ml water plus 2 drops concentrated

HNO_3 and 1 ml 0.1 *M* $AgNO_3$. Finally, fill the crucible with water and suck it through twice. Save all silver washings, etc., in the silver salvage jug provided. Dry the crucibles as before and weigh. Repeated heatings at 130° to 150° may be required. From the ratio Cl/AgCl, calculate the percentage Cl in the sample. Return AgCl to the bottle provided. With care, this method yields results with precision and accuracy better than 1 ppth. However, students often make mistakes in drying to constant weight and in complete precipitation and transfer of the precipitate.

PROJECT 6A. *Solubility study of* $AgBrO_3$

Prepare $AgBrO_3$ in media containing different amounts of common and indifferent ions. The remaining Ag^+ can be titrated by the direct Volhard method and the K'_{sp}, K^0_{sp}, and activity coefficients can be calculated. [This project is adapted from R. W. Ramette, *J. Chem. Educ.* **33,** 610 (1956).]

Definitions. Ionic strength, $I = \frac{1}{2}\sum_i c_i z_i^2$ (see Chapter 9). Activity, $a = fc$, can be applied to each ion:

$$K'_{sp} = [Ag^+][BrO_3^-], \qquad K^0_{sp} = a_{\pm}^2 = f_{\pm}^2 K'_{sp}.$$

See Chapter 9 for extended Debye-Hückel formula and further details.

Experimental. One stock of saturated $AgBrO_3$ may have been prepared for you well ahead of time to equilibrate. The other mixtures are to be made from the stock solutions available. $AgBrO_3$ will precipitate in each. Titration of these saturated solutions of $AgBrO_3$ will tell the $[Ag^+]$ remaining. (If your standard 0.1 *M* $AgNO_3$ is higher than the $KBrO_3$, make a quantitative dilution, such as pipetting 200 ml of it plus 10.00 ml of water into a dry container and mixing well.) Dilute your SCN^- to the 0.02 *M* required (50 ml to 250 ml).

Stock solutions. Dry 4.60 g $KBrO_3$ and weigh. Make up to 250.0 ml. Dry 2.53 g KNO_3. Weigh and make up to 250.0 ml. (Dry both at 110°.) You will need 150 ml of 0.1 *M* $AgNO_3$, standardized. Make the following mixtures in clean dry stoppered bottles and leave in the dark for 20 to 30 hours with occasional swirling. Be sure to add the water and KNO_3 first in each (Why?). Stand them in a tray of water 1 in. deep to hold at even temperature and cover them.

	0.1 *M* $AgNO_3$, ml	0.11 *M* $KBrO_3$, ml	0.1 *M* KNO_3, ml	Water to Make 200 ml
1.	25.00	25.00	0	150.00
2.	25.00	25.00	50.00	100.00
3.	25.00	50.00	25.00	100.00
4.	50.00	25.00	25.00	100.00
5.	25.00	25.00	100.00	50.00

6. The pure water stock of saturated $AgBrO_3$, if available.

Agitate and take the temperature of the bath just before titration. Take 50.00 ml of the saturated solutions. (Start with solution 6 for practice, as you do not have much of your mixtures.) Add 1 ml of 2 *M* Fe(III) indicator and titrate immediately to the red endpoint with 0.02 *M* SCN^- solution. Repeat to check within 5 to 10 ppth. (The endpoint will not be very sharp with such dilute solutions.) Filter each of your mixtures through a dry funnel and paper into a dry erlenmeyer to keep down evaporation. Particles of $AgBrO_3$ must not be pipetted into the titration sample.

Results. Calculate the concentrations of the starting materials to four figures from the weights taken in the stocks. From the $[Ag^+]$ left, calculate the $AgBrO_3$ precipitated, and then, the $[BrO_3^-]$ left. From these you can get the K'_{sp}. Add all the concentrations to get the ionic strength. (I is approximately 0.03 in solution 1, 0.04 in solutions 2, 3, and 4, and 0.07 in solution 5. It is about 0.01 in solution 6). From the extended form of the Debye-Hückel equation, show that you should plot log K'_{sp} versus $\sqrt{I}/(1 + \sqrt{I})$ to extrapolate to find K^0_{sp}. Calculate $f_{\pm}$ from your data (not from the Debye-Hückel equation).

Prepare a neat table of all your results: concentrations of all ions present at equilibrium, I, $\sqrt{I}$, $K'_{sp}, f_{\pm}$. Write the value of the extrapolated K^0_{sp} clearly on your graph. Compare your results with published values and those obtained by other students. Discuss reasons for variations. *Calculate* errors introduced from measurement uncertainties and from a temperature variation of 2°C. Compare your activity coefficients with those from the Debye-Hückel equations or tables.*

SUGGESTIONS FOR ADDITIONAL PROJECTS

Use your standard chloride solution to standardize 0.1 *N* $Hg(NO_3)_2$ with $NaFe(CN)_5NO$ ("nitroprusside"), 1 ml of 10% per 100 ml as indicator. The turbidity endpoint allows one to use this method to determine Cl^- in colored solutions of $CrCl_3$, $FeCl_3$, etc. Such coordination compounds as $Co(NH_3)_6Cl_3$ can be prepared and their purity assayed by this chloride titration. See H. F. Walton, *Inorganic Preparations* (Englewood Cliffs, N.J.: Prentice-Hall, 1948), p. 88–89.

PROJECT 6B. *The solubility of rubidium perchlorate*

The high solubility and resulting uncertainty of interionic effects in saturated solutions of alkali metal compounds make the K_{sp} principle of little value, say for calculating the solubility of NaCl in HCl solutions. A few alkali metal ionic compounds of low solubility should offer solubility behavior relatively free of ion association and hydrolytic effects. This project is a study of $RbClO_4$, which has a solubility (0.07 *M*) significantly less than $KClO_4$ (0.15 *M*), which might also be

* An investigation of equilibria present in this system has been done, in part by undergraduate research students, and reported by R. W. Ramette, *J. Phys. Chem.* **67,** 940 and 944 (1963).

studied. (See the reference cited at the end of this project.) The work introduces an important new precipitation method for potassium, and also for Rb, Cs, NH_4^+, and quaternary ammonium ions. (For a gravimetric K or Rb method see the supplementary laboratory directions, p. 365.) Rb^+ (or the other ions) precipitate with a known excess of standard sodium tetraphenylborate (NaTPB) solution. After partial filtration, an aliquot is back titrated with standard quaternary ammonium ion solution, which gives an indicator reaction when in excess. The aliquot method is used for speed, and because the solubility of the KTPB precipitate gives a high back titration if a total filtration with washing is used for K.

The Ag^+ ion also precipitates with TPB^- (K_{sp} about 10^{-14}). However, methods based on Ag^+ back titrations seem difficult to use with accuracy.

Reagents. Use 0.025 *M* sodium tetraphenylborate (NaTPB): 8.6 g + 5 drops 6 *M* NaOH in 1 liter water (for 10 students). It can be shaken with a few grams of $Al(OH)_3$ and filtered if clarification seems needed.

A solution of 0.025 *M* hexadecyltrimethylammonium bromide (or chloride) (HDTAB) or similar compound (one long-chain R is required) is needed: 2.3 g HDTAB in 250 ml water.

(Both these solutions can be made available in automatic-filling burets to speed the work and save these rather costly reagents. Use a 50 ml buret for NaTPB and a 10 ml buret for HDTAB.)

A 0.04% clayton yellow indicator in water: 40 mg/100 ml is also needed.

Use about 5 g $RbClO_4$ per student. The stock saturated solution, 15 g/liter, is enough for a group of five students. Dissolve at 50° and cool to 25°. (4 oz, 112 g $RbClO_4$ costs about $10 and is enough for about 20 students.) (Leftover solutions can be collected, evaporated, and the $RbClO_4$ crystals filtered out and washed with cold water.)

Prepare a 0.1000 *M* solution of $HClO_4$. For each five students, make one liter (8.5 ml of 70% $HClO_4$ per liter). Standardize and add water to make 0.1000 *M*. Recheck the titer with the standard NaOH.

(If other salt solutions are to be used ($LiClO_4$, $NaClO_4$) they can be standardized by ion exchange. Pass an aliquot through a anion-exchange resin column in the Cl^- form and titrate the resulting Cl^- with standard $AgNO_3$.)

Procedure. In 100 ml volumetric flasks, prepare the mixtures assigned to you. (For individual work, mixtures 1, 2, and 5 make a suitable experiment.) The first, saturated $RbClO_4$, may be available already prepared for the class. For 2, 3, and 4, use a 25 ml pipet to add the volume of 0.1000 *M* $HClO_4$ required. Add 0.5 g solid $RbClO_4$ and fill almost to the mark with saturated $RbClO_4$. Shake for several minutes and make up to the mark with saturated $RbClO_4$ solution. Mix and transfer to a *dry* stoppered 250 ml flask containing a magnetic bar. Set in about 50° water and stir for 5 min to supersaturate (at 25°). Change to a 25° bath controlled to ±0.1° and stir for an hour, or more. Add 0.1 g $RbClO_4$ if needed to keep solid present.

Mixture	1	2	3	4	5
0.1000 *M* $HClO_4$, ml	—	25	50	75	100
$HClO_4$, molarity	0	0.0250	0.0500	0.0750	0.1000

(If you need to make saturated $RbClO_4$ in pure water (mixture 1), use 1.5 g $RbClO_4$ per 100 ml water, warm, stir, and equilibrate at 25° as with the others.) While awaiting equilibrium, standardize the needed solutions with known 0.05 *M* KCl solution as follows.

Titration of Rb^+ (also, K^+, $NH_4{}^+$, Cs^+). Into a 50 ml volumetric flask, pipet 10 ml of the Rb^+ (or K^+) solution. Add 2 drops 6 *M* HCl to neutral samples (none for $HClO_4$ cases). From a buret at a rate no faster than 1 drop/sec, add the 0.025 *M* NaTPB while swirling the flask. Add about 10% excess. Suitable volumes would be: for 0.05 *M* KCl, 22 ml; for mixtures 1 to 5, 32 ml, 26 ml, 23 ml, 20 ml, and 17 ml. Be sure to record the volume NaTPB used to 0.01 ml. Add 15 drops of 6 *M* NaOH, make up to the mark with water, shake well, and let it stand 15 min to coagulate. Filter through a dry, retentive paper into a dry flask. Pipet 40 ml into a titration flask, add 3 drops clayton yellow indicator, and back titrate the excess TPB with standard HDTAB to the pink endpoint. Use a 10 ml buret. (Determine the ratio of TPB to HDTAB by direct titration of 10 ml TPB + 10 drops 6 *M* NaOH.) Convert milliliters HDTAB to milliliters NaTPB and multiply by 1.25, (50 ml/40 ml). Subtract this from the NaTPB taken to get the net milliliters used to precipitate Rb^+ or K^+. Duplicates for each mixture should agree within 5 ppth.

Calculate the apparent molar K'_{sp} for each mixture. Demonstrate that a plot of log K'_{sp} against $\sqrt{I}/(1 + \sqrt{I})$ should give a straight line. What is the intercept at $I = 0$? Prepare a table of data and I, $\sqrt{I}$, $\sqrt{I}/(1 + \sqrt{I})$, K'_{sp}, log K'_{sp}. Plot your data, and class data if assigned, and find K^0_{sp}. Submit the table, graph, and a discussion of errors, reliability, and any special problems met.

Various students may use $NaClO_4$ or $LiClO_4$ in place of $HClO_4$ to test for specific ion effects. RbCl or $RbNO_3$ may also be assigned to test the effect of excess Rb^+ common ion. $KClO_4$ may be investigated in the same way by doubling all concentrations, since $KClO_4$ is twice as soluble as $RbClO_4$. However, the much higher ionic strengths make deviations from simple Debye-Hückel behavior rather large.*

* See R. M. Bozorth, *J. Am. Chem. Soc.* **45,** 2653 (1923).

OXIDATION-REDUCTION STUDIES

TITRATION METHODS FOR IRON AND URANIUM

Determination of either iron or uranium in ores, alloys, fission products, etc., can be achieved by reduction to Fe(II) or U(IV) followed by oxidation with standard dichromate solution to Fe(III) or U(VI) using diphenylaminesulfonate as indicator. Special methods are required if both are present. Iron may also be determined by titration of Fe(III) with a standard reducing solution. Both methods are described below.

Because of the time invested in preparation of standard and unknown samples for titration, it is especially helpful to do practice titrations before wasting good samples. To learn the procedure for the tin(II) reduction and dichromate titration of iron, use 10 ml of a 0.100 *M* Fe(III) solution to carry through the procedure. Use 25 ml of the same solution to practice the procedure for the Hg(I) titration of Fe(III) and for the lead reductor methods described below. The 10 ml size avoids the need to evaporate; just add 10 ml of 12 *M* HCl. If the Fe(III) is not prepared for you, dissolve 4.82 g $FeNH_4(SO_4)_2 \cdot 12H_2O$ and 5 ml 6 *N* H_2SO_4 in water to make a 100 ml solution (or use individual 1 g samples of the ferric alum). If a practice titration of Fe(II) by dichromate, without carrying out the prior reduction step, is desired, 1 g samples of Mohr's salt, $Fe(NH_4)_2(SO_4)_2 \cdot 6H_2O$ can be weighed, dissolved in 100 ml water, and the procedure followed starting at the addition of H_3PO_4-H_2SO_4.

Preparation and standardization of $K_2Cr_2O_7$ solution. Dry 5.0 g of finely-ground highest-grade $K_2Cr_2O_7$ at 120° or higher for 1 hr. Cool, and weigh to 0.1 mg into a 1 liter volumetric flask. Make it up to the mark and calculate the normality from the rational equivalent weight, 49.03.

The normality found by an iron standardization may be slightly different because of an indicator correction. It is therefore suggested that this effective Fe normality be determined for use in tritrations employing the Fe-diphenylamine-sulfonate complex endpoint. It can be done with iron wire dissolved in 10 ml of boiling 6 *N* HCl instead of HNO_3 (see below), or with the tetrachloroferrate standard as described below. The reduction of either by tin (II) or lead can be done as described below.

Tin(II) Reduction and Dichromate Titration of Iron

The sample containing the Fe as Fe(III) and/or Fe(II) should be boiled down, if needed, to 20 ml of rather concentrated HCl. One can boil down to about 10 ml and add 10 ml concentrated HCl. Work on only one sample at a time. To the hot solution in a 500 ml erlenmeyer flask, add 0.3 *M* $SnCl_2$ (in 6 *M* HCl) by drops until the solution changes from yellow to pale green [Fe(II)]. Add 1 to 2 drops excess, no more. Cool by running cold tap water over the flask. Swirl and dump in rapidly 10 ml saturated $HgCl_2$ solution, followed by 200 ml cold water. A small amount of white Hg_2Cl_2 must form in a few seconds or the sample is ruined. Immediately add 25 ml of H_3PO_4-H_2SO_4 mixture (in parts by volume: 40 water, 20 H_3PO_4, and 40 H_2SO_4 in that order; much heat is evolved) and titrate with standard $K_2Cr_2O_7$ solution, swirling and adding 5 drops of indicator after the titration has started. Because of a catalyzed air oxidation of Fe(II), it is important to add most of the $K_2Cr_2O_7$ within 2 min after the $HgCl_2$. However, 30 to 60 sec should be allowed for the slow reaction of $HgCl_2$ with the excess Sn(II). The indicator is 0.1% sodium diphenylaminesulfonate in water.

Hg(I) Titration of Fe(III)

Preparation of Hg(I) solution. In a 600 ml beaker put 5.1 g pure, yellow HgO, 1 ml Hg metal, 20 ml water, and 15 ml concentrated $HClO_4$. Cover and stir magnetically for about 1 hr. Make up to about 500 ml with water. [Fresh $Hg_2(NO_3)_2$ can be used but sometimes contains nitrite which interferes.]

Standardization.

1) Dry and weigh accurately 1 g samples of tetramethylammonium tetrachloroferrate(III), 99.9% pure, formula weight, 271.8.*

2) Use 200 mg of iron wire of known purity. Sandpaper it if it seems rusty. Wipe well with cloth wet with acetone or alcohol. Weigh accurately and dissolve it in 8 ml water and 2 ml HNO_3 added in that order. When dissolved, add 0.5 g sulfamic acid, 10 ml water, and boil to remove oxides of nitrogen and nitrites. (This cannot be used for the $Cr_2O_7^{=}$ method because of the HNO_3 present.) Titrate either, or both, if desired, as follows.

Titration. Make the solution about 50 ml and from 0.1 to 2 *N* in H_2SO_4. If it is already in this range with HNO_3 or HCl, no other acid is needed. Add 1 ml of 6 *M* NH_4SCN for each 10 mg Fe. This is about 20 ml for the usual 200 mg samples taken. Excess is not harmful. Titrate with the Hg(I) solution swirling constantly until the solution is transparent red. Proceed slowly until it is paler orange, then wait 15 sec between drops added. Take the endpoint as a colorless or very pale yellow solution which does not change when another drop of Hg(I) is added.

---

* See L. J. Sacks, *Anal. Chem.* **45,** 1299 (1963).

Lead Reductor Methods for Fe or U

Preparation of column. Use 20 to 100 mesh Pb to make a column about 30 cm high in a 50 ml tube with glass wool plugs at both ends. A funnel in a one-hole stopper can be put in the top. Sift the Pb into the water-filled tube to keep air bubbles out. Before the first use, and any use after storage, wash it with 50 ml 3 *M* HCl containing 1 ml of the Fe(III) solution. Rinse this out with 100 ml 1 *M* HCl to remove the Fe(II). Put through 80 ml 3 *M* HCl and titrate it as a blank, to test for reducing materials. The blank should be only a few drops of $K_2Cr_2O_7$. Keep the liquid level above the Pb at all times—no air must be trapped in the metal. Some reaction to peroxides may occur.

Reduction of samples. Put the sample at a temperature of 25° or warmer, of Fe(III) or U(VI), in 50 to 100 ml 3 *M* HCl, through the column rapidly (1 to 2 min) then follow it by 100 ml 1 *M* HCl to rinse the sample container and to keep liquid always above the top of the metal. Add the wash acid in 4 to 5 portions. (Replace the HCl with water if the column is to be stored.)

Titrations. For Fe, add 25 ml of the H_3PO_4-H_2SO_4 mixture, 5 drops of diphenylaminesulfonate indicator, and titrate with $K_2Cr_2O_7$ solution. For U, do the same after first adding 25 ml 0.1 *M* Fe(III) solution [from $Fe_2(SO_4)_3$ or $FeCl_3$].

Sample Preparations

Iron ores. For approximately 50% Fe ores, weigh 300 mg samples which have been dried for 1 hr at 110° into 500 ml [for Sn(II) reduction] or 300 ml [for Hg(I) titration] erlenmeyer flasks. Add 10 ml concentrated HCl and 5 ml 6 *N* H_2SO_4 and heat gently until dark particles are dissolved. White SiO_2 may remain. If this takes more than $\frac{1}{2}$ hr, replace some of the HCl which evaporates. Proceed with the solution as it is for tin(II) reduction described above. For titration with Hg(I), boil the solution down to about 5 ml to reduce the Cl^- concentration. Cool, add 50 ml water, 20 ml 6 *M* NH_4SCN and titrate with Hg(I) as described above. For Pb reduction, dissolve the ore in a 200 to 400 ml beaker and proceed with lead reduction. Calculate the percent Fe in the samples.

Uranium oxides and ores. (Work in or near the sink and avoid spreading radioactive uranium about.) Dry 1.3 g of uranium oxide sample at 110°. Weigh to 0.1 mg into a 400 ml beaker. Add 10 ml 6 *M* HNO_3 and warm to dissolve. If solution is incomplete, add, after cooling, 2 ml concentrated HNO_3 and 3 ml concentrated H_2SO_4. If it did dissolve in the first step, add only H_2SO_4. Cover with a ribbed watch glass and evaporate to fumes of SO_3. Cool and wash down the beaker sides with a little water from a wash bottle. Cover and evaporate to SO_3 again to remove most of the HNO_3.

Some ores will yield to the above mixed acid treatment. Others require more lengthy treatment. Consult the instructor.

Transfer the solution to a 250 ml volumetric flask, quantitatively. Add enough HCl to make it 3 *M* after dilution to the mark. Put 50 ml aliquots through the Pb column as described above. Calculate the percent U in the sample using the atomic weight 238.0 unless you know it is another isotope.

Method for ores with high uranium content and containing iron. If a paper spot test of the ore solution shows Fe(III) when a drop of 1 *M* SCN^- is added, the dichromate titration is equivalent to the sum of U and Fe. The following simple method uses the intriguing device of making Fe(III) itself the oxidant for U(IV) to get around the interference. It gives fair results, although the endpoint is difficult to fix accurately. Longer and better methods involve sulfide precipitation and cupferron extraction of interfering ions. See the references below.

To the ore solution* reduced with Pb as above, add 5 ml 6 *M* NH_4SCN, heat to 70°C, and titrate with 0.1 *M* Fe(III) solution (48.22 g of $FeNH_4(SO_4)_2 \cdot 12H_2O$ and 6 ml 18 *M* H_2SO_4 per liter). The reaction is slow and reheating to 70° may be required near the end. Take the endpoint as an orange color [red $FeSCN^{++}$ + yellow U(VI)] which persists more than 30 sec at 70°. It fades due to self-oxidation-reduction of $FeSCN^{++}$ which is fairly rapid at this temperature. (An investigation of more stable Fe(III) indicators would be desirable.)

REFERENCES ON URANIUM METHODS

This method was adapted from G. Weiss and P. Blum *C.A.* **42,** 482 (1948), who used Pt electrode indicators for a potentiometric endpoint but added SCN^- as a "catalyst." (*Bull. Soc. Chim. France* **1947,** 735.)

BOOMAN, G. L., and J. E. REIN, "Uranium" in *Treatise on Analytical Chemistry*, ed. by I. M. Kolthoff and P. J. Elving, Part II, Vol. 9. New York: Interscience 1962, p. 163.

STILL, C. W., and H. E. PETERSON, *Anal. Chem.* **24,** 1175 (1952).

"Dead stop" and other endpoint detection methods have been investigated. A recent paper which gives references to previous work is that by R. Whiteker and D. Murphy, *Anal. Chem.* **39,** 230 (1967).

METHODS USING IODINE OXIDATION-REDUCTION

Solutions of 0.1 *N* I_2 and $Na_2S_2O_3$ are to be made and standardized with primary standards. They can then be used to determine a wide variety of oxidizing and reducing agents.

I_2 Solution. (Touch I_2 only with glass or porcelain—no metal or paper.) Since I_2 is expensive, prepare 500 ml unless you are told that more is needed. Put a clean, not dry, 200 to 400 ml beaker on the rough balance and weigh into it about 6.3 g solid I_2 poured directly from the stock bottle. Then weigh 15 g KI on top of the I_2. Add 10 ml water, cover and swirl to dissolve *completely.* Use a wash bottle to transfer it to a 500 ml glass-stoppered storage bottle (not plastic). Fill with water to the shoulder and mix well. Store in a dark place.

* First do a known by carrying 10.0 ml of 0.1 *M* U(VI) through the reduction and titration.

Thiosulfate. Into a clean glass-stoppered 1 liter bottle, put 1 liter freshly distilled water. (It may be boiled and cooled if bacterial contamination is suspected. Cool before use.) Add 26 g $Na_2S_2O_3{\cdot}5H_2O$, 0.1 g (no more) Na_2CO_3, and 1 drop $CHCl_3$. Mix well. The titer should be checked each week. Discard if a precipitate of S forms. If the solution is to be used within 3 to 4 days, no Na_2CO_3 or $CHCl_3$ need be added to preserve it.

The thiosulfate crystals can be weighed to 4 figures and made up to 1 liter in a volumetric flask to check its value as a primary standard.

Starch Indicator. Use a special grade of indicator starch. Boil 500 ml water with 70 g KCl or NaCl added. Stir 5 g starch with 10 ml cold water to a paste and wash it into the hot liquid with a little water. Bring to the boil again; remove from heat and store.

As_2O_3. Dry at 110°, 1.0 g primary-standard grade As_2O_3. Weigh it accurately into a 250 ml volumetric flask. Add 18 ml 6 *M* NaOH and wait for *complete* solution. The flask may be set in warm water if the reaction is slow. Do not heat a volumetric flask directly. Add 100 ml water, 1 drop phenolphthalein, and 6 *M* HCl (about 18 ml) until it becomes acidic, then add 1 ml excess HCl. Add about 4 g $NaHCO_3$ in portions, the last of which should cause no CO_2 formation. You should now have a warm, nearly neutral, arsenite solution. The final pH must be below 9. The heat helps decompose H_2CO_3. Swirl well and make up to the mark with water, when cool. It may be cooled under running water. Calculate its normality from the rational equivalent weight 49.45, or find the number of milliequivalents in the aliquots to be used.

Standardizations with As_2O_3. Pipet 50.00 ml portions of the arsenite solution into 300 ml erlenmeyer flasks. Add about 1 g $NaHCO_3$, 2 ml starch indicator, and titrate with I_2 to a pale blue endpoint.

Repeat with 25.00 ml $Na_2S_2O_3$ solution in place of the arsenite *omitting* the $NaHCO_3$. (If Na_2CO_3 was put in the thiosulfate, add 2 drops of 0.1 *M* acetic acid just before titration starts.) Calculate the normality of the I_2 and $Na_2S_2O_3$ solutions.

Standardizations with $K_2Cr_2O_7$ *a) Copper(II) catalyst method.* Pipet 25.00 ml of standard 0.1 *N* $K_2Cr_2O_7$ (see the previous section on Fe and U methods for preparation) into a 300 ml flask. Add 5 ml 0.0010 *M* $CuSO_4$, 5 ml glacial acetic acid, and 3 g KI dissolved in 30 ml water. Swirl well and titrate with the thiosulfate solution until the brown color fades. Add 2 ml starch indicator and finish titration to the fading of the dark blue-black color. [The final Cr(III) complex here may be red-violet.]

Subtract 0.05 ml for the I_2 formed by the Cu catalyst added. This method is said to be more reliable than the strong acid method (b).*

---

* B. D. Sully, *J. Chem. Soc.* **366,** 1942.

b) *Strong acid method.* Pipet 25.00 ml standard 0.1 *N* $K_2Cr_2O_7$ into a 500 ml flask. Add 5 g KI and 100 ml water. With swirling, add 5 ml 6 *M* HCl. Wash down the sides with water, cover, and stand it in the dark for 5 min. Add 150 ml of water and titrate with the thiosulfate solution, adding 5 ml starch indicator just before the endpoint. Compare the I_2 and $Na_2S_2O_3$ and calculate the normality.

KIO_3 and $KBrO_3$. Primary-standard 0.1 *N* KIO_3 (rational equivalent weight, 35.66) or $KBrO_3$ (rational equivalent weight, 27.83) may be used in a manner similar to (b) above. No extra water or waiting time are needed as with $K_2Cr_2O_7$. Use about 3 ml 6 *M* HCl. Wash down the sides and titrate immediately with thiosulfate. For $KBrO_3$, wait about 1 min before titration as the reaction is slower than that of the KIO_3.

Cu titrations. If Cu is to be determined, the $Na_2S_2O_3$ should be standardized with a known Cu solution.

Weigh accurately 250 mg samples of pure Cu wire or sheet into 300 ml flasks. Add 8 ml 6 *M* HNO_3 to dissolve. Bring to a boil and remove heat. Add 0.5 g urea or sulfamic acid and boil once more. Add 20 ml water and 6 *M* NaOH by drops until some precipitate stays. Just redissolve the precipitate with 6 *M* acetic acid and add 1 ml in excess. Add 20 ml water with 2 g KI in it. Swirl well and titrate with thiosulfate, adding 2 g NH_4SCN and 3 ml starch indicator just before the endpoint. On one sample, get an endpoint before adding the NH_4SCN to observe the I_2 desorbing effect it has upon CuI.

$CuSO_4 \cdot 5H_2O$ (rational equivalent weight, 249.6) may be used as a primary standard if reagent-grade fine crystals have been stored several days in a desiccator over saturated NH_4NO_3 or NaBr solution (about 50% humidity). One-gram samples can be weighed into about 25 ml water, acidified with acetic acid, and the KI added followed by titration as above.

Copper ore. Weigh 1.5 g dried samples (approximately 15% Cu) and add 5 ml concentrated HNO_3 and heat to dissolve. Add 30 ml water and boil. Disregard any small white residue. (A dark residue must be separated and dissolved in HNO_3.) Add 1 g urea and bring to a boil again. Cool and neutralize with NH_3 solution until any Fe(III) precipitates or a little deep-blue $Cu(NH_3)_4^{++}$ forms. Add 6 *M* acetic acid just to dissolve the precipitate or remove the dark blue and add 2 g NH_4HF_2 to complex any Fe(III). Add 3 g KI, swirl, and titrate as above.

Antimony ore (Stibnite, about 50% Sb)(Fe and As absent). Dry at 110° and weigh 0.5 g samples into 500 ml flasks with about 0.5 g KCl in each. Add 10 ml concentrated HCl in a *hood.* Warm gently until the residue is white, silica. Add 3 g tartaric acid and continue warming for 10 min. Add 100 ml water slowly in several portions. Swirl constantly. Add 12 ml 6 *M* NaOH and then solid $NaHCO_3$ slowly until the acid is neutralized and then add 3 g in excess. Swirl and cool well. Add 3 ml starch indicator and titrate with I_2. Calculate the percent Sb in the samples.

PROJECT 7. *Comparison of primary standards*

A large stock of either I_2 or $Na_2S_2O_3$, 0.1 *N*, is made available to the class. Each person then makes the other as described above. Each then standardizes with a different primary standard solid: As_2O_3, $K_2Cr_2O_7$, KIO_3, $KBrO_3$, Cu, $CuSO_4 \cdot 5H_2O$, $Na_2S_2O_3 \cdot 5H_2O$, or others as instructed. At least two people should perform each standardization as a check. Each records his name, standard, and the normality of the stock on a sheet posted for this purpose. All then calculate the average and standard deviation. Consult the literature to explain any obviously divergent values. Do you agree with various authors' estimations of the best standards? In the following unknowns, then, use your own value and the class average value to calculate results. (See Project 11.)

PROJECT 8A. *A chemical investigation of a redox equilibrium*

Redox equilibria are commonly investigated by potentiometric methods. Many systems of quantitative interest go so far in one direction that precise chemical determination of the small amounts of reactants remaining is not feasible. The Fe^{3+}-I^- reaction studied here does not go too extensively to one side under some conditions. Under other conditions, it can be used for quantitative purposes. In this project one finds the equilibrium quotient, the $I_3^- \rightarrow I^-$ half-cell potential, and the conditions for quantitative reaction. The reaction is

$$2Fe^{3+} + 3I^- \rightleftharpoons 2Fe^{++} + I_3^-, \qquad K'_{eq} = \frac{[Fe^{++}]^2[I_3^-]}{[Fe^{3+}]^2[I^-]^3}.$$

Here, K'_{eq} is the molar equilibrium quotient at one ionic strength. The K^0_{eq} can be approximated from K' and activity coefficients of these ions, or by a graphical method if several ionic strengths are studied. (At ionic strength 0.1 *M*, K^0 is about 10 K'.) Two other side equilibria must be considered to obtain the final concentrations of these ions (see Project 11):

$$I_2 + I^- \rightleftharpoons I_3^-, \qquad K_f^0 = 7\bar{5}0;$$
$$Fe(H_2O)_6{}^{3+} \rightleftharpoons Fe(H_2O)_5OH^{++} + H^+, \qquad pK_a^0 = 2.2.$$

The reaction studied is slow enough to allow direct titration of the I° ($I_2 + I_3^-$) at equilibrium if an aliquot is diluted with cool water and titrated rapidly with thiosulfate. (To avoid any possible shift during analysis, CCl_4 extraction can be used to determine the actual I_2 concentration; see Project 11. However, this has the disadvantage of lowering the Fe^{3+} concentration still more. This might be combated by adding Fe^{++}. The extraction method does give results comparable to direct titrations.)

Reagents. Use 0.1000 *M* $Fe(ClO_4)_3$ which is also 0.100 *M* in $HClO_4$. Standardize this by indirect EDTA titration, Pb reduction and $Cr_2O_7^=$ titration, or by direct titration with Hg(I). High accuracy is especially important in the Fe(III) value here.

Freshly made 0.1000 M KI solution is needed. Use dried reagent-grade KI. (Standardize, if desired, by adding known excess $AgNO_3$, to a sample, 200 ml water, 5 ml 6 M $HClO_4$, Fe^{3+} indicator, and back titrating with standard SCN^- solution.)

Use 0.200 M $HClO_4$, 17.4 ml concentrated $HClO_4$ per liter. Check with standard NaOH and add water to make it 0.200 M. Accuracy of 1% here is enough. Use 500 ml of this in making the liter of $Fe(ClO_4)_3$ solution.

You will also need 0.05000 M $Na_2S_2O_3$ and starch indicator as previously prepared.

Procedure. The student puts into volumetric flasks volumes of reagents to make mixtures having initial I^-/Fe^{3+} ratios of $\frac{3}{2}$ to $\frac{2}{1}$. (Why?) In designing his mixtures, the student should keep in mind that ionic strength is to be kept as low as feasible to get sufficient I^0 to titrate, and enough $HClO_4$ should be present to keep much of the Fe^{3+} in the hexaquo form. Outline your experiment, and the volume to be titrated, and discuss it with the instructor before proceeding. One suitable mixture for a 250 ml volumetric flask is (initial concentrations): 0.015 M Fe^{3+}, 0.025 M I^-, and 0.050 M $HClO_4$ (total). The first two should be known to four significant figures.

Stand the mixtures in a beaker of water, or a bath, in the dark for at least 2 hr. Record the temperature. Pipet 50 ml (or the appropriate volume for other mixtures) into 200 ml cold distilled water and titrate rapidly with thiosulfate adding 1 ml starch near the endpoint. Immediately titrate a second sample. (The air added when the flask was opened will slowly oxidize I^- in the acid solution.) For best conditions, air in flasks should be replaced with CO_2 or N_2 when the mixture is made.

The total Fe present can then be found, as a check, by adding 2 g KI, 5 ml 6 N H_2SO_4, and continuing the titration to another endpoint. Warm to about 50°, cool and get the final endpoint if the blue color has returned. The total $S_2O_3^=$ is equivalent to Fe^{3+} taken.

Results. Calculate the number of milliequivalents of $I^0(=Fe^{++})$, the number of millimoles of $(I_2 + I_3^-)$, approximate I^- left, and then from K_f^0 the actual concentrations of I_2 and I_3^- at equilibrium in the mixture. A second approximation of the I^- may be required. Calculate K'_{eq} and K^0_{eq} as defined above. Calculate $\mathcal{E}^0$ for $I_3^- \rightarrow I^-$ taking the $\mathcal{E}^0$ for $Fe^{3+} \rightarrow Fe^{++}$ as 0.771 V (see Chapter 12). Discuss reasons for deviations from the published $\mathcal{E}^0$ of 0.54 V. What are your estimated experimental uncertainty limits on K', K^0, and $\mathcal{E}^0$? Explain how you do this.

Under what conditions will 99.9% of Fe^{3+} be converted to $Fe^{++} + I^0$? Try a titration by $S_2O_3^=$ of 10 ml of the Fe^{3+} stock solution under the conditions you suggested. (Some heat, about 50°, is required just before the final endpoint because the reaction is slow. K_{eq} cannot inform one of this. After heating, the solution must be recooled for the starch indicator to work well.) Do your results agree with the evaluation of this reaction in *Volumetric Analysis*?

OTHER POINTS TO INVESTIGATE

a) Is the two-hour waiting time required? Titrate samples every 5 min to see when equilibrium is reached.

b) Use the extraction method of Project 11 to study this reaction.

c) Make some iron(II) perchlorate solution by ion exchange from $FeSO_4$ and study the reaction from the reverse direction.

REFERENCES

HERSHEY, A., and W. BRAY, *J. Am. Chem. Soc.* **58,** 1760 (1936).

KOLTHOFF, I. M., and R. BELCHER, *Volumetric Analysis*, Vol. III. New York: Interscience, 1957, p. 342.

PROJECT 8B. *Keto-enol equilibrium investigated by redox methods**

The enol form of ethyl acetoacetate reacts rapidly with Br_2, while the keto form does not. The shift from keto to enol is slow enough to make feasible the determination of the amount in the enol form by the reaction:

$$CH_3COH{=}CH{-}COO{-}C_2H_5 + Br_2 \rightarrow CH_3CO{-}CHBr{-}COO{-}C_2H_5 + HBr$$

followed by addition of 2-naphthol to remove the excess Br_2 as 1-bromo, 2-naphthol plus HBr. The enol-Br product then reacts with excess KI to give I_2, which is titrated with thiosulfate solution:

$$CH_3CO{-}CHBr{-}COO{-}C_2H_5 + 2I^- + H^+ \rightarrow CH_3CO{-}CH_2{-}COO{-}C_2H_5 + I_2 + Br^-.$$

This might be understood for redox balance as replacement of a Br^+ by H^+ followed by $Br^+ + 2I^- \rightarrow I_2 + Br^-$.

As with esterification, the apparent equilibrium constant is found to vary with the medium. The K = enol/keto, seems to vary with the dielectric constant of the solvent used. In the pure liquid ethyl acetoacetate, $K = 0.064$.

Experimental Methods. Make 50.00 ml of 2.0 *M* ester (ester means ethyl acetoacetate throughout) (formula weight, 130.1) in your assigned solvent (for example, methanol, *t*-butanol, DMF, DMSO, etc., which are miscible with water and unreactive toward the materials to be added: Br_2, I_2: haloform reaction).

Measure 12.7 ml of the ester into a dry, weighed 50 ml volumetric flask. Weigh to 0.01 g and fill to the mark with solvent at 25°. Mix well and pipet 10.00 ml into a 100 ml flask and fill it to the mark with solvent, at 25°. Stand

* Adapted from C. H. Ward, *J. Chem. Educ.* **39,** 95 (1962) and K. L. Lockwood, *ibid.* **42,** 481 (1965).

these in a 25° bath several hours or overnight. (An insulated plastic ice container works well: the temperature can be held at 25.0° manually for the last hour of equilibration.)

Titrations. Pipet 10.00 ml portions of the 2 *M* stock into 300 ml flasks. To each, and one at a time, add about 15 ml 0.2 *M* Br_2 in methanol. Swirl for a few seconds and immediately add 6 ml 0.7 *M* (10%) 2-naphthol in methanol. Swirl and add 30 ml 0.1 *M* KI in water. Cover and let stand in the dark for 15 min before titrating them. (Use 25 ml aliquots of the 0.2 *M* ester stock, and half the reagent amounts can be used.) Titrate to a constant light color with standard $Na_2S_2O_3$ solution. (Starch is useless in these media.) A simple "dead-stop" endpoint circuit is shown in Fig. 24–7.) Do a blank to discover I_2 reactive impurities (like ethanol or acetone) in the solvent. For ester, substitute a known amount of KIO_3 and add 5 ml 6 *M* HCl with the KI.

Calculations. Each enol requires two moles of thiosulfate. Find the apparent K_{eq} values. Extrapolate to zero ester concentration. Collect the *K*'s of the class in various solvents and those in the literature and make a table in order of increasing dielectric constant of solvents. Define dielectric constant. Discuss errors and the concentration effects seen. For values refer to G. W. Wheland, *Advanced Organic Chemistry* (3rd ed. New York: Wiley, 1960), pp. 667–673. See J. Burdett and M. Rogers, *J. Am. Chem. Soc.* **86,** 2108 (1964) for NMR values. A. Murphy, A. Balasubrananian and C. N. Rao, *Can. J. Chem.* **40,** 2267 (1962) describe a spectral method. (A more recent value for the dielectric constant of DMF is 36.7 at 25°. The value 27 appears in most tables.)

See the titration method for the ester, for purity determination, p. 374.

SUGGESTIONS FOR ADDITIONAL PROJECTS

Different β-diketones can be tried if they have a high enough enol form fraction to be measured by this method: acetylacetone, 2-acetylcyclohexanone. Water may be tried as solvent if more alcohol is added with the 2-naphthol to hold it in solution. The temperature effect can be measured.

The stoichiometry of reactions of Br_2 with phenols, aniline, etc., can be determined.*

For a discussion of the preparation and purity determination of KIO_3 to see if it can be made of high purity by recrystallizations, see H. F. Walton, *Inorganic Preparations* (Englewood Cliffs, N.J.: Prentice-Hall, 1948), p. 152.

* K. L. Lockwood, *J. Chem. Educ.* **42,** 482 (1965). I. M. Kolthoff and B. Belcher, *Volumetric Analysis*, Vol. III. New York: Interscience 1957, p. 534ff.

GAS MEASUREMENTS

MOLECULAR WEIGHTS FROM GAS DENSITIES: CCl_4 AND ACETIC ACID

PROJECT 9. *A dimerization equilibrium constant*

Obtain a Dumas bulb or a 100 ml florence flask with the neck drawn down to about 2 mm diameter in a 2 to 3 cm tip. If it is dry and clean, weigh it to 0.1 mg after wetting the outside and wiping dry. Allow it to stand in the balance case for 1 min. If it is wet or needs cleaning, add a little acetone and then shake it out. Dry by alternate suction and air inrush. Warm it slightly by dipping it in hot water to speed the process. A flame may cause an explosion. Wipe and weigh as above.

a) CCl_4 trials to learn the technique and the accuracy obtained by ideal and van der Waals' equation calculations. Put enough liquid into the bulb to fill it 5 times as a gas. This is about 2 ml CCl_4 for each 100 ml of bulb volume. This can be done easily by warming the bulb slightly and dipping the tip into the desired volume. As the bulb cools, the liquid is sucked into it. Bring a beaker of suitable size, which is about $\frac{2}{3}$ full of distilled water to a boil in the hood. Put a short one-hole stopper or thick-wall rubber tube on the bulb neck and clamp it gently. A thermometer clamp is good for this purpose. If the sealing method is to be used, use asbestos in place of rubber. Lower the bulb into the boiling water up to the clamp. Be sure the bath boils actively and watch for the end of evaporation of the CCl_4. Read the temperature at the bottom and the top of the bath to be sure mixing and thermal homogeneity has occurred. Remove the bulb in one swift motion within 60 sec of the end of evaporation. Dip it immediately into cool water or run tap water over it to cool it. Wipe it and weigh it as before, without delay. Record the temperature of the balance case. Look up the vapor pressure of the CCl_4 at the weighing temperature and correct the weight for the presence of the vapor in the bulb. Calculate the molecular weight with ideal and van der Waals' equations as shown in the example in Chapter 15. To get the volume of the bulb, shake out the CCl_4 and fill the bulb with water. Apply suction from the aspirator pump through a thin rubber tube barely over the bulb tip. Immerse the bulb and tubing into distilled water as you slip the tube off the tip. Repeat, with the bulb upright at first, until it is full. Filling may be completed with a fine dropper if needed. Weigh on an open balance to the precision required to get 4 figures in the volume of the bulb. Take the water temperature and calculate the volume by the usual method from Table 1–2. Correct the hot gas volume for the expansion of the glass by adding $1 \times 10^{-5}(V)(\Delta T)$ to the volume found, V. The ΔT is the bath temperature minus room temperature. The 1×10^{-5} is the cubical coefficient of expansion of borosilicate glass. For soft glass, use 3×10^{-5}. (In a pure water bath, the temperature may be more accurately taken from the published value of the boiling point of water at the barometric pressure of the experiment.)

b) Acetic acid. The purity of the acid may be checked by its freezing point which is 16.6°C for 100% HA. Each 0.1° lowering signifies 0.05_3% water. A calibrated thermometer must be used.

Prepare a bath of glycerin and water which will boil at about 145°. Cover it to keep hot. Use a hot plate in the hood: fire may result from a flame. Put pure HA, 1 to 2 ml per 100 ml of bulb volume, into a Dumas bulb as in (a). Bring the bath to boiling on a hot plate. Read the thermometer and proceed as before. Do a duplicate. (Add a little water to the bath if the boiling point rises due to water evaporation.) Repeat two runs at about 165°. Take the temperatures just as you are ready to remove the bulb.

As an alternative, the weighing problems and vapor corrections can be avoided, if the acid is washed out and titrated with base. To do this, add a few milliliters cold distilled water with a fine dropper. The bulb may have to be set on ice to help suck in the water. Invert the bulb into the titration flask and warm with your hands until the solution is expelled. Wash off the tip and repeat three times to transfer the acetic acid quantitatively. Titrate with standard 0.2 N NaOH to the phenolphthalein endpoint. Calculate the weight of HA present.

If the bulb was weighed, correct for vapor pressure as above. Calculate the number of moles of gas by ideal and van der Waals' equations as shown in the example in Chapter 15. Get the apparent molecular weight and K_P for the dimerization at each temperature. From the van't Hoff equation (Chapter 26):

$$\log (K_1/K_2) = (-\Delta H/2.303R)(T_2^{-1} - T_1^{-1}),$$

calculate the heat of the dimerization, ΔH, where K_1 and K_2 are the K_P values at T_1 and T_2°K. Use R in cal/mole-deg. Discuss your estimate of sources of error and compare with literature results. Assume this dimerization refers to the formation of two hydrogen bonds between two HA molecules.

If more data is available from the class, plot $\log K_P$ versus T^{-1} and find ΔH from the slope $= -\Delta H/2.303R$.

ALTERNATIVE PROJECT

Do the same for H_2O at 120°, 140°, and 160° and for methanol at 85° and 100°. These light substances require careful technique to obtain usable data.

If unknown liquids are assigned, the Dumas bulb should be sealed after complete evaporation in the bath by applying a small hot flame to the tip. It is then cooled and weighed as above. Then the tip is cracked off under water with pliers to allow the bulb to fill with water to determine the volume and check on the amount of air not expelled during the evaporation.

REFERENCES

ANDERSON, H. H., and L. D. SHUBIN, *Anal. Chem.* **29,** 852 (1957).

JOHNSON, E. W., and L. K. NASH, *J. Am. Chem. Soc.* **72,** 549 (1950).

FRITZ, J., and G. HAMMOND, *Quantitative Organic Analysis,* New York: Wiley, 1957, pp. 271 and 229. Purity of acetic acid.

VOLUMETRIC GAS ABSORPTION

Suggested solutions to be used *in the order given* for gas samples are:

For CO_2: Use 30 to 40% by weight KOH solution.

For C_2H_4 and other unsaturates: Add 900 mg Ag_2SO_4 to 150 ml concentrated H_2SO_4.

For O_2: (a) Put 30 g $Na_2S_2O_4$ (dithionite), 3 g indigo carmine, 30 ml of 45% KOH and 175 ml water into a rubber-stoppered flask. Dissolve and transfer to the absorption bulb with as little air contact as possible. The yellow dye activates the absorption of O_2 and turns blue as the dithionite is used up. (b) Put 10 g pyrogallol, 20 ml water, and 130 ml of 45% KOH reagent together and cover well.

For CO: (a) Use Cu(I)-β-naphthol complex. Make Cu_2O as follows: Put 100 g Cu(II) acetate hydrate into 1 liter water, dissolve and filter if solid remains. Put 60 g glucose (dextrose) in 400 ml water. Heat both to boiling and mix. After boiling a few minutes, let the precipitate settle, decant, wash, and filter. Wash with alcohol and dry at room temperature or in a vacuum.

Grind 20 g fresh Cu_2O with 25 g β-naphthol to mix well. Remove it from the mortar and add 225 ml 95% H_2SO_4 to the mortar. Add the mixture a little at a time with grinding to dissolve it. (Heat is produced which can decompose the material.) Filter through glass wool and store in a glass-stoppered bottle. This loses about half its strength in a month's storage at 5°C.* (b) Use Cu(I)-lactate complex (probably slower absorbing than the above). Put 13 g Cu_2O, 20 ml 85% lactic acid, 100 ml water, and 85 ml concentrated NH_3 in a covered beaker. Warm to 60° and put on a magnetic stirrer for 10 to 20 min.

Introductory exercise. Get instructions for the apparatus available. Saturated NaCl solution may be used for the liquid in the buret to reduce gas solubility losses. Determine the percent CO_2 and O_2 in air and breath: 100 ml samples. Take the breath sample in an aspirator (Mariotte) bottle, at the very end of exhalation. Some may do this at rest and some after hyperventilation (running upstairs). See Fig. 15–5 for typical apparatus.

* R. Stewart and D. Evans, *Anal. Chem.* **35,** 1315 (1963).

PROJECT 10. *Reaction products of gas-phase pyrolysis*

Pyrolyze dioxane, or other assigned liquid sample and analyze 100 ml of the water-insoluble products. Try to balance an equation for the reaction.

In a hood put about 30 ml of the pure liquid into a 50 ml distillation flask with a short, 4 cm, side arm. Add a boiling chip. Connect the side arm to a hard glass or quartz combustion tube about 40 cm long and 1 cm in diameter. One-hole stoppers may be used or the ends can be drawn down to fit rubber tube connectors. Warm the tube gently and also start the flask boiling. When the vapor has pushed most of the air out of the tube, increase the heat with two or more Fisher-Meeker burners under the second quarter of the tube. (Do not overheat the rubber.) Distill the liquid very slowly into the tube. Allow the products to go up the hood from a long rubber tube for several minutes to sweep out air. Then connect a short rubber tube from the outlet to the top of an aspirator bottle filled with salt solution. Be sure to open the bottom of the bottle so that the liquid can be displaced to another bottle by the gaseous products. When several hundred milliliters of gas have been collected from the flow system, cut off all burners and disconnect the bottle. Immediately connect it to the gas measuring buret. Rinse the connecting tubes by letting some gas flow in and then out to the air from the buret. Fill the buret to the 100 ml mark with the gas and absorb gases as assigned.

The residue of H_2 and hydrocarbons may be analyzed by combustion if the apparatus is given. Measure and add a four-fold excess of O_2. After combustion, measure the volume contraction and absorb CO_2, O_2, CO. See Chapter 15 for example calculations of the results.

Write possible chemical reactions based on assumptions about the products not determined. Compare your conclusions and products with the literature. Check for mass balance as in the example in Chapter 15.

For dioxane, see L. Küchler and J. Lambert, *Z. physik. Chem.* **B37,** 285 (1937) in *C.A.* **32,** 31 (1938). For dioxolane, see W. B. Guenther and W. D. Walters, *J. Am. Chem. Soc.* **73,** 2127 (1951). For formaldehyde, see J. E. Longfield and W. D. Walters, *J. Am. Chem. Soc.* **77,** 6098 (1955). For acetone, C. H. Klute and W. D. Walters, *J. Am. Chem. Soc.* **67,** 550 (1945). Ketene is produced, for which see W. B. Guenther and W. D. Walters, *J. Am. Chem. Soc.* **81,** 1310 (1959).

Consider the possible sizes of errors introduced by temperature fluctuations, the volume of the connecting tubes in the absorption system, and the lack of ideality of the gases.

REFERENCES

Hurd, C. D., *The Pyrolysis of Carbon Compounds*, ACS Monograph, The Chemical Catalog Co., New York, 1929. See acetone p. 247 ff.

Vogel, A. I., *Quantitative Inorganic Analysis*, 3rd ed. New York: Wiley, 1961, pp. 1079–83 gives details of other gas absorbents, their preparations, uses, and advantages.

SOLVENT EXTRACTION*

PROJECT 11. *Solvent extraction used to determine the formation constant of the I_3^- complex ion*

Solutions. Use 0.02 *M* $HClO_4$ (1.7 ml 12 *M* $HClO_4$ per liter) and 0.1 *N* $Na_2S_2O_3$ and starch (see Iodine Methods). You will also need 0.2000 *M* KI. Weigh 3.320 g KI and make up to 100.0 ml. (Double the quantity if all four points are to be made by each student.) Approximately 0.08 *M* I_2 in CCl_4 is also needed. To prepare, dissolve 5 g I_2 in 250 ml CCl_4. Stir for several hours to dissolve. Decant before use. Each student may do one determination (a) without KI present and (b) one or more of the KI points as assigned. In dry, glass-stoppered bottles, measure (graduated cylinders are adequate as exact volumes are not required unless a check on the total I_2 taken is desired):

a) 70 ml of the I_2 solution in CCl_4 and 250 ml 0.01 *M* $HClO_4$,

b) 70 ml of the I_2 solution in CCl_4 and 150 ml 0.1000 (or 0.05000, 0.02500, 0.01250) *M* KI which is 0.01 *M* in $HClO_4$. (Prepare these by careful dilution with pipets of the proper volumes of 0.2000 *M* KI, 0.02 *M* $HClO_4$, and water.)

(The original KI may be made 0.01 *M* in $HClO_4$ only if it is to be used within a few minutes. Air oxidation of acidic I^- is rapid.) Set each in a 25° water bath beaker and put on the magnetic stirrer for at least $\frac{1}{2}$ hr. Alternatively, swirl occasionally in a bath for 1 hr or more. Keep tightly closed and try to keep the temperature within ±0.1° of 25° for the last 10 min of equilibration.

During this time, titrate one or more 25.00 ml aliquots of your I_2-CCl_4 stock solution and standardize the $Na_2S_2O_3$ if needed.

Titrations. a) Pour the equilibrated mixture into a tall, dry cylinder or beaker to facilitate pipetting the layers. For the mixture without KI, pipet 100.0 ml of the aqueous layer into a flask containing about 1 g KI and titrate immediately with 0.01 *N* $Na_2S_2O_3$ made by quantitative dilution of the standard 0.1 *N* solution. Add 1 ml starch indicator near the endpoint.

b) Titrate 50.00 ml portions of the KI aqueous layers with 0.1 *N* standardized $Na_2S_2O_3$.

---

* Solvent extraction as a separation method is used in the Steel Analysis p. 348.

For the CCl_4 layers, take a dry pipet with a rubber suction bulb. Expel air through the pipet as it is immersed to prevent inflow of the aqueous layer. Pipet 25.00 ml portions into a flask containing about 50 ml water and 1 g KI. Titrate with 0.1 *N* $Na_2S_2O_3$ until the CCl_4 layer seems almost colorless. Add starch and get the endpoint. Swirl well to extract the I_2. (The volume of CCl_4 is too large for it to act as a sensitive extraction indicator in this case.)

Calculations. From the volumes and normality of $Na_2S_2O_3$, find the *molar* concentration of I_2 titrated in each layer. Since we have repressed the reaction of I_2 with water by adding $HClO_4$,

$$I_2 + H_2O \rightleftharpoons HOI + H^+ + I^-, \qquad K_{eq} = \text{about } 10^{-12},$$

we assume that very little I_3^- is present in the mixture without KI added. (In neutral solution, this reaction may make about 1% error in *P*.) In the KI mixtures, the titration gives the total of I_2 and I_3^- in the aqueous layer. Take the partition coefficient, *P*, in concentrations, from the mixture without KI, as:

$$P = \frac{[I_{2\ org}]}{[I_{2\ aq}]}. \tag{a}$$

Take the observed distribution ratio, *D*, for the KI mixtures as:

$$D = \frac{[I_{2\ org}]}{[I_{2\ aq}] + [I_3^-]}. \tag{b}$$

The formation constant for the reaction, $I_2 + I^- \rightleftharpoons I_3^-$, is

$$K_f = \frac{[I_3^-]}{[I_2][I^-]} \quad \text{(all in the aqueous layer).} \tag{c}$$

Combining these gives (assume only I_2 enters the CCl_4 in any case)

$$1/D = 1/P + (K_f/P)[I^-], \tag{d}$$

which can be solved for K_f to give

$$K_f = \frac{P/D - 1}{[I^-]}. \tag{e}$$

Since one can find the $[I^-]$ at equilibrium from the initial $[I^-]_0$ and experimental results, K_f can be calculated. Show that $[I^-]$ is

$$[I^-] = [I^-]_0 - (\text{total } [I_2] \text{ titrated in water} - [I_{2org}]/P). \tag{f}$$

Calculate K_f for each KI mixture from Eqs. (c) or (e).

A further check on the consistency of the results is made from (d) by plotting $1/D$ versus $[I^-]$ with at least three points of individual or group data as assigned. Equation (d) predicts a straight line of slope K_f/P and intercept P^{-1}. Multiply the slope by the experimentally determined *P* to get another K_f. Why does the intercept not give a reliable value of *P*?

Extensive investigations of I_2 solubility have been made.* At 25°, the *M* solubilities reported are: CCl_4, 0.114_4, H_2O, 0.00133. Compare the ratio of these with your *P* value. Compare your K_f values with published ones and point out the major sources of error and uncertainty in the experiment. Support or dispute the contentions:

1. The concentration of $Na_2S_2O_3$ is not required for calculation of *P* or *D*.
2. An uncertainty of $\pm 1\%$ in the normality of $Na_2S_2O_3$ is all one needs to obtain an uncertainty of $\pm 0.2\%$ in $[I^-]$ and in K_f for the 0.1 *M* KI case.
3. *P* does not vary significantly with the total amount of I_2.
4. The Debye-Hückel limiting equation shows that K_f is independent of ionic strength. Is this borne out by the results and literature?

REFERENCES

DANIELS, F., *et al.*, *Experimental Physical Chemistry*, 6th ed. New York: McGraw-Hill, 1962, p. 115 gives other systems in which equilibrium can be investigated by the extraction method.

DAVIES, M., and E. GWYN, *J. Am. Chem. Soc.* **74,** 2748 (1952) gives a summary of previous literature values and a discussion of errors.

JONES, G., and B. B. KAPLAN, *ibid* **50,** 1845 (1928).

---

* W. F. Linke, *Solubilities*, Vol. I. Princeton, N.J.: D. Van Nostrand, 1958, pp. 1254–1288.

EDTA TITRATIONS

This section describes a small selection of the many EDTA methods for determination of metal ions. Make only the solutions assigned for your work. For some later projects, metal chloride or nitrate solutions are required. They may be prepared and standardized by the methods given below. An unknown concentration metal-ion solution may be assigned at this time. For convenience, most methods have been devised using xylenol orange indicator. It is stable in water and gives good results. (For Ca^{++} and Mg^{++} methods, see p. 367.) Successful EDTA titration requires careful attention to pH, ionic strength, competitive complexing, and order of addition of reagents. See the discussions of Chapter 21.

Solutions

EDTA (0.02 *M*). Use 3.730 g in 500.0 ml. Mix well and store in a clean plastic bottle, not in glass. ($Na_2H_2Y \cdot 2H_2O$, formula weight, 372.2, is available in high purity. It usually has a few parts/1000 excess water so that 3.730 g will be 0.01 mole within a few parts/1000. For good four-figure work it must be standardized.)

Zinc (0.02 *M*). Put about 820 mg ZnO into a clean crucible and ignite it at red heat for 20 min to dry and convert any $ZnCO_3$ to ZnO. Cool and weigh to ± 0.1 mg into a 500 ml volumetric flask. Add 5 ml 6 *M* HCl and wash down the walls with a little water. Dissolve and make up to the mark with water. The formula weight of ZnO = 81.4. Calculate the molarity.

Copper (0.02 *M*). Weigh to ± 1 mg 2.5 g of $CuSO_4 \cdot 5H_2O$ which has been stored finely ground in a desiccator over saturated NH_4NO_3 for several days. (This forms the proper hydrate.) Dilute to 500.0 ml and calculate the molarity from the formula weight, 249.7.

Iron (0.02 *M*). a) Weigh to ± 1 mg 2.7 g $N(CH_3)_4FeCl_4$ (formula weight, 271.8). (See the description of the preparation in the section on redox titrations.) Add 5 ml 6 *M* H_2SO_4 and make up to 500.0 ml.

b) Weigh 4.9 g ferric alum and dilute as in (a). The formula weight of $FeNH_4(SO_4)_2 \cdot 12H_2O$ is 482.2.

Bismuth (0.02 *M*). Weigh 4.9 g $Bi(NO_3)_3 \cdot 5H_2O$. Add 10 ml 16 *M* HNO_3 and dilute to 500 ml.

Nickel. Weigh 2.6 g $NiSO_4 \cdot 6H_2O$ (formula weight, 262.9), dilute to 500 ml (0.02 *M*).

Cobalt (0.02 *M*). Weigh 2.8 g $CoSO_4 \cdot 7H_2O$ (formula weight, 281.1), dilute to 500 ml.

Manganese (0.02 *M*). Weigh 1.7 g $MnSO_4 \cdot H_2O$ (formula weight, 169.0), dilute to 500 ml.

Lead (0.02 *M*). Weigh 3.3 g $Pb(NO_3)_2$ (formula weight, 331.2), dilute to 500 ml.

Xylenol orange indicator (0.5% in water). Dissolve 500 mg in 10 ml ethanol and dilute to 100 ml with water. Omit ethanol if the sodium salt of the indicator is used. Alone, it is yellow between pH 1 and 6.2. Its metal complexes are red or violet. Its base form above pH 6.2 is also red-violet.

PAN (0.05% in ethanol). Dissolve 50 mg PAN in 100 ml ethanol.

Titration methods. The Zn, Cu, and Fe (a) solutions described are reliable primary standards if they are carefully prepared. Standardize the EDTA against at least two of them as a cross check on your use of the methods. Report the molarity of EDTA by its own weight, and by the two metal standardizations. Use the average unless you can give a reason for doing otherwise. Determine the molarity of the other metal ion solutions needed by titration with EDTA.

Zinc [Also for Pb(II), Cd(II), and Mn(II)] (Direct titration). Pipet 25 ml of the metal ion solution (or suitable unknown) into a titration flask and add 3 drops of xylenol orange indicator. If the solution is not yellow, add 6 *M* HNO_3 by drops until it is. (Protons displace the metal ion from the indicator.) Add solid hexamine slowly with swirling until red or violet metal-indicator complex forms. Add 1 g excess hexamine. [Add 2 g excess for Mn(II).] Titrate with EDTA solution until there is a sharp change to yellow. (If a solution is very acid, as from ion-exchange separation, neutralize most of the acid with 6 *M* NaOH before starting this procedure, or add the xylenol orange and NaOH until a red or violet color forms.) Hexamine buffers at pH 5 to 6. A pH near 6 is required for Mn(II).

Nickel (Indirect) [May also be used for Co(II), Zn(II), Pb(II), Cd(II), Cu(II), and Mn(II), individually or the sum of any mixture of these]. Pipet 20 ml of the solution of metal ion into a flask. Add 3 drops of xylenol orange indicator, and if the solution is not red-violet, add 6 *M* NH_3 until it becomes so. (If an unknown large amount of acid is present, neutralize to the red color with 6 *M* NaOH, but do not add excess base.) Pipet into it, 25 ml of standard 0.02 *M* EDTA (or excess for an unknown). Add 4 to 6 drops 6 *M* HNO_3 and warm, if needed, until a yellow to green color forms. If it does not, EDTA may not be in excess; pipet 10 ml more. Add 2 g hexamine and back titrate the excess EDTA with standard Zn(II) or Pb(II) solution to the red-violet endpoint. [If Fe(III) is present it will block the indicator. Use method (b) described below for iron.]

Bismuth. Pipet 20 or 25 ml of the Bi(III) solution into a titration flask. Add 5 drops 6 *M* HNO_3 and 3 drops xylenol orange indicator, and titrate with EDTA to the yellow indicator color. The titration may be performed in the reverse direction as well, especially if it is convenient to have the Bi(III) in a buret for the following Fe(III) titration. Calculate the molarity of Bi(III).

Iron. a) Pipet 20 ml of 0.02 *M* Fe(III) solution, which is not over 0.1 *M* in chloride. Add 6 *M* NaOH by drops until deep red-brown Fe-OH polymers and/or precipitate of $Fe(OH)_3$ form. (If the solution is too dilute for this to be visible, use phenolphthalein.) Redissolve, or discharge color, with 6 *M* HNO_3 and add 4 drops in excess. Pipet 25 ml 0.02 *M* EDTA (an excess) into it, wash down the sides and swirl, taking at least one minute to allow the slow complexing of Fe(III) by EDTA to occur. (This does not react well above pH 3. Be sure the solution is properly acidified in the previous step.) Add 3 drops xylenol orange indicator only after allowing the EDTA to complex Fe(III), otherwise the indicator combines irreversibly with Fe(III). Back titrate the excess EDTA with standard Bi(III) solution. Iron may be determined in this way at pH about one without interference by Zn(II), Pb(II), Mn(II), Ni(II), Cu(II) and the alkaline earth ions. Higher concentrations of chloride seem to inhibit the endpoint color formation.

b) Fe(III) can be determined at higher pH (for the back titration) as was done for various ions in the method described above for nickel. Proceed as in (a) and add 1 g of hexamine just before the back titration which should be made with standard Zn(II) or Pb(II) solution. This method will, of course, give the total of iron and +2 ions in the solution, except alkaline earth ions.

Copper-PAN method. This direct titration is faster and often sharper than the method described for nickel. Pipet 20 or 25 ml of Cu(II) solution into a flask. Add about 20 ml water. If the acidity is unknown, neutralize with 6 *M* NH_3 until $Cu(OH)_2$ precipitates or blue NH_3 complexes form. (If these are not visible, use phenolphthalein and NaOH.) Return to acid solution with 6 *M* HNO_3 and add 3 drops in excess. Add 50 ml ethanol or acetone. (The indicator precipitates with Cu(II) in water alone.) Add 1 g hexamine (or sodium acetate) to buffer about pH 5. Add 3 drops PAN indicator and titrate with EDTA until the violet changes to yellow. This method is recommended for the Cu(II) titrations in the ion-exchange projects.

REFERENCES

These methods were adapted from the following sources:

PRIBL, R., and V. VESELY, *Chemist-Analyst* **52,** 5 (1963) and **50,** 100 (1961).

REILLEY, C. N., *et al., J. Chem. Educ.* **36,** 555 and 619 (1959).

VOGEL, A. I., *Quantitative Inorganic Analysis,* 3rd ed. New York: John Wiley, 1961, Chapter 4.

ION EXCHANGE

PROJECT 12. *Equilibrium and separation with ion-exchange resin*

Determination of batch equilibrium distribution, and column separation curves, as well as unknown separation and determination can be carried out. Investigation of equilibria of metal ions has been facilitated by development of EDTA titrations. They are used here to study equilibria of transition-metal chloro-anions with anion-exchange resin. The total exchange capacity of the resin is found by titration of the Cl^- released by a weighed sample. The ideas involved are discussed in Chapter 23.

Materials. Obtain strongly basic anion-exchange resin in the chloride form, 100 to 200 mesh of the type Dowex 1-X8 (about 30 g per student and about 30 g in a column for 3 to 4 students).

Solutions. A 0.0200 *M* solution of metal ion chloride, standardized (100 ml per student) is needed. [Ni(II), Co(II), Cu(II), Fe(III), Zn(II), or Mn(II) may be used as desired.]

Use about 250 ml per student of 0.0400 *M* EDTA standard (dilute to 0.02 and 0.01 as required).

Also needed are: 0.0200 *M* standard Zn^{++} (100 ml per student) and HCl: 12, 6, 5, 1, 0.5 *M*, HNO_3: 3 *M* (if Zn is used on the column) and 6 *M* NaOH (about 250 ml each, per student). Use xylenol orange indicator (PAN for Cu). See the section on EDTA titrations.

Procedures (a) and (b) below are independent. Either or both may be assigned. Each student may determine a full set of D_e values for an ion, or may combine points with others, each doing only one or two HCl concentration batch experiments. The unknown solution can be given for simultaneous determination of the elution curve and total of each metal ion in (b). Approximate time for (a) and (b) is four laboratory periods if standards are already prepared.

Procedure

a) Determinations of batch distribution coefficients. Wash about 30 g of the anion-exchange resin in a tall beaker by stirring it with two 50 ml portions of 3 *M* HCl, decanting after each, and the same amount of ethanol and water. Transfer with water to filter paper in a funnel and allow it to drain well. Press it between filter papers to remove water. Dry it in a large dish at about 55° for

2 to 4 hr. Cool to room temperature in open air and store in a tightly capped jar. Weigh 1.00 g samples of resin into each of 2 to 10 bottles (depending on the number of points assigned), which hold 30 to 50 ml and have tight plastic or glass stoppers. At the same time, weigh two 1.00 g samples into titration flasks. For a complete set of points, pipet 5.00 ml of 0.0200 *M* metal chloride solution and 20.0 ml of HCl solutions into the 10 bottles, so as to provide 25 ml of the following HCl molarities:

For Co, Fe, Cu, or Mn: 0.5, 1, 2, 3, 4, 5, 6, 7, 8, and 9 *M* HCl.
For Zn: 0.01, 0.05, 0.1, 0.5, 1, 1.5, 2.0, 3, 4, and 5 *M* HCl.

Make these from the proper volumes of 6 or 12 *M* HCl and water in a 25 ml graduated cylinder. About 5% accuracy is sufficient. Each bottle now contains 1.00 g resin and 25 ml of solution originally 0.00400 *M* in metal ion and containing the number of mmoles of HCl needed to give the molarities listed as appropriate to the ion. (For example, one takes 4.2 ml 6 *M* HCl, fills to 20 ml with water, and adds this to a sample bottle to obtain the 1 *M* HCl sample.) Calculate these and enter the values in the table suggested below for further use. Close the bottles tightly and agitate for 1 hr or more at 25° ± 1°.

To the resin samples in the titration flasks, add 10 ml 0.2 *M* KNO_3, 30 ml water, and 2 ml 0.25 *M* K_2CrO_4 indicator and titrate with standard 0.1 *M* $AgNO_3$ to the reddish endpoint. Calculate the resin capacity in milliequivalents/gram for the moisture conditions used. This step may be omitted if D is to be expressed in gram units.

Titration of samples. Filter the contents of each bottle through a dry filter into a dry flask and pipet 20.00 ml of the solution into a titration flask. Add enough 6 *M* NaOH to react with 95% of the HCl in that 20 ml sample. Add 10.00 ml of 0.01 *M* standard EDTA and continue with pH adjustment and Zn^{++} back titration as described previously for that metal ion (see the discussion of EDTA titrations). First titrate 5.00 ml samples of the metal ion stock solution for practice and to check the standardizations. Prepare a table in your notebook with the column headings: *M* HCl, ml 6 or 12 *M* HCl taken, g resin, ml 6 *M* NaOH for neutralization, ml EDTA, ml back titration, mmole metal left in total 25 ml solution, mmole in resin, D_e (or D_g if assigned).

Calculate D_e and plot log D_e versus *M* HCl, for all ions done in the class, on one graph:

$$D_e = \frac{\text{mmole metal ion/meq resin}}{\text{mmole metal ion/ml solution}}.$$

b) Determination of elution curves for metal ion separations. From the D curves in (a) or from published data (Chapter 23) plan a column-separation scheme for Fe(III), Co(II), and Ni(II) or others as assigned. [When D_e is below 10 (log D_e = 1), the ion elutes with a reasonable volume of solvent.] The following directions should be adjusted for conditions found for the resin in use.

If a column is not provided, wash about 30 g of resin as before and pour it into a column 1 to 2 cm in diameter (a 50 ml buret with a glass wool plug at the bottom can be used). Keep it covered with water and keep air bubbles out of the resin. Put a funnel in a one-holed stopper in the top with the funnel tube delivering liquid onto a pad of glass wool at the top of the resin.

Weigh approximately (or use the unknown) 1 mmole of each metal chloride. Dissolve them in about 5 ml of 9 *M* HCl. Put 20 ml of 9 *M* HCl into the column and let it down to the top of the resin. Add the sample and let it down into the resin. (Never let air down into the resin.) Rinse the sample container with three 3-ml portions of 9 *M* HCl letting each down to the resin top before adding the next. Put about 50 ml of 9 *M* HCl through the column at about 1 ml/min (1 drop/sec). Collect 10 ml portions in a graduated cylinder and store in stoppered test tubes. When the yellow-green $NiCl^+$ can be seen flowing from the resin, take several 5.0 ml samples to get a well-defined elution curve. Take at least two 10 ml samples when the Ni seems passed.

Change to the next HCl molarity [about 5 *M* for Co(II)] and proceed just as with Ni elution. At different portions, Co will be blue, as $CoCl_4^=$, and then pink as water replaces Cl^- in more dilute HCl solution. (The 3 *M* HCl suggested in literature for Co, sweeps Fe(III) down the column too soon with some resin samples.) Elute Fe(III) with 0.5 *M* HCl. This often takes a larger volume; let two drops fall into a test tube with 3 drops of 1 *M* SCN^- to test for the absence of Fe(III). If Zn(II) is present, elute it with 3 *M* HNO_3, using at least 100 ml. Finally, wash the HNO_3 out of the resin with 1 *M* HCl and store it full of water. (Save all resins as they are expensive and actually improve with use.)

Titrate each sample using EDTA back-titration methods. Neutralize the HCl with 6 *M* NaOH as described in (a). Plot an elution curve. It is convenient to express the concentrations of ions in mmole/liter. Note that the volume should be the total number of milliliters taken from the start of the elution to the *middle* of the sample titrated, since one finds the average concentration over the range of the sample volume. (More correctly, one may plot straight-line segments for a stair-step diagram of the elutions.) Indicate changes of eluant on the graph as shown in Chapter 23.

Unknown determinations. Use an unknown solution just as in (b). It must be of small volume and 8 to 12 *M* in HCl. If not, evaporate it and take up in 5 ml 9 *M* HCl. Proceed as in (b) except that eluant is collected in 500 ml titration flasks, one for each component. Use about 60 ml 9 *M* HCl for Ni, 60 ml 5 *M* HCl for Co, and 100 ml 0.5 *M* for Fe(III). Add phenolphthalein indicator to each and neutralize the HCl with 3 *M* NaOH. Try to add very little excess. Discharge the red base color with drops of 6 *M* HCl. Add 25.00 ml 0.0400 *M* EDTA (must be in excess for Fe case), 5 drops 6 *M* HCl, 1 g hexamine, 4 drops xylenol orange indicator. If the solution is now reddish-violet, excess EDTA was not added. (For Ni and Co, one may continue by warming and adding 10.00 ml more EDTA.) Titrate the yellow-green solution with standard Zn(II) to the red-violet endpoint.

(It is wise to practice known titrations of these ions in the presence of these large concentrations of ionic materials.)

From the net EDTA required, the number of mmoles and weight of metal in the unknown can be determined.

SUGGESTIONS FOR ADDITIONAL PROJECTS

Stainless steel can be analyzed by a combination of ion exchange with oxidation to chromate. Both Ni and Cr(III) go straight through the resin together. See Chapter 23 and the laboratory experiment on steel methods described in the following section.

Try to separate more difficult pairs: Mn(II)-Co(II), Co(II)-Cu(II), Fe(III)-Zn(II). Smaller samples and longer columns should help achieve this.

Cation-exchange resins can be investigated. See the papers referred to in Chapter 23 and the well-detailed paper of Strelow, Rethmeyer, and Bothma [*Anal. Chem.* **37,** 106 (1965)].

MULTIPLE-COMPONENT MIXTURES

STAINLESS STEEL: ANALYSIS FOR IRON, NICKEL, AND CHROMIUM

Weigh accurately three or four 900 mg samples into tall-form 250 ml beakers. Add 10 ml water, 10 ml concentrated HCl, and 1 ml concentrated HNO_3, in that order. Cover with a watch glass and warm if needed to dissolve, adding 1 ml more HNO_3 after a few minutes. [All Fe must be taken to Fe(III).] In a hood, evaporate until some crystals form, not to dryness. Add 3 ml concentrated HCl and evaporate almost to dryness to remove most of the HNO_3.

Extraction of Iron

Get three plastic-stopcock separatory funnels of 125 to 250 ml size and set up three rings to support them one above the other. Transfer the sample (filter with Whatman No. 54 paper if silica is noticed) into the top funnel with 8 *M* (7 *M* for methyl isobutyl ketone) HCl—about 50 ml in four to five portions. Do one sample at a time. Add about 50 ml of your extractant (diisopropyl ether, *n*-butyl acetate, or methyl isobutyl ketone). Shake and allow to separate. Be sure the tip of the funnel is always in the mouth of the one below to catch any drops which may have escaped upon pressure equalization.

Quantitatively drain the acid layer into the second funnel. Wash the organic layer in the first funnel with two or three 10 ml portions of the HCl used, draining these into the acid (second) funnel. Now extract the total acid fraction with two or three [or more if Fe(III) color is still seen in the extractant] 30 ml portions of the extractant. Drain the acid from the first of these into the third funnel and change places with it and the second funnel to continue. Put the last acid into a 600 ml beaker.

Finally, collect all the acid portions in a 600 ml beaker, cover and save for Ni determination. To the extractant, all in one funnel, add 50 ml portions of water to strip out the Fe(III) until no further color extracts. Collect all the aqueous iron portions in a 600 ml beaker and continue with the urea homogeneous precipitation.

Homogeneous precipitation of basic Fe(III) formate. To each sample containing about 600 mg Fe(III), add 10 g NH_4Cl and water to make about 350 ml total volume. Put an 8 in. rod in each beaker to remain during the whole process and to be used in final filtration. Cover with a watch glass. Add 2 ml of formic acid and 10 g urea. At the pH meter, add HCl (or NH_3) to adjust the pH to 1.6. Wash off the pH electrodes into the solution. Bring the mixture to a boil and adjust the flame to keep the temperature just under boiling for 2 hr or until the pH is above 4. Bubbles of CO_2 should form steadily—do not mistake this for boiling. A precipitate should form within 30 min. If it does not, a drop of NH_3 may be added every minute or two until the precipitate starts to form. This will not be needed if the original solution was properly adjusted.

When the pH is above 4, add 5 ml 3% H_2O_2, 10 ml 0.02% gelatin, and a tablet of filter paper pulp (accelerator). Allow to stand hot for several minutes to oxidize any Fe(II) and to coagulate the precipitate. Use a fast paper (Whatman No. 40 or 540) in a long-stemmed 60° funnel.

Fold the paper in half and then almost in quarters so as to leave about 2 mm unmatched at the edges. This makes the paper cone larger than 60°. Tear off a third of the corner of the shorter "quarter" and fit this next to the wet funnel with water and pressing to make the top half fit tightly. Pour the liquid down the rod to fill the paper $\frac{2}{3}$ full. The funnel stem should stay full of liquid to give rapid filtration. (A 58° funnel may be used with perfect quarter folds.)

Make a wash solution, about 150 ml for each sample, of hot 1% NH_4NO_3 with 2 drops NH_3 added. After the liquid in the beaker has been filtered, use three to five 10 ml portions of the wash liquid to transfer the solid to the filter. (If there is solid that cannot be removed with a rubber policeman, add 1 ml concentrated HCl and heat to reflux the acid over the walls and cover. Wash down the cover and walls with water and precipitate the Fe(III) with a slight excess of NH_3. Add 30 ml water and boil to coagulate. Filter.) Wash the total solids in the funnel with the remaining ten small portions of hot wash solution.

Put the paper with the solids into a crucible which has been ignited to constant weight (± 0.2 mg). Char the paper with a low flame and a cover on the crucible. Increase the heat to redness and ignite with a Meeker burner for 30 min uncovered. Cool 1 min in air and then 15 min in a desiccator and weigh. Repeat the ignition until the weight is constant to ± 0.2 mg. Care in using the same times and procedure for the empty and full crucible is required if good results are to be obtained.

Calculate the percent Fe in the sample based on the final weight of pure Fe_2O_3.

This procedure was adapted from *Precipitation From Homogeneous Solution* by L. Gordon, M. Salutsky, and H. Willard (New York: Wiley, 1959, pp. 32–33).

The prior separation from Cr(III) was required since Cr(III) would also precipitate at these pH values.

Homogeneous Formation of Dimethylglyoximatonickel(II)

Slow oximation of biacetyl(2,3-butanedione) with hydroxylamine in the presence of Ni(II) produces large pure crystals of bis(dimethylglyoximato)nickel(II). Fresh biacetyl is required. (About 35 ml may be distilled in a small fractionating column. Collect 12 ml in the boiling range 87.5 to 90.2°C at 750 torr, or, better, vacuum distill.) Dilute 12 ml biacetyl to 1 liter with water, for about 20 samples.

Evaporate the highly acidic samples from the extraction to about 50 ml. Do this in the hood with ribbed or raised watch glasses. A burner may be used. The evaporation takes about 3 hr. The samples must not splash in boiling. In fact, no actual boiling action is needed in this case. During this time crucibles for this and the Fe(III) determination may be prepared. For Ni, sintered glass or porcelain crucibles are washed, dried, and weighed to constant weight, ± 0.2 mg as usual. The process of boiling down may be started while the Fe(III) work is being done.

Add 200 ml water, 10 g sodium citrate, and 6 *M* NH_3 until pH 7.5 ± 0.1 is reached (use a pH meter). If solid $Cr(OH)_3$ appears during neutralization, stop, add 1 to 2 g citric acid, and then continue. Traces of flocculant white solid are probably SiO_2, which must be filtered out before the precipitation of nickel. Cool; add 50 ml of 1.2% biacetyl and 50 ml $NH_2OH{\cdot}HCl$. (For each sample, prepare 2.2 g $NH_2OH{\cdot}HCl$ in 50 ml water, adding NH_3 until pH 7.5 is reached.) Precipitation begins within $\frac{1}{2}$ hr. Cover and leave for at least 24 hr (18 is not enough). Heat at 80° to 90° for 2 hr. Cool and filter through the weighed crucibles. Test the filtrate with 1% alcoholic DMG solution for complete precipitation. Wash with water and dry each crucible at 120° to 140° in a protecting beaker. Cool and weigh in a reproducible manner to constant weight. Calculate the percent Ni based on the dimethylglyoximate as 20.32% Ni.*

If a titrimetric finish is desired, filter the red precipitate through fast paper (Whatman No. 54) washing with water. Lift out the paper and wash the crystals into a 600 ml beaker with a stream of water. Boil several minutes with 2 ml 16 *M* HNO_3 to dissolve it and decompose the DMG. Cool and add NH_3 until the solution becomes just basic [blue $Ni(NH_3)_4{}^{++}$]. Add dilute HA until the blue color just disappears. Add excess EDTA and 5 ml of 5.5 buffer (NaA-HA) and back titrate to the xylenol orange endpoint with standard Zn(II) solution.

Chromium by Peroxydisulfate Oxidation and Fe(II) Titration

Start with new samples or aliquots containing about 60 mg Cr. Ni and Fe do not interfere. The large amount of citric acid and other organic matter prevents the use of the remainder after Ni determination.

Boil the new samples, which are dissolved as before, in 500 ml flasks, with 10 ml H_2SO_4 and 10 ml H_3PO_4, to drive off most of the HCl. Cool and add 100 ml water, 0.5 g $AgNO_3$ (or 40 ml 0.1 *M* $AgNO_3$) and 3 g $(NH_4)_2S_2O_8$. Boil *gently* for 15 min. (The presence of some AgCl solid does no harm, but Ag^+ must be in excess of Cl^-.) This quantitatively oxidizes Cr(III) to $Cr_2O_7{}^{=}$ and decomposes the excess peroxydisulfate. If the orange color of $Cr_2O_7{}^{=}$ does not form at the start of heating, more $AgNO_3$ may be needed. Ag(II) is formed to catalyze the oxidation. (If purple $MnO_4{}^-$ forms, add 5 ml 6 *M* HCl and boil 10 min more to reduce it or any MnO_2.)

---

* This method is adapted from the work of E. D. Salesin and L. Gordon, *Talanta* **5**, 81 (1960).

Cool and titrate with standard Fe(II) solution, adding a few drops of diphenylaminesulfonate indicator toward the end. It forms a deep violet color only when more Fe(II) is added. This goes to pale green at the endpoint. [The standard Fe(II) solution is made by dissolving 9.81 g $Fe(NH_4)_2(SO_4)_2 \cdot 6H_2O$ in a 250.0 ml volumetric flask, with 0.1 *M* H_2SO_4.] This is satisfactory for three-figure results on Cr; however, it may be checked against standard $K_2Cr_2O_7$ solution. Report the percent Fe, Ni, Cr and see what kind of alloys listed in the handbooks have this composition. Can you suggest faster titrimetric methods for combinations of these metals? Would they have equal accuracy? Give references.

BRASS ALLOY: DETERMINATION OF Sn, Cu, Pb, Ni, Fe, AND Zn IN A MIXTURE

Alloys with major components Cu, Sn, Pb, Zn, and which contain small amounts of other metals can be analyzed in many ways. To illustrate some important methods, a brass is treated as follows to determine up to six components:

Determination of	Methods
Sn	Dissolve sample in HNO_3. Filter out SnO_2. Dissolve SnO_2 in H_2SO_4, determine by EDTA.
Cu, Pb	Simultaneous electrodeposition. Weigh Cu and PbO_2.
Ni, Fe, Zn	From 6 *M* HCl, absorb $FeCl_4^-$ and $ZnCl_4^=$ on anion-exchange resin. Wash out Ni(II) with 6 *M* HCl, Fe(III) with 0.5 *M* HCl, and Zn(II) with 3 *M* HNO_3. Titrate each with EDTA.

This method was developed for a brass containing about 80% Cu, 5% Sn, 5% Pb, 5% Zn and 0.1 to 1% Ni and Fe.

Solution and Tin Separation

Weigh three or four 1 g samples to four to five figures and put each into a 250 ml beaker. Add 20 ml 6 *M* HNO_3 and cover with watch glasses. When the first rapid reaction subsides, warm to effect complete reaction. If any metal particles remain, add a few drops of concentrated HNO_3 and heat further. Prop up the covers with glass hooks and evaporate slowly to a volume of 5 to 10 ml, not dry. Wash down the covers and sides adding a total of about 60 ml water to each. Add $\frac{1}{2}$ tablet of filter paper pulp (accelerators) and keep the solutions hot to digest for at least $\frac{1}{2}$ hr. Heating a few minutes then leaving overnight is even better. This coagulates the SnO_2 and leaches soluble ions out of the precipitate.

Tin

Heat each sample and filter it hot through a slow paper (Whatman No. 42) into tall-form 250 ml beakers. Use five to six 5 ml portions of hot 0.2 *M* HNO_3 to rinse the beakers and the filter papers, allowing each portion to drain well. (The object is to get good washing with little addition to the volume of solution.) If the filtrate is cloudy, refilter it. If it fills the 250 ml tall beaker more than half-way, evaporate it down to that point. There is no need to get all SnO_2 off the walls of the first beaker. Save the filtrate for the copper and lead determination.

Put the wet paper containing the SnO_2 into the first 250 ml beaker. Add 6 ml concentrated HNO_3 and 8 ml oxidizing acid. (Mix 13 ml water, 54 ml H_2SO_4, and 33 ml $HClO_4$ to make each 100 ml oxidant needed.) Heat each covered sample gently for 5 min. Increase the heat and evaporate to a volume of 2 to 4 ml. Much SO_3 will be evolved. This treatment oxidizes the paper, dissolves the SnO_2, and removes HNO_3 which can reprecipitate SnO_2 later. (If $HClO_4$ is not used, repeated $HNO_3 + H_2SO_4$ treatments eventually dissolve and oxidize the paper. The $HClO_4$ added *after* the HNO_3 is quite safe. This heating should be performed in a closed hood. Wear safety glasses when examining the beaker.)

Cool, wash down the sides and cover, adding at least 25 ml water. Pipet into it an excess of standard EDTA solution (25 ml 0.02 *M* for 5% tin samples). The EDTA must be added before the next step. If any SnO_2 precipitates here, the sample is ruined. Add a drop of thymol blue indicator, or use a pH meter, and add solid ammonium acetate until pH 2 to 3 is reached, a yellow indicator color. (One may add 0.1 g thiourea to mask any Cu present.) Add 5 drops xylenol orange indicator and back titrate with standard Bi(III) solution to a red endpoint. From the net EDTA calculate the percent of Sn. (Alternatively, a gravimetric SnO_2 determination can be performed by igniting the papers as was done earlier for Fe.)

Copper and Lead

The apparatus for the electrodeposition of copper and lead is illustrated in Fig. L–2.

Before starting, and between samples, clean the platinum electrodes with dilute HNO_3; add a few milliliters of H_2O_2 to the HNO_3 to dissolve PbO_2 on the anode. Rinse with water and acetone or alcohol, being careful not to touch the gauze with fingers at any time. Dry a few minutes in the oven or over a colorless flame. Cool and weigh to 0.1 mg.

To the filtrate from the tin separation, add 5 to 6 ml of HNO_3 (for 100 ml), 2 drops 18 *M* H_2SO_4, and only 1 drop of 0.1 *M* HCl. (This assumes that about 3 ml HNO_3 remain in the sample from previous additions.) Add about 1 g urea and electrolyze onto the two Pt gauzes for about 20 min at 2 to 3 amp and 2 to 2.5 V with magnetic stirring. The anode should be immersed to its top, and the cathode may have about $\frac{1}{5}$ its length above the surface.

Add another gram of urea, wash down the cover and walls and continue the electrolysis for 20 min at about 2 amp and 2 V. Again add urea, 2 ml 6 *M* NH_3, and water to cover the cathode. Continue for 10 min. If any new Cu is seen on the top of the cathode, continue for 10 min more. The blue Cu(II) color is usually gone after the first 20 min.

Lower the beaker, with current still on, and simultaneously wash down the gauzes with a gentle stream of water. Immediately bring a beaker of water up around the gauzes. Remove each one and rinse with acetone. Dry the Cu in the

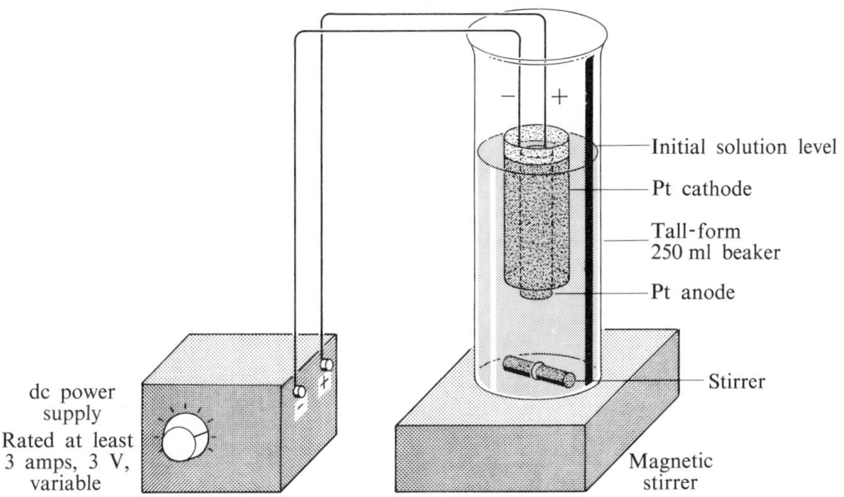

Fig. L–2. Simple constant-voltage electrodeposition assembly for platinum gauze electrodes. Arrangement for simultaneous deposition of Cu and PbO_2.

oven for a few minutes only. Suspend the anode with a pinch clamp in a small beaker so that nothing touches the fragile layer of PbO_2. Dry the PbO_2 at least $\frac{1}{2}$ hr at 140°. Cool in air and weigh each. Calculate the percent Cu and Pb using an empirical factor of 0.864 rather than the theoretical 0.866 for Pb/PbO_2. This accounts for water held by PbO_2 dried this way.

Iron, Nickel, and Zinc

(If instructed that Fe and Ni are very low or absent, the total metal content of the solution after the copper and lead determination may be determined by adding excess EDTA, adjusting pH to 5.5, and back titrating as detailed in the previous section on EDTA methods. Report as percent Zn.)

Evaporate the solution from the previous step down to 10 to 20 ml. Add 10 ml concentrated HCl and evaporate almost to dryness. Add 3 ml HCl and evaporate almost to dryness again to remove most of the HNO_3. Cool, add 5 ml 6 *M* HCl and transfer quantitatively to an ion-exchange column with further 5 ml portions of 6 *M* HCl (a column about 1.6 cm in diameter containing about 6 cm length of 100 to 200 mesh Dowex-1 anion-exchange resin washed with 6 *M* HCl). Wash the Ni(II) through the column with about 60 ml more 6 *M* HCl into a 500 ml titration flask. Follow this with about 90 ml 0.5 *M* HCl into a new flask for Fe(III). Follow this with 90 ml 3 *M* HNO_3, for Zn(II), into a third flask. (See Project 12 for instructions on operation of the ion exchanger.)

To each flask add excess known EDTA, xylenol orange indicator, and NH_3 just until a red color appears. Add 6 *M* acetic acid until the yellow color returns. Add 10 ml 5.5 buffer (3 *M* NaA and 0.5 *M* in NA) and back titrate with standard

Zn(II) solution to the red endpoint. Remember to wait a minute before adding indicator to the Fe(III). From the net EDTA, calculate the percent of Ni, Fe, and Zn in the samples.

If possible, run one known synthetic sample of Ni, Fe, Zn in 6 *M* HCl through the ion exchange and titrations, before your brass. The back-titration method prevents indicator troubles if there is blocking by traces of Fe(III) in the Ni or Zn fractions. Excellent results can be obtained by this procedure if care is taken in adjusting conditions as directed.

DETERMINATION OF FORMULAS AND EQUILIBRIUM CONSTANTS OF COMPLEXES

PROJECT 13. *Bjerrum's method*

Since it is rarely possible to determine each species in the stepwise equilibria of complexes, other approaches through several equations in as many unknowns can be tried. The first experiment presents the methods for NH_3 complexes developed by Bjerrum.*

Here the ligand left uncomplexed affects the pH. The pH is used to find $[NH_3]$, and from this and the initial amounts of metal ion and NH_3, $\bar{n}$, the average number of ligands per metal ion, is calculated. Several methods then lead to the K_n values.

A high and constant $[NH_4{}^+]$ is used, 2 *M*, to prevent OH^- complexing and to provide a medium of constant ionic strength. Under these conditions, from the K_a for $NH_4{}^+$, the student may show that:

$$[NH_3]_1[H^+]_1 = [NH_3]_2[H^+]_2$$

and

$$\Delta \log [NH_3] = \Delta \text{pH},$$

so that the change in pH can be used as an accurate measure of the change in pNH_3 when small amounts of metal ion complex some of the NH_3 in these 2 *M* NH_4NO_3 solutions.

An accurately known volume and concentration of metal ion in 2 *M* NH_4NO_3 is "titrated" at the pH meter with a dilute NH_3 solution in 2 *M* NH_4NO_3. Then $\bar{n}$ values at points are calculated and the formation curve, $\bar{n}$ versus $\log [NH_3]$ is plotted. From this, K_n values can be estimated by the half-integral $\bar{n}$ approximation and refined by further use of the $\bar{n}$ relation and K_n expressions. The metal-ion concentration is determined with EDTA, and the NH_3 with HCl titrations. Collect the required materials so that the measurements may be made rapidly to reduce temperature change and NH_3 evaporation errors. The NH_3 stock solution must be titrated on the same day that the rest of the experiment is performed unless it is tightly contained in a plastic bottle.

---

* J. Bjerrum, *Metal Ammine Formation in Aqueous Solution*, Copenhagen: Haase and Son, 1957, p. 123ff.

Solutions. To prepare solutions of metal ions, put into a 250 ml volumetric flask 40.0 g NH_4NO_3 and the nitrate of the metal ion to be investigated:

0.03 *M*: $Cu(NO_3)_2{\cdot}3H_2O$, 1.81 g, $Co(NO_3)_2{\cdot}6H_2O$, 2.18 g, $Ni(NO_3)_2{\cdot}6H_2O$, 2.18 g, $Zn(NO_3)_2{\cdot}6H_2O$, 2.23 g;

0.05 *M*: $AgNO_3$, 2.125 g.

(Only $AgNO_3$ may be considered a primary standard. The others should be titrated with standard EDTA as described later.) Dissolve with about 200 ml water, warm to room temperature, and make up to the mark. (The solution gets very cold.) Mix well.

To prepare 0.2 *M* ammonia solution, put into a 250 ml volumetric flask 50 ml 1 *M* NH_3 or 3.4 ml concentrated NH_3 (approximate, to be standardized later) and 40.0 g NH_4NO_3. Dissolve, warm to room temperature, and make up to the mark with water. Mix well.

Measurements. Standardize the pH meter with a known buffer solution. Rinse the electrodes and immerse them in a small volume of the 0.2 *M* NH_3 stock solution. Record the pH. Use this solution to rinse a 50 ml buret, then fill it with fresh 0.2 *M* NH_3. Pipet 50.00 ml of the metal-ion solution into a dry 250 ml beaker containing a magnetic stirring bar. Set it on the stirrer, immerse the electrodes, and add the 0.2 *M* NH_3 from the buret according to the following schemes. (The buret tip should just touch the liquid surface, as no water may be used to wash off the drop on the tip.)

For 0.03 *M* metal ions add 0, 3, 4, 7, 11, 12, 13, 18, 19, 25, 26, 27, 30, 40, 50 ml of 0.2 *M* NH_3.

For 0.5 *M* Ag^+ add 0, 2, 6, 6.5, 7, 12, 12.5, 13, 18, 18.5, 19, 24, 25, 30, 35 ml of 0.2 *M* NH_3.

Read the buret and pH accurately after each of these approximate additions. Do not delay and stir only briefly after each addition to minimize evaporation of NH_3. Record the solution temperature. Repeat, omitting points 2 to 5, as a check with less time for evaporation.

Titrations. (Omit for Ag^+.) Before leaving the pH meter, add 1 *M* acetic acid until the pH is about 5.6. Add 3 drops of xylenol orange indicator and titrate, if the ion is Zn(II), directly with standard 0.04 *M* EDTA to the yellow endpoint. For Cu, Ni, or Co, add 50.00 ml of standard 0.04 *M* EDTA, 50 ml water, and back titrate with standard Zn(II) solution (0.02 to 0.04 *M*). (Cu may be titrated directly with EDTA if PAN indicator is used and an equal volume of acetone or ethanol is added.) Check the titration value with another aliquot of the metal-ion solution or with the repeat run.

Find the accurate molarity of the 0.2 *M* NH_3 solution by titrating 25.00 ml of it with standard HCl to the bromcresol green (pH 5) endpoint. Work quickly and do not agitate the NH_3 until near the endpoint, or NH_3 evaporation will give low results. Have 50 ml cold water in the flask before pipetting NH_3.

Further measurements. To get improved values at the high $\bar{n}$ end, further measurements should be made, especially for Ni, Co, or Zn, as follows: Pipet 50.00 ml of the 0.2 *M* NH_3 solution into the beaker and read the pH. Pipet into this and read the pH after the addition of each of four portions of 0.03 *M* metal ion: 10.00 ml, and three 25.00 ml portions.

A covered container or a 3-neck flask may be used to reduce evaporation. More concentrated NH_3 may be tried if it seems needed to establish K_4 values, especially for Zn(II).

Calculations. Set up a table for calculation. Include in it temperature, total mmole metal ion, the pH and $[NH_3]$ of the stock 0.2 *M* NH_3 solution. Use as column headings: volume and mmole NH_3 added at each step, total volume, pH, $\Delta \log [NH_3]$, $p[NH_3]$ left uncomplexed, $[NH_3]$, mmole NH_3 uncomplexed, mmole NH_3 complexed, and finally, $\bar{n}$ (the mmole NH_3 complexed/total mmole metal ion). Plot $\bar{n}$ versus $\log [NH_3]$ left uncomplexed. Estimate K_n at half-integral $\bar{n}$ values and refine with the complete $\bar{n}$ equation. See the detailed examples in Chapter 20.

This experiment is an expanded version of the one for Cu alone published by the author in *J. Chem. Educ.* **44,** 46 (1967).

REFERENCES TO MORE EXTENSIVE PROJECTS

GOLDBERG, D. E., *J. Chem. Educ.* **39,** 328 (1962).

SCHROEDER, K. H., "Direct Calculation of Successive Stability Constants from an Experimental Formation Curve," *Acta Chemica Scandinavica* (in English) **20,** 1401 (1966).

PROJECT 14. *Spectrophotometric investigation of complexes*

The Nickel-EDTA Complex

Job's method can be used to establish the formula of the blue Ni-EDTA complex since it differs significantly from the green Ni(II) aquo ion in the visible absorption spectrum. If the molar absorptivity of the nickel ion and the complex are determined at an appropriate wavelength, corrections for uncomplexed Ni(II) can be made. These can also be used to calculate the formation constant from the absorbance of a solution in which proton competition for the ligand frees a measurable amount of Ni(II) from the EDTA complex:

$$K_f = \frac{[NiY^=]}{[Ni^{++}][Y^{4-}]} = \frac{[NiY^=]}{[Ni^{++}]C_Y\alpha_{0Y}}.$$

If C_Y is the total of all forms of EDTA not in $NiY^=$, and pure $NiY^=$ was taken to start, $[Ni^{++}] = C_Y$, so that

$$K_f = \frac{[NiY^=]}{[Ni^{++}]^2\alpha_{0Y}}.$$

The Ni(II) species can be found spectrophotometrically and the α_{0Y} is known at a given pH from the K_a values of EDTA. α_{0Y} is the fraction of EDTA in the Y^{4-} form.

The conditional formation constant, K_f', is calculated from experimental data alone, for the stoichiometric 1:1 solution

$$K_f' = K_f \alpha_{0Y} = \frac{[NiY^{=}]}{[Ni^{++}]^2}.$$

It is constant at one pH, ionic strength, and total Ni(II) concentration. The K_f calculated from α_{0Y} for EDTA of course includes the assumption that only Y^{4-} enters into complexing equilibrium. The theory and equations are presented in Chapter 21. Obtaining concentrations by spectrophotometry is discussed in Chapter 24.

Solutions. Use 0.1 *M* $Ni(NO_3)_2$ and EDTA solutions each standardized* to within 2 ppth. Dilute 100.0 ml of the more concentrated solution with the correct volume of water to make the two solutions of equal concentration.

Job's method plot. Measure to 0.01 ml, 2, 4, 6, and 8 ml of one solution into dry test tubes. Add, in the same order, 8, 6, 4, and 2 ml of the other and 400 mg of solid hexamine. This gives four tubes with 10.0 ml of solutions at pH 5 to 6 where $NiY^{=}$ formation is effectively quantitative.

A larger stock of 1:1 solution is needed. Pipet 25.00 ml of each into a dry stoppered flask. Mix and remove 10 ml to a test tube with 400 mg hexamine for the pH 5 sample. (If so instructed, determine the full visible spectrum of the pH 5, 1:1 sample of $NiY^{=}$ and of 0.1 *M* $Ni(NO_3)_2$. Absorbance readings at 586 mμ, at least, are required on each of these.) Set the spectrophotometer at zero and 100% transmission with the cells filled with water and the instrument set at 586 mμ. Read the absorbance of each mixture, at pH 5 to 6, at 586 mμ in 1 cm cells. Subtract the absorbance due to Ni^{++} from the readings of solutions having excess Ni^{++}. Plot the Job curve (Chapter 20) with both experimental and corrected absorbance values.

Is there any indication of the presence of complexes other than $NiY^{=}$?

Formation-constant determination. Adjust a new 20 ml portion of the 1:1 $NiY^{=}$ solution to an accurately read pH near 1.0 by adding drops of 6 *M* $HClO_4$ (or HNO_3) at the pH meter. Count the drops added and estimate their volume. This should be a small correction on the concentrations of the species present by increase in the total volume. Neglect the correction if it is less than 2%, about 0.4 ml.

Read the absorbance of this solution at 586 mμ.

---

* Standardize by dilution of portions to 0.02 *M* and titration as described for Ni in the EDTA section.

Calculations. The molar absorptivities of Ni^{++} and $NiY^{=}$ are calculated from the absorbances of 0.1 *M* Ni^{++} and 0.05 *M* $NiY^{=}$ at pH 5 at 586 mμ (see Chapter 24). These are used to correct the absorbances of Job's ratio solutions in which Ni^{++} is in excess of EDTA. Then, the concentrations of both Ni^{++} and $NiY^{=}$ are found in the 1:1 solution at pH 1. If $[Ni^{++}]$ is x and $[NiY^{=}]$ is $(0.05 - x)$, in 1 cm cells (Chapter 24):

$$A = \epsilon_1 x + \epsilon_2(0.05 - x).$$

The adjustment to low pH was required to make x nonnegligible in this equation. Now calculate K_f'. Look up the α_{0Y} values at the low pH used (Fig. 21–2) and calculate K_f. Compare with published values. (Show that the ionic strength used here was about 0.1 *M*.) Show with a dotted line on the graph what the Job curve should be like if all solutions were at pH 1.

The complex of Ni(II) with an indicator like xylenol orange might be investigated by similar means. What changes would be required by the higher color intensity?

Compare results and methods with the study of Hughes and Martell [*J. Phys. Chem.* **57**, 694 (1953)]. Listings of K_f' data at several pH values are found in the tables in A. Ringbom, *Complexation in Analytical Chemistry* (New York: Interscience, 1963).

Iron(III) Complexes

Weigh to 3 figures the solids needed to prepare 250 ml stock solutions of 0.00400 *M* Fe(III) and of tiron (disodium dihydroxybenzene disulfonate) making both also 0.001 *M* in $HClO_4$ to repress OH^- complexing of iron (K_a for $Fe^{3+} = 10^{-2.2}$). More acid reduces the basic ligand concentration too much. (Instead of tiron, sulfosalicyclic acid, thiocyanate, or azide may be tried.)

Rinse and fill burets with the stocks and into clean dry test tubes measure 1 through 9 ml of each solution such that the ratios will be $\frac{1}{9}$, $\frac{2}{8}$, $\frac{3}{7}$, etc., at total volume 10 ml. Measure to 0.01 ml precision. If greater precision is desired, use five times these volumes of the stock solutions for a total volume of 50.00 ml of each mixture.

Examine the visible spectrum of the 1:1 mixture in the spectrophotometer. Also look at the spectrum of the stock solutions. Choose an absorption peak of the complex at which the stocks are nearly transparent, or a correction may be applied. (See the directions for the Nickel-EDTA complex.) Read the absorbance, *A*, of each mixture, plot the data, and determine K_f as described in Chapter 20. Discuss sources of error. Try to find published data, K_f, and any evidence for higher complex formation. See *Stability Constants* by Sillen and Martell (Special Publication No. 17, The Chemical Society, London, 1964).

Some of the complexes are light-sensitive and fade. They should be mixed and measured as soon as possible. Since HSCN is a strong acid, 0.1 *M* $HClO_4$ may be used to advantage.

The Mole-Ratio Method Applied to Co(II) Complexes

Stock solutions. Prepare a 0.010 *M* Co(II) solution: Weigh 1.830 g $Co(ClO_4)_2{\cdot}6H_2O$ (formula weight, 366.0), dissolve in acetone, and make up to 500 ml. Check its molarity with standard EDTA. [$Co(NO_3)_2{\cdot}6H_2O$ (formula weight, 291.0) may be substituted.]

Prepare a stock solution of 0.020 *M* LiCl (formula weight, 42.40): Put about 0.9 g into 1.000 liter acetone. Find the molarity with standard $AgNO_3$ and adjust with acetone to be twice the molarity of the Co(II) stock. (0.020 *M* LiBr, LiI, or 0.010 *M* NH_4SCN may be prepared and adjusted as for LiCl if their anions are to be investigated. Note that Li salts are used when available because NH_4^+, K^+, and Na^+ might not dissolve in acetone in some of the mixtures, especially with perchlorate present.)

Avoid water. The final mixtures will be about 0.3 ppth water as a result of the water introduced with the solids. More will complex some Co(II).

Next make the series of ratio solutions with constant total Co(II) at 0.002 *M* for the halides and 0.001 *M* for the SCN^- system. Fill burets with the stocks and wipe the tip because acetone evaporates easily to leave solute on the tip. Make a large table of the volumes to be taken and the wavelengths to be read. Ratios should be made in 0.20 intervals from 0.40 to 5.00 for ligand/Co(II). Make all the ratios, or the region assigned to you. For the mixtures put 5.00 ml of the Co(II) in each 25 ml volumetric flask [a 50 ml flask for SCN^-, or halve the Co(II)]. Then add 1.00, 1.50, 2.00, 2.50 ml etc., of the LiCl (or other) stock to each successive flask, dilute to the mark with acetone and mix well.

With your instructor present, fill a blank spectrophotometer 1 cm cell with acetone and another with the mixture of $\frac{4}{1}$ ratio. Adjust the instrument according to the manufacturer's instructions and scan the visible region to get an idea of the peaks present. (If told, record the spectrum from 800 to about 340 mμ. Repeat with each stock, and discuss the choice of wavelengths with the instructor.) Record the absorbance, *A*, in your table for each mixture at each chosen wavelength. Work rapidly and cover the cells to avoid evaporation and temperature changes. Some suggested wavelengths are:

Cl^-	SCN^-	Br^-	I^-
550	360	590	400
590	565	620	620
616	616	635	660
640	650	670	670
690		700	700
			775

Plot *A* observed versus L/Co ratios and draw the best straight lines through the points lying between the integral ratios. What complexes seem definitely present? Are others definitely absent? Estimate K_n values where possible by methods outlined in Chapter 20. Discuss the assumptions and difficulties involved. Consult

Fine's work [*J. Am. Chem. Soc.* **84,** 1139 (1962).] and also, for SCN^-, Brubaker and Johnson [*J. Am. Chem. Soc.* **80,** 5037 (1958)].

In the ammine systems one measures directly the free ligand concentration. Here, there is no easy determination of the concentration of any species in the K_n values. A rough approximation may be tried by assuming that only the stoichiometric complex absorbs at an integral ratio at a wavelength which gives a maximum in the plot of A versus ratio. Then the extrapolation method given in Chapter 20 for Job's method can be applied, if one further assumes that the K_n values decrease from 1 to n. This means that the stoichiometric complex is in equilibrium with only its lower dissociation complex species for calculation purposes.

Other systems. An interesting case is that of Ni(II) which accepts only one halide in water but forms three and four halo complexes in acetone. See D. A. Fine, *Inorganic Chem.* **4,** 345 (1965).

SUPPLEMENTARY LABORATORY DIRECTIONS

USE OF THE pH METER

This important instrument is frequently used in this course. A few introductory tests may be desirable to familiarize the student both with its operation and with some pH concepts. The nature of the instrument is discussed in Chapter 24.

1) Rinse the electrodes with a stream of water from the wash bottle. Remove any hanging drops with a light touch of absorbent paper. (Take care never to bump or scratch the glass electrode.) Open the vent of the reference electrode to attain atmospheric pressure and proper flow. Put a known reference buffer into a small beaker and immerse the electrodes in it. Follow the directions for the specific instrument to set the reading at the correct pH. (Table 7–2 lists some standard buffers.) Note the temperature. Rinse and recheck the pH, until the reading is constant.

2) Rinse the electrodes as above and use a different buffer. How close an agreement of the pH reading should be expected for the instrument? What are some of the factors involved? Repeat with other solutions as assigned.

3) Make a buffer by pipetting together equal volumes of 0.200 *M* acetic acid and sodium acetate. Rinse the electrodes and read the pH as before. Pipet 25.00 ml of this solution into a clean 250 ml volumetric flask and dilute to the mark with fresh distilled water. Mix it well and determine its pH. Make one or two more ten-fold dilutions. How do the pH readings agree with $-\log$ (activity H^+) calculated from K_a^0 and activity coefficients? Prepare a table of experimental and calculated pH values. (This exercise may be incorporated into Project 5, p. 317, where acetate buffers must be used for the bromcresol green study.)

4) *Water.* While doing the previous tests, set about 200 ml of distilled water to boil in a 250 ml conical flask. After a few minutes' boiling, cover it and set in cold water to cool.

Meanwhile, rinse the electrodes and read the pH of the laboratory stock of distilled water. Stir it and read again. Blow on it, stir, and read again. Replace this water with a little of the boiled, cooled water. (Use a clean thermometer to be sure it is at 25°, or the same temperature used for the other water.) Discard it and repeat with a fresh sample of this water. Blow on it, stir, and read as before. Explain your observations. Find the pH of tap water (not distilled). See if you can find out what chemical treatment is given the water supply and what its pH usually is when it is pumped from the water plant.

5) Dilute 25.0 ml of 0.200 *M* acetic acid to 250 ml with distilled water. Read its pH. Add 0.58 g NaCl to 100 ml of the 0.0200 *M* acid, dissolve, and read the pH. Explain. Repeat the NaCl addition to 100 ml of a 1:1 buffer which has been made 0.001 *M* in both acetic acid and sodium acetate. Read the pH before and after adding the NaCl. Explain.

6) Make and read the pH of 0.10 *M* and 0.010 *M* HCl. Explain why the readings are not 1.00 and 2.00. Repeat with 0.10 *M* and 0.010 *M* NaOH solutions. Do this last because the glass electrode may need some recovery time after the strong base exposure.

After using the pH meter, rinse the electrodes with 0.1 *M* HCl and leave them immersed in distilled water. Turn the instrument to stand-by or off as directed.

METHODS FOR ALKALI AND ALKALINE EARTHS

The colorful and interesting chemistry of the majority of metal ions should not blind one to the importance of the "simpler" ions of the Group I and II elements. Mg, Ca, and Na are among the most abundant elements of the earth's crust. Good analytical methods for separating and determining the members of these groups have had to await the development of new precipitants and solvents and EDTA, ion-exchange, and flame-photometry methods. Some of the problems and their solutions are presented here both for their practical importance and because they illustrate chemical structure reasoning.

In contrast with most other cations, alkali and alkaline earth ions form relatively weak complexes with anions in water solutions. The size and charge of ions here has a strong effect on crystal-lattice energy and solubility.* The rough generalization that high crystal energy (low solubility) is favored by small cations in compounds with small anions, and large with large, is of some analytical use. Table L–2 illustrates this. Often, high hydration energy, as with hydroxides, overcomes the lattice-energy factor so that regular trends are not found.

Separations of the Group I Ions

If we were limited to water solutions, only LiF and the perchlorates of K, Rb, and Cs would seem to offer hope for separation methods based on solubility. However, other solvents and solutes change the solubilities to allow some separations.

An interesting application of the common-ion effect is made to remove large amounts of Na^+ from solutions. HCl gas is passed in, which reduces the NaCl solubility to less than 0.1 *M* in concentrated HCl. Large amounts of K^+ can be removed by adding $HClO_4$. However, these methods are not quantitative separations. Other anions larger than ClO_4^- have been found which can precipitate K^+ (and Rb^+, Cs^+, NH_4^+ if present) from aqueous solution. Most im-

* See a good discussion by C. S. G. Phillips and R. J. P. Williams, *Inorganic Chemistry*, Vol. II. London: Oxford University Press, 1966, Chapter 20.

Table L–2. Molal Solubilities in Water at 25° (Increasing Anion Size Within Charge Type to the Right) (Moles/1000 g Water)

	OH^-	F^-	Cl^-	I^-	NO_3^-	ClO_4^-	$CO_3^=$	$SO_4^=$
Li	5.6	0.05	19	12	10	4.4	0.2	3
Na	27	1.0	6	12	11	9	2	4
K	21	17	5	9	3	0.15	8	0.6
Rb	19	12	8	7	4	0.07	10	1.8
Cs	25	24	11	3	1	0.09	8	5
Mg	3×10^{-4}	0.002	6	5	5	4	0.0001	3
Ca	0.018	0.0003	7	7	7	8	0.00006	0.008
Sr	0.086	0.0009	4	5	3	11	0.00004	0.0006
Ba	0.27	0.012	2	5	0.4	6	0.00004	0.00001

portant now is the tetraphenylborate ion whose Li and Na compounds are quite soluble. Others of historical interest are periodate, hexachloroplatinate(IV), hexanitrocobaltate(III) and dipicrylaminate ions. Some relevant molar solubilities of potassium compounds (at 25°) are:

$$KB(C_6H_5)_4 = 1.8 \times 10^{-4}, \qquad K_2NaCo(NO_2)_6 = 0.002,$$
$$K_2PtCl_6 = 0.01, \qquad KClO_4 = 0.15.$$

Organic solvents have been found to help in separations. LiCl is remarkably more soluble in alcohols than the other alkali chlorides. In the comparison below, solubility is given in g/100 ml solvent.

	H_2O	*n*-hexanol	2-ethylhexanol
LiCl	85	6	3
NaCl	36	0.0008	0.0001
KCl	35	0.00004	0.00001

A mixture of alkali metal ions can be evaporated with HCl and 2-ethylhexanol and heated to 135° to remove water and precipitate NaCl and KCl. Filtration removes the solution of LiCl which can be evaporated and weighed. Usually one adds H_2SO_4 to form the less deliquescent Li_2SO_4 for weighing.

Sodium can next be separated from the rest by the solubility of its perchlorate or tetraphenylborate. Nonaqueous solvents increase the separation factor as shown in Table L–3. For example, when a mixture of 200 mg each of $NaClO_4$ and $KClO_4$ is treated with 5 ml ethyl acetate all but 0.07 mg of the $KClO_4$ is left, while all the $NaClO_4$ dissolves. More solvent will be needed to wash the precipitate, but the loss can easily be held below 0.2 mg or 1 ppth. The $KClO_4$ can be dried and weighed, and $NaClO_4$ calculated by difference.

Potassium can better be separated and determined as the tetraphenylborate, the first truly quantitatively insoluble compound discovered for potassium. Only Rb^+, Cs^+, NH_4^+, Hg^{++}, and Ag^+ interfere. EDTA removes heavy metal ion

Table L–3. Solubility of Perchlorates in Several Solvents, g/100 ml Solvent

	H_2O	CH_3OH	C_2H_5OH	nC_4H_9OH	$C_2H_5OOCCH_3$
$LiClO_4$	47	89	79	49	63
$NaClO_4$	114	36	11	1.5	8.4
$KClO_4$	2.0	9	0.009	0.004	0.0013
$RbClO_4$	1.3	0.05	0.007	0.002	0.0014
NH_4ClO_4	22	5.3	1.5	0.014	0.029

interference, while the reaction between formaldehyde and NH_3 in basic solution removes NH_4^+ interference. (In rare cases when Rb or Cs are present, their chlorides can be dissolved away from KCl with ethanol saturated with HCl gas.) The flocculant white $KB(C_6H_5)_4$ is easily filtered on a fritted glass filter crucible, dried, and weighed. Several titrimetric finishes have been developed.

Other precipitants for Li, Na, and K have been sought with slight success. These are discussed by Kallman in *Treatise on Analytical Chemistry* (Part II, Vol. 1. New York: Interscience, 1961, pp. 301–447).

Procedures

A. Potassium content of silicate materials. This method is suitable for potassium determination of powdered samples of rock, clay, glass, cement, and soils. Classical methods involved either the attack of the silicate with HF or basic fusion with CaO. Both are difficult without practice. Molten NaOH (melting point, 318°C) more easily converts the silicates to soluble forms. The large excess of sodium does not interfere with the potassium determination.

Dry the finely ground sample at 110° for 1 hr. Weigh out 1 to 3 g samples (for 3 to 0.5% K) into large nickel crucibles holding 100 ml. Spread the powder around the bottom of the crucible and add 10 g solid NaOH (or 13 ml 50% NaOH) for each gram of sample. Cover and heat gently to drive off water and melt the NaOH. Use tongs to swirl the fluid gently from time to time while heating for 1 hr with a flame just high enough to keep it molten. Finally, heat more strongly for a minute and then allow to cool. Carry a 20 g NaOH blank through the procedure to determine its K content.

Wash down the cover and walls with water, adding about 50 ml. Warm to dissolve and transfer quantitatively to a 600 ml beaker. Calculate the volume of HCl needed to neutralize the NaOH. Dilute it with water and add it slowly to the beaker. Since a large amount of Na_2CO_3 was formed, there will be foaming. Add a drop of indicator and more acid if needed. Add 1 ml excess HCl and boil the solution down to 20 ml or less to coagulate the silica. Add about 30 ml water, heat, and filter hot through a large suction funnel through fast paper. The silica gel clogs paper badly so that gravity filtration is hopeless. Add three successive 30 ml portions of hot wash water before the cake hardens. Return the filtrate to a clean beaker and boil. If more silica forms, add a filter accelerator, boil, and refilter. Cool and dissolve in 20 ml water a weight of sodium tetraphenylborate equal to 12 times the expected weight of potassium. Add it to the solution of K, swirl and wait several minutes before filtering through a weighed sintered glass filter crucible. Wash with three 5 ml portions of cool water. Dry at 110° for 30 min and weigh. [$KB(C_6H_5)_4$ is 10.91 %K.] Subtract the blank.

Detailed discussion of tetraphenylborate methods including an interesting titrimetric finish with Hg(II)-EDTA is given by H. Flaschka and A. J. Barnard in *Advances in Analytical Chemistry and Instrumentation* (ed. by C. N. Reilley, Vol. I. New York: Interscience, 1960).

A coulometric titration of the excess tetraphenylborate ion with electrogenerated silver ion is described in a paper by G. J. Patriarche and J. L. Lingane [*Anal. Chem.* **39,** 168 (1967)]. Excellent results for quantities of K, Rb, and Cs on the order of 1 to 10 mg were obtained. The coulometric method is discussed in Chapter 24. A new value for the formal K_{sp} of $AgB(C_6H_5)_4$ at 25° in 0.4 *M* $NaNO_3$ is given as 8×10^{-14}. The student might read, in the section on experimental techniques in this paper, their sources of materials and standards for K, Rb, and Cs.

B. Lithium, sodium, and potassium. The sample should contain about 100 mg Li and Na, and 20 mg K. For larger amounts, aliquots can be taken before the appropriate steps. If the anions are known to be only carbonate or chloride, proceed with the lithium separation. Otherwise, pass the dissolved sample through a column of anion-exchange resin in the Cl^- form.

LITHIUM. Add 1 ml HCl to the sample and evaporate to dryness. Do not overheat. Moisten with a few drops of water, add 20 ml 2-ethylhexanol, and heat at 135° for several minutes after all steam has been evolved. Cool and filter through a dry, weighed sintered glass crucible. Wash with several small portions of 2-ethylhexanol which has just been boiled to dehydrate it. Cool it before use. Dry the crucible at 210° and weigh the NaCl + KCl. Reserve it for K.

Evaporate the filtrate and washings in a weighed dish or crucible. Cool the solid LiCl and add 10 drops H_2SO_4 and 1 drop HNO_3. Flame gently to decompose the organic matter and convert LiCl to Li_2SO_4. When it is dry, increase the flame to heat the container to dull redness for several minutes. Cool, and weigh the Li_2SO_4.

POTASSIUM. Wash the NaCl and KCl from the crucible with water. Make the volume about 100 ml and the HCl concentration about 0.1 *M* and proceed with the potassium determination by means of tetraphenylborate as described in Part A above. Calculate the Na content from the known total weight of NaCl and KCl obtained above.

Alkaline Earth Elements

Classical methods of separation and determination of Mg, Ca, Sr, and Ba were developed from the solubility differences of their carbonates, oxalates, sulfates, and chromates. All four together present a difficult problem. Nonaqueous solvent methods similar to those discussed for the alkali metals have been found for the chlorides and nitrates.

For barium (if Sr, Ca, and Pb are absent) the famous $BaSO_4$ precipitation can be used. It is a commonly used sulfate-determination method. It is also infamous as the subject of numerous studies of its pronounced ability to coprecipitate many other ions (Chapter 11).

Calcium can be separated from Mg^{++} by oxalate precipitation at pH 4. Chromate precipitation effects fair separations of Ba, Sr, and Ca ions at controlled pH values. At pH 4 to 5 only $BaCrO_4$ forms ($K_{sp} \sim 10^{-10}$). At pH as high as 8 or 9, however, $SrCrO_4$ ($K_{sp} \sim 10^{-5}$) is precipitated, and acetone is added to reduce its solubility.

A common problem in the study of minerals, water, and biological materials is the determination of Mg and Ca (Sr and Ba are quite rare). The gravimetric $CaC_2O_4{\cdot}H_2O$ (pH 4) and Mg 8-hydroxyquinolate (pH 9) precipitations can be used. However, complexometric titration methods are now available and preferred for speed. An example follows:

Procedure (determination of calcium and magnesium). Dry at 110° and weigh into a tall beaker about 0.8 g of a dolomite or a limestone or cave formation with high Mg content. Cover and warm with 10 ml 1 *M* HCl to dissolve. Boil to remove excess CO_2. Disregard any silica, but test for complete solution by adding 1 ml more HCl during heating, after the first effervescence has ceased. Cool, and dilute quantitatively to 250.0 ml in a volumetric flask.

A. Total Ca + Mg. Pipet 25.00 ml of the solution into a titration flask. Add an equal volume of water and about 100 mg ascorbic acid. Swirl for a minute and add 1 ml 6 *M* NaOH and about 50 mg KCN. Warm to 40 to 50° and wait for any precipitate to redissolve. Add 5 ml of pH 10 buffer (9 *M* NH_3 with 1.4 *M* NH_4Cl), 3 drops of indicator (calmagite or erio T), and titrate while warm with 0.22 *M* standard EDTA to a clear blue endpoint. Repeat to get 3 checks and calculate the sum of the number of mmoles of Ca + Mg present.

The ascorbic acid reduces Fe(III) to Fe(II), and the CN^- complexes Fe and other heavy metals which can block the indicator.

B. Ca alone. With fresh 25 ml aliquots, repeat the procedure used in Part A substituting 4 ml NaOH (no buffer) and calcon indicator. At this pH (12 to 13) $Mg(OH)_2$ precipitates and is not titrated. The endpoint should be approached slowly so that any $CaCO_3$ formed may redissolve and react. Ascorbic acid and KCN are used just as in Part A. Do checks and calculate the number of mmoles of Ca and Mg. Calculate the percentage of $CaCO_3$ and $MgCO_3$ in the original sample.

If desired, Fe can be determined on fresh aliquots by indirect EDTA titration at pH 1 to 2 as directed in the section on EDTA titrations. Mg and Ca do not interfere.

REFERENCES

DIEHL, H., *Calcein, Calmagite, and o,o′-Dihydroxyazobenzene Titrimetric, Colorimetric, and Fluorometric Reagents for Calcium and Magnesium*, Columbus, Ohio: G. Frederick Smith Chemical Co., 1964 is a detailed book, 124 pages, giving EDTA titrations of Ca and Mg.

FRITZ, J. S., and H. WAKI, *Anal. Chem.* **35,** 1079 (1963) report good anion-exchange resin separations of Ca and Mg with 0.5 *M* HNO_3 in 90% 2-propanol. Mg elutes first in about 3 column volumes, then Ca is washed through with aqueous 0.02 *M* HNO_3.

PAPER CHROMATOGRAPHY

Simple paper strip and circular paper methods are described here for student practice, since they are widely used in separations and identifications. Rough quantitative estimations can be obtained if one prepares a set of standard chromatograms with a series of known amounts of the substances in question. See the references in Chapter 22 for sources of descriptions of other methods. In this discussion, general techniques are given first followed by a discussion of solvents and color developers for the chromatography of amino acids and some metal ions.

A. General Methods

Ascending paper strip method. Cut off a piece of $\frac{1}{2}$ to 1 in. chromatography paper (Whatman No. 1 or a similar type) long enough to reach the bottom of a glass cylinder to be used as the chamber [Fig. L–3(a)]. A 100 to 500 ml cylinder will serve if the paper does not touch the sides. Keep the paper and all apparatus quite

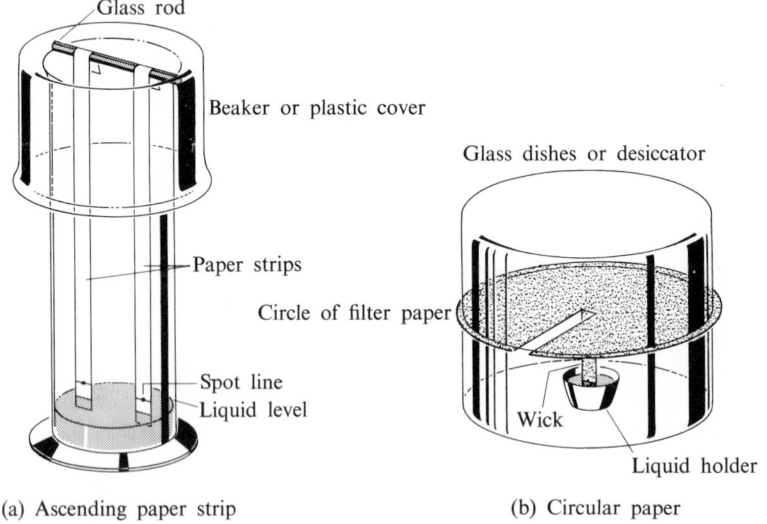

(a) Ascending paper strip (b) Circular paper

Figure L–3

clean. Fold one end so that the paper can hang from a glass rod across the top of the cylinder and reach within 5 mm of the bottom. Remove the paper and place solvent 1 to 2 cm deep in the cylinder. Cover it to allow vapor equilibrium to be attained. Meanwhile on a very clean surface, draw a light *pencil* line horizontally 2 cm from the bottom of the paper strip. With a lambda pipet, place 1 to 20 microliters, depending on concentration, of the solution to be tested along the line. (The pipet is filled and emptied by capillarity. Practice by letting water rise in it to the line and then touching it to paper to draw out the water.) Dry it 5 min in air or in a 50° oven.

Hang it in the chamber so that it dips only 2 to 10 mm into the solvent. Cover tightly and allow the solvent to rise from $\frac{1}{2}$ to 3 hr. Separation of 2 or 3 components of well-spaced R_f values may require only 10 to 20 cm rise while other mixtures may require 30 to 40 cm to effect visible separation. Plastic film and a rubber band will cover the cylinder tightly to maintain a saturated atmosphere. Several strips can be run at once if they do not touch each other.

When finished, remove the strip and immediately mark the top of the solvent front with a pencil before it evaporates. Hang it in a hood over a warm hotplate to dry, if the solvent interferes with the color tests to be used. Spray with a color reagent and a preservative as appropriate for the materials.

Horizontal paper circle method. Cut a wick 2 to 5 mm wide to the center of a paper circle which fits the chamber (a dry, empty desiccator or two Petri dishes). Fold the wick down so that it can dip into the solvent [Fig. L–3(b)]. Spot the sample at the center on the fold, and proceed as above until the solvent front approaches the edge of the chamber. Dry and spray. This method is faster and often gives sharper separations than the strip.

B. Separations and Identifications

1. Amino acids. Make an aqueous solution of 1 to 10 mg per ml of each amino acid. Spot 1 to 10 microliters of it on the paper. With unknowns, several trials with different amounts may be required to obtain good separations. Develop chromatograms with one or both solvents (in separate chambers). After drying, cut the strips vertically in half and spray each half with different color reagents. Using two solvents and two color tests in this way will distinguish a large number of amino acids. See Table L–4 for some values. More tables can be found in the sources listed in the references. Calculate the R_f value for each spot as the distance from the starting line to its center, divided by the distance from the starting line to the solvent front line. The circular paper gives sharper separations.

Solvent I, parts by volume	Solvent II, parts by volume
1 water, 4 phenol Warm to dissolve. (Danger: painful burns with skin contact.)	100 water, 100 *n*-butanol, and 12 acetic acid. Shake well in a separatory funnel. Use upper layer.

Table L–4. R_f Values ($\times$ 100) for Amino Acids

Compound	Solvent I	Solvent II	Reported color with	
			Ninhydrin	Isatin
α-alanine	60	39	purple	lavender
β-alanine	66	54	purple	none
α-amino *n*-butyric	71	62	purple	blue
arginine	89	19	purple	
asparagine	40	29	brown-yellow	
aspartic acid	19	33	blue	pink to blue
cystine	15	17	blue	blue
glutamic acid	31	37	purple	pink to blue
glycine	41	33	blue-pink	
hydroxyproline	63	41	brown-yellow	blue (weak)
isoleucine	84	68	purple	
leucine	84	72	purple	
lysine	81	18	purple	
methionine	81	57	purple	
phenylalanine	85	66	grey-brown	
proline	88	53	yellow	blue
serine	36	31	brown-red	brown
tryptophan	75	61	yellow-brown	
valine	78	56	purple	

It should be repeated that these values are a guide. Temperature, solvent composition, paper thickness, etc., all contribute to variations in observed R_f values. The table helps choose likely conditions and aids preliminary identifications. Known amino acids must be tested to verify the behavior of the suspected unknown under the conditions used. Compiled from the sources listed in the references for Chapter 22, especially R. Block, E. Durrum, and G. Zweig, *Paper Chromatography and Paper Electrophoresis*, 2nd ed. New York: Academic Press, 1958, Chapter V.

Color reagents. *Ninhydrin*, 0.25%, weight/volume in acetone. Spray in a hood, or dip quickly, and dry. Color develops overnight or in $\frac{1}{2}$ to 1 hr at 50°. It appears as purple, blue, or brown spots.

Isatin, 0.2% in acetone. Treat the paper as with ninhydrin. Most amino acids give pink spots which fade. Colors depend somewhat on conditions and amounts. It is best to make a spot test with a known on the same paper being used.

2. Metal ions. a) *Iron-Cobalt-Nickel.* About 10 mg per ml of Fe(III), Co(II), and Ni(II) in dilute HCl can be used. Spot 1 to 10 microliters and develop with solvent made with 8.3 parts 6 *M* HCl, 87 parts acetone, and water to make 100 volumes. The R_f values are: Fe = 1, Co = 0.3, Ni = 0. These are so widely separated that a drop of appropriate reagent can be applied where each is expected, without danger of overlap. Try saturated NH_4SCN in acetone for Fe (red) and Co (blue) and alcoholic dimethylglyoxime for Ni (red—may need exposure to NH_3 vapor). This simple method takes as little as 10 min since a 10 cm rise suffices. It is of value in qualitative analysis where test-tube separations of these ions is tedious.

b) *Al, Bi, Cd, Co, Cu, Fe, Hg, Ni, Zn.* The solution should contain 10 to 100 mg of each per milliliter in 2 *M* HCl. Spot 1 to 10 microliters and develop with solvent made of 4 parts *n*-butanol and 1 part 12 *M* HCl, by volume. Dry the paper and spray with 1% 8-hydroxyquinoline in 70% ethanol. Expose to the vapor over concentrated NH_3 and dry. All give yellow, except Fe(III) black, in daylight. Long-wavelength ultraviolet (3700 Å) light, however, serves well to discriminate between adjacent ions like Al-Ni and Cd-Hg. The colors and R_f values follow:*

Ion	Al(III)	Ni(II)	Co(II)	Cu(II)	Bi(III)	Zn(II)	Cd(II)	Hg(II)	Fe(III)
$R_f \times 100$	3	4	19	40	51	78	83	84	93
Color, ultraviolet	yellow	red	red	red	red	yellow	yellow	red	purple

HEAT, FREE ENERGY, AND ENTROPY CHANGES IN AQUEOUS NEUTRALIZATIONS

This experiment illustrates some uses of the thermal data which is easily obtained from the temperature change upon reaction in solution. Several acids and bases will be mixed to determine the calories per mole evolved in neutralization, ΔH. From the acid K_a^0 values—available from a titration curve if required—one can find the ΔG^0 for acid dissociation reactions:

$$\Delta G^0 = -RT \ln K_a^0.$$

Hence, one can get the entropy change, approximately,

$$\Delta G^0 = \Delta H^0 - T\,\Delta S^0.$$

(The ΔH obtained by experiment will not be exactly the ΔH^0 for all ions and water at unit activity.) These relations and this experiment are discussed in Chapter 26.

Materials. A thermometer which can be estimated to 0.02° or less, and with a range from about 18 to 32°C is required.

Use a well-insulated reaction vessel such as a Dewar flask. Plastic foam hot-drink cups are excellent, as they have very low density (7 oz or smaller size). A tall-form 250 ml beaker wrapped in paper has rather high heat capacity, but can be used.

Solutions of 1.00_0 *M* HCl and NaOH (low carbonate) are needed. Make about 250 ml of each, slightly high in molarity. Standardize with a known solu-

* Values from W. Reeves and T. Crumpler, *Anal. Chem.* **23,** 1576 (1951).

tion and add to 200.0 ml, the volume of water calculated to make each one 1.00_0 *M*. (Within 5 ppth is satisfactory here.)

Approximately 1.02 *M* NH_3, which is just slightly more concentrated than the HCl, is required.

Make 1.00_0 *M* $NaHCO_3$ and NH_4Cl by weighing dry, reagent-grade solids to give 100 ml of each.

Experimental procedure. As soon as possible, place all five solutions in a water bath which is about 2° below room temperature. Shake them often to bring them to the same temperature (about $\frac{1}{2}$ hr). While waiting, you might make a practice reaction.

Arrange to suspend the thermometer in the vessel to touch the bottom. Do the following as rapidly as possible:

Rinse a large test tube with the acid solution and drain it 5 sec only. Pipet into it 25.00 ml of the acid and clamp it in the water bath. Put the thermometer into it. Pipet 25.00 ml of base solution into the vessel. Read the acid temperature as precisely as possible. Drain any acid from the thermometer bulb. Wipe it and put it into the base in the vessel. Read and record its temperature. Pour the acid from the test tube (wrap in a towel) into the vessel and drain 5 sec. Immediately move and read the thermometer every 5 sec until a constant temperature is reached or a falling temperature curve it established. Repeat until ΔT agrees within 0.1°. Do the other three pairs, so that data are available for:

$HCl + NaOH$, $HCl + NH_3$, $NH_4Cl + NaOH$, $NaHCO_3 + NaOH$.

Calculations. Average the initial temperatures of acid and base. Subtract it from the maximum temperature observed. (Extrapolate to zero time if a falling curve was observed in some cases.) The specific heat in the table tells the calories which raise 1 g of the *product* solution one degree. Thus the calories absorbed by the solution must be:

$$\text{calories} = (\text{specific heat cal/g-deg})(\Delta T\ \text{deg})(50.0\ \text{ml})(d\ \text{g/ml}).$$

From the specific heats and densities in the table, calculate the calories for each reaction. A slight correction should be added for the heat absorbed by the vessel and thermometer. Estimate the weight of plastic or glass in contact with the solution. (Specific heat of plastic = 0.3 cal/g-deg, of glass = 0.2 cal/g-deg.)

TABLE OF DATA NEEDED

0.500 *M* final solutions	NaCl	NH_4Cl	$NH_3 + NaCl$	Na_2CO_3
Specific heat, cal/g-deg	0.96	0.97	1.00 (estimated)	0.94
Density, g/ml	1.01	0.97	1.00	1.05

With the plastic cups, only about 3 ppth of the heat goes into the vessel. Speed helps to reduce the unknown amount of heat lost to the surroundings. Calculate ΔH per mole. (You used $\frac{1}{40}$ mole in each case.) Calculate ΔG^0 and ΔS^0 as shown in Chapter 26. Find data for comparison in thermodynamic tables.

Check for internal consistency (first law) by seeing if the sum of the two reactions involving NH_3 (which is $H^+ + OH^- \rightarrow H_2O$) does give the heat observed with HCl and NaOH. Explain why this should be so.

SUGGESTIONS FOR ADDITIONAL EXPERIMENTS

Find the heats of neutralization of other weak acids with NaOH (acetic, formic, and bisulfate ion) and interpret their free energy and entropy changes.

TITRATIONS IN NONAQUEOUS SOLVENTS

Two broadly useful methods are discussed here. The ideas involved and references to other methods and works on the subject are included in Chapter 25. A valuable laboratory manual is, *Acid-Base Titrations in Nonaqueous Solvents*, by James S. Fritz, published by the G. F. Smith Chemical Co., Columbus, Ohio, in 1952.

Glacial Acetic Acid

Glacial acetic acid is useful for weak bases or materials convertible to bases (such as sodium acetate, amines, amino acids, and ionic halides by means of the mercuric acetate method).

Reagents. To prepare 0.1 *M* $HClO_4$, use 4.3 ml 12 *M* $HClO_4$, 400 ml acetic acid, and 10 ml acetic anhydride diluted to about 500 ml with acetic acid. Allow one day for the anhydride to react with the water added in the $HClO_4$.

To prepare 0.1 *M* $NaC_2H_3O_2$, use 4.1 g anhydrous sodium acetate or 2.650 g anhydrous Na_2CO_3 for 500 ml. If Na_2CO_3 is used, dry at 130°, weigh to 4 figures, and add it in small portions to part of the HA. Make up to 500.0 ml with glacial acetic acid.

For indicator, use 100 mg methyl violet in 50 ml chlorobenzene.

Standardizations. Dry at 110° and weigh to 4 figures, 0.5 g portions of potassium acid phthalate. Dissolve each in about 50 ml of pure acetic acid by heating. Cool, add 3 drops indicator, and titrate with the 0.1 *M* $HClO_4$ to the disappearance of the last violet tinge. (Carry all subsequent titrations to this same color.) Repeat with 25.00 ml portions of the 0.1 *M* $NaC_2H_3O_2$. Calculate the molarity of the acid and the base stock solutions.

(Any of the following titrations can be scaled down to smaller burets as may be required for the availability of the samples.)

Determinations. For *amines* (anilines, *p*-toluidine, quinoline, etc.) and alkali or alkaline earth *salts of carboxylic acids*, weigh out 2 to 4 meq of sample and dissolve it in 50 ml HA. (Benzene or chlorobenzene are recommended for the amines to get sharper endpoints.) Titrate with 0.1 *M* $HClO_4$ to the same color used in the standardization with methyl violet.

For *amino acids*, weigh out about 3 meq (usually 100 to 200 mg). Pipet into it 50.00 ml of the standard 0.1 *M* $HClO_4$. Dissolve and back titrate with standard $NaC_2H_3O_2$ solution to the appearance of the violet tinge of methyl violet.

For *ionic chlorides or halides* (for example, amine hydrochlorides, quaternary ammonium halides, thiamine hydrochloride), weigh 0.5 to 3 meq of sample (use an appropriate size buret for small samples.) Dissolve in 50 ml hot HA. Cool, add 10 ml 6% mercuric acetate in HA and titrate with standard 0.1 *M* $HClO_4$ to the methyl violet endpoint as above. Pure NaCl can be used to practice the method with a known.

Dimethylformamide

Dimethylformamide is useful for acidic materials like carboxylic acids, enols, imides, phenols, sulfonamides.

Reagents. To prepare 0.1 *M* base, dilute 30 ml of 10% tetrabutylammonium hydroxide in methanol (available commerically) to 100 ml with benzene. If the solid is used, dissolve it in 10 ml methanol and 90 ml benzene.

To prepare 0.04 *M* benzoic acid standard, dry at 100° and weigh to 4 figures 500 mg pure benzoic acid. Make it up to 100.0 ml with dimethylformamide.

For azo violet indicator, use saturated *p*-nitrobenzeneazoresorcinol in benzene.

Determinations. (If possible, connect the base stock with glass-to-glass connections through vinyl tubing to a two-way stopcock buret, 5 or 10 ml size. Pump the solution into the buret with air passed through ascarite to remove water and CO_2. This also reduces evaporation changes.)

Weigh samples or take aliquots containing 0.3 to 0.9 meq in DMF. Add 2 drops azo violet indicator. Titrate with the base until the red color has changed completely to blue-violet. Standardize the base with the benzoic acid (10.00 ml for a 5 ml buret, 20.00 ml for a 10 ml buret). Estimate buret readings to ± 0.001 ml.

SUGGESTIONS FOR ADDITIONAL PROJECTS

A few recent articles from the *Journal of Chemical Education* are listed which give or suggest projects on equilibrium and reactions of interest in the quantitative chemistry course.

K_a of Iodic Acid and K_{sp} of $Cu(IO_3)_2$. R. W. Ramette, **36,** 191 (1959).

K_a of HSO_4^- and K_{sp} of $PbSO_4$. R. W. Ramette, **33,** 610 (1956).

Dissolved Silver Acetate Species. R. W. Ramette, **43,** 299 (1966).

Multiple Equilibria, $PbCl_2$ Precipitation and Complex Ions. G. M. Fleck, **42,** 106 (1965).

Stoichiometry of Redox Reactions. H. R. Tietze, **40,** 344 (1963).

Periodate Cleavage of Glycols. G. Schenk, **39,** 33 (1962).

As-I_2 Redox Reactions: Rates and Equilibrium. D. Britton and Z. Hugus, **40,** 607 (1963).

Fractional Distillation. R. D. Campbell, **39,** 348 (1962).

Determination of Column Efficiency by Gas Chromatography. A. Ault, **41,** 432 (1964).

Quantitative Paper Chromatography of Co, Cu, Ni, and Zn. W. Frierson, *et al.*, **40,** 409 (1963).

Test Tube and Glass Rod TLC. R. Ikan and E. Rapaport, **44,** 297 (1967). Thin layers of silica gel on rods are easily prepared for chromatography of amino acids and carbohydrates.

Indicators. C. B. Leonard, Jr., **44,** 363 (1967). A quantitative determination of a countercurrent distribution curve of two indicators, with light absorbance measurements.

Equilibrium Constant of $FeSCN^{++}$. R. W. Ramette, **40,** 71 (1963).

Composition and Reactions of Solid Metal-Ammine Salts. G. P. H. Haight, **42,** 468 (1965).

Formation Constants of a Metal-Ammine System. D. E. Goldberg, **39,** 328 (1962).

Formation Constants of a Metal-Anionic Ligand System. D. E. Goldberg, **40,** 344 (1963).

GENERAL REFERENCES

Theories of equilibrium and chemical measurements

Butler, J. N., *Ionic Equilibrium*, Reading, Mass.: Addison-Wesley, 1964. Tables A–1, A–5, A–6, A–7, and A–8 are substantially taken from this text.

Fleck, G. M., *Equilibria in Solution*, New York: Holt, Rinehart and Winston, 1966.

Freiser, H., and Q. Fernando, *Ionic Equilibria in Analytical Chemistry*, New York: John Wiley, 1963.

Laitinen, H. A., *Chemical Analysis*, New York: McGraw-Hill, 1960.

Walton, H. F., *Principles and Methods of Chemical Analysis*, 2nd ed. Englewood Cliffs, N. J.: Prentice-Hall, 1964.

Laboratory methods

Kolthoff, I. M., and V. A. Stenger, *Volumetric Analysis*, Vol. II, New York: Interscience, 1947. Acid-base methods.

Kolthoff, I. M., and R. Belcher, *Volumetric Analysis*, Vol. III, New York: Interscience, 1957. Redox methods.

Vogel, A. I., *Practical Organic Chemistry*, New York: Longmans, Green and Co., 1958.

Vogel, A. I., *A Textbook of Quantitative Inorganic Analysis and Elementary Instrumental Analysis*, 3rd ed. New York: John Wiley, 1961.

Compilations of data

Seidell, A., *Seidell's Solubilities of Inorganic and Metal-Organic Compounds*, 4th ed, 2 vols, ed. by W. Linke. Washington: American Chemical Society, 1958, 1965. Actual tables of solubilities are given rather than equilibrium constants.

Sillén, L. G., and A. E. Martell, *Stability Constants of Metal-Ion Complexes*, Special Publication No. 17, The Chemical Society, London, 1964. (A second edition of Nos. 6 and 7.) This is a clear, complete, and systematic list of published results for acidity, solubility, and electrode-potential equilibrium constants.

APPENDIX

Table A–1. Selected Electrode Potentials

Half-reaction	Electrode potential, volts
$Li^+ + e^- \rightleftharpoons Li(s)$	—3.045
$Na^+ + e^- \rightleftharpoons Na(s)$	—2.714
$Zn^{++} + 2e^- \rightleftharpoons Zn(s)$	—0.763
$Fe^{++} + 2e^- \rightleftharpoons Fe(s)$	—0.440
$Cr^{+++} + e^- \rightleftharpoons Cr^{++}$	—0.41
$2H^+ + 2e^- \rightleftharpoons H_2(g)$	0.000
$S(s) + 2H^+ + 2e^- \rightleftharpoons H_2S(g)$	+0.141
$Cu^{++} + e^- \rightleftharpoons Cu^+$	+0.153
$AgCl(s) + e^- \rightleftharpoons Ag(s) + Cl^-$	+0.222
$Cu^{++} + 2e^- \rightleftharpoons Cu(s)$	+0.337
$I_2(s) + 2e^- \rightleftharpoons 2I^-$	+0.5355
$MnO_4^- + e^- \rightleftharpoons MnO_4^=$	+0.564
$O_2(g) + 2H^+ + 2e^- \rightleftharpoons H_2O_2$	+0.682
$Fe^{+++} + e^- \rightleftharpoons Fe^{++}$	+0.771
$Hg_2^{++} + 2e^- \rightleftharpoons 2Hg(l)$	+0.789
$Ag^+ + e^- \rightleftharpoons Ag(s)$	+0.7991
$Hg^{++} + e^- \rightleftharpoons \frac{1}{2}Hg_2^{++}$	+0.920
$Br_2(l) + 2e \rightleftharpoons 2Br^-$	+1.0652
$MnO_2(s) + 4H^+ + 2e^- \rightleftharpoons Mn^{++} + 2H_2O$	+1.23
$Cr_2O_7^= + 14H^+ + 6e^- \rightleftharpoons 2Cr^{+++} + 7H_2O$	+1.33
$Cl_2(g) + 2e^- \rightleftharpoons 2Cl^-$	+1.3595
$Mn^{+++} + e^- \rightleftharpoons Mn^{++}$	+1.51
$MnO_4^- + 8H^+ + 5e^- \rightleftharpoons Mn^{++} + 4H_2O$	+1.51
$H_2O_2 + 2H^+ + 2e^- \rightleftharpoons 2H_2O$	+1.77
$F_2(g) + 2e^- \rightleftharpoons 2F^-$	+2.65

* Data from Latimer's *Oxidation Potentials.* Because the reactions in this table are written as reductions, in accordance with the IUPAC convention, the signs of the electrode potentials are opposite from the signs of the oxidation potentials given in Latimer's tables.

Table A–2. Some Useful Formal Potentials (Observed Potentials at Unit Concentrations)

Half-reaction	($\mathcal{E}^0$)	$\mathcal{E}$ in 1 *M* HCl	H_2SO_4	1 *M* $HClO_4$
$Fe(III) + e^- \rightarrow Fe(II)$	0.771	0.70	0.68 (0.1 to 4 *M*)	0.74
$Cr_2O_7^= + 14H^+ + 6e^- \rightarrow 2Cr(III) + 7H_2O$	1.33	1.00	1.08 (0.5 *M*)	1.025
$Ce(IV) + e^- \rightarrow Ce(III)$ ($\mathcal{E}$ = 1.61 in 1 *M* HNO_3)	1.7	1.28	1.44 (0.5 to 2 *M*)	1.70

Some approximately known values: $Sn(IV) + 2e^- \rightarrow Sn(II)$, $\mathcal{E} = 0.15$,
$Pb(IV) + 2e^- \rightarrow Pb(II)$, $\mathcal{E} = 1.7$,
$PbO_2 + 4H^+ + 2e^- \rightarrow Pb(II) + 2H_2O$, $\mathcal{E} = 1.46$.

Table A–3. Acidity Constants,* pK_a^0 at 25°C (see note on facing page)

Monoprotic acids	pK_a^0	Monoprotic acids	pK_a^0
$HB(OH)_4$ (boric, below 0.025 *M* only)	9.24	Formic	3.75
HCN	9.21	Acetic	4.756
HN_3	4.7	Chloroacetic	2.86
HNO_2	3.3	Bromoacetic	2.86
HSO_4^-	1.99	Dichloroacetic	1.3
HF	3.17	Trichloroacetic	0.7
HIO_3	0.78	Propionic	4.874
NH_4^+	9.24	*n*-butyric	4.820
$CH_3NH_3^+$	10.7	Lactic	3.858
$(CH_3)_2NH_2^+$	10.9	Pyruvic	2.49
$(CH_3)_3NH^+$	9.9 (at 15°)	Benzoic	5.80
$C_2H_5NH_3^+$	10.67		

Polyprotic acids	pK_1	pK_2	pK_3	pK_4
Carbonic, H_2CO_3	6.35	10.33		
Hydrosulfuric, H_2S	7.0	12.9		
Oxalic, $H_2C_2O_4$	1.25	4.28		
Tartaric, $(HOOC)_2(CHOH)_2$	3.036	4.366		
Phthalic, $(HOOC)_2C_6H_4$	2.950	5.408		
Ethylenediammonium, $C_2H_4(NH_3^+)_2$	7.0	9.96		
Phosphoric, H_3PO_4	2.15	7.21	12.32	
Citric, $(HOOC)_3C_3H_4OH$	3.13	4.76	6.40	16
EDTA, $(HOOCCH_2)_4C_2H_4N_2$	2.07	2.75	6.24	10.34 (I = 0.1 at 20°)
EDTA, $(HOOCCH_2)_4C_2H_4N_2$	1.95	2.62	6.00	10.08 (I = 0.2 at 20°)
Glycine (H^+)	2.35	9.78		
Alanine (H^+)	2.34	9.87		
Aspartic (H^+)	1.91	3.63	9.47	
Lysine ($2H^+$) (at I = 0.01)	2.18	9.18	10.72	

Table A–4. Acidity Constants for Some Metal Ions in Water*

Ion	pK_a	Ion	pK_a
Ag^{+}	12	Al^{3+}	4.9
Mg^{++}	11.4	Cr^{3+}	3.9
Ca^{++}	12.6	Fe^{3+}	2.2
Ba^{++}	13.2	$CrCl_2(H_2O)_4{}^{+}$	5.7
Fe^{++}	8.3	$Cr(NH_3)_4(H_2O)_2{}^{3+}$	5.5
Ni^{++}	10.6	$Co(NH_3)_4(H_2O)_2{}^{3+}$	5.2
Cu^{++}	8.0	$Co(NH_3)_6{}^{3+}$	>14
Zn^{++}	9.7	$Co(en)_3{}^{3+}$	>14
Cd^{++}	9.0	$Pt(en)_3{}^{4+}$	5.5
Hg^{++}	3.7	$Os(en)_3{}^{4+}$	strong acid
Pb^{++}	7.8		

* Water to fill the coordination sphere is assumed. These are the pK_1 values for the formation of one H_3O^+.

From F. Basolo and R. Pearson, *Mechanisms of Inorganic Reactions*, New York: John Wiley, 1958, pp. 387–388. See also p. 32, Second Edition, 1967.

Note to Table A–3:

* Negative logarithms of thermodynamic acidity constants (zero ionic strength extrapolation or estimation, except where another I value is noted). Water activity is *one*. Selected from *Stability Constants*, Special Publication No. 17 of the Chemical Society, London, 1964, compiled by Lars Gunnar Sillén and Arthur E. Martell. In some cases, chemical stability and other experimental difficulties limit the precision available. Bases are tabulated as acidity constants for the protonated form, i.e., the K_1 and K_2 for the acid $C_2H_4(NH_3{}^+)_2$ rather than K_b's for ethylenediamine.

The following may be treated as strong acids in water solution below ~1 M: HCl, HBr, HI, HNO_3, $HClO_4$, $HClO_3$, $HBrO_3$, H_2SO_4 ($1H^+$), HSCN, H_2SeO_4, ($1H^+$). (But not $HIO_4 = H_5IO_6$ in water.) HIO_3 is in Table A–3.

Table A–5. Stepwise Formation Constants for Mononuclear Complexes

Ligand	Central ion	Logarithm of equilibrium constant						Medium and ionic strength
		K_1	K_2	K_3	K_4	K_5	K_6	
Cl^-	Ag^+	2.85	1.87	0.32	0.86			0.2*M* $NaClO_4$
	Cd^{++}	1.32	0.90	0.09	−0.45			4.5*M* $NaClO_4$
	Hg^{++}	6.74	6.48	0.85	1.00			0.5*M* $NaClO_4$
	Pb^{++}	0.88	0.61	−0.40	−0.15			1.0*M* KCl
	In^{+++}	1.42	0.81	1.00	−0.2			1.0*M* $NaClO_4$
	Fe^{+++}	0.62	0.11	−1.40	−1.92			1.0*M* $NaClO_4$
	Fe^{++}	0.36	0.04					2.0*M* $NaClO_4$
Br^-	Ag^+	4.15	2.96	0.84	0.94			0.1*M* $NaClO_4$
	Cd^{++}	1.56	0.46	0.23	0.41			1.0*M* $NaClO_4$
	Hg^{++}	9.05	8.28	2.41	1.26			0.5*M* $NaClO_4$
I^-	Cd^{++}	2.08	0.87	2.09	1.59			4.5*M* $NaClO_4$
	Hg^{++}	12.87	10.95	3.78	2.23			0.5*M* $NaClO_4$
CN^-	Cd^{++}	5.48	5.14	4.56	3.58			3.0*M* $NaClO_4$
	Hg^{++}	18.00	16.70	3.83	2.98			0.1*M* $NaNO_3$
SCN^-	Ag^+	4.59	3.70	1.77	1.20			4.0*M* $NaClO_4$
	Ni^{++}	1.18	0.46	0.17				1.0*M* $NaClO_4$
	Cr^{+++}	3.1	1.7	1.0	0.3	−0.7	−1.6	0 corr (50°C)†
	Fe^{+++}	1.96	2.02	−0.41	−0.14	−1.57	−1.51	1.8*M* KNO_3. Values vary widely with medium.
$S_2O_3^{=}$	Ag^+	8.82	4.64	0.69				0 corr (20°C)

Table A–6. Stepwise Formation Constants of Metal Ammine Complexes

Central ion	Log of equilibrium constant*					
	K_1	K_2	K_3	K_4	K_5	K_6
Ag^+	3.20	3.83				
Hg^{++}	8.8	8.7	1.00	0.78		
Zn^{++}	2.37	2.44	2.50	2.15		
Mg^{++}	0.23	−0.15	−0.42	−0.7	−0.95	−1.3
Cd^{++}	2.65	2.10	1.44	0.93	−0.32	−1.66
Cu^{++}	4.15	3.50	2.89	2.13	−0.5	−2.5
Ni^{++}	2.80	2.24	1.73	1.19	0.75	0.03
Co^{++}	2.11	1.63	1.05	0.76	0.18	−0.62
Co^{+++}	7.3	6.7	6.1	5.6	5.05	4.41

* Mg^{++} and Hg^{++} data measured at 23°C in 2 molar NH_4NO_3. All other data measured at 30°C in 2 molar NH_4NO_3. The basic ionization constant of ammonia is:

pK_b	Temperature °C	Ionic medium
4.75	25	0 corr
4.39	23	$2M$ NH_4NO_3
4.67	30	$2M$ NH_4NO_3

These data were taken from J. Bjerrum, *Metal Ammine Formation in Aqueous Solution.* Copenhagen: P. Haase and Son, 1941.

Table A–7. Solubility Products at 25°C

Ions of equal charge		Ions of unequal charge	
Salt	pK_{s0}*	Salt	pK_{s0}*
TlCl	3.72	Ag_2SO_4	4.80
$AgBrO_3$	4.28	$Ag_2C_2O_4$	11.30
Hg_2SO_4†	6.17	BaF_2	5.76
$SrSO_4$	6.55	$Cu(IO_3)_2$	7.13
$AgIO_3$	7.52	MgF_2	8.18
$PbSO_4$	7.80	SrF_2	8.54
AgCl	9.75	CaF_2	10.40
$BaSO_4$	9.96	$Mg(OH)_2$	10.74
AgSCN	12.00	$Pb(IO_3)_2$	12.59
AgBr	12.28	Hg_2Cl_2†	17.88
AgI	16.08	$Ce(IO_3)_3$	9.50
		$La(IO_3)_3$	11.21

* K_{s0} has been extrapolated to zero ionic strength.

† Hg_2^{++} is a single ion.

Table A–8. Alignment Chart for Calculating Activity Coefficients

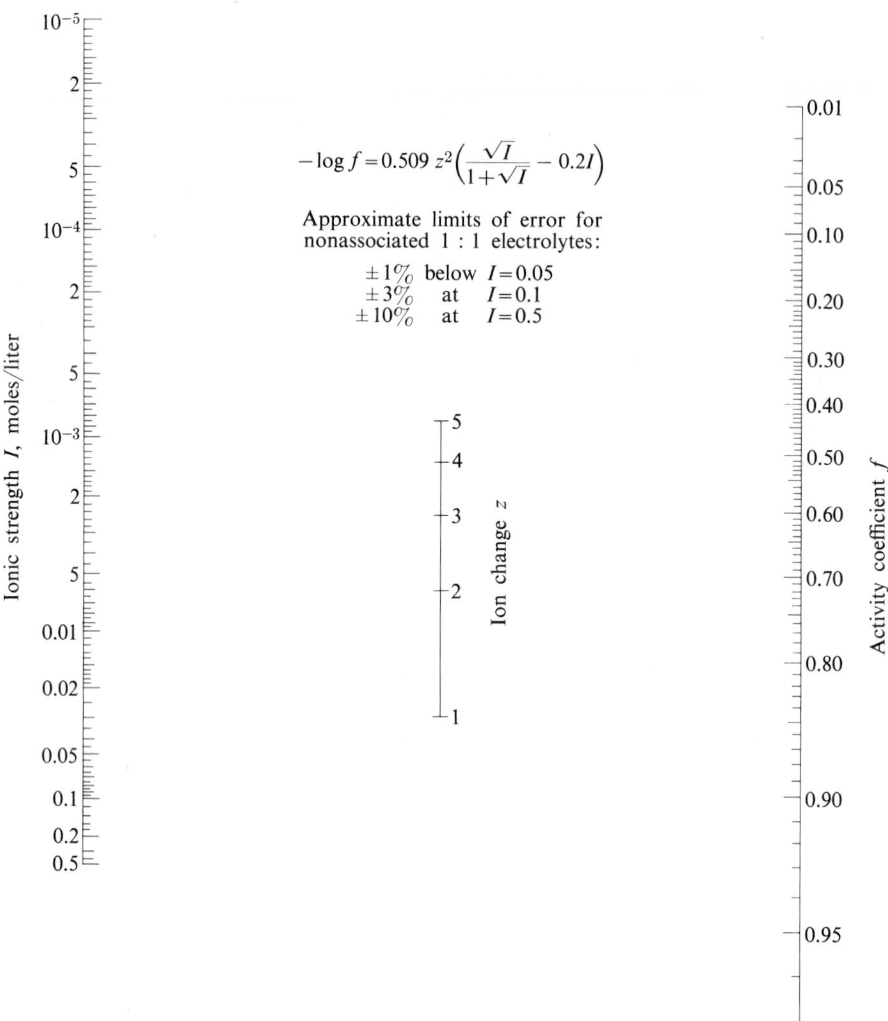

Table A–9. Kielland Table of Ionic Activity Coefficients Arranged by the Sizes of Ions

Charge	Size* *a*	Ions	I = 0.0005	0.001	0.0025	0.005	0.01	0.025	0.05	0.1
1	2.5	Rb^+, Cs^+, Ag^+, NH_4^+, Tl^+	0.975	0.964	0.945	0.924	0.898	0.85	0.80	0.75
	3	K^+, Cl^-, Br^-, I^-, CN^-, NO_3^-, NO_2^-, OH^-, F^-, ClO_4^-	0.975	0.964	0.945	0.925	0.899	0.85	0.805	0.755
	4	Na^+, IO_3^-, HCO_3^-, HSO_3^-, $H_2PO_4^-$, ClO_2^-, $C_2H_3O_2^-$	0.975	0.964	0.947	0.928	0.902	0.86	0.82	0.775
	6	Li^+, $C_6H_5COO^-$	0.975	0.965	0.948	0.929	0.907	0.87	0.835	0.80
	9	H^+	0.975	0.967	0.950	0.933	0.914	0.88	0.86	0.83
2	4.5	Pb^{++}, Hg_2^{++}, $SO_4^=$, $CrO_4^=$, $CO_3^=$, $SO_3^=$, $C_2O_4^=$, $S_2O_3^=$, H citrate$^=$	0.903	0.867	0.805	0.742	0.665	0.55	0.455	0.37
	5	Sr^{++}, Ba^{++}, Cd^{++}, Hg^{++}, $S^=$, $WO_4^=$	0.903	0.868	0.805	0.744	0.67	0.555	0.465	0.38
	6	Ca^{++}, Cu^{++}, Zn^{++}, Sn^{++}, Mn^{++}, Fe^{++}, Ni^{++}, Co^{++}, Phthalate$^=$	0.905	0.870	0.809	0.749	0.675	0.57	0.485	0.405
	8	Mg^{++}, Be^{++}	0.906	0.872	0.813	0.755	0.69	0.595	0.52	0.45
3	4	PO_4^{3-}, $Fe(CN)_6^{3-}$, $Cr(NH_3)_6^{3+}$	0.796	0.725	0.612	0.505	0.395	0.25	0.16	0.095
	9	Al^{3+}, Fe^{3+}, Cr^{3+}, Sc^{3+}, In^{3+}, and rare earths	0.802	0.738	0.632	0.54	0.445	0.325	0.245	0.18

* Note that these sizes are rounded values for the *effective* size in water solution and are not the size of the simple ions, unhydrated. For a more detailed discussion see the original paper from which these values are taken [J. Kielland, *J. Am. Chem. Soc.* **59,** 1675 (1937)]. Calculated from

$$\log f = \frac{-0.509\, z^2 \sqrt{I}}{1 + 0.328\, a\sqrt{I}}$$

at 25°C, where a is the effective diameter in angstroms. Note I is not M for 2 and 3 charge ions.

Table A–10. Physical constants, numerical factors, and conversions.

Atmosphere, standard (760 torr)*	1,013,250 dynes/cm^2
Avogadro number, N	6.0225×10^{23} $mole^{-1}$
Boltzmann constant, R/N	1.38054×10^{-16} erg/deg
Faraday constant, $\mathfrak{F}$	96,487 coul/equivalent
	23,061 cal/volt-equivalent
Gas law constant, R	0.082054 liter-atm/mole-deg
	1.9872 cal/mole-deg
	8.3143 joules/mole-deg
Light velocity, c	2.99793×10^{10} cm/sec
Planck constant, h	6.6256×10^{-27} erg-sec

ln ( ) = 2.3026 log ( )
R ln ( ) = 4.5758 log ( ) cal/mole-deg
298.15 R ln ( ) = 1364.3 log ( ) cal/mole
298.15 $R/\mathfrak{F}$ ln ( ) = 0.05916 log ( ) volt-equiv/mole
1 eV/molecule = 23,061 cal/mole

*A defined constant

NOTATION FOR EQUILIBRIUM

In this book, the notation used for equilibria in general follows that used in *Stability Constants of Metal-Ion Complexes* by Sillén and Martell (Special Publication No. 17, The Chemical Society, London, 1964), in J. N. Butler's *Ionic Equilibrium* (Reading, Mass.: Addison-Wesley, 1964), and in A. Ringbom's *Complexation in Analytical Chemistry* (New York: Interscience, 1963). Some of the ways in which this usage differs from that found in earlier American literature are mentioned here.

Equilibrium constants. The stepwise formation constants of metal complexes, K_n, refer to addition of the nth group to the $n - 1$ complex. For example, from the Cu(II)-NH_3 system (Eq. 19–1) for $n = 4$,

$$Cu(NH_3)_3^{++} + NH_3 \rightleftharpoons Cu(NH_3)_4^{++}, \qquad K_4 = \frac{[Cu(NH_3)_4^{++}]}{[Cu(NH_3)_3^{++}][NH_3]} = 10^{2.13}.$$

The cumulative (overall) constant is called β_4 (Eq. 19–2),

$$\beta_4 = \frac{[Cu(NH_3)_4^{++}]}{[Cu^{++}][NH_3]^4} = K_1K_2K_3K_4 = 10^{12.67}.$$

Polyprotic acids. Traditionally, acid constants are presented as dissociations rather than formations. However, in the book *Stability Constants*, they are expressed as formation constants of H^+ complexes of the central basic group A^{-m}, in complete analogy with the metal-ion formation equilibria. Thus, in that book, K_1 for PO_4^{3-} refers to

$$PO_4^{3-} + H^+ \rightleftharpoons HPO_4^{=}.$$

American chemists are accustomed to speaking of the reverse reaction with K_3 for H_3PO_4. These traditional acid constants are used in this text and written K_{an}, acidity constants, where any ambiguity might arise. Thus, for H_3PO_4,

$$K_{a3} = \frac{[H^+][PO_4^{3-}]}{[HPO_4^{=}]}.$$

Distribution fractions. The expression α_n refers to the fraction of the total central group present as the complex having n ligands. In these cases, for uniformity, the formation direction is always used. The α_3 for the Cu(II)-NH_3 system refers to the fraction of $Cu(NH_3)_3^{++}$ present; the α_3 for the H_3PO_4 solutions refers to the fraction of H_3PO_4 present. Thus n is always the number of added ligands, whether they are bases or protons. Some publications use n for the number of protons lost from an acid (i.e., the charges on the anion). Some use β for the fractions in metal complexes and α in acids. However, in this text, β has the other significance described above.

Table of International Atomic Weights 1961
Based on nuclidic mass of $C^{12} = 12$

(Courtesy International Union of Pure and Applied Chemistry)

Element	Symbol	Atomic No.	Atomic weight	Element	Symbol	Atomic No.	Atomic weight	Element	Symbol	Atomic No.	Atomic weight
Actinium	Ac	89		Gold	Au	79	196.967	Praseodymium	Pr	59	140.907
Aluminum	Al	13	26.9815	Hafnium	Hf	72	178.49	Promethium	Pm	61	
Americium	Am	95		Helium	He	2	4.0026	Protactinium	Pa	91	
Antimony	Sb	51	121.75	Holmium	Ho	67	164.930	Radium	Ra	88	
Argon	Ar	18	39.948	Hydrogen	H	1	*1.00797	Radon	Rn	86	
Arsenic	As	33	74.9216	Indium	In	49	114.82	Rhenium	Re	75	186.2
Astatine	At	85		Iodine	I	53	126.9044	Rhodium	Rh	45	102.905
Barium	Ba	56	137.34	Iridium	Ir	77	192.2	Rubidium	Rb	37	85.47
Berkelium	Bk	97		Iron	Fe	26	†55.847	Ruthenium	Ru	44	101.07
Beryllium	Be	4	9.0122	Krypton	Kr	36	83.80	Samarium	Sm	62	150.35
Bismuth	Bi	83	208.980	Lanthanum	La	57	138.91	Scandium	Sc	21	44.956
Boron	B	5	*10.811	Lead	Pb	82	207.19	Selenium	Se	34	78.96
Bromine	Br	35	†79.909	Lithium	Li	3	6.939	Silicon	Si	14	*28.086
Cadmium	Cd	48	112.40	Lutetium	Lu	71	174.97	Silver	Ag	47	†107.870
Calcium	Ca	20	40.08	Magnesium	Mg	12	24.312	Sodium	Na	11	22.9898

Californium	Cf	98		Manganese	Mn	25	54.9380	Strontium	Sr	38	87.62
Carbon	C	6	*12.01115	Mendelevium	Md	101		Sulfur	S	16	*32.064
Cerium	Ce	58	140.12	Mercury	Hg	80	200.59	Tantalum	Ta	73	180.948
Cesium	Cs	55	132.905	Molybdenum	Mo	42	95.94	Technetium	Tc	43	
Chlorine	Cl	17	†35.453	Neodymium	Nd	60	144.24	Tellurium	Te	52	127.60
Chromium	Cr	24	†51.996	Neon	Ne	10	20.183	Terbium	Tb	65	158.924
Cobalt	Co	27	58.9332	Neptunium	Np	93		Thallium	Tl	81	204.37
Copper	Cu	29	63.54	Nickel	Ni	28	58.71	Thorium	Th	90	232.038
Curium	Cm	96		Niobium	Nb	41	92.906	Thulium	Tm	69	168.934
Dysprosium	Dy	66	162.50	Nitrogen	N	7	14.0067	Tin	Sn	50	118.69
Einsteinium	Es	99		Nobelium	No	102		Titanium	Ti	22	47.90
Erbium	Er	68	167.26	Osmium	Os	76	190.2	Tungsten	W	74	183.85
Europium	Eu	63	151.96	Oxygen	O	8	*15.9994	Uranium	U	92	238.03
Fermium	Fm	100		Palladium	Pd	46	106.4	Vanadium	V	23	50.942
Fluorine	F	9	18.9984	Phosphorus	P	15	30.9738	Xenon	Xe	54	131.30
Francium	Fr	87		Platinum	Pt	78	195.09	Ytterbium	Yb	70	173.04
Gadolinium	Gd	64	157.25	Plutonium	Pu	94		Yttrium	Y	39	88.905
Gallium	Ga	31	69.72	Polonium	Po	84		Zinc	Zn	30	65.37
Germanium	Ge	32	72.59	Potassium	K	19	39.102	Zirconium	Zr	40	91.22

* The atomic weight varies because of natural variations in the isotopic composition of the element. The observed ranges are boron, ±0.003; carbon, ±0.00005; hydrogen, ±0.00001; oxygen, ±0.0001; silicon, ±0.001; sulfur, ±0.003.

† The atomic weight is believed to have an experimental uncertainty of the following magnitude: bromine, ±0.002; chlorine, ±0.001; chromium, ±0.001; iron, ±0.003; silver, ±0.003. For other elements the last digit given is believed to be reliable to ±0.5.

COMMON LOGARITHMS

N	0	1	2	3	4	5	6	7	8	9
0	....	0000	3010	4771	6021	6990	7782	8451	9031	9542
1	0000	0414	0792	1139	1461	1761	2041	2304	2553	2788
2	3010	3222	3424	3617	3802	3979	4150	4314	4472	4624
3	4771	4914	5051	5185	5315	5441	5563	5682	5798	5911
4	6021	6128	6232	6335	6435	6532	6628	6721	6812	6902
5	6990	7076	7160	7243	7324	7404	7482	7559	7634	7709
6	7782	7853	7924	7993	8062	8129	8195	8261	8325	8388
7	8451	8513	8573	8633	8692	8751	8808	8865	8921	8976
8	9031	9085	9138	9191	9243	9294	9345	9395	9445	9494
9	9542	9590	9638	9685	9731	9777	9823	9868	9912	9956
10	0000	0043	0086	0128	0170	0212	0253	0294	0334	0374
11	0414	0453	0492	0531	0569	0607	0645	0682	0719	0755
12	0792	0828	0864	0899	0934	0969	1004	1038	1072	1106
13	1139	1173	1206	1239	1271	1303	1335	1367	1399	1430
14	1461	1492	1523	1553	1584	1614	1644	1673	1703	1732
15	1761	1790	1818	1847	1875	1903	1931	1959	1987	2014
16	2041	2068	2095	2122	2148	2175	2201	2227	2253	2279
17	2304	2330	2355	2380	2405	2430	2455	2480	2504	2529
18	2553	2577	2601	2625	2648	2672	2695	2718	2742	2765
19	2788	2810	2833	2856	2878	2900	2923	2945	2967	2989
20	3010	3032	3054	3075	3096	3118	3139	3160	3181	3201
21	3222	3243	3263	3284	3304	3324	3345	3365	3385	3404
22	3424	3444	3464	3483	3502	3522	3541	3560	3579	3598
23	3617	3636	3655	3674	3692	3711	3729	3747	3766	3784
24	3802	3820	3838	3856	3874	3892	3909	3927	3945	3962
25	3979	3997	4014	4031	4048	4065	4082	4099	4116	4133
26	4150	4166	4183	4200	4216	4232	4249	4265	4281	4298
27	4314	4330	4346	4362	4378	4393	4409	4425	4440	4456
28	4472	4487	4502	4518	4533	4548	4564	4579	4594	4609
29	4624	4639	4654	4669	4683	4698	4713	4728	4742	4757
30	4771	4786	4800	4814	4829	4843	4857	4871	4886	4900
31	4914	4928	4942	4955	4969	4983	4997	5011	5024	5038
32	5051	5065	5079	5092	5105	5119	5132	5145	5159	5172
33	5185	5198	5211	5224	5237	5250	5263	5276	5289	5302
34	5315	5328	5340	5353	5366	5378	5391	5403	5416	5428
35	5441	5453	5465	5478	5490	5502	5514	5527	5539	5551
36	5563	5575	5587	5599	5611	5623	5635	5647	5658	5670
37	5682	5694	5705	5717	5729	5740	5752	5763	5775	5786
38	5798	5809	5821	5832	5843	5855	5866	5877	5888	5899
39	5911	5922	5933	5944	5955	5966	5977	5988	5999	6010
40	6021	6031	6042	6053	6064	6075	6085	6096	6107	6117
41	6128	6138	6149	6160	6170	6180	6191	6201	6212	6222
42	6232	6243	6253	6263	6274	6284	6294	6304	6314	6325
43	6335	6345	6355	6365	6375	6385	6395	6405	6415	6425
44	6435	6444	6454	6464	6474	6484	6493	6503	6513	6522
45	6532	6542	6551	6561	6571	6580	6590	6599	6609	6618
46	6628	6637	6646	6656	6665	6675	6684	6693	6702	6712
47	6721	6730	6739	6749	6758	6767	6776	6785	6794	6803
48	6812	6821	6830	6839	6848	6857	6866	6875	6884	6893
49	6902	6911	6920	6928	6937	6946	6955	6964	6972	6981
50	6990	6998	7007	7016	7024	7033	7042	7050	7059	7067
N	0	1	2	3	4	5	6	7	8	9

COMMON LOGARITHMS

N	0	1	2	3	4	5	6	7	8	9
50	6990	6998	7007	7016	7024	7033	7042	7050	7059	7067
51	7076	7084	7093	7101	7110	7118	7126	7135	7143	7152
52	7160	7168	7177	7185	7193	7202	7210	7218	7226	7235
53	7243	7251	7259	7267	7275	7284	7292	7300	7308	7316
54	7324	7332	7340	7348	7356	7364	7372	7380	7388	7396
55	7404	7412	7419	7427	7435	7443	7451	7459	7466	7474
56	7482	7490	7497	7505	7513	7520	7528	7536	7543	7551
57	7559	7566	7574	7582	7589	7597	7604	7612	7619	7627
58	7634	7642	7649	7657	7664	7672	7679	7686	7694	7701
59	7709	7716	7723	7731	7738	7745	7752	7760	7767	7774
60	7782	7789	7796	7803	7810	7818	7825	7832	7839	7846
61	7853	7860	7868	7875	7882	7889	7896	7903	7910	7917
62	7924	7931	7938	7945	7952	7959	7966	7973	7980	7987
63	7993	8000	8007	8014	8021	8028	8035	8041	8048	8055
64	8062	8069	8075	8082	8089	8096	8102	8109	8116	8122
65	8129	8136	8142	8149	8156	8162	8169	8176	8182	8189
66	8195	8202	8209	8215	8222	8228	8235	8241	8248	8254
67	8261	8267	8274	8280	8287	8293	8299	8306	8312	8319
68	8325	8331	8338	8344	8351	8357	8363	8370	8376	8382
69	8388	8395	8401	8407	8414	8420	8426	8432	8439	8445
70	8451	8457	8463	8470	8476	8482	8488	8494	8500	8506
71	8513	8519	8525	8531	8537	8543	8549	8555	8561	8567
72	8573	8579	8585	8591	8597	8603	8609	8615	8621	8627
73	8633	8639	8645	8651	8657	8663	8669	8675	8681	8686
74	8692	8698	8704	8710	8716	8722	8727	8733	8739	8745
75	8751	8756	8762	8768	8774	8779	8785	8791	8797	8802
76	8808	8814	8820	8825	8831	8837	8842	8848	8854	8859
77	8865	8871	8876	8882	8887	8893	8899	8904	8910	8915
78	8921	8927	8932	8938	8943	8949	8954	8960	8965	8971
79	8976	8982	8987	8993	8998	9004	9009	9015	9020	9025
80	9031	9036	9042	9047	9053	9058	9063	9069	9074	9079
81	9085	9090	9096	9101	9106	9112	9117	9122	9128	9133
82	9138	9143	9149	9154	9159	9165	9170	9175	9180	9186
83	9191	9196	9201	9206	9212	9217	9222	9227	9232	9238
84	9243	9248	9253	9258	9263	9269	9274	9279	9284	9289
85	9294	9299	9304	9309	9315	9320	9325	9330	9335	9340
86	9345	9350	9355	9360	9365	9370	9375	9380	9385	9390
87	9395	9400	9405	9410	9415	9420	9425	9430	9435	9440
88	9445	9450	9455	9460	9465	9469	9474	9479	9484	9489
89	9494	9499	9504	9509	9513	9518	9523	9528	9533	9538
90	9542	9547	9552	9557	9562	9566	9571	9576	9581	9586
91	9590	9595	9600	9605	9609	9614	9619	9624	9628	9633
92	9638	9643	9647	9652	9657	9661	9666	9671	9675	9680
93	9685	8689	9694	9699	9703	9708	9713	9717	9722	9727
94	9731	9736	9741	9745	9750	9754	9759	9763	9768	9773
95	9777	9782	9786	9791	9795	9800	9805	9809	9814	9818
96	9823	9827	9832	9836	9841	9845	9850	9854	9859	9863
97	9868	9872	9877	9881	9886	9890	9894	9899	9903	9908
98	9912	9917	9921	9926	9930	9934	9939	9943	9948	9952
99	9956	9961	9965	9969	9974	9978	9983	9987	9991	9996
100	0000	0004	0009	0013	0017	0022	0026	0030	0035	0039
N	0	1	2	3	4	5	6	7	8	9

ANSWERS AND EXPLANATIONS

Chapter 1

1. Each new weight should be one more than the sum of all smaller weights. *Answer:* seven weights at 1, 2, 4, 8, 16, 32, 64 values.
2. Five weights: 1, 3, 9, 27, 81. This is the basis of some well-known puzzles. See the article by Lang and Peck cited in the references to Chapter 1.
3. +0.6 ppth
4. The correction for salt is about 0.3 ppth, while for water it is 1.1 ppth.
5. 47.0872 g. The buoyancy on the H_2 is 0.1207 g, while it weighs only 0.0077 g.
6. It does not work. The gas pressure outside the barometer is not opposed by any weight of mercury, which will thus fill the tube.
7. 0.99990 for Pt, 1.0003 for Al. One is more, the other less dense than the weights.
8. 0.2009 *M* from the fraction expansion of water, assuming dilute solutions expand the same
9. 6 ml by pure water approximation

Chapter 2

1. *Volumetric:* Temperature uncertainty of $\pm 2°$ affects volumes about ± 0.5 ppth. Buret uncertainties in 40 ml also affect volumes about ± 0.5 ppth. Thus 1 ppth, or four figures is a practical limit for usual work.
   Gravimetric: Purity (dryness) may be hard to improve above 99.9% for most precipitated solids. An exception is silver halides.
2. Mean 65.10, median, 65.10, $Q = 0.43, 0.40$; no rejections
3. $\overline{7}.{}_5$, 25.84, 25.86, 25.7. (25.98 may be rejected in third set.)
   $s = 0.9_5, 0.04, 0.08, 0.16$
4. 0.18 pH units, assuming 50% error means 1.5 times the former value.
5. 1.9%
6. 32%
7. $K = 0.0111 \pm 0.015$: $\pm 14\%$
8. 1.6%, 8% (maximum)
9. 1.3%. An impurity having higher chloride content than NaCl (LiCl).
10. $s = 0.067$, $t = 0.6$. Critical t values at $n = 7$ are 2.5 and 3.7 for 95 and 99% levels. There is no significant difference.

11. There are two rather different approaches to this problem.
 1) Interpolate:

$$11.0093 - 10.0129 = 0.9964, \qquad (0.804 \pm 0.001)(0.9964) = 0.801 \pm 0.001.$$

 Then

$$10.0129 + 0.801 = 10.814 \pm 0.001.$$

 2) Carry through the uncertainties: (If one fraction increases, the other must decrease by the same amount if only two isotopes exist.)

$$\begin{aligned} 11.0093(0.804 \pm 0.001) &= 8.851 \pm 0.011 \\ 10.0129(0.196 \mp 0.001) &= \underline{1.962 \mp 0.010} \\ & 10.814 \pm 0.001 \end{aligned}$$

Chapter 4

1. To decide, compare the K_b and K_a of the conjugate base and acid of the cation and anion. The larger predominates. HBO_2, acidic; NH_4CN, basic; NH_4Cl, acidic; K_2CO_3, basic; $Ba(C_2H_3O_2)_2$, basic; $NaBO_2$, basic; KHC_2O_4, acidic; $HN(CH_3)_3C_2H_3O_2$, basic.
2. $HPO_4^{=}$, $pK_{a3} = 12.3$, is a far weaker acid than NH_4^+, $pK_a = 9.2$. Thus PO_4^{3-} removes protons from NH_4^+ to give $(NH_4)_2HPO_4$ crystals.
3. 0.0184 N_b, 18.4 ml
4. 19 M, 25 ml
5. 0.1888 N_a
6. 0.1033 N_b
7. 6.114 N_a, 35.82 g [*Note:* not 35.85 g, the weight *in vacuo*.]
8. a) 2.1 ± 0.2 g, b) 32.7 ml

Chapter 5

1. 6.79 pH. Use the quadratic equation to solve the K_w expression. Let x be the $[OH^-]$, then $[H^+]$ is $10^{-7} + x$.
2. pH 10 and 4; second trial, pH 9 and 5
3. pH 10 and 7.4; second trial, pH 9 and 8.5
4. About 18 ml
5. About 6 ml. NaA only increases the acetate concentration, while NaOH both removes HA and produces acetate at the same time. The same is true for NH_3: it is as efficient a base as OH^- below pH 5.
6. Ratio $5NaOH/2H_3Cit$
7. d) pH = 12.5, 5.1, 9.5, 12.5, 9.2, 11.0
8. pH = 4.1_6 (See Example 4 in Chapter 9 p. 100 for the use of activity effects.)
9. 58 and 42 ml. It is easily found after deciding the K_2 must be the major equilibrium.
10. pH 7.8
11. pH 9.2
12. pH 8.5
13. pH 3.05 (The quadratic formula must be used here.) No. K_{sp} for $Fe(OH)_3$ is barely exceeded: supersaturated. Actually, polymerization slows the formation of a precipitate which does occur on long standing.

14. About 55 ml 15. pH 2.35 and 9.78 16. pH 9.86

17. Glycine, zwitterion; alanine, zwitterion; aspartic acid, −1 ion; lysine, +1 ion. The forms are deduced from K_a values.

Chapter 6

1. The method is described in the chapter. The student should make up examples to test the effects of a variety of K values and concentrations.
2. $KCl = 0.010$, $K_2CO_3 = 0.030$; $La_2(SO_4)_3 = 0.15$
3. a) 0.001 M approximate: $\sqrt{K_aC} = 10^{-3.88}$, exact pH = 3.91 ($f = 1$). 10^{-6} M approximate pH = 5.39, exact pH = 6.02 ($f = 1$).
   b) These values are rapidly found by using the results in (a) as first approximations for refinement in the exact equation. For 0.0010 M, pH = 3.82; and for 10^{-6} M, pH = 6.010.
4. The equations are derived in the chapter. Show the order of magnitude of each term for $H_2C_2O_4$ and H_2S. Assume that ionic strength is zero.
5. a) approximate pH = 2.43, correct pH = 2.50
   b) approximate (pK_a^0) = 2.86. At $I = 0.01$ M, $pK_a = 2.77$. The exact pH = 2.89.
6. The methods and equations are analogous to the diprotic cases in the chapter.

Chapter 7

1. Use the approximate equation of Chapter 5 to get pH at start and halfway to each equivalence point. Sketch the approximate curves from these.
2. Use major species ($CO_3^=$, HCO_3^-, and H_2CO_3) approximations (Chapter 5) to estimate the pH at each point, use the complete equations given in this chapter at 9 to 11 ml.
3. Slope (a) 80 pH/ml, (b) 42, (c) 0.5. Indicator: (a) thymol blue or phenolphthalein, (b) phenolphthalein, (c) not feasible.
4. About $\frac{2}{3}$
5. 0.75 meq. of some strong acid and 1.00 mmole of a weak acid, H_3A. This is deduced because the curve at 14 ml shows some buffering (pH should be higher) H_3A has apparent $pK_1 = 2.1$, $pK_2 = 7.2$, $pK_3 \sim 12$.
6. 24.00 ± 0.04% NaOH, 74.20 ± 0.11% Na_2CO_3
7. About pH 6.1
8. Use the points in Problem 1 answer above.
9. phosphate ratio = 1/4.15, carbonate ratio = 1/15.4

11. 97.8 ml citrate^{-3} and 2.2 ml Hcitrate$^=$

Chapter 8

1. pH 2.0

2–6. See the methods used for the citrate examples worked in the chapter.

7. For pH 4, citrate: $\alpha_3 = 0.10$, $\alpha_2 = 0.76$, $\alpha_1 = 0.13$. This could be made with a ratio of 1 mole Na_3 citrate to 1.95 moles HCl, since the ratio from these α values is 1.95 for total H^+/total citrate.

8. Take logarithms of the K_a and K_w expressions and differentiate them with respect to pH.
9. It breaks down if $C_a - [H^+]$ is not nearly equal to C_a.

Chapter 9

1. a) 0.020, 0.060, 0.160
   b) From the simple Debye-Hückel limiting equation:

$$AgCl, f_{\pm} = 0.85, 0.76, 0.63, \qquad CaSO_4 = 0.52, 0.33, 0.15,$$
$$La_2(SO_4)_3 = 0.37, 0.18, 0.06.$$

2. a) At $I = 0$, 0.0030 M, at $I = 0.015$, 0.0048 M
   b) At $I = 0$, 0.0014 M, at $I = 0.020$, 0.00316 M
   c) At $I = 0$, 1.38×10^{-5} M (Table 9–1), at $I = 0.05$, 8.6×10^{-5} M
   d) At $I = 0$, 1.9×10^{-8} M, at $I = 0.06$, 8.5×10^{-7} M
3. About 26% increase by simple Debye-Hückel equation (9–2)
4. The $f_{=}$ for $C_2O_4^{=}$ has greater effect; about 150% increase or 2.5 fold
7. Since pH $= -\log(a_{H^+})$, and $(a_{H^+})^2 = K_a^0 \times C_a$ = a constant, if C_a = [HA] is valid: not too dilute.
8. With $pK_2^0 = 7.21$, $I = 0.100$, and the Kielland table f values, pH 6.89. (See also, Butler, *Ionic Equilibrium*, p. 441.)

Chapter 10

1. First show that $I = 0.043$. [*Answer:* 0.08 ml or 2 ppth]
2. 0.06 ml. The f values nearly cancel in the calculation process.
3. Published K_{sp}^0 values are 1.4 to 1.7×10^{-5} at 25°.
4. $K_{sp}^0 = 1.7 \times 10^{-5}$. Note that $[SO_4^{=}]$ is 0.0271; much is converted to HSO_4^-.
6. $I = 3.6 \times 10^{-4}$, $K_{sp} = 4.7 \times 10^{-9}$, $K_{sp}^0 = 3.9 \times 10^{-9}$
7. a) 2×10^{-6} b) 2.4 to 2.6×10^{-6} d) 1 part in 10^4
8. See Eq. (10–7)
9. Formulate an equation of the sum of the moles of NaCl and KCl equal to the moles of Cl^- found. [*Answer*. 27.8% NaCl. An error of 0.05 ml (1 ppth) changes the percent NaCl by 12 ppth.]
10. a) 354.5 mg b) 584.4 mg
11. 0.0705 M
12. At pH 2, $10^{0.20}$, at pH 7, $10^{-1.08}$
15. At pH 0, $10^{-1.58}$, at pH 3, $10^{-2.04}$
16. At pH 3, $10^{-3.68}$

Chapter 11

1. Old scale, 107.878; new scale, 107.872
2. Ratio changed 0.17 ppth
3. 107.875_5
4. Old scale, 18.9987; new scale, 18.9979; 0.026 ppth, 26 ppm
5. 326 mg

6. 28.9% NaCl, 71.1% KCl. Point out where you lose the fourth significant figure in a subtraction when the simultaneous equations are combined.
7. a) 35 ppth b) 0.6 ppth
8. 2 g

Chapter 12

1. [*Hint:* What should be plotted to give straight-line relations for various common functions? What are the activity effects?]
2. For Cr(II), $\mathcal{E}^0 = 0.95$ V, $K^0_{eq} = 10^{32}$, yes
3. a) For K_{10}, $\mathcal{E}^0 = 0.059$ V. b) 10^{17}
4. a) 0.35 V b) 0.07 V
5. 6.0×10^{-5}
6. 0.07 V
7. 0.071_5 V

Chapter 13

1. a) About 0.2 b) 70%, >99.99%
2. $\mathcal{E}$ at equivalence = 1.06 V
3. See Problem 1.
4. $10^{-8.5}$

Chapter 14

1. 0.0840 N
2. 0.01106, 0.03316, 0.0840
3. 14.4, 21.6 ml
4. 1.86% Fe, 0.57% U
5. 4.35%

Chapter 15

1. Give your observed slopes and intercepts and compare with those predicted by the equations.
2. 23°K
3. $H_2/O_2 = \frac{4}{1}$. The second stage could start with a ratio $\frac{16}{1}$, etc.
5. Choose V and calculate P with van der Waals' equation. The dip around 0.1 liter is a result of this cubic function. Check the points: at $V = 1, p = 32$ atm; at $V = 0.2$, $p = 53$.
8. 40% CH_2O, $C_5H_{10}O_2$
9. [*Hint:* $C_2H_6 + H_2$ is indistinguishable from $2CH_4$.]
10. Ideal, 0.224; van der Waals, 0.07. Get 3 figures.

Chapter 16

1. 132°
2. 20° 97 torr
3. $3\bar{2}00$ atm

Chapter 17

1. One started on the water side of the azeotrope, therefore the initial distillate contains more water in fractionation than in simple distillation and the remainder approaches the azeotrope at a lower percent distilled.
3. Fraction of benzene in the liquid = 0.803, fraction in the vapor = 0.686

Chapter 18

2. For $P = 1, 10, 100$, the fractions are given in Table 18–1. For $P = 2$, fractions are $\frac{1}{3}$, $\frac{1}{4}$, near $\frac{1}{5}$, under $\frac{1}{5}$; the limit is 0.136.
3. Compare your plot with Fig. 18–2. Tubes 6, 7, 8, 9 have fractions 0.14, 0.23, 0.26, 0.20. Note that powers like 3^{10} can be found in Handbook tables as 3^5 squared.
4. 96.8%, 99.90%, 99.997%
5. $P = 86$; the equation is: f_n (left in CCl_4) $= (1 + 100/86(10))^{-n}$. Solve for the n which makes $f = 0.01$. [*Answer:* 42]

Chapter 19

1. Check your answers on the α diagram, Fig. 19–1 (a or b).
2. 0.114 moles NH_3
3. Maximum $\alpha_1 = 0.188$ at free $[NH_3]$ $10^{-3.52}$
4. a) Assuming $[HgCl^+] = [Cl^-]$, K_1 gives $[Hg^{++}] = 10^{-6.74}$ and K_2 gives $[Cl^-] = 1.3 \times 10^{-4}$
   b) $[HgCl_2] = 0.026\ M$, $[HgCl_3^-] = 0.013\ M$, $[HgCl_4^=] = 0.011\ M$
   c) $[Hg^{++}] = 0.069\ M$, $[HgCl^+] = 0.057\ M$, $[HgCl_2] = 0.025\ M$
   These values are found by getting $\bar{n}$ first and using the diagrams to find α values. See the examples in the chapter.
6. With $[Cl^-] = 1\ M$, α_0 is 0.092; α_1, 0.39; α_2, 0.50; α_3, 0.02; α_4, 0.0002
8. $[NH_3] = 10^{-3.90}$; α_0, 0.25; α_1, 0.48; α_2, 0.24; α_3, 0.03
11. A distribution diagram for the hypothetical case, M-A, with $K_1 = K_2 = K_3 = K_4 = 10^2$ (similar to the Zn(II)-NH_3 system) is shown below.

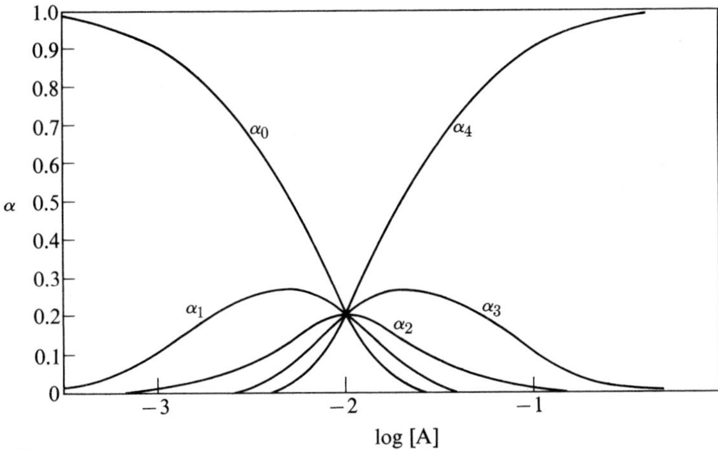

Chapter 20

3. First crossing $[I^-] = 10^{-12.9}\ M$
4. First show that $P = C_{org}/C_{aq}\alpha_2 = D/\alpha_2$. Then, omitting small terms $(1 + K_1[I^-])$ from the α_2 expression, solve simultaneous equations at the two points to get $K_3 = 5.3 \times 10^3$ and $K_4 = 1.3 \times 10^2$.
7. a) $K_1 = 4.17$ b) 0.20

Chapter 21

1. $[Hg^{++}] = 10^{-11.2}, 10^{-6.7}, 10^{-3.9}$. Be sure that the assumed species present are consistent with the Cl^- found. For the last point, if there is 0.45 mmole $HgCl_2$ and 0.1 mmole $HgCl^+$, K_2 gives $[Cl^-] = 10^{-5.8}$, which is consistent with the species assumed. This is seen on the α diagram in the chapter and also the value $\bar{n} = 1.87$ by this assumption, checks with the $\bar{n}$ diagram for this system.
2. pH = 4.0, 2, and <2
3. Ratios: 3, 10^3, 10^5. R becomes quantitative about pH 5(10^4)
5. 10^{-12} M, 0.005 ml after
6. p[Cu] at equivalence, 7.2(pH 5) and 5.8(pH 10)
7. At pH 5, 0.02 M and $10^{-7.2}$ M; at pH 10, $10^{-10.4}$ M and $10^{-14.6}$ M.
8. 100 mg

Chapter 23

1. 50
3. 38% Ni, 47% Co, 15% Fe
5. 120,220 ml to each maximum. The first 170 ml give the Co, the next 100 ml contain the Cu.

Chapter 24

2. $\frac{1}{2}$, $\frac{4}{7}$
4. a) $A = 0.991$, $\epsilon = 48\bar{2}0$, $a = 24.8$ b) 0.320, 0.496 c) 0.690, 69.6%
5. 10^{-4}, 0.040
6. 21%
7. a) −0.64 V b) Change 1.1 V and 0.06 V c) 0.9 V and reversed
8. 25.5 min
9. 0.58 micrograms, 11.6 micrograms

Chapter 25

3. HA 7.2, $HClO_4$ 2.9

Chapter 26

1. $10^{5.3}$
2. $10^{5.7}$
3. $10^{-23.6}$

INDEX*

*Laboratory directions are included on pp. 303 to 375.